BIOETHICS
in Canada

BIOETHICS
in Canada

Edited by
Charles Weijer
Anthony Skelton
Samantha Brennan

OXFORD
UNIVERSITY PRESS

OXFORD
UNIVERSITY PRESS

Oxford University Press is a department of the University of Oxford.
It furthers the University's objective of excellence in research, scholarship,
and education by publishing worldwide. Oxford is a registered trade mark of
Oxford University Press in the UK and in certain other countries.

Published in Canada by
Oxford University Press
8 Sampson Mews, Suite 204,
Don Mills, Ontario M3C 0H5 Canada

www.oupcanada.com

Library and Archives Canada Cataloguing in Publication

Bioethics in Canada / edited by Charles Weijer, Anthony Skelton & Samantha Brennan.

Includes bibliographical references and index.
ISBN 978-0-19-544015-7

1. Bioethics—Canada—Textbooks. 2. Medical ethics—Canada—Textbooks.
I. Weijer, Charles, 1964– II. Skelton, Anthony, 1972–
III. Brennan, Samantha, 1964–

R724.B562 2013   174.20971   C2012-906485-8

Cover image: Roy Ritchie/Stone+/Getty Images

Oxford University Press is committed to our environment.

This book is printed on Forest Stewardship Council® certified paper and comes from responsible sources.

Printed and bound in Canada

2 3 — 16 15

Contents

Preface

We offer this anthology to those teaching bioethics in colleges and universities who seek to relate its core issues to the public policy context in Canada. In this volume, we have made a conscious effort to include articles from colleagues whose work we greatly respect but, for whatever reason, have not been included in prior bioethics anthologies. We hope the reader will, as a result, better appreciate the rich reservoir of talent present among those working in bioethics in Canada and Canadian bioethicists working abroad. In addition, we have intentionally aimed to educate the reader about the policies and laws that regulate the most important and pressing bioethical problems facing Canadians. We hope that the reader will develop a nuanced view of the nature, importance, and impact of bioethics in Canada.

This project would not have been possible without the invaluable assistance and hard work of a number of people. Jennifer Epp, Jason Marsh, and Angela White, doctoral students at the Rotman Institute of Philosophy, expertly edited all of the articles in the volume. Rob Read, administrative assistant at the Rotman Institute, coordinated our meetings, scanned the articles, and supervised the copyediting process. The editorial team at Oxford University Press, including Stephen Kotowych and Meagan Carlsson, supported us throughout the creation of the book. We owe you all a debt of gratitude.

Each of us would like to thank additional people. Samantha Brennan thanks her colleagues in philosophy at Western, Dean Michael Milde, and her family for supporting her during her term as department Chair, making it possible for a Chair to have an active research life, of which this book is part. Anthony Skelton wishes to thank Meena Krishnamurthy, Carolyn McLeod, Sandra Raponi, Anne Skelton, and (especially) Charles Weijer for helpful comments on previous drafts. Charles Weijer is grateful to Anthony Skelton and Anthony Belardo for their helpful comments on previous drafts.

Acknowledgements

We would also like to acknowledge the following reviewers and those who wished to remain anonymous for providing insightful comments and suggestions:

Iva Apostolova, University of Ottawa
Kirstin Borgerson, Dalhousie University
Diane Gall, Medicine Hat College
Kenneth Kirkwood, Western University
Michael Stingl, University of Lethbridge

Finally, we invite readers of this anthology to send us suggestions for topics and articles to be included in future editions. These can be sent to Charles Weijer (cweijer@uwo.ca).

About the Authors

Charles Weijer

Charles Weijer is a professor in the Departments of Philosophy and Medicine, Canada Research Chair in Bioethics and the co-founder of the Rotman Institute of Philosophy at Western University, Canada. He is a fellow of the Hastings Center, fellow of the Royal College of Physicians and Surgeons of Canada, fellow of the American College of Physicians, and fellow of the Canadian Academy of Health Sciences.

He is a widely published and respected physician and philosopher whose research is focused on the ethics of human experimentation.

Anthony Skelton

Anthony Skelton is an associate professor and member of the Rotman Institute of Philosophy in the Department of Philosophy at Western University, Canada, where he specializes in ethics and the history of ethics. Recent articles have appeared in *Journal of the History of Philosophy* and *Utilitas*. He is currently working on a series of papers dealing with the issue of what it is to fare well as a child and a book provisionally entitled *Henry Sidgwick and the Conflicts of Ethics*.

Samantha Brennan

Samantha Brennan is a professor in the Department of Philosophy, a member of the Rotman Institute of Philosophy, and an affiliate member of the Department of Women's Studies and Feminist Research, at Western University, Canada. Her main research interests are in contemporary normative ethics, including feminist approaches to ethics. A complete list of her publications can be found on her homepage, http://publish.uwo.ca/~sbrennan.

Introduction

This is a textbook in bioethics. Bioethics is an area of moral philosophy focusing on ethical problems in the medical and life sciences, including genetics and biology. The purpose of this book is to familiarize students with the most pressing problems in contemporary bioethics. It therefore focuses on such issues as the morality of using human embryos, adults and non-human animals in medical research; the morality of abortion and procreation; the morality of assisted suicide and euthanasia; justice in health care; the nature of informed consent, competency, disease and death; and the ethical issues associated with the cosmetic use of pharmaceuticals and the promotion of public health, among others. To situate ourselves, it is useful to begin with an actual bioethical case that raises difficult and not uncommon moral problems. This is the case of Baby Joseph.

Joseph Maraachli was born on 22 January 2010 in Windsor, Ontario. At birth, he appeared to be a healthy and normal infant. However, later that same year, on 31 May, he had a seizure and was admitted to a hospital in Windsor. He was later transferred to a hospital in Detroit, where it was discovered that he had neurological problems. Some months later, on 17 October, he stopped breathing while driving with his parents, and he ended up in a hospital in Ingersoll, Ontario. He was subsequently moved to the London Health Sciences Centre, in London, Ontario, and was placed on a ventilator. Physicians at the LHSC determined that he had a severe and progressive neurological disorder called Leigh's disease. It was possible for his seizures to be controlled, but no effective treatment for the disorder existed. Indeed, in the form that Baby Joseph had it, the disease is always fatal. While in hospital, Baby Joseph's condition deteriorated. He was unable to feed himself and to breathe spontaneously, and several attempts to remove him from the ventilator failed. Physicians later concluded that he had lapsed into a persistent vegetative state, and that it would be best to disconnect him from life support and to let him die. Baby Joseph's parents rejected this option, and instead asked the physicians to perform a tracheotomy on him, which is required for those needing a breathing machine permanently in place. This would allow his parents to care for him at home. However, the doctors refused on the grounds that keeping Baby Joseph alive would be "futile and cruel."

This response must have come as a shock to Baby Joseph's parents, since this was not the first time that they had encountered a scenario of this sort. Eight years earlier, Baby Joseph's sister Zina was born, and like Joseph, developed Leigh's disease, which is an inherited condition. Like her brother, Zina suffered from seizures, and eventually lost the ability to feed and to breathe without the aid of a machine. As in the case of Baby Joseph, rather than have her remain in hospital, Zina's parents requested that doctors perform a tracheotomy on her so that they could care for her at home. Unlike in the case of Baby Joseph the doctors complied with the request. She died a few months later at the age of 18 months.

The disagreement over the proper course of treatment for Baby Joseph led the eight physicians in charge of his care to conclude that his parents were no longer capable of making decisions in his best interests. They appealed to the Consent and Capacity Board of Ontario, a body that deals with conflicts of this variety, and the Board concurred with Baby Joseph's physicians. In essence, the Consent and Capacity Board argued that the physicians had the balance of reasons in their favour: Baby Joseph had "suffered enough human indignities" and it was reasonable to expect that a tracheotomy would lead to "exacerbated difficulties." It would be better, all things considered, for Baby Joseph to be taken off life support: keeping him alive had an unfavourable cost/benefit ratio. The parents appealed this decision, but it was upheld by the Ontario Superior Court of Justice on 17 February 2011.

The case did not end here. Several weeks after the court ruling, an American-based right-to-life organization calling itself Priests for Life intervened on behalf of the parents. Although many American hospitals refused to take Baby Joseph, with the help of Priests for Life he was flown to Cardinal Glennon Children's Medical Center in St. Louis, Missouri, on 13 March. Some days later, physicians at the hospital performed the desired procedure. This allowed Baby Joseph to breathe with a portable breathing machine, and his parents returned home to Windsor on 21 April. Although he regained the ability to breathe on his own and his condition seemed to be improving, he died slightly more than six months later, on 27 September 2011.

How do we determine the right course of action in this situation? How do we decide which party in this dispute has the most compelling moral reasons? Was the course of action recommended by the LHSC and supported by other institutions and medical experts wrong? Or was it impermissible for Baby Joseph's parents to put their son through a set of medical procedures appearing to have no benefit to him? Which factors matter to the morality of these decisions and courses of action? Which factors appear to be the most morally salient? The different parties in this case need to make decisions. What resources, moral and otherwise, ought they to draw on?

In order for us to begin answering these questions we must view moral debate as a practice that is governed at least in part by reason. That is, we have to agree that morality is something about which we can argue. Whether this is so, is a matter of long-standing philosophical debate. The best way to deal with it is by noting how difficult it is to avoid presupposing that some moral decisions are better justified than others. Indeed, as we see in the case of Baby Joseph no one suggested that anything goes with respect to his medical or other treatment. No one threw up their hands and declared that it was all a matter of opinion or emotion, and that there was no truth about what ought to be done. Instead, what we find is each party in the conflict attempting to provide reasons and trying to identify factors that they think matter morally. That is, we find that each party in the dispute is trying to move the other by rational means. This should come as no surprise to us, for we have a conception of ourselves according to which our intentional acts are not the product of arbitrary and random forces. On the contrary, we think of our intentional actions as being justified or as being backed up by reasons that others at least recognize or might be in a position to accept. These at least in part are what move us to act. We simply cannot accept that anything goes or that what we do is permissible only because we think or want it to be so. Otherwise, why would we agonize over the issues and problems that we do?

But what does moral reasoning look like? What counts as a moral reason? Answers to these questions are also a matter of long-standing philosophical debate. It is important for our purposes to avoid

controversy and, more significantly, to avoid assuming what readers of this anthology will decide for themselves about what matters morally. However, it is important to note that moral reasons are distinct from legal reasons, on the one hand, and religious reasons, on the other. Though these can and often do overlap, the three kinds of reasons remain distinct. A legal reason is one that is typically found in a statute or a legal precedent; a religious reason typically derives from a religious text of some kind (e.g., the Koran). Some of these reasons are moral reasons, too, but not necessarily. It is of course difficult to say what makes a reason a moral reason, but typically moral reasons have to do with human rights, well-being, justice, virtue, fidelity to promises, dignity, and respect for individual autonomy. In addition, moral reasons are not codified in the way that legal and religious reasons are. Finally, moral reasons typically have a much broader reach than either legal or religious reasons. Indeed, we rely on moral considerations to assess and sometimes criticize law and religion. These are factors that seem to matter regardless of what law and religion dictate.

With these considerations in mind, we may be able to make sense of what bioethical or moral reasoning would look like in the case of Baby Joseph. To begin, it is important that moral disputants agree on the facts. Sometimes moral disagreements are the result of factual disagreements, such that once the factual disagreements are cleared up the moral disagreements evaporate or become more tractable. The disagreement between Baby Joseph's physicians and his parents appeared to turn on disagreements about his medical status. One physician commenting on the case stated that withdrawing a feeding tube would not necessarily be painful but that a tracheotomy might be, and that you have to weigh this cost against any benefit to Baby Joseph. But Baby Joseph's parents were sceptical of the claim that a tracheotomy would be painful. He appeared to possess a level of consciousness that was inconsistent with him feeling anything at all. In addition, the parents disputed the claim that Baby Joseph was in a persistent vegetative state. According to the Priests for Life website, Baby Joseph was instead in a near-vegetative state (http://www.priestsforlife.org/articles/3620-baby-joseph-is-home-and-breathing-free). It is possible that had these facts been agreed to by the physicians in charge of Baby's Joseph's care that they would have performed a tracheotomy as physicians had in the case of Baby Joseph's sister.

However, there is reason to think that the factual disagreements are of only minor significance in this case. Instead, there appear to be deep moral disagreements between Baby Joseph's parents and his physicians. In a newspaper article, Baby Joseph's father, Moe Maraachli, is reported to have said "Let me take him home and let him breathe . . . If he will die, he will die because he's sick, naturally." The reason that Mr. Maraachli wanted to take his son home had less to do with his attitudes about his son's condition and more to do with his attitudes regarding the best way for him to die. Mr. Maraachli seemed to think that it would be worse for Baby Joseph to die from not breathing, which would have happened had his breathing tube been removed in the hospital, than from the underlying disease from which he was suffering. This was further confirmed by the fact that upon Baby Joseph's death a spokesperson for the family, Paul O'Donnell, is reported to have said that "What they [Baby Joseph's parents] wanted was to let their baby die peacefully and naturally when God decides and not have that imposed by the hospital or the courts."

It was assumed by all that Baby Joseph's interests were of importance. But his parents also considered another factor to be important in their decision-making: they wanted more time with Joseph. This was, to them, a benefit to be weighed against the cost of the treatment. In a newspaper article, it was reported that Baby Joseph's parents enjoyed the extra time they had with Zina and that they wanted to have the same experience with Joseph. It seemed that the parents were including a benefit that the physicians had simply ignored, the benefit to Baby Joseph's parents of having him at home and of caring for him until he died. This benefit to the parents may well have been thought to outweigh the risks that the surgery posed to their son.

The reasons in favour of respecting the choices of Baby Joseph's parents are very strong. They seemed to be relying in part on their core and deeply held religious convictions (Mr. Maraachli is a Muslim, while Baby Joseph's mother, Sana Nader, is a Catholic). Furthermore, the parents had a more detailed and nuanced knowledge of their child and of caring for children of this sort, and they were more than willing to assume the bulk of Baby Joseph's care (though a nurse looked after him from midnight to 0700h while he was at home). Finally, there is a strong presumption in the common law and in ethical thinking that medical decisions of the sort at issue in this case are the sole responsibility of the parents.

The family's decisions and the reasons that speak in favour of them seem to be of the utmost importance in cases like this. Nonetheless, it is important to consider the other moral factors that matter. The health care team that was responsible for the care of Baby Joseph had equally strong reasons for the decision that they made. They are experts in the care of infants suffering from the condition that afflicted Baby Joseph, and they deal with these cases on a routine basis. The decision that they made in this case concurred with the decisions that other experts typically make in similar situations; and in some jurisdictions decisions of this sort are mandated by law irrespective of the parent's wishes. The health care workers have a duty to care for the infant to the best of their ability and to do so with only the infant's best interests in mind. Most important of all, they have a duty not to perform surgery that is unlikely to produce a benefit for the patient. A less compelling reason, but no less worthy of note, is that physicians have to think of the opportunity costs of sustaining lives like Baby Joseph's. If the physicians believed that there was no benefit to keeping Baby Joseph alive, then it would be unfair to others who might benefit from such care for the physicians to continue to care for him.

Aside from the two parties immediately involved in the situation, it is important to consider two further groups: the administrators of LHSC, and society at large. The administrators of LHSC have to manage the care of a plurality of patients in a way that is efficient and designed to produce the most desirable outcomes for all. In order to do this they have to adopt general principles or best practices to guide their choices. This involves not only thinking about what certain principles imply for particular cases, but what these principles imply for all cases of the same nature. The administrators must decide how to handle cases like these and must avoid permitting exceptions that might set undesirable precedents. Finally, they have to decide issues on the basis of sound scientific evidence, rather than expediency, which would imperil the medical and scientific integrity of their institution.

The second group that it is important to consider is the community in general. The decisions that Baby

Joseph's doctors made are not isolated decisions. They take place within a society, and it is important to understand the general effects of permitting people to act in certain kinds of ways. On the one hand, one might plausibly worry that licensing physicians to act in ways that were suggested by Baby Joseph's own physicians might have a corrosive effect on how well patients like Baby Joseph are treated. On the other hand, one might worry that permitting parents to make the ultimate choice as to the sorts of medical procedures their children undergo may undermine the legitimate authority of medical and similar practitioners and result in problematic outcomes for vulnerable children and for the care of other patients.

The solution to this case involves thinking about all of the reasons enumerated above. It is determined in particular by how you weigh the various reasons against each other. This is aided by judgment, reflection, sympathy, and a keen understanding of the case's context and the particular and general outcomes of decisions about it. This is therefore a case that defies easy resolution. Most important of all, the case of Baby Joseph is not atypical. It is the sort of case that is the stock and trade of people working in bioethics and related fields. This book examines the issues raised by cases like this by relying on arguments, theories, and concepts developed by philosophers working in moral theory and political philosophy. However, the presupposition of this book is that it is a mistake to think that we can deal with these issues simply by applying a normative moral or political framework directly to them. Instead, we think that such theories are often too poorly defined and the issues too complex for this to be an option. The complexity of the case of Baby Joseph seems, quite clearly, to demonstrate this fact. It is far from obvious what the standard theories imply for this case. Our view is that it is much more productive to explore bioethical issues directly, to determine their ethical dimensions and their social complexity, and only then to rely on theories to help with the process of ethical decision-making. This set of claims runs contrary to the common idea that bioethics is simply just one part of what is often called "applied ethics," which, roughly speaking, involves the top-down and sometimes mechanical application of a moral or political theory to practical moral issues. The idea in applied ethics is that one assumes a particular moral outlook, which one then applies to some practical problem and from which one receives

a practical directive. Our orientation is that this is an impoverished view of ethics, one that is particularly ill-suited to bioethical reasoning.

Our view of the role of moral and political theory in bioethical reasoning is reflected in the organization of this book. This volume begins and ends with chapters focusing exclusively on problems in bioethics. Its core focus—in its first 12 chapters—is the most urgent bioethical problems arising between the conception and the death of the typical human being. It does not begin with a chapter in which various moral theories are outlined and explained in isolation from the problems that they help to deal with. Instead, this book is designed so that certain theoretical orientations emerge in each of the readings as part of the natural course of reasoning about what we ought to do with respect to the specific bioethical problem under consideration. We believe that this is a pedagogically more valuable way to assess the role and importance of moral theory to bioethical reasoning. It is of little value to students of bioethics to discuss theories in complete isolation from bioethical problems. The main problem that we see with the "free floating" discussion of ethical theories is that it does not do justice to the ways in which theories actually relate to practical ethical problems and are altered and modified in light of these problems. It is of little value to explain Kantianism or utilitarianism in the abstract and then to turn, for example, to the morality of medical research using adults. It is better in our view to first begin with the issues raised by such research and only then to discuss how a particular theory might deal with the issue in this context.

In addition, the thematic focus of this book's core chapters reflects the fact that bioethics is not, in our view, primarily focused on the moral problems that arise in the treatment of the autonomous human adult and only secondarily on those who fall outside this category, e.g., human embryos and children. The book's core chapters deal instead with each segment in the typical human life span and the moral problems that are germane to it. It does not treat these segments as mere deviations from the norm of the autonomous adult. Our approach to bioethical problems has the advantage of beginning with a question that is important to any ethical discussion, namely, who has moral standing? We begin by examining whether human embryos and fetuses deserve direct consideration. We stop, in chapter three, to deal with the issue of what sort of child a parent should want to produce and what sort of care they are required to provide. We then move to the issue of how we treat those with full moral standing in a variety of contexts, including medical treatment, research, the health system, and end of life care. This involves discussions of justice, both national and international, and many important conceptual issues, e.g., the definition of death, informed consent, competency, equipoise, and so on.

We believe that this book possesses a number of helpful features. First, it focuses for the most part on Canadian bioethical cases and bioethical issues raised in Canadian public policy and law. In addition, it features a substantial number of Canada's leading philosophers working in bioethics. This is therefore a book for those studying in Canada and wanting to learn about what Canada's leading minds in bioethics have to say about its most pressing problems. Second, the book includes a variety of useful tools for students. Each of the seventeen chapters comprises the following features: a set of readings designed to reflect a plurality of approaches to a single moral issue, all of which have been edited for length to better reveal its argumentative structure; a set of study questions at the conclusion of each reading, which help to focus the reader; a set of study questions at the conclusion of each chapter, which focus on the similarities and differences between the chapter's readings; a passage from one of the readings for critical analysis, which is designed to help students hone skills of analysis and criticism; a case study that is realistic and relevant to Canadian society, i.e., which deals with Canadian practices and policies; and finally, a list of suggestions

for further reading, including many online sources, for use by instructors and students looking to examine an issue more thoroughly.

There are of course many ways an instructor might use this book. Our main aim has been to provide instructors with a self-contained introductory course in bioethics lasting twelve or thirteen weeks. The book is not designed to give instructors many options within a chapter; each chapter's articles are meant to provide both diverse and often competing approaches to a problem. Time may not allow an instructor to discuss all three of the articles in each chapter. In this case, it should be noted that the first two articles in each chapter are considered its core articles, while the last is considered supplementary. We envision instructors relying heavily on the chapters in the core section of this book, chapters 1 to 12, since these chapters survey the most divisive and compelling issues in contemporary bioethics. However, some of these could be replaced or supplemented by the non-core chapters, 13 to 17. These chapters cover a range of issues, including the nature of disease, ethical issues associated with the promotion of public health, the morality of using non-human animals in research, neuroenhancement, and sexual justice and health care. The following Content Correlation Grid might be of use to instructors who choose to use this book in a way other than what is suggested by its explicit editorial design. Highlighting various themes, the grid should act as a guide when coordinating your course with the text. These are just some of the possibilities and our hope is that this book will be of use to even the most imaginative instructor.

Content Correlation Guide

	Moral Standing	Health And Justice	Ethics of Killing	Reproductive Ethics	Research Ethics	Bioethics and Autonomy	Feminism and Bioethics	Bioethics and the Marginalized
CHAPTER 1: Conception and Embryos	X		X	X	X		X	
CHAPTER 2: Fetuses	X		X	X			X	
CHAPTER 3: Procreation and Child Rearing				X			X	X
CHAPTER 4: Adults and Decision-making						X		
CHAPTER 5: Conflict about Appropriate Treatment		X				X		
CHAPTER 6: Equipoise and Clinical Research		X			X	X		
CHAPTER 7: Justice and Access to Health Care		X						
CHAPTER 8: Obligations to the Global Poor		X						X
CHAPTER 9: Assisted Suicide and Euthanasia			X			X	X	
CHAPTER 10: Defining Death	X							
CHAPTER 11: Harvesting Organs from the Dead						X		
CHAPTER 12: Bioethics in a Pluralistic Society		X						

CHAPTER 13: What is Disease?								X
CHAPTER 14: Public Health		X				X		
CHAPTER 15: Research on Non-human Animals	X		X		X			
CHAPTER 16: Neuroenhancement						X		
CHAPTER 17: Sexual Justice and Health Care		X					X	X

Conception and Embryos

I s it permissible to destroy human embryos in the context of medical research? This question is urged on us by the fact that the study of human embryos and their parts promises great health and other benefits to humans. Human embryos contain, among other things, embryonic stem cells. The study of these cells may give us insight into cell specialization, that is, into how stem cells become, for example, liver or brain cells. This in turn may provide insight into disease and its amelioration, since some diseases (e.g., cancer) occur due to problems in cell differentiation, as well as insight into the regeneration of diseased or damaged organs. In addition, research on human embryos helps to produce more effective reproductive technologies (e.g., in vitro fertilization or IVF). The cost of these benefits is, of course, that human embryos are destroyed.

> **Human embryonic stem cells**
> Undifferentiated human cells located in the human embryo with the capacity to renew themselves by means of cell division and to develop into more specialized cells, e.g., brain and liver cells.

In Canada, it is legal to create and destroy embryos for the purpose of facilitating the improvement of and instruction in assisted reproductive technology. It is also permissible (under strict conditions) to destroy embryos in the context of research on stem cells. To make sense of the morality of these and other uses of human embryos in scientific and medical research one must develop an account of moral standing, i.e., determine the class of beings who count morally. Such an account or criterion would tell us whom to consider in deliberating about the appropriate ways of pursuing our scientific and medical ambitions. An account of moral standing is a necessary feature of all ethical frameworks. We might agree that we ought to respect rights and that we ought to relieve suffering. But in order to follow these requirements it is important to determine whose suffering matters and which beings have rights. A criterion of moral standing will assist in determining this. It will specify a feature or set of features that an individual or collective must possess in order to count morally. A full interpretation of moral standing will tell us how to treat these entities.

If human embryos and perhaps some of their constituent parts matter morally, then there are moral restrictions (however weak) on what we are permitted to do to them in seeking scientific knowledge and medical benefits for humans. At some stage after the fusion of a human egg and a human sperm, or conception, an individual human embryo emerges. It is undeniable that this embryo is a member of the species Homo sapiens. What is far less clear is whether this individual is a being with moral status. It is common to assume that being Homo sapiens is a sufficient condition of having moral standing. It is, thus, by virtue of our chromosomal structure that we matter morally from the moment we come into existence. Despite its prevalence this view is difficult to defend, for it is hard to see why mere species membership provides the basis of moral standing. It seems as implausible as taking sexual orientation or race as the basis of moral standing. These things just do not seem to be the sort of features that matter. None of the authors whose works are included in this chapter seeks to defend a view based in species membership.

A more promising line of argument is that a human embryo has moral standing because it has the potential to develop into a being like you or me, an individual that clearly possesses moral standing. Because most human embryos have this potential, the argument goes, they possess moral standing, and therefore we have direct obligations to them. In particular, we have the obligation not to destroy them without compelling moral justification. This position is the focus of the first article of this chapter. In "The Moral Status of Stem Cells," Agata Sagan and Peter Singer argue that if we admit that human embryos have moral standing because they have the potential to become beings like us, there is no reason for rejecting the claim that the parts of those same embryos (e.g., stem cells) have standing, for they, too, have the potential to become beings like us. The authors argue that this is absurd and so the position that human embryos have moral standing for this reason should be rejected. They add to this that the view attributing moral standing to human embryos on the grounds that each embryo is a distinct individual with a rational nature is flawed, since an embryo does not currently possess the ability to reason. They believe that human embryos have no standing whatsoever, and that therefore we are free to use them for scientific and medical purposes.

In "The Ethical Case against Stem Cell Research," Soren Holm rejects common arguments both for and against granting human embryos moral standing. In his view, these positions lead to highly counterintuitive implications, and therefore they ought not to be relied on in seeking public policies regulating the use of human embryos in medical research. He argues further that "appeal to consistency" arguments, intended to drive people to accept the use of all manner of research on human embryos on the grounds that we already allow some embryo research, are problematic. According to Holm, it does not follow from the fact that in Canada we permit the creation and destruction of human embryos in the context of research on human reproduction and on improving reproductive technologies that we ought to permit it for the purpose of generating other medical and health benefits, since the goods at stake in each case are distinct. He suggests that the most plausible account of moral standing is gradualist in nature: moral standing develops gradually as the human develops. Accordingly, Holm contends that human embryos have some standing but less than that of the average mature adult human being. This is sufficient in his view to place a justificatory burden on those who want to destroy human embryos for medical and scientific purposes.

The third article focuses on the fact that technological advancement does not affect all members of society equally. Reproductive technology threatens to affect women more seriously than men, since they gestate and undergo reproductive therapies. Accordingly, feminist philosophers have taken a keen interest in research on human embryos. In "Feminists on the Inalienability of Human Embryos," Carolyn McLeod and Françoise Baylis argue that feminists should be wary of arguments that reject the use or commodification of human embryos on grounds that these embryos are morally inalienable to the women who produce them. This position has potentially deleterious effects on women's autonomy and reproductive freedom, in part because it fails to take account of the diversity of experience among women. Not all women view embryos that have been created using their eggs as inalienable to them. Arguments that rely on this assumption risk perpetuating the norm that women should view their embryos as inalienable. Although McLeod and Baylis do not take a stand on the moral status of human embryos, they contend that any comprehensive view must take account of the oppression and exploitation of women.

ONE The Moral Status of Stem Cells

Agata Sagan and Peter Singer | *Metaphilosophy* 2007; 38: 264-84.

Introduction

Most ethical objections to the use of stem cells are directed at the use of human embryonic stem cells—in particular, at the destruction of human embryos in order to obtain these cells. . . . But is the destruction of embryos really the key ethical issue concerning the use of human embryonic stem cells?

Embryonic stem cells are mainly derived from the inner cell mass of the embryo, from which the later stages of a human being develop. . . . This inner cell mass can, if moved to another trophoblast, develop into an adult. Do these cells perhaps have some moral status themselves, independently of the status of the embryo of which they once formed a part? . . . To set the stage for that discussion, we need to give closer attention to the nature of embryos and to the question of what human entities can develop into a mature human being. . . .

> **Trophoblast**
> The outer layer of the early embryo (or blastocyst) which attaches the embryo to the uterine wall and functions as the nutritive pathway; in addition, it plays a role in the development of the placenta.

> **Moral status (or moral standing)**
> A conception of moral standing determines the range of beings toward whom moral agents have obligations. Such a conception will tell you the feature or set of features a being must possess to count morally. For example, some argue that if an individual has the capacity to suffer, then that individual has moral standing and therefore moral agents have direct obligations to that individual.

The Beginnings of Human Life

The Definition of the Embryo

The standard sense of the term "embryo," in reference to mammals, is usually understood to refer to the entity resulting from the fertilization of the egg by the sperm, creating the zygote, until around the time when organs begin to form. . . . Although the very concept of something being an "embryo" suggests that it has the capacity to or is likely to develop into some more mature stage or adult form, in practice the term is also applied to entities that—perhaps because of some defect or because they have developed in the fallopian tube rather than in the uterus—have no possibility of developing to maturity. . . .

What Is Crucial for Development into a Being with Uncontested Moral Standing?

What, then, is crucial for the entity to be able to develop into a being that has uncontested moral standing? It seems that there must be a nucleus, with the genes needed for development, and probably some cytoplasm. (The cytoplasmic components contain resources in addition to those in the nucleus.) Everything else that is required seems to be the environment in which life develops. . . .

Stem Cells

Where Do Stem Cells Fit among the Possible Origins of a New Individual?

It is clear that even a single embryonic stem cell can, by the transfer of its nucleus into an enucleated egg, be the beginning of a new human life (Wakayama 1999). Indeed, other stem cells (with the possible exception of germ stem cells) can also be the beginning of a new human life, but it seems that embryonic stem cells, because they are not so differentiated, are better suited for cloning than any other cells. . . .

If something can develop into a new human being, should we think of it as having the moral status of an embryo? If what is important is that an entity can become an adult human being, then should not that entity have the same status as an embryo that can develop into a mature human being? . . .

Those who do think that the embryo is precious because of its potential to become a mature human being seem to be required to regard an embryonic stem cell as precious for the very same reason. One could imagine differences in the value accorded to the stem cell and the embryo, just as there could be differences between the embryo and the newborn infant, but it would seem that if the human embryo has moral standing and is entitled to protection in virtue of what it can become, then the same must be true of human embryonic stem cells. . . .

Implications of Granting Stem Cells Moral Status

If a new life is precious and entitled to protection, it seems that a minimal implication of this is that we should, if other things are equal, protect the new life from destruction and do our best to enable it to develop. What, then, would the inclusion of stem cells in the circle of precious entities require from us?

The most obvious implication is that we would not be permitted to use stem cells, no matter whether they originated from newly destroyed embryos or from stem cell lines that have been in existence for many years, or were obtained by some other method not involving the destruction of embryos at all. We would not even be permitted to use stem cells derived from adults, children, fetuses, or umbilical-cord blood. All these entities can develop into adult human beings. But that is not all. Should we allow all embryonic stem cells to grow into adults? If we accept that such entities are precious, then we would have to take the same view of all the cells of the embryo. Should we then split the early embryo and, when the resulting embryos have grown, split them again? . . . Should we also try to locate all other cells in our body that have the potential to develop into more mature human beings, take as many as possible, and enable them to do so? . . . No society on earth . . . does any of this. We do not even consider ourselves obliged to split the early embryo, which is an easy and reliable way of allowing its cells to develop into human beings. Nor do we support research that will facilitate future attempts to allow all of these entities to realize their potential. We don't seriously entertain the notion of striving to actualize the potential of every entity that could become an adult human being. . . .

Objections

In a recent essay, Patrick Lee and Robert George (2006a) have responded to claims that are in some respects similar to those that we have made above. . . . Ultimately Lee and George assert that the embryo has a right to life not because it is a potential human being but because "*as a matter of basic biological fact* human embryos are *actual* human beings in the earliest stages of their natural development. (2006a)" To support this claim, they seek to draw a line between what is and what is not a human being in a way that does not imply that every cell that could become a human being is also an actual human being. . . .

What Entities have a **Rational Nature**?

The final two paragraphs of Lee and George's essay give the crucial steps in their argument:

> **Rational nature**
> The capacity to reason freely about what to do and about what to believe.

"*Some entities have intrinsic value and basic rights and other entities do not. Such a radical moral difference logically must be based on a radical onto-logical difference (that is, a radical difference among those entities themselves). And so the basis for that moral difference (a difference in the way they should be treated) must be the natures of those entities, not their accidental characteristics which involve merely quantitative differences,* or *differences in degree. (By "accidental" qualities, we mean those attributes that do not help to define the nature of an entity. In humans, age, size, stage of development, state of health, and so forth are accidental qualities.) The immediately exercisable capacity to reason and make free choices is only the development of the underlying basic, natural capacity for reasoning and free choice, and there are various degrees of that development along a continuum. But one either is or is not a distinct subject with a rational nature (the traditional definition of "*person*"). So, Singer is correct to say that the right to life must be based on what is true of the entity now, not just what is true of its future. But it is true of the human embryo now that he or she is a distinct individual with a rational nature, even though it will take him or her several years fully* to actualize his or her basic, natural capacities so they are immediately exercisable.

> **Ontological**
> Ontology is the study of the ultimate constituents of the universe. To make an ontological claim is to make a claim about the nature and characteristics of what exists in the universe.

> **Person**
> A philosophically controversial notion. A person is an individual (not necessarily human) possessing certain higher order cognitive capacities and abilities (e.g., the capacity for self-awareness and awareness of one's self over time).

Our conclusion: Every human being, irrespective of age, size, condition of dependency, or stage of development—or the means by which he or she is produced—is intrinsically valuable as a subject of rights and deserves full moral respect."

An obvious question to ask about this passage is whether the notion of "development" is sufficiently distinct from the notion of "potentiality" to bear the weight here placed upon it. Given that we all agree that the human embryo in its present form cannot reason, has never been able to reason, and will not be able to reason for a long time, or possibly will never be able to reason, is it more accurate to say that the human embryo "is a distinct individual with a rational nature" or to say that the human embryo "is a distinct individual with the potential to become a rational being?" In our view, the former description is misleading. The embryo does not have "a rational nature." What it has is the genetic coding that may, under favourable circumstances, lead it to develop into a being with a rational nature. . . .

From the Factual Claim to the Moral Claim

Even if we were to accept Lee and George's ontological claim, that would bring us no nearer to the moral conclusion they set forth in the final paragraph of their essay, that the embryo "is intrinsically valuable as a subject of rights and deserves full moral respect." For if we define "rational nature" as they define it, we can still resist the claim that having a rational nature . . . suffices for being a subject of rights, or being intrinsically valuable, or deserving of moral respect. Rather, it would seem that the morally relevant characteristic on which such claims of value should be based is "the immediately exercisable capacity to reason and make free choices."

> **Intrinsically valuable**
> If a thing (e.g., pleasure) has intrinsic value, then it is worth having or pursing for its own sake, which need not rule out that it is worth having or pursuing for other reasons.
>
> **Rights**
> A specific kind of moral constraint on what it is permissible to do in the service of some worthy goal. If you have a right against torture, then at the very least others have a reason not to torture you to, e.g., promote social well-being or security.

Why do we say this? Consider the grounds on which we may hold that gratuitously killing a being "like us" is an especially grave wrong—that is, a wrong that far exceeds any wrong we may commit in gratuitously killing a dog or a pig. . . . We might say that to kill a being like us is an especially grave wrong because it involves the violation of the autonomous will of the being who is killed. Or we might say that it is an especially grave wrong because it thwarts the hopes and desires that beings like us have for the future. . . . But it is not a being's "rational nature" in the Lee and George sense that gives rise to a violation of autonomy or the thwarting of hopes and desires for the future. Rather, it is the immediately exercisable—or at least, to take account of cases of temporary unconsciousness, previously exercised—capacity to reason that is required for killing to have these effects. This strongly suggests that these aspects of a person's existence are more relevant to the wrongness of killing than whether the being is of such a nature that it will eventually be able to exercise a capacity to reason.

When Lee and George assert that a radical moral difference between entities that have intrinsic value and basic rights and entities that lack such value and rights must be based on "the natures of those entities, not their accidental characteristics," they beg several questions. They seem to assume a sharp dichotomy between, on the one hand, beings that have intrinsic value and basic rights and, on the other hand, beings that lack such value and rights. Such a dichotomy may be convenient for law and public standards of ethics, but we should not assume that it exists in nature. We may grant that rocks have no intrinsic value or basic rights, and that beings capable of exercising a capacity to reason do have both intrinsic value and basic rights, but there are many intermediate cases. The gradual development of the embryo, fetus, and child suggests one ground for the existence of intermediate cases. . . .

More significantly, the question of whether a given characteristic defines the nature of an entity or is accidental to it cannot be used as an argument that seeks to answer the question, what kind of beings have intrinsic value and rights? *First* we must decide what kind of being has intrinsic value and rights, and only then can we say what characteristics define its nature and what are accidental to it. We must not here say, "We already know that all and only human beings have intrinsic value and rights, so the answer is that you must be a human being." That assumes the conclusion that Lee and George need to establish. There may be better answers. We might, for instance, answer that it is conscious beings who have intrinsic value and rights. Or we could say that it is self-aware beings, or beings with an exercisable or previously exercised capacity to reason, who have this special moral status. If we give such answers, then "the nature of the entities" that gives them intrinsic value and basic rights just *is* their consciousness or self-awareness or exercisable or previously exercised capacity to reason, and these things are not "accidental" to that nature—they are its defining characteristics. Being human, on the other hand, or having a particular genetic code then becomes accidental, since conscious and self-aware beings do not have to be human or have any specific genetic code. Lee and George simply assume that we must be looking for the kind of "nature" that persists through all stages of a being's biological life, and they label some features as "accidental" from this perspective. . . .

Conclusion

Once we understand the full range of biological possibilities of producing new human beings, we have a new perspective on the beginning of life. These biological possibilities raise particular difficulties for the claim that the embryo should be protected because it has the potential to become a more mature human being. To cling to this view, we would have to take seriously all its far-reaching implications and make choices over a vast number of potential human lives.

How would we make such choices? One possible answer is that, in a world with more than a billion people living below the World Bank's poverty line, and millions of people dying every year from poverty-related causes, any prima facie obligation we might have to facilitate the development of additional human beings is overwhelmed by the fact that they would compete for scarce resources with those who already exist and would add to existing pressures on the natural environment. If, however, we believe that we should protect at least some of those entities with the potential to become mature human beings, how are we to decide which ones to protect? . . . Some people will not be comfortable with making such choices,

> **Prima facie**
> A Latin phrase meaning "at first glance" or "apparent."

on a large scale, especially when the choices will be between identical cells from the same embryo or adult, and we have to decide which among them will live and which will not. But not choosing is a kind of choice too, because it means that the cell will never develop as it could. Not choosing means that a possible human being will not exist.

These implications amount to something very close to a reductio ad absurdum of the claim that human embryos must not be destroyed because of their potential. It is, if not strictly a logical absurdity, at least a position that no one could seriously set out to put into practice.

Finally, we have considered and rejected one argument for the view that the human embryo is not merely potentially but actually a being of intrinsic value with basic rights. . . .

> **Reductio ad absurdum**
> A form of argumentation that attempts to show that we should reject an argument's conclusion or one of its premises on the basis of the fact that it has implications that are absurd or impossible to accept.

The most obvious way to avoid the difficulties we have considered is to turn to the alternative view that at the beginning of life human entities lack the requirements for moral status. They lack not only those attributes that are linked to personhood, like self-awareness, but also more basic things, like sentience or the capacity to feel pain. Therefore unless there is some other reason to keep them alive—for example, the wishes of their parents—we may use them as we please. . . . Our judgment is that human entities at the beginning of life do not have moral status, and hence the use of them for research purposes is justifiable. Moreover, because this research could lead to cures for diseases that are now fatal, it might be obligatory.

> **Sentience**
> The capacity to feel or experience pleasure and pain.

Study Questions

1. Which two positions claiming that embryos have moral status do Sagan and Singer evaluate?

2. Why do Sagan and Singer describe their main argument against the claim that human embryos have moral status because they have the potential to develop into mature human beings as "very close to a reductio ad absurdum"?

3. What would we have to presuppose about ethical obligations to justify the claim that it would be obligatory to use stem cells for scientific research?

References

American Association for Advancement of Science and Institute for Civil Society. 1999. *Stem Cell Research and Application: Monitoring the Frontiers of Biomedical Research*, http://www.aaas.org/spp/sfrl/projects/stem/report.pdf (last accessed 12 December 2006).

Austriaco, Nicanor Pier Giorgio. 2005. "Are Teratomas Embryos or Non-embryos? A Criterion for Oocyte-Assisted Reprogramming." *National Catholic Bioethics Quarterly 5*, no. 4 (Winter):697-706.

Bailey, Ronald. 2001a. "Are Stem Cells Babies? Only if Every Other Human Cell Is, Too." *Reason Online* (11 July), http://reason.com/rb/rb071101.shtml (last accessed 12 December 2006).

———. 2001b. "My Critics Are Wrong: Why Using Human Embryonic Stem Cells for Medical Research Is Moral." *National Review Online* (25 July), http://www.nationalreview.com/comment/comment-baileyprint072501.html (last accessed 12 December 2006).

Bush, George W. 2001. "President Discusses Stem Cell Research." White House news release (9 August), http://www.whitehouse.gov/news/releases/2001/08/20010809-2.html (last accessed 12 December 2006).

———. 2005. "President Discusses Embryo Adoption and Ethical Stem Cell Research." White House news release (24 May), http://www.whitehouse.gov/news/releases/2005/05/20050524-12.html (last accessed 12 December 2006).

———. 2006. "President Discusses Stem Cell Research Policy." White House news release (19 July), http://www.whitehouse.gov/news/releases/2006/07/20060719-3.html (last accessed 12 December 2006).

Chen Ying, Zhi Xu He, Ailian Liu, Kai Wang, Wen Wei Mao, Jian Xin Chu, Yong Lu, Zheng Fu Fang, Ying Tang Shi, Qing Zhang Yang, Da Yuan Chen, Min Kang Wang, Jin Song Li, Shao Liang Huang, Xiang Yin Kong, Yao Zhou Shi, Zhi Qiang Wang, Jia Hui Xia, Zhi Gao Long, Zhi Gang Xue, Wen Xiang Ding, and Hui Zhen Sheng. 2003. "Embryonic Stem Cells Generated by Nuclear Transfer of Human Somatic Nuclei into Rabbit Oocytes." *Cell Research* 13, no. 4:251-63.

Coalition for the Advancement of Medical Research Dedicated to Advancing Stem Cell Research. No date. "Alternative Methods of Producing Stem Cells: No Substitute for Embryonic Stem Cell Research," http://www.stemcellfunding.org/resources/Why_Alternatives_Summary.htm (last accessed 12 December 2006).

Colman, Alan. 1999. "Review of *Somatic Cell Nuclear Transfer in Mammals: Progress and Applications*." *Cloning* 1, no. 4:185-200.

Congregation for the Doctrine of Faith. 1987. *Instruction for Respect for Human Life*. Vatican City: Vatican Polyglot Press.

Hochedlinger, K., and R. Jaenisch. 2002. "Generation of Monoclonal Mice by Nuclear Transfer from Mature B and T Donor Cells." *Nature* 415, no. 6875:1035-38.

Huang, Steve C., et al. (Helen Lin, JingQi Lei, David Wininger, Minh-Thanh Nguyen, Ruchi Khanna, Chris Hartmann, Wen-Liang Yan, and Steve C. Huang). "Multilineage Potential of Homozygous Stem Cells Derived from Metaphase II Oocytes." *Stem Cells* 21, no. 2:152-61.

Hudson, Kathy L., Joan Scott, and Ruth Faden. 2005. *Values in Conflict: Public Attitudes on Embryonic Stem Cell Research*. Washington, D.C.: Genetics and Public Policy Center, Phoebe R. Berman Bioethics Institute, Johns Hopkins University, http://www.dnapolicy.org/images/reportpdfs/2005ValuesInConflict.pdf (last accessed 12 December 2006).

Hurlbut, William B. 2004. "Altered Nuclear Transfer as a Morally Acceptable Means for the Procurement of Human Embryonic Stem Cells." Commissioned working paper discussed at the President's Council on Bioethics at the meeting in December 2004, http://www.bioethics.gov/background/hurlbut.html (last accessed 12 December 2006).

Jaenisch, R., et al. (Kevin Eggan, Kristin Baldwin, Michael Tackett, Joseph Osborne, Joseph Gogos, Andrew Chess, Richard Axel, and Rudolf Jaenisch). 2004. "Mice Cloned from Olfactory Sensory Neurons." *Nature* 428, no. 6978:44-49.

Kono Tomohiro, Yayoi Obata, Quiong Wu, Katsutoshi Niwa, Yukiko Ono, Yuji Yamamoto, Eun Sung Park, Jeong-Sun Seo, and Hidehiko Ogawa. 2004. "Birth of Parthenogenetic Mice That Can Develop to Adulthood." *Nature* 428, no. 6985:860-64.

Kuhse, Helga. 1987. *The Sanctity-of-Life Doctrine in Medicine: A Critique*. Oxford: Clarendon Press.

Landry, Donald W., and Howard A. Zucker. 2004. "Embryonic Death and the Creation of Human Embryonic Cells." *Journal of Clinical Investigation* 114, no. 9:1184-86.

Lanza, Robert, et al. (Irina Klimanskaya, Young Chung, Sandy Becker, Shi-Jiang Lu, and Robert Lanza). 2006. "Human Embryonic Stem Cell Lines Derived from Single Blastomeres." *Nature* 444, no. 7118:481-85.

Lee, Patrick, and Robert George. 2001a. "Reason, Science and Stem Cells: Why Killing Embryonic Human Beings Is Wrong." *National Review Online* (20 July), http://www.nationalreview.com/comment/comment-georgeprint072001.html (last accessed 12 December 2006).

———. 2001b. "The Stubborn Facts of Science: Human Embryos Are Human Beings." *National Review Online* (30 July), http://www.nationalreview.com/comment/comment-georgeprint073001.html (last accessed 12 December 2006).

———. 2006a. "Human-Embryo Liberation: A Reply to Peter Singer." *National Review Online* (25 January), http://www.nationalreview.com/comment/lee_george200601250829.asp (last accessed 12 December 2006).

———. 2006b. "Fundamentalists? We? Bad Science, Worse Philosophy, and McCarthyite Tactics in the Human-Embyro Debate." *National Review Online* (3 October), http://article.nationalreview.com/?q=OTNiYWM2ZjJi YWVlN2IyMzFjOWYwMDZmMTc4MzU2MGU (last accessed 12 December 2006).

———. 2006c. "Silver Lining: A Reply to Lee Silver." *National Review Online* (19 October), http://article. nationalreview.com/?q=MjNmZmYyN2NhNjFkYW RhNmExMDA2YzhiMDY5YzMyYTI=(last accessed 12 December 2006).

Melton, Douglas A., et al. (Chad A. Cowan, Jocelyn Atienza, Douglas A. Melton, and Kevin Eggan). 2005. "Nuclear Reprogramming of Somatic Cells after Fusion with Human Embryonic Stem Cells." *Science* 309, no. 5739:1369-73.

Nagy, A., J. Rossant, R. Nagy, W. Abramow-Newerly, and J. C. Roder. 1993. "Derivation of Completely Cell Culture–Derived Mice from Early-Passage Embryonic Stem Cells." *Proceedings of the National Academy of Sciences of the USA* 90, no. 18:8424-28.

NIH Stem Cell Task Force. 2005. "Alternative Methods of Obtaining Embryonic Stem Cells." Presented by James F. Battey, Subcommittee on Labor, Health and Human Services, Education, and Related Agencies, Committee on Appropriations, United States Senate (12 July), http:// stemcells.nih.gov/policy/statements/20050712battey. asp (last accessed 12 December 2006).

Ozil, J. P. 1983. "Production of Identical Twins by Bisection of Blastocysts in the Cow." *Journal of Reproduction and Fertility* 69, no. 22:463-68.

Peters, Ted. 2001. "The Stem Cell Controversy." *Dialog: A Journal of Theology* 40, no. 4 (Winter):290-3.

Peters, Ted, and Gaymon Bennett. 2001. "Theological Support of Stem Cell Research." *Scientist* 15, no. 17 (3 September): 4.

Savulescu, Julian. 1999. "Should We Clone Human Beings?" *Journal of Medical Ethics* 25, no. 2:87-98.

Schnieke, Angelika, E. Alexander, J. Kind, William A. Ritchie, Karen Mycock, Angela R. Scott, Marjorie Ritchie, Ian Wilmut, Alan Colman, and Keith H. S. Campbell. 1997. "Human Factor IX Transgenic Sheep Produced by Transfer of Nuclei from Transfected Fetal Fibroblasts." *Science* 278, no. 5346:2130-33.

Silva José , Ian Chambers, Steven Pollard, and Austin Smith. 2006. "Nanog Promotes Transfer of Pluripotency after Cell Fusion." *Nature* 441, no. 7096:997-1001.

Silver, Lee M. 2006a. *Challenging Nature: The Clash of Science and Spirituality at the New Frontiers of Life*. New York: Ecco.

———. 2006b. "Human Issues." *National Review Online* (19 October), http://article.nationalreview.com/?q=Mjg2 Y2RkNDM1MzlkMGMyMjI3NjhkYmE0ZTRjOTgyZDE (last accessed 12 December 2006).

Singer, Peter. 1993. *Practical Ethics*. 2nd edition. Cambridge: Cambridge University Press.

———. 2001. *Animal Liberation*. 2nd edition. New York: Ecco.

Steinbock, Bonnie, and Alastair Norcross (editors). 1994. *Killing and Letting Die*. 2nd edition. New York: Fordham University Press.

Stice, S. L., and C. L. Keefer. 1993. "Multiple Generational Bovine Embryo Cloning." *Biology of Reproduction* 48, no. 4:715-19.

Stojkovic, M., P. Stojkovic, C. Leary, V. J. Hall, L. Armstrong, M. Herbert, M. Nesbitt, M. Lako, and A. Murdoch. 2005. "Derivation of a Human Blastocyst after Heterologous Nuclear Transfer to Donated Oocytes." *Reproductive BioMedicine* 11, no. 2:226-31.

Takahashi, Kazutoshi, and Shinya Yamanaka. 2006. "Induction of Pluripotent Stem Cells from Mouse Embryonic and Adult Fibroblast Cultures by Defined Factors." *Cell* 126, no. 4:663-76.

Wakayama, Teruhiko, Ivan Rodriguez, Anthony C. F. Perry, Ryuzo Yanagimachi, and Peter Mombaerts. 1999. "Mice Cloned from Embryonic Stem Cells." *Proceedings of the National Academy of Sciences of the USA* 96, no. 26:14984-89.

Wakayama, Teruhiko, Yoichi Shinkai, Kellie L. K. Tamashiro, Hiroyuki Niida, D. Caroline Blanchard, Robert J. Blanchard, Atsuo Ogura, Kentaro Tanemura, Makoto Tachibana, Anthony C. F. Perry, Diana F. Colgan, Peter Mombaerts, and Ryuzo Yanagimachi. 2000. "Cloning of Mice to Six Generations." *Nature* 407, no. 6802:318-19.

Wikipedia. No date. S.v. "Humanzee," http://en.wikipedia. org/wiki/Humanzee (last accessed 12 December 2006).

Wilcox, A. J., C. R. Weinberg, J. F. O'Connor, D. D. Baird, J. P. Schlatterer, R. E. Canfield, E. G. Armstrong, and B. C. Nisula. 1988. "Incidence of Early Loss of Pregnancy." *New England Journal of Medicine* 319, no. 4:189-94.

Willadsen, S. M. 1979. "A Method for Cultured Micromanipulated Sheep Embryos and Its Use to Produce Monozygotic Twins." *Nature* 277, no. 5694:298-300.

———. 1986. "Nuclear Transplantation in Sheep Embryos." *Nature* 320, no. 6057:63-5.

Wilmut, I., A. E. Schnieke, J. McWhir, A. J. Kind, and K. H. S. Campbell. 1997. "Viable Offspring Derived from Fetal and Adult Mammalian Cells." *Nature* 385, no. 6619:810-13.

Yang, X., Tao Cheng, et al. (Li-Ying Sung, Shaorong Gao, Hongmei Shen, Hui Yu, Yifang Song, Sadie L Smith, Ching-Chien Chang, Kimiko Inoue, Lynn Kuo, Jin Lian, Ao Li, X. Cindy Tian, David P. Tuck, Sherman M. Weissman, Xiangzhong Yang, and Tao Cheng). 2006. "Differentiated Cells Are More Efficient than Adult Stem Cells for Cloning by Somatic Cell Nuclear Transfer." *Nature Genetics* 38, no. 11:1323-28.

TWO   The Ethical Case against Stem Cell Research

Soren Holm | *Cambridge Quarterly of Health Care* 2003; 12: 372-383.

Introduction

The possibility of creating human embryonic stem cell lines from the inner cell mass of blastocysts has led to considerable debate about how these scientific developments should be regulated. Part of this debate has focused on the ethical analysis and part on how this analysis should influence policymaking.[1]

> **Blastocyst**
> A very early stage of the embryo. It contains an inner-cell mass from which stem cells are derived, fluid, and an outer layer of cells known as the trophoblast.

In this paper, I want to look at both issues and present the best arguments against the derivation of human stem cells in a way that leads to the destruction or killing of the human entity of which they are a part. . . .

The discussion falls in three parts. I first present a critical analysis of the most common arguments showing that the derivation and use of stem cells are morally unproblematic. I then look at the arguments showing that the derivation and use of stem cells are problematic. . . . Following this, I analyze the policy stalemate that these two opposing views lead to and consider the suggestion that the stalemate can be resolved by requiring consistency between different areas of regulation.

The Reductio of the Pro-Stem Cell Arguments

By far the most common pro-stem cell argument is that derivation of human embryonic stem cells is morally innocuous because human embryos have no moral status. By analyzing their characteristics, we can see that they are not persons and that it is not wrong to kill them, and we can also see that they do not qualify for any kind of "lower" moral status (for instance, based on sentience). . . . I call this "the standard liberal argument."

One main problem with this argument is that it proves far too much. . . . First, and perhaps most important, it justifies the (nonpainful) killing and use of any prepersonal human entity from the fertilized egg to the prepersonal infant. Such a killing can be justified by any kind of net benefit to others. In the current context, it can therefore just as easily justify the killing of infants for their stem cells as it can the destruction of embryos for the same purpose. There is no in principle difference between the two killings.[2]

Second, it places no restrictions on the use of biological material from prepersonal human entities that can justify the destruction of these entities, as long as those uses are beneficial. The derivation of a new and effective antiwrinkle cream can therefore be a perfectly acceptable justification for the production and destruction of embryos (or fetuses or infants, although the price would probably be quite high for the infant-derived variety). . . .

Another type of pro-stem cell argument tries to bypass the question of moral status by showing that stem cell derivation is justified on direct consequentialist grounds. If the good that can be attained is of a sufficient magnitude, then it can outweigh the killing of a certain number of human entities. It is justified to sacrifice some for the benefit of others. . . .

> **Consequentialism**
> The moral view stating that the rightness or wrongness of an action or rule or policy is determined solely by the goodness or badness of the states of affairs that it produces.

This kind of argument may again prove too much—for instance, that it is also justified to sacrifice some adults if the benefits to others are sufficient. . . .

The Anti-Stem Cell Arguments

The direct arguments against the derivation of human embryonic stem cells, like the standard liberal argument, focus on the moral status of the embryo. The standard restrictive argument proceeds from the premise that the life of human individuals is intrinsically valuable at all stages of life. Killing or destroying a human being is, therefore, always *pro tanto* wrong (or, to put it differently, the act always contains at least one wrong-making feature).

The most radical version of the standard restrictive argument claims that all human beings have the same value. On this view, destroying embryos is just as bad as destroying adults, and it seems to rule out any kind of destructive stem cell derivation from embryos (at least if the direct consequentialist argument discussed above does not go through). This view leads to a number of counterintuitive conclusions in other areas if it is pursued rigorously. It rules out abortion in most, or perhaps all, cases and would, for instance, definitely rule out abortions in cases of rape. It would also put a stop to all kinds of IVF involving the generation of supernumerary embryos and all destructive embryo experiments aimed at improving IVF. It would, finally, also commit us to doing much more to prevent loss of embryos or fetuses during normal reproduction.

Others, including myself, have argued that, although human life is intrinsically valuable at all stages of life, it generally becomes more valuable during the development from fertilized egg to adult human being. This is either argued on the basis of potentiality or on the basis that as the developing human being acquires new characteristics the act of killing it entails more and more wrong-making features (because it deprives it of more and more of what it has, as well as of everything it will get in the future). . . . [3]

On a gradualist analysis of the moral status of the human being through its developmental stages, destroying embryos is always wrong to some degree and cannot be done just for any kind of benefit. One great advantage of a gradualist analysis applied to stem cell research is that it can explain why destructive use of embryos for stem cell production is less problematic than the destructive use of fetuses, or infants.

But if embryos have value, the question is whether the benefits of stem cell research are of the right kind and large enough to justify the destruction of some valuable embryos. The benefits definitely seem to be of the right kind. Helping or perhaps even curing people who are suffering from horrendous diseases is clearly an ethically worthwhile activity and a good goal to pursue.[4] But what about the magnitude of the benefit; is it also large enough?

One way of answering this question is by finding some other analogous activity where we sacrifice embryos to produce some good. It has been argued by my colleague John Harris that "normal" reproduction is such an activity.[5] For every pregnancy brought to term, on average 3–5 embryos fail to implant or undergo spontaneous abortion some time during pregnancy. Harris argues that, if we accept that loss of embryos by engaging in reproduction (or just not protecting against reproduction), we are forced by

reasons of consistency also to allow similar sacrifice of embryos for goals of equal importance. Let us for the sake of argument accept Harris' analysis.[6] How much embryonic stem cell research would it commit us to allowing?

If the trade-off is one life produced for every six embryos used, probably not very much. First, we have to remember that we cannot just count lives saved by stem cell therapies and assume that if we save one life for every six embryos destroyed we will be ethically all right. We can save the same life many times, and it is questionable whether every new saving counts equally. If I am hand-ventilating a patient, do I save his life anew with every compression of the ventilation bag?[7] We also have to take account of the fact that many stem cell therapies are not lifesaving but life extending or quality-of-life enhancing. We therefore need a metric that can take account of all of these considerations. One such metric is the QALY (quality adjusted life year). QALYs have many problems, but none of them should be of relevance to the following analysis. Assuming a low-average life span of 72 years for a newborn, the "normal" trade-off works out as 12 life years per embryo, or, if we assume that some of these are of lower quality than others so that the net QALY gain per newborn is only 60 QALYs, we still have a trade-off of 10 QALYs per embryo.

A recent paper from one of the well-known groups in the field reports the generation of one definite and two possible embryonic stem cell lines from 50 blastocysts (and 101 fertilized eggs).[8] If we assume that all the cell lines are true embryonic stem cells, this is equivalent to a 1 in 16.6 ratio between embryo use and cell line production.

If all three cell lines turned out to be therapeutically useful, it would thus seem that they would each have to produce health improvements equivalent to at least 166 QALYs to be equivalent to normal human reproduction.[9] It is, however, unlikely that all the cell lines generated will ever have any therapeutic usefulness. Many will only be used for basic research, and others will be discarded because they are less easy to work with than other similar lines. It might also be the case that the use of adult stem cell lines derived in nondestructive ways will become the preferred option in a number of therapeutic areas, or we may be able to create stem cells without the involvement of embryos, both developments leaving the derived embryonic stem cell lines unproductive. We are still at such an early stage of development that we have no way of estimating how many of the stem cell lines that are derived will eventually be used for therapeutic purposes. But, all in all, the considerations here indicate that on this type of consistency argument the stem cell lines that are actually used would have to produce major therapeutic benefits. . . .

The Policy Stalemate

A policy stalemate can be discerned in every country where public policy has been formulated on human embryonic stem cells. Neither side of the debate has a policy that is consistent with the full implications of its arguments,[10] and neither side seems very interested in pressing for such a fully consistent policy!

This situation should perhaps in itself make us wary of trying to decide public policy based purely on consistency arguments (because they seem to be very selectively employed), but let us nevertheless as good philosophers try to see how far consistency will get us when applied to the regulation of stem cell research.

When consistency is invoked concerning public policy, the claim is that certain features of current regulation in a specific area logically (or perhaps slightly weaker, morally) commit regulators to regulate new areas in a specific way for reasons of consistency or parity of reasoning.[11] This type of argument occurs in two subtypes. The first subtype is:

1. Authority X promulgates regulation R.
2. X puts forward an incomplete argument A supporting R.
3. A can be made complete by the addition of premises P1–Pn.
4. The complete argument A will (perhaps with the addition of some further premises that X accepts) also support regulation C.
5. X is therefore, by parity of reasoning, committed to accept regulation C.

The second subtype is:

1. Authority X promulgates regulation R.
2. The justification for R can be reconstructed as argument A*.
3. The argument A* will (perhaps with the addition of some further premises that X accepts) also support regulation C.

4. X is therefore, by parity of reasoning, committed to accept regulation C.

These "official policy" based arguments may fail if our reconstruction and completion of the underlying arguments are wrong, but a further possible mode of failure occurs if the regulation R has been promulgated in a situation where R is the result of a compromise, either because X has openly engaged in a compromise with some other group or because X has already taken the views of some other group into account when drafting the regulation (for instance, to ensure a smooth passage through the political process). If a regulation is based on a political compromise, it may well be the case that no one wants to defend or justify the position reached in the regulation, except as a legitimate result of a legitimate political process. . . .[12]

A consistency argument based on official policy also needs to take into account that there are limits to the preciseness with which one can draft regulation and that ethically extraneous factors play a role. . . .

In evaluating official policy it is also very important not to forget that the ideal policy has to be both locally and globally coherent and consistent and that maximal coherence in a body of regulations may be achieved by allowing some local inconsistencies. . . .

In the context of stem cell research, one particular consistency argument is often put forward claiming that, because destructive research using embryos for certain purposes is already allowed in a given jurisdiction, consistency requires that we allow the destructive use of embryos for stem cell research.[13,14]

Many countries that presently allow experiments on embryos restrict these experiments to those related to improving reproductive technologies and increasing our understanding of the biology of human reproduction. Many types of stem cell research fall outside this restriction and are therefore not permitted even though the jurisdictions in question allow other forms of research on embryos.

Can a restriction of embryo research to reproductive matters be justified?

The decision to allow embryo research for a restricted range of research questions could possibly be reconstructed as an attempt to achieve consistency in a situation where embryo research is believed to be (somewhat) ethically problematic.[15] Most legal regulation of embryo research occurs within the broader context of regulation of assisted reproductive technologies, and it is evident that these technologies could only have been developed, and can only be improved, if embryo research is permitted. Any legislation that allows the use of assisted reproductive technologies and prohibits embryo research could therefore be charged with a form of performative inconsistency, by prohibiting a necessary step in the development and improvement of a permitted technique.[16]

Would it then be inconsistent not to allow research using embryos with no connection to reproduction?

Michael Walzer has famously argued that society contains several separate "spheres of justice" and that the application of principles of justice from one sphere to another is not necessarily warranted.[17] Maybe there are also separate "spheres of consistency" when we discuss the consistency of public regulations. This is not as strange an idea as it might perhaps initially seem. Walzer's argument for different spheres of justice is that different social goods are different and that, unless we understand and take account of this difference in our analysis of justice, we will go wrong. He writes:

> "No account of the meaning of a social good, or of the sphere within which it legitimately operates, will be uncontroversial. Nor is there any neat procedure for generating or testing different accounts. At best, the arguments will be rough, reflecting the diverse and conflict-ridden character of the social life that we seek simultaneously to understand and to regulate—but not to regulate until we understand. I shall set aside, then, all claims made on behalf of any single distributive criterion, for no such criterion can possibly match the diversity of social goods."[18]

In the same way as different social goods are different, the different social practices aimed at producing these social goods are different. The practices involved in reproduction and in securing the goods secured by reproduction are different from the practices involved in research. There is thus no prima facie

reason to believe that arguments and conclusions valid in one of these areas can be transferred without modification to the other area. Let me try to illustrate this.

In the area of reproductive ethics the idea that there is a strong right to reproductive freedom or reproductive liberty has gained currency in recent years. If a given permissive legal regulation has been passed because of an appreciation of this right (for instance, concerning the creation, use, and destruction of embryos in the sphere of ARTs [assisted reproductive technologies]), then it is not immediately obvious that consistency requires the same kind of permissive regulation outside of the sphere of reproduction. A right to reproductive liberty cannot, for instance, in itself support a permission to use embryos for nonreproduction-related purposes, such as stem cell research! And, given that the right to reproductive liberty is most often justified by arguments pointing to the central position of reproductive projects in the lives of (most) people, it also follows that the consideration justifying a right to reproductive liberty cannot directly support the production of embryos for nonreproduction-related purposes (whether they be research or other purposes). . . . .

Conclusion

These conclusions are all negative but should not, on reflection, be terribly controversial.[19] The positive, but controversial, conclusion is that at least some of these problems can be resolved by adopting a gradualist position on the moral status of the embryo. If we adopt a gradualist position, we will find that we need good reasons to perform any kind of experiments on embryos but that such experiments are not ruled out tout court. This means that it is up to the scientists to present convincing arguments that destructive embryonic stem cell research is necessary to produce cures and treatments for important human diseases.

Tout court
To rule something out in this way means ruling it out without qualification or completely.

Study Questions

1. What reasons does Holm give for rejecting what he calls "the standard liberal argument"?

2. What is Holm's argument for the claim that we cannot rely on consistency arguments to move from

the fact that we permit the destruction of human embryos in the context of research on human reproduction to the claim that we ought to permit their destruction in medical research relating to disease and its amelioration?

3. Holm argues that a gradualist position on the moral standing of the embryo is the most plausible conception of moral standing. What would such a view look like? What would moral status in this case be based on?

Notes

1. For a review of the debate, see: Holm S. Going to the roots of the stem cell controversy. *Bioethics* 2002;16:493–507.
2. We might try to say that, if we want to kill the prepersonal infant for its stem cells, we need the permission of its parents and that the parents are then obliged to take the best interests of the infant into account (and presumably not allow the killing). This may be correct in law, because the law considers every born human being as a person, but it is not morally justifiable on the standard argument. If the infant is not a person, the parents are not proxy decision makers but simply decision makers for a piece of property in which they have invested time and resources.
3. Holm S. The moral status of the pre-personal human being: the argument from potential reconsidered. In: Evans D, ed. *Conceiving the Embryo*. Dordrecht: Kluwer; 1996:193–220.
4. Whether the same can be said about basic biological research using human embryonic stem cells is another matter.
5. Harris J. The ethical use of human embryonic stem cells in research and therapy. In: Burley J, Harris J, eds. *A Companion to Genetics*. Oxford: Blackwell; 2002:158–74.
6. Most gradualists would probably argue that embryos have more value than one-sixth of an adult life and that the reason we "allow" loss of embryos in reproduction is not primarily connected to the value of the embryos.
7. This issue is quite complex, and intuitions may vary from case to case. Here is one more case supporting the line I take on repeated savings. Let us imagine that by killing one person and removing his organs we can get five organs that are life saving for others. This might, on a utilitarian analysis, justify the killing as shown by John Harris in his famous survival lottery paper. But would it also justify killing the one person in a situation where we knew that a person would need the five organs sequentially over a period of 25 years—that is, where we had five lifesaving episodes, but all of these were lifesaving for the same person? In my book, this would be to kill one person to save the life of one other person—not killing one to save five.
8. Lanzendorf SE, Boyd CA, Wright DL, Muasher S, Oehninger S, Hodgen GD. Use of human gametes obtained from anonymous donors for the production of human embryonic stem cell lines. *Fertility and Sterility* 2001;76(1):132–7.
9. This, by the way, indicates that it is quite unlikely that this consistency argument could ever show individually targeted stem cell production (for instance, by nuclear replacement) to be ethically acceptable. Unless longevity increases enormously it will simply be close to impossible to generate the requisite number of QALYs or unadjusted life years. This will be the case even if you could use the same cell line for a number of different therapies in the same person. It will still be very difficult to cram 166 QALYs into one life.
10. It is important to note that this is true both in restrictive and liberal jurisdictions. The restrictive regulations of the United States are not nearly restrictive enough and the liberal regulations of the United Kingdom not nearly liberal enough to match the philosophical arguments.
11. The following section is a slightly amended section from my paper Parity of reasoning arguments in bioethics—some methodological considerations. In Häyry M, Takala T, eds. *Scratching the Surface of Bioethics*. Amsterdam: Rodopi; 2003:45–56.
12. It is usually accepted that a political decision can be legitimate even in cases where it can be argued not to be optimal.
13. Harris J. The ethical use of human embryonic stem cells in research and therapy. In: Burley J, Harris J, eds. *A Companion to Genetics*. Oxford: Blackwell; 2002:158–74.
14. The possible policy responses to stem cell research also raise a number of other consistency issues that will not be discussed in detail here. These include questions of consistency with regard to (1) legal permission of certain kinds of stem cell research and prohibition of public funding of the same kinds of research, and (2) legal prohibition of derivation of stem cell lines from embryos and permission to import and use cell lines derived elsewhere.
15. Many public policies seem to indicate that people are "closet gradualists" with regard to the moral status of embryos and fetuses.
16. It is unclear whether any formal inconsistency would be implied. It is still an open question whether subsequent use of research data obtained in unethical experiments (e.g., the Nazi concentration camp experiments) is in itself ethically problematic.
17. Walzer M. *Spheres of Justice: A Defence of Pluralism and Equality*. Oxford: Blackwell; 1983.
18. See note 17, Walzer 1983:21.
19. Even the most insistent liberal and conservative philosophers usually shy back if asked whether they want to implement the full implications of their position as social policy.

THREE Feminists on the Inalienability of Human Embryos
Carolyn McLeod and Françoise Baylis | *Hypatia* 2006; 21: 1-14.

One of the many ethical issues with human embryo research—especially when the research involves the destruction of embryos—is that it risks commodifying, or resulting in the commodification of, that which perhaps ought not to be commodified, namely, women's reproductive labor and human reproductive tissues or their derivatives. Feminists and women's health activists have insisted upon the importance of the first of these two issues—the commodification of women's reproductive labor (Dickenson 2001; Dodds 2003). . . . Of equal concern, however, is the potential commodification of human oocytes and, in particular, of human embryos.

> **Commodification**
> To commodify a thing is to treat it as a good or service that can be exchanged or traded for other goods and services, including money; this is problematic in cases where the thing in question (sex cells, sexual services) is not naturally conceived of as a commodity.
>
> **Feminist**
> As regards philosophy, feminism is the philosophical position which examines how the articulation and solution of philosophical problems impacts the oppression and exploitation of women.
>
> **Oocyte**
> An unfertilized female gamete or sex cell (e.g., ovum).

Arguments against the commodification of human embryos are many and varied. The most obvious, perhaps, start with the premise that human embryos are persons with full moral standing and conclude that like other persons (for example, adult humans with inalienable rights to life and security of the person), they should not be commodified. Other arguments that oppose the commodification of human embryos attempt to draw the same conclusion, but the starting premise is nuanced. The claim is not that human embryos are persons, but rather, that they are undeniably human, they are potential persons, or they are "symbols of human life." For one or all of these reasons, they should be treated as full-fledged persons, or at the very least should be accorded special moral status, and therefore ought not to be commodified. Still other arguments against the commodification of embryos stipulate that embryos are morally inalienable from us (irrespective of whether they are inside or outside of the body) and for this reason should not be commodified. Here, the claim is that human embryos are a part of, or contribute to, the personhood of full persons (but are not themselves persons, actually, potentially, symbolically, or otherwise) and that this fact precludes their legitimate commodification. The underlying assumption is that human embryos could not be commodified without at the same time partially commodifying the full persons to whom they are intimately connected.

In this essay, we aim to make sense of how human embryos could be intimately connected to, but not identical with, persons, such that embryos are inalienable from persons and for this reason alone should not be commodified. Our main goal is to encourage resistance to this line of argument, among feminists in particular, because it is insufficiently respectful of women's reproductive autonomy; and, more generally, it is inconsistent with a feminist understanding of persons as relational embodied beings. As we suggest, such criticism is compatible with asserting that *some* human embryos are inalienable to some persons, including to some women, which could require restrictions of some sort on the commodification of human embryos. . . .[1]

Clarifying what commodification and alienability mean is important to understanding the position on commodifying human embryos that we critique in this essay. . . .

Commodification

When we commodify something, we take that which is not already a commodity and make it into, or treat it as though it were, a commodity. . . . Karl Marx provided the most thorough modern exposition on this topic. For Marx, "a commodity is, in the first place, an object outside us, a thing that by its properties satisfies human wants of some sort or other (1867/1954, 43). . . ." According to Marx, a commodity has more than use value, however. It also has exchange value completely independent of its use value; . . . a coat that can be traded for food or for gold (which for Marx represents the "value form" or the "money form" of the coat) is a commodity. As such, a commodity is a complex of two things: use value and exchange value. The use value is the physical form of the commodity (for example, the coat), which is a synthesis of matter and labor, whereas the exchange value is the value or monetary form of the commodity. . . . It follows that to commodify something is to make it into an article of commerce. . . .

Importantly, for our analysis, commodification can be morally benign or malign. That is, the act of commodifying a thing can be morally permissible or impermissible depending upon: (1) whether the thing commodified has intrinsic value that is incompatible with its being either fully or even partially commodified;[2] (2) whether moral constraints exist on the alienability of the thing from persons; or (3) whether the consequences of making the thing alienable and of commodifying it are, or are not, favourable. . . .

> **Moral constraint**
> A moral constraint is a moral restriction or prohibition placed on certain actions, despite the fact that such actions promise to produce desirable outcomes.

Alienability

Alienability is related to commodification in that it informs the assessment of whether a particular trade for money is benign or malign. Arguably, commodification is benign when the thing traded for a price is normatively alienable to us—meaning that it can rightly lie "outside us," (Marx 1867/1954, 43) for it can be traded or forfeited without doing harm to our person.[3] We can rid ourselves of our material belongings and remain intact as persons, for example. But we cannot divest ourselves of our autonomy or of our basic human rights (for example, to life, security of the person, or dignity) without harming our person. At issue in some debates about the permissibility of commodifying human embryos (where embryos are not considered persons actually, potentially, symbolically, or otherwise), is whether human embryos are of a kind that they are or are not alienable to us (that is, separable from us) without damaging our person, and so can or cannot rightly be transferred to another. . . .

Personhood

We focus here on recent feminist perspectives on personhood, which insist that persons are relational beings—socially and politically constituted selves—as well as embodied beings, and that both of these aspects of personhood are essential to autonomy.[4]

According to most feminists, persons are so profoundly embedded in social relations that one can neither individuate them, nor explain how they came to be, independently of those relations. Persons identify themselves, and others identify them, using descriptions whose meanings are deeply sociocultural. . . . Feminists tend to speak of "relational autonomy," because relations that foster autonomy skills are crucial to being autonomous (Mackenzie & Stoljar 2000; Meyers 1989; Sherwin 1988). In fact, much of the skill and knowledge of persons originates not simply from within them, but also from feedback or information from others. . . . Because others help persons to understand and give meaning to their experiences, they would suffer intense alienation without their connection to these others.

> **Relational autonomy**
> The view according to which one's autonomy is constituted at least in part by one's social, political and moral relations with the members of one's society or social group.

Feminists tend to agree that contexts in which persons are rooted are not merely social, but also political (at least in the world as we know it). The identity categories we use to individuate persons include not only social roles and psychological traits, but also membership in groups divided along lines of race, ethnicity, gender, class, ability, and the like. These groups are privileged or oppressed to varying degrees. . . .

For feminists, persons are not only relational in sociocultural and sociopolitical senses, but they are also embodied. This insight comes from feminist attention to the bodily experiences of women, including pregnancy and menstruation—experiences that make women's embodied nature undeniable. Serious bodily changes, such as those that occur in pregnancy, show what having a different body can allow one to do, or hinder one from doing, and therefore reveal how one's embodiment contributes to one's autonomy (Young 1990). . . . On this feminist understanding of persons as relational embodied beings, what is inalienable to persons, and what therefore should not be commodified, are autonomy and bodily integrity, along with the socio-cultural-political relations that support these states of being. . . .

Human Embryos as Inalienable to Persons

Suzanne Holland and Cynthia Cohen are among those who have recently argued that human reproductive tissues (including gametes and embryos) are inalienable to persons, and therefore should not be commodified. . . . In "Contested Commodities at Both Ends of Life," Holland claims that we, as persons, have inherent moral worth that is incompatible with us being treated as commodities, and that our bodies and their parts, including gametes and embryos, have a special connection to our personhood (2001, 265). . . . They are constitutive of us and therefore should not be commodified. . . . Holland spends considerable time discussing the facts surrounding the downstream commodification of gametes, embryos, and other body tissues; however, in our view, her stance against this practice is poorly developed. For example, she says little about why bodies and body parts are an aspect of personhood; and she also fails to distinguish body parts that may be essential to, or constitutive of, persons from those that normally are not (including hair and spit) (Cohen 1999, 291). In our view, body parts are inalienable to us only insofar as they instantiate the self, facilitate autonomous action, or promote bodily integrity, namely, they are "integral to the functioning of human beings." We assume that this status is never true for all body bits (although some bits may be integral to the functioning of some, but not all, persons) and specifically that this status may not be true for gametes and embryos. A crucial difference therefore must exist between the claim that persons are embodied selves and the idea that all parts of the body are constitutive of the self. Holland fails to name and explore this difference and so, not surprisingly, fails to provide an argument for why gametes and embryos are intimately connected to our personhood through their connection to our bodies. . . .

Perhaps Holland could draw on Cohen's argument, which is similar to her own in that it too begins with our embodiment. Cohen says that since our bodies are the "medium[s] through which [we] act" or "express ourselves," they have special moral worth (Cohen 1999, 295, 291).[5] This worth does not extend to all body parts, however, but only to those that are "integral to the functioning of human beings," or of human persons (291).[6] These parts are noncommodifiable, according to Cohen. . . .

For Cohen, gametes are not essential body parts, integral to the functioning of whole persons. *Nonetheless*, in her view, they have special moral worth—what she calls "derivative dignity"—because of "five interrelated features that they bear":

1. They are derived from human beings—beings with a special dignity and worth.

2. They are "*life-giving*-bodily parts . . . integral to a function of special import to human beings, reproduction."

3. They convey the distinctiveness of their progenitors, which itself has moral worth.

4. They are "the medium through which unique human beings are created."

5. They are integral to the formation of special biological, ethical, and social relations among human beings (Cohen 1999, 296-8).

To buttress her argument that embryos are inalienable to persons, Holland could appeal specifically to features 2, 3, and 5 to argue that embryos express what is distinctive about us and allow us to fulfill important ends in terms of reproduction and having biological relations with others. The problem with any argument that human embryos are inalienable to persons, however, will be that it violates basic tenets of feminism. . . .

The claim that human embryos are inalienable to us should be deeply problematic for feminists because of: (1) the pronatalist streak that runs through this view; (2) the threat that this view represents to women's reproductive autonomy; (3) the lack of respect it shows for different understandings of bodily integrity among women; and (4) the biological reductionism that it reinforces. . . .

> **Pronatalist**
> An individual who promotes the production, rearing and parenting of children. Such an individual typically takes a dim view of abortion and other such limits on procreation.

First, if embryos are inalienable to persons, and for this reason persons cannot detach themselves from them, then persons can never escape their fertility; they cannot be free to lead a life in which reproduction does not occur, or is a nonissue. On the view that embryos are inalienable beings, people discover part of who they are as persons by actualizing their reproductive potential. Such pronatalism is inimical, however, to the reproductive autonomy of both women and men. Pronatalist views permeate Cohen's theory and are particularly evident in her claims that reproduction is a "function of special import to human beings (1999, 296)" and that the "most significant" relationships are "those affected by conception and birth (297)." The first statement may be true of human beings as a species, but is certainly not true of every individual human being. But Cohen uses the point to justify a moral constraint on any individual selling her gametes.

Since pronatalism is already rampant in most women's lives, in particular, feminists should be concerned as feminists about the pronatalism involved in saying that embryos are inalienable to persons. While many women may see their gametes, embryos, or fetuses as inseparable parts of their selves, they may not choose to do so in a meaningful sense; yet even if they did choose to do so, it would not follow, of course, that women as a class hold this view, or should hold it.

Second, while it is true that claims about the inalienability of human embryos do not confer upon embryos the status of persons, these claims do suggest that killing embryos is morally wrong. Killing off any inalienable (that is, constitutive) part of ourselves would degrade us as persons and therefore be wrong. As such, the view that embryos are inalienable to us constitutes a clear threat to women's reproductive freedom.

Third, the narrower view that embryos are inseparable from women is incompatible with respect for women's bodily integrity, which is crucial to their autonomy and which again, includes their ability to perceive their bodies authentically. Some women do not see, and do not wish to see, their gametes, embryos, or fetuses as constitutive parts of themselves, and it is not obvious that they should, anymore than they should see other non-life-sustaining bits as constitutive of themselves. . . .

Fourth, feminists would be perturbed as feminists by the biological reductionism that may be inherent to the view we are criticizing and that is certainly present in Cohen's theory.[7] She cherishes some relationships because of mere biology, and also implies that embryos are inalienable to persons because "they . . . convey the distinctiveness of the human being[s] who produce . . . them (1999, 296)." The "they" here are not so much embryos, but the bundle of genes found within them, which suggests a form of gene worshipping that is problematic from the perspective of most philosophers of biology, and that is politically threatening to women from a feminist perspective. If

women's distinctiveness as women were purely biological, then they might be locked forever into social roles in which they serve men and children.

For these and possibly other reasons, arguments against the commodification of human embryos in embryo research that are grounded in claims about the inalienability of human embryos are deeply flawed, particularly from a feminist perspective. . . . The theoretical problem stems from an incompatibility between this view of embryos and a feminist conception of persons as relational embodied beings. The political concern lies in the apparent lack of support for women's reproductive autonomy.

In closing, at the outset of this essay we identified three categories of arguments against the commodification of human embryos: (1) arguments according to which human embryos are persons, and like all persons ought not be treated as property in the marketplace; (2) arguments that arrive at the same conclusion, but on the basis of more modest claims about the moral status of embryos as *potential* persons or "important symbols of human life;" and (3) arguments to the effect that embryos are inalienable to persons and so cannot rightly be considered as objects outside of us that can be traded for a price. We have critically examined the last of these arguments and shown that embryos are not by definition inalienable to persons (though they may be inalienable to specific persons, for specific personal reasons), given a feminist understanding of persons. Hence, from a feminist perspective, embryos are not de facto noncommodifiable by virtue of being inalienable. Whether feminists should condemn or accept the commodification of embryos is still at issue, however. . . .

> **De facto**
> A Latin term used in the law meaning "in fact."

If feminists deem embryos to have intrinsic moral value as potential persons, then very likely they will not consider them fully commodifiable. If, in the alternative, feminists simply characterize embryos as body tissues that are not intimately connected to our personhood, then they may decide that embryos are fully commodifiable. Since the commodification of embryos is an option in either scenario, feminists will also have to pay careful attention to the *consequences* of commodification, and try to constrain and direct this process so that it does not cause social harms, in particular the exploitation and oppression of women.

Study Questions

1. What do McLeod and Baylis mean by commodification?

2. What is relational autonomy? Why is it relevant to the main line of argument that McLeod and Baylis pursue?

3. McLeod and Baylis argue that "body parts are inalienable to us only insofar as they instantiate the self, facilitate autonomous actions, or produce bodily integrity." Is this view plausible? Why?

Notes

1. For example, there could be restrictions on the "downstream commodification" of embryos (that is, commodification downstream from an initial sale or donation; Holland 2001, pp. 266) by embryo providers who retain an intimate connection to their embryos despite the act of sale or donation. (We discuss this possibility below.)

2. Margaret Radin (1996) emphasizes that the process of commodification can be complete or incomplete, meaning that a product may be fully or only partially commodified. With the former, no restrictions exist on the trading of the item; it is available for exchange on an open market. With the latter— that is, incomplete or partial commodification—the relevant market is closed in certain respects.

3. On inalienablity and alienablity, see Radin (1996, pp. 16–18) and Sandra Lee Bartky (1990, pp. 33–37).

4. For feminist perspectives on the selves of human persons, see Diana Meyers' edited collection *Feminists Rethink the Self* (1997), and, in particular, Susan Brison's article therein (1997, pp. 13–31).

5. Here Cohen follows Kant, whom she interprets as saying, "any body part that is necessary for the functioning of the whole person ... is endowed with the dignity of that person" (292).

6. Throughout, Cohen uses human being and person interchangeably.

7. It would be inherent to it if among the only somewhat plausible reasons for thinking that embryos are inalienable to persons is that they bear the distinctiveness of persons.

References

Baier, Annette. 1985. *Postures of the mind: Essays on mind and morals.* Minneapolis: University of Minnesota Press.

Bartky, Sandra Lee. 1990. Narcissism, femininity, and alienation. In *Femininity and domination: Studies in the phenomenology of oppression.* New York: Routledge.

Brison, Susan J. 1997. Outliving oneself: Trauma, memory, and personal identity. In *Feminists rethink the self*, ed. Diana Tietjens Meyers. Boulder, Colo.: Westview Press.

Cohen, Cynthia. 1999. Selling bits and pieces of humans to make babies: "The gift of the magi" revisited. *Journal of Medicine and Philosophy* 24 (3): 288–306.

Dickenson, Donna. 2001. Property and women's alienation from their own reproductive labour. *Bioethics* 15 (3): 205–17.

Dodds, Susan. 2003. Women, commodification, and embryonic stem-cell research. In *Biomedical ethics reviews: Stem cell research*, ed. James Humber and Robert F. Almeder. Totowa, N.J.: Humana Press.

Donchin, Anne. 1996. Feminist critiques of new fertility technologies: Implications for social policy. *Journal of Medicine and Philosophy* 21 (5): 475–98.

Holland, Susan. 2001. Contested commodities at both ends of life: Buying and selling gametes, embryos, and body tissues. *Kennedy Institute of Ethics Journal* 11 (3): 263–84.

Mackenzie, Catriona. 1992. Abortion and embodiment. *Australian Journal of Philosophy* 70 (2): 136–55.

——— and Natalie Stoljar, eds. 2000. *Relational autonomy: Feminist perspectives on autonomy, agency, and the social self.* New York: Oxford University Press.

Marquis, Don. 1989. *Why abortion is immoral.* Journal of Philosophy 86 (4): 183–202.

Marx, Karl. 1867/1954. *Capital.* Trans. Samuel Moore and Edward Aveling, ed. Frederick Engels. Moscow: Progress.

Meyers, Diana Tietjens. 1989. *Self, society, and personal choice.* New York: Columbia University Press.

——— ed. 1997. *Feminists rethink the self.* Boulder, Colo.: Westview Press.

Nussbaum, Martha C. 1992. Human functioning and social justice: In defense of Aristotelian essentialism. *Political Theory* 20 (3): 202–46.

Radin, Margaret Jane. 1996. *Contested commodities: The trouble with trade in sex, children, body parts, and other things.* Cambridge, Mass.: Harvard University Press.

Scheman, Naomi. 1983. Individualism and the objects of psychology. In *Discovering reality: Feminist perspectives on epistemology, metaphysics, methodology, and philosophy of science*, ed. Sandra Harding and Merrill B. Hintikka. Boston: D. Reidel.

Sherwin, Susan. 1998. A relational approach to autonomy in health care. In *The politics of women's health: Exploring agency and autonomy*, ed. Feminist Health Care Ethics Research Network. Philadelphia: Temple University Press.

Tooley, Michael. 1972. Abortion and infanticide. *Philosophy and Public Affairs* 2: 37–65.

Young, Iris Marion. 1990. Pregnant embodiment. In *Throwing like a girl and other essays in feminist philosophy and social theory*. Bloomington: Indiana University Press.

Chapter Study Questions

1. Sagan and Singer, and Holm appear to agree that in some cases the destruction of embryos for medical benefit is permissible. What are the differences between their positions? Who articulates the more defensible view?

2. In what ways is the feminist analysis found in McLeod and Baylis distinct from the analysis found in Sagan and Singer and in Holm? In what ways is the analysis compatible? In what ways is it incompatible?

3. It is clear that a conception of moral standing plays an important role in determining the morality of the use of human embryos in medical research. Consider the various conceptions of moral standing discussed in the three articles found in this chapter. Which seems most plausible to you? What would help you decide in favour of a certain conception of moral standing?

Critical Analysis

Consider the following from the article by Holm:

"The most radical version of the standard restrictive argument claims that all human beings have the same value. On this view, destroying embryos is just as bad as destroying adults, and it seems to rule out any kind of destructive stem cell derivation from embryos . . . .This view leads to a number of counterintuitive conclusions in other areas if it is pursued rigorously. It rules out abortion in most, or perhaps all, cases and would, for instance, definitely rule out abortions in cases of rape. It would also put a stop to all kinds of IVF involving the generation of supernumerary embryos and all destructive embryo experiments aimed at improving IVF. It would, finally, also commit us to doing much more to prevent loss of embryos or fetuses during normal reproduction."

Outline Holm's argument in your own words, paying particular attention to the premises that he relies on to support his main conclusion. Choose one of the premises for evaluation. Try to think of at least one objection to this premise.

Case Study

On 29 March 2004, the *Assisted Human Reproduction Act* received Royal Assent in the House of Commons in Ottawa. The Act regulates human reproductive research, among other things. It maintains that it is permissible to create an in vitro human embryo for the purpose of producing a human being or for the purpose of improving or providing instruction in assisted reproductive technologies. However, it forbids the creation of a human embryo for any other purpose. In particular, it forbids creating an embryo for the sole purpose of conducting medical research on stem cells and other related matters. The only situation in which it is permissible to use and destroy human embryos in the conduct of this research is when the embryos in question are "surplus" embryos created by in vitro fertilization having the following characteristics: they are no longer wanted by those for whom they were created, the embryos are freely and consensually donated by those for whom they were created, and the gametes from which the embryos themselves were made were not obtained by means of a commercial transaction. The Act lists a set of guiding principles, including the following: "the health and well-being of children born through the application of assisted human reproductive technologies must be given priority in all decisions respecting their use," that "the benefits of assisted human reproductive technologies and related research for individuals, for families and for society in general can be most effectively secured by taking appropriate measures for the protection and promotion of human health, safety, dignity and rights in the use of these technologies and in related research," and that "while all persons are affected by these technologies, women more than men are directly and significantly affected by their application and the health and well-being of women must be protected in the application of these technologies."

1. Do the principles listed in the preceding justify the provisions of the *Assisted Human Reproduction Act*?

2. Do you think these principles are persuasive?

3. Do you agree that there is a principled reason for permitting the creation and eventual destruction of embryos for the purpose of conducting research on assisted reproductive technologies but not for the purpose of conducting other medical research?

Further Reading

Canada's Assisted Human Reproduction Act (2004, c. 2) [Internet]. Available from: http://laws.justice.gc.ca/PDF/Statute/A/A-13.4.pdf. Date Accessed: 5 June 2012.

Canadian Institutes of Health Research. Updated Guidelines for Human Pluripotent Stem Cell Research [Internet]. Available from: http://www.cihr-irsc.gc.ca/e/42071.html. Date Accessed: 5 June 2012.

Dickenson DL. The lady vanishes: what's missing from the stem cell debate, *J Bioethic Inq* 2006 3:43-54.

Marquis D, The moral-principle objection to human embryonic stem cell research, *Metaphilosophy* 2007 38:190-206.

Siegel A. Ethics of stem cell research. In: Zalta EN, editor. Stanford Encyclopedia of Philosophy [Internet]. 2008. Available from: http://plato.stanford.edu/entries/stem-cells/. Date Accessed: 05 June 2012.

Fetuses

In this chapter, our focus is the ethics of abortion. Abortion involves intentionally killing a human fetus by means of some medical or surgical procedure. This fetus lives inside a woman's body and it depends on her for life and sustenance. It is for these reasons that abortion is a hotly contested ethical and political matter. Determining the morality of abortion involves appealing to a full theory of moral standing. This involves the development of a theory of what is valuable and a theory of moral requirement, which will tell us not only whether a fetus has moral standing, but also how to treat it once it has moral standing. This is not all. An analysis of the morality of abortion will need to possess an account of the nature of both the physical and the social relationship between a woman and a fetus.

There is, it seems, agreement that if a fetus possesses moral standing, then there exists a constraint on killing it without compelling justification. The problem is that there is deep disagreement over the issue of whether or not the fetus has moral standing. On this issue, political discussion tends to be quite polarized. Opponents of abortion often think that a fetus has moral standing at or at some point very near conception, and that therefore most abortions are morally forbidden. Their rivals, meanwhile, often assume that a woman has a right over her own body and that this permits abortion at any point in pregnancy. It is therefore difficult to imagine how one could reach consensus on the issue of the morality of abortion. In their own way the articles in this chapter seek to overcome this polarization.

The articles by Don Marquis and L. Wayne Sumner focus on the issue of moral standing. In his article "Why Abortion is Immoral," Marquis argues that the vast majority of abortions are immoral. The basis of his position is that what makes it wrong to kill a fully functioning adult human being is that doing so denies that being a future of value, a future of pleasurable experiences, rich relationships, and achievements. He argues that since the typical fetus that is aborted has a future of value just like the typical adult human being, it is therefore wrong to kill it. The fact that the standard fetus has a future of value gives it the same degree of moral protection that a typical adult human being has against being killed. Marquis argues that only in very rare circumstances, e.g., when a fetus has no value lying in its future, is abortion permissible. He therefore argues for an extremely conservative account of the morality of abortion.

In his article "A Third Way," Sumner rejects both extremely conservative and extremely liberal views of the morality of abortion. He advocates a middle position between the two. The key feature of this third way is an account of moral standing according to which an individual has such standing when it is sentient; that is, when it has the capacity (however minimal) to experience pleasure and pain. It is at this point that a being has interests and therefore rights that we ought to take account of in our thinking about what to do. He argues that this criterion of moral standing entails that a fetus has no standing whatsoever in the period of its life before the emergence of sentience. In aborting a fetus in the early stages of its development a woman does nothing wrong. However, when a fetus develops the capacity to feel pleasure and pain (which occurs at some point in the second trimester of pregnancy) a fetus has moral standing, and therefore a right to life. In the later stages of pregnancy a more restrictive approach to abortion is therefore appropriate. Abortion in this case is more like (though not identical to) infanticide, and only a serious threat to a woman's health or well-being or severe fetal deformity justifies abortion.

Marquis and Sumner believe that the key to determining the morality of abortion turns on whether or not a fetus has moral standing. This is contestable. In Canada, if a woman lives in a remote northern community or in rural Nova Scotia or in Prince Edward Island, she must travel significant distances to procure a safe, legal abortion. This places serious restrictions on the reproductive autonomy and the safety and security of the women who live in these communities. Abstract discussions of the moral status of the fetus seem not to take account of this, and therefore ignore the importance of the lived experience of (especially unwanted) pregnancy. Margaret Little addresses this issue in the third article in this chapter.

In her article "Abortion, Intimacy, and the Duty to Gestate," Little argues that a legal policy restricting abortion forces women to gestate. This is harmful to women because pregnancy is a kind of intimacy: it involves a woman being intertwined and enmeshed with a fetus. To be forced to gestate is tantamount to being forced to be intimate with another human being, and is therefore harmful like non-consensual sex, itself a form of forced intimacy. In addition, she argues that a full account of the morality of abortion involves developing an account of the basis of the duty to gestate. Her view is that the mere biological connection between a woman and a fetus generates a duty to be open to entering into a relationship with the fetus. It does not, however, generate a duty to carry it to term. The duty to let a fetus make use of one's body depends on a thicker kind of relationship, involving a lived personal relationship similar to the relationship that occurs in many cases between children and parents, and the existence of this depends on one's conceptualization of the nature of the relationship one is in with the fetus.

ONE   Why Abortion is Immoral
Don Marquis | *The Journal of Philosophy* 1989; 86: 183-202.

The view that abortion is, with rare exceptions, seriously immoral has received little support in the recent philosophical literature. . . . This essay sets out an argument that purports to show, as well as any argument in ethics can show, that abortion is, except possibly in rare cases, seriously immoral, that it is in the same moral category as killing an innocent adult human being. The argument is based on a major assumption: . . . that whether or not abortion is morally permissible stands or falls on whether or not a fetus is the sort of being whose life it is seriously wrong to end.

This essay will neglect issues of great importance to a complete ethics of abortion. Some anti-abortionists will allow that certain abortions, such as abortion before implantation or abortion when the life of a woman is threatened by a pregnancy or abortion after rape, may be morally permissible. This essay will not explore the casuistry of these hard cases. The purpose of this essay is to develop a general argument for the claim that the overwhelming majority of deliberate abortions are seriously immoral.

A sketch of standard anti-abortion and pro-choice arguments exhibits how those arguments possess certain symmetries that explain why partisans of those positions are so

> **Casuistry**
> Reasoning about ethical matters on a case-by-case basis, by beginning with judgments about clearer cases and then applying this reasoning to difficult ethical cases involving exceptions to and conflicts amongst moral principles.

convinced of the correctness of their own positions, why they are not successful in convincing their opponents, and why, to others, this issue seems to be unresolvable. An analysis of the nature of this standoff suggests a strategy for surmounting it.

Consider the way a typical anti-abortionist argues. She will argue or assert that life is present from the moment of conception or that fetuses look like babies or that fetuses possess a characteristic such as a genetic code that is both necessary and sufficient for being human. Anti-abortionists seem to believe that (1) the truth of all of these claims is quite obvious, and (2) establishing any of these claims is sufficient to show that abortion is morally akin to murder.

A standard pro-choice strategy exhibits similarities. The pro-choicer will argue or assert that fetuses are not persons or that fetuses are not rational agents or that fetuses are not social beings. Pro-choicers seem to believe that (1) the truth of any of these claims is quite obvious, and (2) establishing any of these claims is sufficient to show that an abortion is not a wrongful killing. . . .

Now, how might one deal with this standoff? The standard approach is to try to show how the moral principles of one's opponent lose their plausibility under analysis. It is easy to see how this is possible. On the one hand, the anti-abortionist will defend a moral principle concerning the wrongness of killing which tends to be broad in scope in order that even fetuses at an early stage of pregnancy will fall under it. The problem with broad principles is that they often embrace too much. In this particular instance, the principle "It is always prima facie wrong to take a human life" seems to entail that it is wrong to end the existence of a living human cancer-cell culture, on the grounds that the culture is both living and human. Therefore, it seems that the anti-abortionist's favored principle is too broad.

> **Prima facie**
> A Latin phrase meaning at first sight or until proven otherwise.

On the other hand, the pro-choicer wants to find a moral principle concerning the wrongness of killing which tends to be narrow in scope in order that fetuses will *not* fall under it. The problem with narrow principles is that they often do not embrace enough. Hence, the needed principles such as "It is prima facie seriously wrong to kill only persons" or "It is prima facie wrong to kill only rational agents"

do not explain why it is wrong to kill infants or young children or the severely retarded or even perhaps the severely mentally ill. Therefore, we seem again to have a standoff. The anti-abortionist charges, not unreasonably, that pro-choice principles concerning killing are too narrow to be acceptable; the pro-choicer charges, not unreasonably, that anti-abortionist principles concerning killing are too broad to be acceptable. . . .

Passions in the abortion debate run high. There are both plausibilities and difficulties with the standard positions. Accordingly, it is hardly surprising that partisans of either side embrace with fervor the moral generalizations that support the conclusions they preanalytically favor, and reject with disdain the moral generalizations of their opponents as being subject to inescapable difficulties. It is easy to believe that the counterexamples to one's own moral principles are merely temporary difficulties that will dissolve in the wake of further philosophical research, and that the counterexamples to the principles of one's opponents are as straightforward as the contradiction between A and O propositions in traditional logic. This might suggest to an impartial observer (if there are any) that the abortion issue is unresolvable.

There is a way out of this apparent dialectical quandary. The moral generalizations of both sides are not quite correct. The generalizations hold for the most part, for the usual cases. This suggests that they are all *accidental* generalizations, that the moral claims made by those on both sides of the dispute do not touch on the *essence* of the matter. . . . All this suggests that a necessary condition of resolving the abortion controversy is a more theoretical account of the wrongness of killing.

In order to develop such an account, we can start from the following unproblematic assumption concerning our own case: it is wrong to kill *us*. Why is it wrong?

What primarily makes killing wrong is . . . its effect on the victim. The loss of one's life is one of the greatest losses one can suffer. The loss of one's life deprives one of all the experiences, activities,

> **A and O propositions**
> In traditional or categorical logic, an 'A proposition' is a statement that is both universal and affirmative (e.g., "All fetuses are persons") and an 'O proposition' is both particular and negative (e.g., "Some fetuses are not persons"). When they contain the same subject (e.g., "fetuses") and predicate (e.g., "persons"), A and O propositions are natural contradictories, meaning that both statements cannot be true.

projects, and enjoyments that would otherwise have constituted one's future. Therefore, killing someone is wrong, primarily because the killing inflicts (one of) the greatest possible losses on the victim. To describe this as the loss of life can be misleading, however. The change in my biological state does not by itself make killing me wrong. The effect of the loss of my biological life is the loss to me of all those activities, projects, experiences, and enjoyments, which would otherwise have constituted my future personal life. These activities, projects, experiences, and enjoyments are either valuable for their own sakes or are means to something else that is valuable for its own sake. Some parts of my future are not valued by me now, but will come to be valued by me as I grow older and as my values and capacities change. When I am killed, I am deprived both of what I now value which would have been part of my future personal life, but also what I would come to value. Therefore, when I die, I am deprived of all of the value of my future. Inflicting this loss on me is ultimately what makes killing me wrong. This being the case, it would seem that what makes killing *any* adult human being prima facie seriously wrong is the loss of his or her future. . . .[1]

The claim that what makes killing wrong is the loss of the victim's future is directly supported by two considerations. In the first place, this theory explains why we regard killing as one of the worst of crimes. Killing is especially wrong, because it deprives the victim of more than perhaps any other crime. In the second place, people with AIDS or cancer who know they are dying believe, of course, that dying is a very bad thing for them. They believe that the loss of a future to them that they would otherwise have experienced is what makes their premature death a very bad thing for them. . . .

The view that what makes killing wrong is the loss to the victim of the value of the victim's future gains additional support when some of its implications are examined. In the first place, it is incompatible with the view that it is wrong to kill only beings who are biologically human. It is possible that there exists a different species from another planet whose members have a future like ours. Since having a future like that is what makes killing someone wrong, this theory entails that it would be wrong to kill members of such a species. Hence, this theory is opposed to the claim that only life that is biologically human has great moral worth, a claim which many anti-abortionists have seemed to adopt. . . .

In the second place, the claim that the loss of one's future is the wrong-making feature of one's being killed entails the possibility that the futures of some actual nonhuman mammals on our own planet are sufficiently like ours that it is seriously wrong to kill them also. . . .

In the third place, the claim that the loss of one's future is the wrong-making feature of one's being killed does not entail, as sanctity of human life theories do, that active euthanasia is wrong. Persons who are severely and incurably ill, who face a future of pain and despair, and who wish to die, will not have suffered a loss if they are killed. It is, strictly speaking, the value of a human's future which makes killing wrong in this theory. This being so, killing does not necessarily wrong some persons who are sick and dying. . . .

> **Sanctity of human life**
> Holders of the sanctity of human life doctrine typically believe that human life has a unique and special value simply by virtue of the fact that it is human life. There may well be differences between its exponents on the precise way life acquires this value.

In the fourth place, the account of the wrongness of killing defended in this essay does straightforwardly entail that it is prima facie seriously wrong to kill children and infants, for we do presume that they have futures of value. Since we do believe that it is wrong to kill defenseless little babies, it is important that a theory of the wrongness of killing easily account for this. . . .

The claim that the primary wrong-making feature of a killing is the loss to the victim of the value of its future has obvious consequences for the ethics of abortion. The future of a standard fetus includes a set of experiences, projects, activities, and such which are identical with the futures of adult human beings and are identical with the futures of young children. Since the reason that is sufficient to explain why it is wrong to kill human beings after the time of birth is a reason that also applies to fetuses, it follows that abortion is prima facie seriously morally wrong.

This argument does not rely on the invalid inference that, since it is wrong to kill persons, it is wrong to kill potential persons also. The category that is morally central to this analysis is the category of having a valuable future like ours. . . .

Of course, this value of a future-like-ours argument, if sound, shows only that abortion is prima facie wrong, not that it is wrong in any and all circumstances. Since the loss of the future to a standard fetus, if killed, is, however, at least as great a loss as the loss of the future to a standard adult human being who is killed, abortion, like ordinary killing, could be justified only by the most compelling reasons. The loss of one's life is almost the greatest misfortune that can happen to one. Presumably abortion could be justified in some circumstances, only if the loss consequent on failing to abort would be at least as great. Accordingly, morally permissible abortions will be rare indeed unless, perhaps, they occur so early in pregnancy that a fetus is not yet definitely an individual. Hence, this argument should be taken as showing that abortion is presumptively very seriously wrong, where the presumption is very strong—as strong as the presumption that killing another adult human being is wrong.

How complete an account of the wrongness of killing does the value of a future-like-ours account have to be in order that the wrongness of abortion is a consequence? This account does not have to be an account of the necessary conditions for the wrongness of killing. Some persons in nursing homes may lack valuable human futures, yet it may be wrong to kill them for other reasons. Furthermore, this account does not obviously have to be the sole reason killing is wrong where the victim did have a valuable future. This analysis claims only that, for any killing where the victim did have a valuable future like ours, having that future by itself is sufficient to create the strong presumption that the killing is seriously wrong. . . .

One strategy for avoiding these anti-abortion consequences involves limiting the scope of the value of a future argument. More precisely, the strategy involves arguing that fetuses lack a property that is essential for the value-of-a-future argument (or for any anti-abortion argument) to apply to them.

One move of this sort is based upon the claim that a necessary condition of one's future being valuable is that one values it. Value implies a valuer. Given this one might argue that, since fetuses cannot value their futures, their futures are not valuable to them. Hence, it does not seriously wrong them deliberately to end their lives.

This move fails, however, because of some ambiguities. Let us assume that something cannot be of value unless it is valued by someone. This does not entail that my life is of no value unless it is valued by me. I may think, in a period of despair, that my future is of no worth whatsoever, but I may be wrong because others rightly see value—even great

value—in it. Furthermore, my future can be valuable to me even if I do not value it. This is the case when a young person attempts suicide, but is rescued and goes on to significant human achievements. Such young people's futures are ultimately valuable to them, even though such futures do not seem to be valuable to them at the moment of attempted suicide. A fetus' future can be valuable to it in the same way. Accordingly, this attempt to limit the anti-abortion argument fails. . . .

In this essay, it has been argued that the correct ethic of the wrongness of killing can be extended to fetal life and used to show that there is a strong presumption that any abortion is morally impermissible. If the ethic of killing adopted here entails, however, that contraception is also seriously immoral, then there would appear to be a difficulty with the analysis of this essay.

But this analysis does not entail that contraception is wrong. Of course, contraception prevents the actualization of a possible future of value. Hence, it follows from the claim that futures of value should be maximized that contraception is prima facie immoral. This obligation to maximize does not exist, however; furthermore, nothing in the ethics of killing in this paper entails that it does. The ethics of killing in this essay would entail that contraception is wrong only if something were denied a human future of value by contraception. Nothing at all is denied such a future by contraception, however.

Candidates for a subject of harm by contraception fall into four categories: (1) some sperm or other, (2) some ovum or other, (3) a sperm and an ovum separately, and (4) a sperm and an ovum together. Assigning the harm to some sperm is utterly arbitrary, for no reason can be given for making a sperm the subject of harm rather than an ovum. Assigning the harm to some ovum is utterly arbitrary, for no reason can be given for making an ovum the subject of harm rather than a sperm. One might attempt to avoid these problems by insisting that contraception deprives both the sperm and the ovum separately of a valuable future like ours. On this alternative, too many futures are lost. Contraception was supposed to be wrong, because it deprived us of one future of value, not two. One might attempt to avoid this problem by holding that contraception deprives the combination of sperm and ovum of a valuable future like ours. But here the definite article misleads. At the time of contraception, there are hundreds of millions of sperm, one (released) ovum and millions of possible combinations of all of these. There is no actual combination at all. Is the subject of the loss to be a merely possible combination? Which one? This alternative does not yield an actual subject of harm either. Accordingly, the immorality of contraception is not entailed by the loss of a future-like-ours argument simply because there is no nonarbitrarily identifiable subject of the loss in the case of contraception.

The purpose of this essay has been to set out an argument for the serious presumptive wrongness of abortion subject to the assumption that the moral permissibility of abortion stands or falls on the moral status of the fetus. Since a fetus possesses a property, the possession of which in adult human beings is sufficient to make killing an adult human being wrong, abortion is wrong. . . .

Study Questions

1. According to Marquis, what makes killing wrong?

2. Marquis produces an argument to the effect that the vast majority of abortions are seriously immoral. However, he intimates that some abortions are permissible when "they occur so early in pregnancy that a fetus is not yet definitely an individual." Which abortions does this permit (if any)?

3. Why does Marquis think that, while most abortions are immoral, the use of contraception is morally permissible?

Notes

1. I have been most influenced on this matter by Jonathan Glover, *Causing Death and Saving Lives* (New York: Penguin, 1977), ch. 3; and Robert Young, "What Is So Wrong with Killing People?" *Philosophy*, LIV, 210 (1979):515–28.

TWO   A Third Way

L. Wayne Sumner | Dwyer S, Feinberg J. *The Problem of Abortion* (3rd ed.). Wadsworth Publishing Company; 1997: 98-117.

. . . In most countries in the West, public discussion of abortion has been distorted by the dominance of two views. The liberal view, espoused by "pro-choice" groups, holds that (voluntary) abortion is always morally innocuous and (therefore) that the only acceptable abortion policy is one which treats abortion as another variety of minor elective surgery. The conservative view, espoused by "pro-life" groups, holds that abortion is always morally serious and (therefore) that the only acceptable abortion policy is one which treats abortion as another variety of homicide.

The central issue in the morality of abortion is the moral status of the fetus. Let us say that a creature has *moral standing* if, for the purpose of moral decision-making, it must be counted for something in its own right. We may, for the purpose of the present discussion, make this rather vague notion more precise by adopting the rights vocabulary favored by both of the established views. We will suppose that having (some) moral standing is equivalent to having (some) right to life. The central issue in the morality of abortion is then whether fetuses have moral standing in this sense.[1]

The conservative view, and also the more naive versions of the liberal view, selects a precise point (conception, birth, etc.) as the threshold of moral standing, implying that the transition from no standing to full standing occurs abruptly. In doing so they rest more weight on these sudden events than they are capable of bearing. A view that avoids this defect will allow full moral standing to be acquired gradually. . . . Both of the established views attribute a uniform moral status to all fetuses, regardless of their dissimilarities. . . .

A consequence of the uniform approach adopted by both of the established views is that neither can attach any significance to the development of the fetus during gestation. Yet this development is the most obvious feature of gestation. A view that avoids this defect will base the (differential) moral standing of the fetus at least in part on its level of development.

Gestation
The period from conception to birth during which the fetus grows and develops inside the womb; pregnancy.

It will thus assign undeveloped fetuses a moral status akin to that of ova and spermatozoa, whereas it will assign developed fetuses a moral status akin to that of infants.

So far, then, an adequate view of the fetus must be gradual, differential, and developmental. It must also be derived from a satisfactory criterion of moral standing. Such a criterion must be general (applicable to beings other than fetuses), it must connect moral standing with the empirical properties of such beings, and it must be morally relevant. Its moral relevance is partly testable by appeal to intuition. . . . An adequate view of the fetus promises a morally significant division between early abortions (before the threshold stage) and late abortions (after the threshold stage). It also promises borderline cases (during the threshold stage). Wherever that stage is located, abortions that precede it will be private matters, since the fetus will at that stage lack moral standing. Thus the provisions of the liberal view will apply to early abortions: they will be morally innocent (as long as the usual conditions of maternal consent, etc., are satisfied) and ought to be legally unregulated (except for rules equally applicable to all other medical procedures). Early abortion will have the same moral status as contraception.

Abortions that follow the threshold stage will be interpersonal matters, since the fetus will at that stage possess moral standing. Thus the provisions of the conservative view will apply to late abortions: they must be assessed on a case-by-case basis and they ought to be legally permitted only on appropriate

Empirical
Empirical properties are those that can be discovered by means of the senses or by means of standard scientific methodology.

Intuition
A moral intuition is a sober, reflective attitude regarding some moral or evaluative matter, e.g., that slavery is wrong and that children have moral standing.

grounds. Late abortions will have the same moral status as infanticide, except for the difference made by the physical connection between fetus and mother.

A third way with abortion is thus a moderate and differential view, combining elements of the liberal view for early abortions with elements of (a weakened version of) the conservative view for late abortions. The policy that a moderate view will support is a moderate policy, permissive in the early stages of pregnancy and more restrictive (though not as restrictive as conservatives think appropriate) in the later stages. . . .

Infanticide
The intentional killing of an infant or neonate.

We are assuming that for a creature to have moral standing is for it to have a right to life. Any such right imposes duties on moral agents; these duties may be either negative (not to deprive the creature of life) or positive (to support the creature's life). Possession of a right to life implies at least some immunity against attack by others, and possibly also some entitlement to the aid of others. As the duties may vary in strength, so may the corresponding rights. To have some moral standing is to have some right to life, whether or not it may be overridden by the rights of others. To have full moral standing is to have the strongest right to life possessed by anyone, the right to life of the paradigm person. Depending on one's moral theory, this right may or may not be inviolable and indefeasible and thus may or may not impose absolute duties on others.

To which creatures should we distribute (some degree of) moral standing? . . . A criterion of sentience (or consciousness) is promising. Sentience is the capacity for feeling or affect. In its most primitive form it is the ability to experience sensations of pleasure and pain, and thus the ability to enjoy and suffer. Its more developed forms include wants, aims, and desires (and thus the ability to be satisfied and frustrated); attitudes, tastes, and values; and moods, emotions, sentiments, and passions. Consciousness is a necessary condition of sentience, for feelings are states of mind of which their owner is aware. But it is not sufficient; it is at least possible in principle for beings to be conscious (percipient, for instance, or even rational) while utterly lacking feelings. . . . Sentience is rooted in a being's affective and conative

Conative
Pertaining to a being's will to perform an act or volition.

life. It is in virtue of being sentient that creatures have interests, which are compounded either out of their desires or out of the experiences they find agreeable (or both). If morality has to do with the protection and promotion of interests, it is a plausible conjecture that we owe moral duties to all those beings capable of having interests. But this will include all sentient creatures. . . .

It makes sense to think of sentience as admitting of degrees. Within any given mode, such as the perception of pain, one creature may be more or less sensitive than another. But there is a further sense in which more developed (more rational) creatures possess a higher degree of sentience. The expansion of consciousness and of intelligence opens up new ways of experiencing the world, and therefore new ways of being affected by the world. More rational beings are capable of finding either fulfillment or frustration in activities and states of affairs to which less developed creatures are, both cognitively and affectively, blind. It is in this sense of a broader and deeper sensibility that a higher being is capable of a richer, fuller, and more varied existence. The fact that sentience admits of degrees (whether of sensitivity or sensibility) enables us to employ it both as an inclusion criterion and as a comparison criterion of moral standing. The animal kingdom presents us with a hierarchy of sentience. Nonsentient beings have no moral standing; among sentient beings the more developed have greater standing than the less developed, the upper limit being occupied by the paradigm of a normal adult human being. Although sentience is the criterion of moral standing, it is also possible to explain the relevance of rationality. The evolutionary order is one of ascending intelligence. Since rationality expands a creature's interests, it is a reliable indicator of the degree of moral standing which that creature possesses. Creatures less rational than human beings do not altogether lack standing, but they do lack full standing. . . .

A criterion of sentience can thus allow for the gradual emergence of moral standing in the order of nature. It can explain why no moral issues arise (directly) in our dealings with inanimate objects, plants, and the simpler forms of animal life. It can also function as a moral guideline in our encounters with novel life forms on other planets. If the creatures we meet have interests and are capable of enjoyment and suffering, we must grant them some moral standing.

We thereby constrain ourselves not to exploit them ruthlessly for our own advantage. The kind of standing that they deserve may be determined by the range and depth of their sensibility, and in ordinary circumstances this will vary with their intelligence. We should therefore recognize as equals beings who are as rational and sensitive as ourselves. The criterion also implies that if we encounter creatures who are rational but nonsentient—who utterly lack affect and desire—nothing we can do will adversely affect such creatures (in morally relevant ways). We would be entitled, for instance, to treat them as a species of organic computer. . . .

> **Organic computer**
> An artificially created computer made from living neurons that seems to be able to perform rudimentary computations.

A criterion of sentience also requires gentle usage of the severely abnormal. Cognitive disabilities and disorders may impair a person's range of sensibility, but they do not generally reduce that person to the level of a nonsentient being. Even the grossly retarded or deranged will still be capable of some forms of enjoyment and suffering and thus will still possess (some) moral standing in their own right. This standing diminishes to the vanishing point only when sentience is entirely lost or never gained in the first place. If all affect and responsivity are absent, and if they cannot be engendered, then (but only then) are we no longer dealing with a sentient creature. This verdict accords well with the contemporary trend toward defining death in terms of the permanent loss of cerebral functioning. Although such patients are in one obvious sense still alive (their blood circulates and is oxygenated), in the morally relevant sense they are now beyond our reach, for we can cause them neither good nor ill. . . .

The adoption of sentience as a criterion determines the location of a threshold of moral standing. Since sentience admits of degrees, we can in principle construct a continuum ranging from fully sentient creatures at one extreme to completely nonsentient creatures at the other. . . .

There is no doubt that a newborn infant is sentient—that it feels hunger, thirst, physical pain, the pleasure of sucking, and other agreeable and disagreeable sensations. There is also no doubt that a zygote, and also an embryo, is presentient. . . .

The information we now possess does not enable us to date with accuracy the emergence of fetal sentience. Of some judgments, however, we can be reasonably confident. First-trimester fetuses are clearly not yet sentient. Third-trimester fetuses probably possess some degree of sentience, however minimal. The threshold of sentience thus appears to fall in the second trimester. More ancient and primitive than cognition, the ability to discriminate simple sensations of pleasure and pain is probably the first form of consciousness to appear in the ontogenetic order. Further, when sentience emerges it does not do so suddenly. The best we can hope for is to locate a threshold stage or period in the second trimester. It is at present unclear just how far into that trimester this stage occurs. . . . We are therefore inevitably confronted with a class of fetuses around the threshold stage whose sentience, and therefore whose moral status, is indeterminate.

A criterion based on sentience enables us to explain the status of other putative thresholds. Neither conception nor birth marks the transition from a presentient to a sentient being. A zygote has not one whit more consciousness than the gametes out of which it is formed. Likewise, although a neonate has more opportunity to employ its powers, it also has no greater capacity for sensation than a full-term fetus. Of thresholds located during gestation, quickening is the perception of fetal movement that is probably reflex and therefore preconscious. Only viability has some relevance, though at one remove.

A fetus is viable when it is equipped to survive in the outside world. A being that is aware of, and can respond to, its own inner states is able to communicate its needs to others. This ability is of no use in utero but may aid survival in an extrauterine environment. A fetus is therefore probably sentient by the conventional stage of viability (around the end of the second trimester). Viability can therefore serve as a (rough) indicator of moral standing.

> **Quickening**
> Usually considered the point in pregnancy when a woman feels her fetus move.

> **Viability**
> The point at which a fetus is able to live outside the uterine environment.

> **In utero**
> Pertaining to the environment inside the uterus or womb.

> **Extrauterine**
> Pertaining to the environment outside the uterus or womb.

Our common moral consciousness locates contraception and infanticide in quite different moral categories. This fact suggests implicit recognition of a basic asymmetry between choosing not to create a new life in the first place and choosing to destroy a new life once it has been created. The boundary between the two kinds of act is the threshold at which that life gains moral protection. Since gametes lack moral standing, contraception (however it is carried out) merely prevents the creation of a new person. Since an infant has moral standing, infanticide (however it is carried out) destroys a new person. A second-trimester threshold of moral standing introduces this asymmetry into the moral assessment of abortion. We may define an early abortion as one performed sometime during the first trimester or early in the second, and a late abortion as one performed sometime late in the second trimester or during the third. An early abortion belongs in the same moral category as contraception: it prevents the emergence of a new being with moral standing. A late abortion belongs in the same moral category as infanticide: it terminates the life of a new being with moral standing. The threshold of sentience thus extends the morality of contraception forward to cover early abortion and extends the morality of infanticide backward to cover late abortion. . . . The moral issues raised by early abortion are precisely those raised by contraception. It is for early abortions that the liberal view is appropriate. Since the fetus at this stage has no right to life, early abortion (like contraception) cannot violate its rights. But if it violates no one's rights, early abortion (like contraception) is a private act. . . . If a woman elects an early abortion, then, whatever the circumstances and whatever her reasons, she does nothing immoral.[2]

The moral issues raised by late abortion are similar to those raised by infanticide. It is for late abortions that (a weakened form of) the conservative view is appropriate. Since the fetus at this stage has a right to life, late abortion (like infanticide) may violate its rights. But if it may violate the fetus' rights, then late abortion (like infanticide) is a public act. There is, however, a morally significant difference between late abortion and infanticide. A fetus is parasitic upon a unique individual in a manner in which a newborn infant is not. That parasitic relation will justify late abortion more liberally than infanticide. Since we have already explored the morality of abortion for those cases in which the fetus has moral standing, the general approach to late abortions is clear enough. Unlike the simple and uniform treatment of early abortion, only a case-by-case analysis will here suffice. We should expect a serious threat to the woman's life or health (physical or mental) to justify abortion, especially if that threat becomes apparent only late in pregnancy. We should also expect a risk of serious fetal deformity to justify abortion, again especially if that risk becomes apparent (as it usually does) only late in pregnancy. On the other hand, it should not be necessary to justify abortion on the ground that pregnancy was not consented to, since a woman will have ample opportunity to seek an abortion before the threshold stage. If a woman freely elects to continue a pregnancy past that stage, she will thereafter need a serious reason to end it.

A differential view of abortion is therefore liberal concerning early abortion and conservative (in an extended sense) concerning late abortion. The status of the borderline cases in the middle weeks of the second trimester is simply indeterminate. We cannot say of them with certainty either that the fetus has a right to life or that it does not. Therefore we also cannot say either that a liberal approach to these abortions is suitable or that a conservative treatment of them is required. What we can say is that, from the moral point of view, the earlier an abortion is performed the better. . . .

A liberal view of early abortion in effect extends a woman's deadline for deciding whether to have a child. . . . A deadline in the second trimester allows a woman enough time to discover that she is pregnant and to decide whether to continue the pregnancy. If she chooses not to continue it, her decision violates neither her duties nor any other being's rights. From the point of view of the fetus, the upshot of this treatment of early abortion is that its life is for a period merely probationary; only when it has passed the threshold will that life be accorded protection. . . .

Settling on sentience as a criterion of moral standing thus leads us to a view of the moral status of the fetus, and of the morality of abortion, which satisfies the constraints set out above. It is gradual, since it locates a threshold stage rather than a point and allows moral standing to be acquired incrementally. It is differential, since it locates the threshold stage during gestation and thus distinguishes the moral status of newly conceived and full-term fetuses. It is developmental, since it grounds the acquisition of moral standing in one aspect of the normal development of the fetus. And it is moderate, since it distinguishes the moral status of early and late abortions, and applies each of the established views to that range of cases for which it is appropriate. . . .

Study Questions

1. What is the main problem that Sumner finds with both the liberal and the conservative views of abortion?

2. On Sumner's account, what is the basis of moral standing?

3. In Sumner's view, when is a late-stage abortion justified?

Notes

1. The adoption of this working definition of moral standing should not be construed as a concession that rights are the appropriate category for dealing with the moral issues posed by abortion. But since both of the established views employ the rhetoric of rights, there is some point to showing how that rhetoric is equally available to a moderate view. For a generalized notion of moral standing freed from all connection with rights, see L. Wayne Sumner, *Abortion and Moral Theory*. Princeton, NJ: Princeton University Press, 1981, Section 23.

2. Unless there are circumstances (such as extreme underpopulation) in which contraception would also be immoral.

THREE   Abortion, Intimacy, and the Duty to Gestate
Margaret Olivia Little | *Ethical Theory and Moral Practice* 1999; 2: 295-312.

Introduction: The Method Question

It is often said that the public debate on abortion, in addition to being politically intractable, is too crude: any reasoning proffered (as opposed to the more usual fist-pounding) fails to capture the subtleties and ambivalences that suffuse the issue. . . .

I want to argue that this is no accident. The topics that abortion touches on, including motherhood and intimacy, and again vulnerability and responsibility, are amongst those least explored by mainstream theory. Most profoundly of all, abortion is about a kind of interconnection that our inherited theories are particularly ill-suited to address. . . . A question of method thus shadows all discussions of abortion, whether acknowledged or not. Abortion asks us to face the morality and politics of intertwinement and enmeshment with a conceptual framework that is, to say the least, poorly suited to the task. A tradition that imagines persons as physically separate might be expected not to do well when analyzing situations in which persons *aren't* as it imagines them. And this is, in fact, precisely what we find. Let me give as an example of this distortion the way in which the legal debate has proceeded in the United States.

In the United States, it is fair to say that the landscape of mainstream public discussion on abortion is dominated by two positions: a pro-life position that likens abortion to murder, and the pro-choice position as it is developed in the famous *Roe* v. *Wade* decision, which stresses a fundamental right to privacy. These two positions are obviously in deep conflict with one another, and the continued intractable public debate gives witness to just how deep the divide goes. It is all the more striking, then, to see that there are two key features they share in common.

First, both agree that the legal permissibility of abortion turns on the question of fetal personhood. That is, while they disagree vehemently about whether a fetus qualifies as a person, they agree on what would follow if it did. Persons have a fundamental right to life, after all; and abortion would be the type of action that violates such a right: if the fetus were a person, both sides find it obvious that abortion should be outlawed. Second, neither takes as pivotal the fact that gestation occurs inside of someone's body. . . . On mainstream views, if abortion is the type of action that violates a right to life, and the fetus turns out to be the sort of creature that has such a right, then abortion must be prohibited whatever hardships unwanted pregnancies involve for women; for we simply don't take hardships as justification for murder. . . .

In wondering whether abortion is murder the issue is not just a matter of deciding whether or when the fetus is a person: it is a matter of determining the contours of the right to life in the rather distinctive circumstance of being gestated. It asks us how we should classify the action of "ending a pregnancy" (that there is no neutral terminology here is precisely the point). But we are encouraged by mainstream pro-life *and* pro-choice views to miss this question. It turns out, that is, that the two features I isolated above as shared ground of these mainstream positions are deeply related. In not highlighting the fact that gestation happens inside of bodies, we can end up thinking of fetuses, not just as persons, but as persons *atomistically situated*, as physically individuated and separate—as though the bundle of specified rights at issue for the fetus is the same bundle we commonly face walking down the street in everyday life. . . .

Of course, even if we decide that abortion isn't best construed as a violation of the right to life, the law might still have reasons for wanting to prohibit it, and ethics a basis for protesting it. Indeed, to my way of thinking, the most interesting sources of concern about abortion would still remain: these are concerns grounded in the idea that the woman who aborts is not so much violating the fetus' right to life as she is reneging on *positive responsibilities* she has towards the fetus, either as a matter of general decency or in virtue of some special maternal relationship. The really interesting questions about abortion, I think, are questions about whether or when one has a duty to continue gestating when one finds oneself pregnant. But, while this question is more interesting, it must also be handled with care. If we are to assess the positive responsibility to gestate, we must assess it in full appreciation of the fact that gestation is an *intimacy*. Let me explore the difference this appreciation might make to our views about the moral and legal status of abortion, beginning with the legal question.

Intimacy without Consent

What harm is visited, what burden imposed, when the state forces someone to continue gestating?

To be pregnant is to be *inhabited*. It is to be *occupied*. It is to be in a state of physical *intimacy* of a particularly thorough-going nature. The fetus intrudes on the body massively; whatever medical risks one faces or avoids, the brute fact remains that the fetus shifts and alters the very physical boundaries of the woman's self. To mandate continuation of gestation is, quite simply, to force continuation of such occupation. To mandate that the woman remain pregnant is to mandate that she remain in a state of physical intertwinement against her consent. . . . The complaint is with the idea of forcing a woman to be in a state of physical intimacy with and occupation by this unwitting entity. For, unwitting or not, it still intertwines and intrudes on her body; and whatever the state's beneficent motives for protecting the interests of the fetus, it matters that the method used for that protection involves forcing others to have another entity live inside them. . . .

Mandating gestation against a woman's consent is *itself* a harm—a liberty harm. . . . However joyful pregnancy under consent may be—yearned for or tolerated as a means to an end you endorse—gestation mandated against consent is itself a harm. . . .

However joyful, meaningful, or just plain fun sex under consent may be, sex against consent is itself a harm—even if there are no bruises or broken ribs. So, too, forced gestation against consent is a liberty harm, however meaningful pregnancy under consent— even if there are no further harms such as medical complications or social cost. The extent to which this harm is absent in the mainstream literature is startling. I don't mean that it is mentioned and too quickly disregarded; I mean it is rarely on the table. . . .

Morality and Intimate Duties

The matter of lived urgency to so many women, of course, is not so much whether they should have a legal right to abort, but whether and when it is moral to *exercise* that right. In my experience, mainstream discussions of this question are disturbingly off-base. To be asked to gestate is to be asked to share one's very body—and likely, by the end, one's heart. To gestate is to be engaged in an *intimacy* of deep proportions. The ethical issues salient to questions of intimate actions, though, have been almost universally ignored in traditional philosophy. . . .

What we need in thinking about abortion is a moral approach that does justice to the ethics of intimacy; what we have is a moral approach that rarely uses the word.

Let me explore the issue by focusing on what is one of the strongest—if usually tacit—concerns about the morality of abortion. If truth be known, many reservations about the permissibility of abortion are grounded in an idea of what mothers owe their children; for many people, moral questions about abortion are, if you like, a species of the ethics of parenthood. If this is true, then we need an adequate ethics of parenthood: we need to understand what makes someone a parent in a thickly normative sense, and what the contours of the responsibility really are. I want to argue that parenthood can have different layers—biological, legal, but also personal relationship—and that, crucially, different moral responsibilities attach to different layers. Let me give the general framework and then show how it applies to the special case of gestation.

In its paradigmatic form, parenthood is a lived, personal relationship, not just a legal status, one that, in the ideal, involves a restructuring of psyches, a lived emotional interconnection, and a history of shared experiences. It is because of that lived intertwinement, indeed, that parents' motivation to sacrifice is so often immediate (why parenthood thickly lived is one of the few sites of genuinely virtuous, as opposed to merely continent, action). But it is also because of the lived intertwinement that the child has legitimate expectations of enormous sacrifice, and why failure to provide such assistance would, absent unusual circumstances, be so problematic—it becomes a betrayal of the relationship itself. . . .

Some parental responsibilities, I want to suggest, are functions, of the lived and personal relationship that so often accompany them, and that responsibilities to share one's very *body*, like responsibilities of the heart, are paradigmatic of those that are relationship-based.

This isn't, though, the end of the story. In ethics, if we notice relationships at all, we tend to focus only on questions about what morally flows from or governs relationships once they have been entered.[1] But there is another layer to the ethics of relationships: considerations surrounding whether one *ought* to enter—or be open to entering—a relationship, and again, when it is permissible to exit. There are some very general virtues at the level of entering: it is a sign of good character to be appropriately open to new relationships (a mild requirement, to be sure, given that one can be open but decline because, as it were, one's dance card is full). . . . If biology *per se* carries any relevance, I want to argue, it is at this level. The biological connections definitive of what we might call thin parenthood count as a substrate of parenthood thickly understood—of parenthood as personal relationship. They provide children with a moral claim that the person so related be open toward developing a deeper relationship. . . . My point is only that, if biology is morally salient, it is salient as a claim toward a further relationship—our intuitions on the subject are often intuitions about the moral legitimacy of yearning for personal relationship with those of biological connection, and sense of betrayal if the reasons for declining are too casual or callous.

There are, then, moral claims that flow from extant personal relationships and also moral claims about being open to entering such relationships. . . . This matters especially for the responsibilities—and the abnegations—of parenthood. The anatomy of parental abandonment is a complicated thing. It is a form of abandonment callously to refuse openness to a child with whom one stands in biological connection, and it is a form of abandonment blithely to refuse a sacrifice that would, against a lived relationship, be reasonably expected: but they are not the same abandonment. . . . Gestation, I've claimed, is an intimacy of the first order—it is even more intimate than donating an organ, for it involves an intertwinement and on-going occupation. This means, on the above approach, that a responsibility to gestate does not arise merely from the fact of being in biological relationship with the fetus: pregnant women do not have an automatic, role-based moral duty to gestate.[2] But this doesn't mean that pregnancy is not a moral moment. For one thing, just as there are mild virtues of openness to relationship, it is a general virtue to be welcoming of germinating human

life that comes one's way (a virtue that is perfectly consistent with using birth control—one may try one's best to avoid guests and yet think it a virtue to welcome them if they show up on your doorstep). More importantly, the biological substrate of being connected to the child in one's belly grounds a special claim of openness to further relationship. . . .

What I now want to suggest is that this framework of relationship ethics helps to make sense of what can otherwise seem to be rather puzzling features of certain intuitions about the moral responsibilities of gestation. More specifically, it can help to capture and to make sense of the fact that intuitions about the moral responsibility to gestate are, at one and the same time, *varied*, *urgently felt*, and curiously *underdetermined*. For if responsibilities to share one's body turn on the specifics of the lived relationship at hand, the lived relationship accompanying gestation is itself varied, urgently felt, and curiously underdetermined. Let me explain.

Just as women differ in their conceptions of the fetus' status, they differ in how they conceptualize the relationship they are in with that fetus. Some women feel from the start that they are in a special personal relationship with the growing fetus. They conceptualize themselves as a mother, thickly construed, in relationship with an entity that is "their child," whatever the further metaphysical details. The structure of their psyche has already shifted, the fetus' welfare is inextricably bound with their own, and it is unthinkable not to gestate—or it would, at the least, take enormously weighty reasons to refuse. For others, the sense of relationship grows, as most personal relationships do, slowly: the pregnancy begins as mere biological relationship but, as the day-to-day preoccupations of decisions involving the welfare of another (of mediating what she eats, how she sleeps) accumulate, and she finds herself in personal relationship. For other women, the relationship is never one of motherhood thickly construed: she is simply in biological relationship with a germinating human organism. For still others, the sense of relationship shifts throughout pregnancy: a conception of motherhood is tried on, then dispatched, or arrives fully formed out of the blue.

For purposes of the woman's *integrity*, her conception is determinative. Her own sense of what type of reasons she would need to end a pregnancy is in large part a function of how she understands the particular relationship she is experiencing in gestating (including its other relatum). For a woman one who conceives of herself as already intertwined as mother, and the fetus as her child, it would take reasons approaching life and death to decline gestating; for one who conceives of herself as in a biological relationship with burgeoning life, lesser reasons will suffice.

From an external or objective perspective, though, it is very difficult to get a foothold on what expectations and claims we might press on behalf of the fetus—to determine, as it were, which woman's conception is correct. And this, crucially, is not just because it's hard to garner evidence, but because there *isn't* much to determine what the relationship is. . . . With gestation, it is hard to determine what reasonable expectations we might press on behalf of the fetus; and this is because there simply *is* little to the relationship, *as* a relationship, other than the biological substrate and the woman's experience and conception of it.

Now mentioning the woman's conception of the pregnancy and fetus makes many people nervous. It can sound as though we are ceding far too much power to her subjective experience (as do some crude conventionalists, according to whom the woman's view of the fetus determines its metaphysical and normative status). But the claim here is not that the woman's assessment of the pregnancy determines the fetus' status. . . . The point here is a specific and contained one. Not everything about one's moral duties to fetuses (or again to newborns) trades on personal relationship. There are all sorts of duties that have nothing to do with those particulars. But some responsibilities, including, I've urged, responsibilities of gestation, do. The only claim about the woman's conception is that it's the only thing we have, other than mere biology, to tell whether there is a personal relationship extant and what its textures are like. We might say that her conception is largely determinative of what the relationship is, and that her moral responsibilities follow its suit; or—better, I think— we may simply say that there is too little going on for there to be a fact of the matter of what responsibilities are objectively owed. . . .

One of the most common reasons women seek abortions is that they do not have room in their life just then to be a mother, but they know if they continue the pregnancy they will not be able to give up the child. What has seemed paradoxical (and indeed ethically confused) to many strikes me as a perfectly sensible, and often wise, appreciation of the different moral contours involved with entering, existing in, and exiting relationships. . . .

Study Questions

1. What are Little's two objections to the mainstream treatment of the morality of abortion?

2. Little relies heavily on the idea that pregnancy involves a kind of intimacy and intertwinement. How does she define these terms?

3. Little argues that the biological connection between a fetus and its mother is the basis of some duties to the fetus, but not the duty to gestate. What is the basis of the duty to gestate? What role does a woman's integrity play in the grounding of this duty?

Notes

1. Barbara Katz Rothman briefly discusses the crucial difference between entering and exiting relationships in her article Redefining Abortion (1989).

2. This is not meant to settle whether she has a perfect duty of beneficence to gestate, only to urge that she does not have a special duty grounded in the role of motherhood.

References

Feinberg, J., Abortion, in *Freedom and Fulfillment: Philosophical Essays*. Princeton: Princeton University Press, 1992, pp. 37–75.

Kamm, F.M., *Creation and Abortion: A Study in Moral and Legal Philosophy*. New York: Oxford University Press, 1992.

Koppelman, A., Forced Labor: A Thirteenth Amendment Defense of Abortion. *Northwestern University Law Review* 84 (1990), pp. 480–535.

MacKinnon, C., Reflections on Sex Equality Under Law. *Yale Law Journal*, 100 (1991), p. 1314.

McDonagh, E., *Breaking the Abortion Deadlock: From Choice to Consent*. Oxford: Oxford University Press, 1996.

Rothman, B.K., Redefining Abortion, in *Recreating Motherhood: Ideology and Technology in a Patriarchal Society*. New York: Norton, 1989, pp. 106–24.

Thomson, J.J., A Defense of Abortion. *Philosophy and Public Affairs* 1 (1971).

West, R., Gender and Jurisprudence, in Patricia Smith (ed.), *Feminist Jurisprudence*. Oxford: Oxford University Press, 1993, pp. 493–530.

Wreen, M., Abortion and Pregnancy Due to Rape. *Philosophia* 21 (1992), pp. 201–20.

Chapter Study Questions

1. The authors of the articles in this chapter agree that some abortions are permissible. To what extent do they agree? To what extend do they disagree?

2. Marquis and Sumner seem to defend theories according to which infanticide is permissible.

What is the main difference (if any) between them on this question?

3. Little raises various objections to the mainstream treatment of the morality of abortion. Do the analyses provided by Sumner and Marquis avoid these objections? Explain your answer.

Critical Analysis

Consider the following from the article by Marquis:

"The claim that the primary wrong-making feature of a killing is the loss to the victim of the value of its future has obvious consequences for the ethics of abortion. The future of a standard fetus includes a set of experiences, projects, activities, and such which are identical with the futures of adult human beings and are identical with the futures of young children. Since the reason that is sufficient to explain why it is wrong to kill human beings after the time of birth is a reason that also applies to fetuses, it follows that abortion is prima facie seriously morally wrong."

Outline Marquis' argument in your own words, paying particular attention to the premises that he relies on to support his main conclusion. Choose one of the premises for evaluation. Try to think of at least one objection to this premise.

Case Study

In the 1988 *R. v. Morgentaler* case, the Supreme Court of Canada ruled that law then governing abortion was in violation of the *Charter of Rights and Freedoms*. As a result, Canada currently has no law specifically governing abortion, except those laws that govern surgical procedures more generally. This makes it possible for a person to obtain an abortion during the late stages of pregnancy (especially in large urban centres). Although this turns out to be quite rare, it does happen in Canada. Consider the following case.

A young woman has newly arrived in Canada from a foreign country for the purpose of studying engineering at a university in a large urban centre. She is 34 weeks pregnant. She is not married and has only a very small income and no partner with which to raise the child. She is visiting Canada only for the purpose of her studies. However, if she is forced to return to her home country she fears being ostracized and being punished for being pregnant out of wedlock. The fetus is well beyond the point of viability and it is only a few weeks away from being considered full term. She does not claim to have been raped or to have had sexual relations that suggest the baby is a product of incest. She does, however, appear confused and distressed when she enters a clinic that performs abortions. She appears competent to consent to medical procedures, and the clinic permits her having an abortion.

1. Do you think it permissible for a woman to obtain an abortion at this late stage of pregnancy?

2. Which factors matter to your answer to the first question?

3. If the woman in question was carrying a fetus with a serious birth defect, would you change your mind about the morality of the abortion in question?

Further Reading

Boonin D. *A defence of abortion*. Oxford: University Press; 2003.

Pope John Paul II, Evangelium Vitae (1995) [Internet]. Available from: http://www.vatican.va/edocs/ENG0141/_INDEX.HTM. Date Accessed: 5 June 2012.

R. v. Morgentaler [Internet]. Available from: http://www.canlii.org/en/ca/scc/doc/1988/1988canlii90/1988canlii90.pdf. Date Accessed: 5 June 2012.

Richer K. Abortion in Canada: Twenty years after *R. v. Morgentaler*. Library of Parliament; 2008. Available from: http://www.parl.gc.ca/Content/LOP/researchpublications/prb0822-e.pdf. Date Accessed: 5 June 2012.

Sherwin, S. Abortion through a feminist lens, *Dialogue* 1991 30:327–42.

Procreation and Child Rearing

What sort of child is it good to desire or to seek to produce? A vast majority of people believe that one ought to want a healthy and happy child, and that one ought to take the steps most likely to facilitate this outcome. These obligations are most palpable during pregnancy, infancy and early childhood. The prevailing wisdom is that anyone considering assuming responsibility for a child is encouraged to educate her- or himself about parenting. Women are urged to eat correctly, to avoid smoking and consuming alcohol during pregnancy and to breastfeed their baby during the first year of life and to thereafter offer only the most nutritious food and the highest quality stimulation. Men are prodded to be active and engaged parents and to be especially supportive of new and nursing mothers and emotionally vulnerable infants and toddlers. There is in general a strong demand that parents do what they can to enhance their child's mental and physical health and welfare.

The conventional means of satisfying this demand for the most part involve maximizing the potential of an existing fetus or infant. However, for those relying on in vitro fertilization (IVF), technology offers a larger menu of options for producing healthy, happy children. IVF is a process in which an embryo that is fertilized in a laboratory is subsequently implanted in a womb. Before an embryo is transferred it is possible to employ a technique known as pre-implantation genetic diagnosis or PGD. This procedure makes it possible to determine the genetic makeup of an embryo and in particular to test for chromosomal abnormalities or genetic mutations known to be associated with certain diseases. This knowledge can then be used to reject embryos that have increased propensity for certain diseases (e.g., sickle-cell anemia and cystic fibrosis) and to select embryos that have traits that are positively correlated with health and well-being. The embryos that are considered desirable are then implanted.

PGD is legal in Canada. It is currently employed in some fertility clinics, though it is difficult to determine how frequently it is used and for what purposes. There are few norms governing it beyond those covering medical procedures in general. The *Assisted Human Reproduction Act*, which regulates PGD, among other things, forbids it only for the purpose of selecting for or against a particular sex for non-medical reasons. This means that in Canada many genetic conditions might be used as the basis for selecting an embryo. PGD might therefore be used to produce a happy, healthy and socially well-adjusted child.

But ought individuals to avail themselves of all possible means of producing the child with the rosiest life prospects? The first two papers in this chapter deal with this question. In "Procreative Beneficence: Why We Should Select the Best Children," Julian

Savulescu argues that for those using IVF it is obligatory to use PGD to select the best child possible. Savulescu's case for this claim begins with the uncontroversial assumption that well-being matters. That something makes a life better, all things considered, gives us a strong but defeasible reason to promote it. There are a number of both disease conditions (e.g., asthma) and non-disease conditions (e.g., impulse control) that make a difference to the quality of one's life. PGD is able to help us avoid producing children with asthma and may in the future assist us in producing children with greater impulse control. PGD is therefore capable of helping us promote welfare by helping us to produce children who, given the evidence, will live better lives. Hence there is strong reason to employ PGD in cases in which one has employed IVF and to select the embryo that one expects to have the best prospects.

In her article "'Healthy' Human Embryos and Symbolic Harm," Elizabeth Gedge urges us to consider the negative implications of PGD. She is in particular concerned with what is known as the expressivist critique, according to which PGD and related technologies are problematic because they send a message that the lives of the disabled are not worth living. She is keen to provide this argument with a firm backing. She starts by distinguishing between two kinds of harms: consequentialist, and symbolic; and she thinks that the use of PGD is capable of producing both kinds of harms for the disabled, though her focus is on symbolic harm. She thinks that the use of PGD can produce symbolic harm in two ways: by dehumanizing, and by subordinating those with disabilities. PGD is dehumanizing because it involves drawing distinctions between embryos that are healthy and those that are unhealthy, and this in turn implies that the disabled fall short of the genetic ideal, a view that is inconsistent with proper concern and respect. PGD subordinates the disabled because, as a social practice that is supported by medical and governmental institutions, it sends a message that the disabled are inferior to the abled, putting the rights and the entitlements of the disabled in jeopardy. Gedge is not, however, in favour of banning or limiting the use of PGD since she is keen to protect reproductive freedom. She hopes that it is possible to respect this freedom while limiting its negative effects on the most vulnerable.

In the literature on bioethics, reproductive ethics tends to be equivalent to the study of the ethical issues arising during pregnancy and the early stages of life. In the final paper of this chapter, "Measuring Mothering," Rebecca Kukla argues for a reconsideration of this focus. She argues that reproductive ethics ought instead to "refer to the ethics of creating and caring for new generations." She is concerned in particular with the norms governing mothering. There is a tendency to measure mothering by reference to a set of signal moments rather than by reference to extended narratives. It is common to think that a good mother is one who behaves according to socially enforced norms when giving birth to her child and when feeding her child in the early stages of life. Kukla thinks that many of these norms are dubious and that, more importantly, they reinforce privilege and distract us from developing policies and programs that encourage good mothering over the long term.

ONE   Procreative Beneficence: Why We Should Select the Best Children

Julian Savulescu | *Bioethics* 2001; 15: 413-26.

Introduction

Imagine you are having in vitro fertilization (IVF) and you produce four embryos. . . . One is to be implanted. You are told that there is a genetic test for predisposition to scoring well on IQ tests (call this intelligence). If an embryo has gene subtypes (alleles) A, B there is a greater than 50 per cent chance it will score more than 140 if given an ordinary education and upbringing. If it has subtypes C, D there is a much lower chance it will score over 140. Would you test the four embryos for these gene subtypes and use this information in selecting which embryo to implant? . . .

Many people believe that research into the genetic contribution to intelligence should not be performed, and that if genetic tests which predict intelligence, or a range of intelligence, are ever developed, they should not be employed in reproductive decision-making. I will argue that we have a moral obligation to test for genetic contribution to non-disease states such as intelligence and to use this information in reproductive decision-making. . . .

> **Genetic tests which predict intelligence**
> Intelligence is the result of both genetic and non-genetic factors, making it a trait that is difficult to select for. Any such test that is developed for this trait is likely to be prone to error.

Procreative Beneficence: The Moral Obligation To Have The Best Children

I will argue for a principle which I call Procreative Beneficence:

> *"Couples (or single reproducers) should select the child, of the possible children they could have, who is expected to have the best life, or at least as good a life as the others, based on the relevant, available information."*

I will argue that Procreative Beneficence implies couples should employ genetic tests for non-disease traits in selecting which child to bring into existence and that we should allow selection for non-disease genes in some cases even if this maintains or increases social inequality.

By "should" in "should choose," I mean "have good reason to." I will understand morality to require us to do what we have most reason to do. In the absence of some other reason for action, a person who has good reason to have the best child is morally required to have the best child. . . .

Definitions

A disease gene is a gene which causes a genetic disorder (e.g., cystic fibrosis) or predisposes to the development of disease (e.g., the genetic contribution to cancer or dementia). A non-disease gene is a gene which causes or predisposes to some physical or psychological state of the person which is not itself a disease state, e.g., height, intelligence, character (not in the subnormal range).

Selection

It is currently possible to select from a range of possible children we could have. This is most frequently done by employing fetal selection through prenatal testing and termination of pregnancy. Selection of embryos is now possible by employing in vitro fertilization and pre-implantation genetic diagnosis (PGD). There are currently no genetic tests available for non-disease states except sex. However, if such tests become available in the future, both PGD and prenatal testing could be used to select offspring on the basis of non-disease genes. . . .

> **Pre-implantation genetic diagnosis**
> A technique allowing for the genetic evaluation of embryos that have been created using in vitro fertilization. A biopsy is performed on the embryo and the cells are screened for various genetic mutations or chromosomal abnormalities. Knowledge gained from this is typically used to determine which embryos to transfer to the uterus.

An Argument For Procreative Beneficence

Consider the *Simple Case of Selection for Disease Genes.* A couple is having IVF in an attempt to have a child. It produces two embryos. A battery of tests for common diseases is performed. Embryo A has no abnormalities on the tests performed. Embryo B has no abnormalities on the tests performed except its genetic profile reveals it has a predisposition to developing asthma. Which embryo should be implanted?

Embryo B has nothing to be said in its favour over A and something against it. Embryo A should (on pain of irrationality) be implanted. . . .

Why shouldn't we select the embryo with a predisposition to asthma? What is relevant about asthma is that it reduces quality of life. Attacks cause severe breathlessness and in extreme cases, death. Steroids may be required to treat it. These are among the most dangerous drugs which exist if taken long term. Asthma can be lifelong and require lifelong drug treatment. Ultimately it can leave the sufferer wheelchair bound with chronic obstructive airways disease. The morally relevant property of "asthma" is that it is a state which reduces the well-being a person experiences.

An Objection to Procreative Beneficence in the Simple Case

The following objection to Procreative Beneficence is common. "If you choose Embryo A (without a predisposition to asthma), you could be discarding someone like Mozart or an Olympic swimmer. So there is no good reason to select A."

It is true that by choosing A, you could be discarding a person like Mozart. But it is equally true that if you choose B, you could be discarding someone like Mozart without asthma. A and B are equally likely (on the information available) to be someone like Mozart (and B is more likely to have asthma). . . .

Moving From Disease Genes To Non-disease Genes: What is the "Best Life?"

It is not asthma (or disease) which is important, but its impact on a life in ways that matter which is important. Non-disease genes may prevent us from leading the best life.

By "best life," I will understand the life with the most well-being. There are various theories of well-being: hedonistic, desire-fulfilment, objective list theories.[1] According to hedonistic theories, what matters is the quality of our experiences, for example,

that we experience pleasure. According to desire-fulfilment theories, what matters is the degree to which our desires are satisfied. According to objective list theories, certain activities are good for people, such as achieving worthwhile things with your life, having dignity, having children and raising them, gaining knowledge of the world, developing one's talents, appreciating beautiful things, and so on.

On any of these theories, some non-disease genes will affect the likelihood that we will lead the best life. Imagine there is a gene which contributes significantly to a violent, explosive, uncontrollable temper, and that state causes people significant suffering. Violent outbursts lead a person to come in conflict with the law and fall out of important social relations. The loss of independence, dignity and important social relations are bad on any of the three accounts. . . .

Does being intelligent mean one is more likely to have a better life? At a folk intuitive level, it seems plausible that intelligence would promote well-being on any plausible account of well-being. On a hedonistic account, the capacity to imagine alternative pleasures and remember the salient features of past experiences is important in choosing the best life. On a desire-fulfilment theory, intelligence is important to choosing means which will best satisfy one's ends. On an objective list account, intelligence would be important to gaining knowledge of the world, and developing rich social relations. Newson has reviewed the empirical literature relating intelligence to quality of life. Her synthesis of the empirical literature is that "intelligence has a high instrumental value for persons in giving them a large amount of complexity with which to approach their everyday lives, and that it equips them with a tool which can lead to the provision of many other personal and social goods."[2] . . .

Objections to the Principle of Procreative Beneficence Applied to Non-Disease Genes

Harm to the Child

One common objection to genetic selection for non-disease traits is that it results in harm to the child. There are various versions of this objection, which include the harm which arises from excessive and overbearing parental expectations, using the child as a means, and not treating it as an end, and closing off possible future options on the basis of the information provided (failing to respect the child's "right to an open future").

There are a number of responses. Firstly, in some cases, it is possible to deny that the harms will be significant. Parents come to love the child whom they have (even a child with a serious disability). Moreover, some have argued that counselling can reduce excessive expectations.[3]

Secondly, we can accept some risk of a child experiencing some state of reduced well-being in cases of selection. One variant of the harm to child objection is: "If you select embryo A, it might still get asthma, or worse, cancer, or have a much worse life than B, and you would be responsible." Yet selection is immune to this objection. . . .

Imagine you select Embryo A and it develops cancer (or severe asthma) in later life. You have not harmed A unless A's life is not worth living (hardly plausible) because A would not have existed if you had acted otherwise. A is not made worse off than A would otherwise have been, since without the selection, A would not have existed. Thus we can accept the possibility of a bad outcome, but not the probability of a very bad outcome. (Clearly, Procreative Beneficence demands that we not choose a child with a low predisposition to asthma but who is likely to have a high predisposition to cancer.) . . .

Inequality

One objection to Procreative Beneficence is that it will maintain or increase inequality. For example, it is often argued that selection for sex, intelligence, favourable physical or psychological traits, etc. all contribute to inequality in society, and this is a reason not to attempt to select the best.

In the case of selection against disease genes, similar claims are made. For example, one version of the *Disability Discrimination Claim* maintains that prenatal testing for disabilities such as Down syndrome results in discrimination against those with those disabilities both by:

- the statement it makes about the worth of such lives; and
- the reduction in the numbers of people with this condition.

Even if the Disability Discrimination Claim were true, it would be a drastic step in favour of equality to inflict a higher risk of having a child with a disability on a couple (who do not want a child with a disability) to promote social equality.

Consider a hypothetical rubella epidemic. A rubella epidemic hits an isolated population. Embryos produced prior to the epidemic are not at an elevated risk of any abnormality but those produced during the epidemic are at an increased risk of deafness and blindness. Doctors should encourage women to use embryos which they have produced prior to the epidemic in preference to ones produced during the epidemic. The reason is that it is bad that blind and deaf children are born when sighted and hearing children could have been born in their place.

> **Rubella**
> An infection also known as German measles. If a pregnant woman is infected, this can result in her fetus being infected with congenital rubella syndrome, which can produce a range of health problems, including mental retardation and congenital heart disease.

This does not necessarily imply that the lives of those who now live with disability are less deserving of respect and are less valuable. To attempt to prevent accidents which cause paraplegia is not to say that paraplegics are less deserving of respect. It is important to distinguish between disability and persons with disability. Selection reduces the former, but is silent on the value of the latter. There are better ways to make statements about the equality of people with disability (e.g., we could direct savings from selection against embryos/fetuses with genetic abnormalities to improving well-being of existing people with disabilities).

These arguments extend to selection for non-disease genes. It is not disease which is important but its impact on well-being. In so far as a non-disease gene such as a gene for intelligence impacts on a person's well-being, parents have a reason to select for it, even if inequality results.

This claim can have counterintuitive implications. Imagine in a country women are severely discriminated against. They are abandoned as children, refused paid employment and serve as slaves to men. Procreative Beneficence implies that couples should test for sex, and should choose males as they are expected to have better lives in this society, even if this reinforces the discrimination against women.

There are several responses. Firstly, it is unlikely selection on a scale that contributes to inequality would promote well-being. Imagine that 50 per cent of the population choose to select boys. This would result in three boys to every one girl. The life of a male in such a society would be intolerable.

Secondly, it is social institutional reform, not interference in reproduction, which should be promoted. What is wrong in such a society is the treatment of women, which should be addressed separately to reproductive decision-making. Reproduction should not become an instrument of social change, at least not mediated or motivated at a social level. . . .

Limits on Procreative Beneficence: Personal Concern for Equality or Self-Interest

Consider the following cases. David and Dianne are dwarves. They wish to use IVF and PGD to select a child with dwarfism because their house is set up for dwarves. Sam and Susie live a society where discrimination against women is prevalent. They wish to have a girl to reduce this discrimination. These choices would not harm the child produced if selection is employed. Yet they conflict with the Principle of Procreative Beneficence.

We have here an irresolvable conflict of principles:

- personal commitment to equality, personal interests and Procreative Autonomy; and
- Procreative Beneficence.

> **Procreative Autonomy**
> Being able to direct one's procreative decisions by reference to one's rationally chosen reproductive goals.

Just as there are no simple answers to what should be done (from the perspective of ethics) when respect for personal autonomy conflicts with other principles such as beneficence or distributive justice, so too there are no simple answers to conflict between Procreative Autonomy and Procreative Beneficence.

For the purposes of public policy, there should be a presumption in favour of liberty in liberal democracies. So, ultimately, we should allow couples to make their own decisions about which child to have. Yet this does not imply that there are no normative principles to guide those choices. Procreative Beneficence is a valid principle, albeit one which must be balanced against others.

The implication of this is that those with disabilities should be allowed to select a child with disability, if they have a good reason. But the best option is that we correct discrimination in other ways, by correcting discriminatory social institutions. In this way, we can achieve both equality and a population whose members are living the best lives possible.

Conclusions

With respect to non-disease genes, we should provide:

- information (through PGD and prenatal testing);
- free choice of which child to have; and
- non-coercive advice as to which child will be expected to enter life with the best opportunity of having the best life.

Selection for non-disease genes which significantly impact on well-being is *morally required* (Procreative Beneficence). "Morally required" implies moral persuasion but not coercion is justified.

If, in the end, couples wish to select a child who will have a lower chance of having the best life, they should be free to make such a choice. That should not prevent doctors from attempting to persuade them to have the best child they can. In some cases, persuasion will not be justified. If self-interest or concern to promote equality motivate a choice to select less than the best, then there may be no overall reason to attempt to dissuade a couple. But in cases in which couples do not want to use or obtain available information about genes which will affect well-being, and their desires are based on irrational fears (e.g., about interfering with nature or playing God), then doctors should try to persuade them to access and use such information in their reproductive decision-making.

> **Liberal democracies**
> Societies such as Canada's in which the population has some measure of control over the government and in which individual rights and freedoms are paramount and legally protected.

Study Questions

1. What is the central value on which Savulescu's argument relies?

2. Why is Savulescu unconvinced that PGD is harmful to a child?

3. Do you agree that we should seek to produce the child with the very best life rather than the child that is free from conditions that significantly impact well-being?

Notes

1. D Parfit. 1984. *Reasons and Persons.* Appendix I, pp. 493–502. Oxford. Clarendon Press: Part IV; J Griffin. 1986. *Well-Being.* Oxford. Clarendon Press.

2. A Newson. The value of intelligence and its implications for genetic research. *Fifth World Congress of Bioethics,* Imperial College, London, 21-4 September 2000.

3. J Robertson. Preconception Sex Selection. *American Journal of Bioethics* 1:1 (Winter 2001).

TWO   "Healthy" Human Embryos and Symbolic Harm

Elizabeth Gedge | In: Nisker J, Baylis F, Karpin I, McLeod C, Mykitiuk R. *The Healthy Embryo: Social, Biomedical, Legal and Philosophical Perspectives.* Cambridge University Press, 2010: 233-50.

Introduction

The term *genohype* is used by some writers (Caulfield et al. 2001) to refer to the excessive preoccupation with genetic medicine, the exaggerated claims made on its behalf, and various associated dangers. . . .

A primary application of genetic medicine is in the reproductive sphere, where prenatal or pre-implantation testing for embryo "health," reproductive counselling and the offer of selective termination are increasingly seen as routine aspects of good reproductive care. Many persons with disabilities claim that testing for "healthy" embryos and the conceptualization implicit within it not only stigmatize disabled persons as deviant, but send a message that their lives are not worth living or that they are not welcome. . . . The target of the objection is the evaluative attitude expressed by practices that seek to prevent the birth of persons with disabilities. This view has been labelled expressivism. . . I consider whether it can be given a sound rendering.

> **Prenatal testing**
> Genetic testing performed during pregnancy to detect chromosomal and other genetic abnormalities. This usually involves testing fetal tissue or amniotic fluid. It is routine in Canada and similar countries.

Expressivism claims that prenatal diagnosis (PND) and pre-implantation genetic diagnosis (PGD) send a message that devalues and poses a threat to persons with disabilities. The claim has two logically distinct components. . . . The threat of unwanted intervention, increased discrimination or reduced service alleged (Saxton 2000; Wates 2005) to be implicit in the lower status assigned by the practice to persons with disabilities points to a potential consequentialist harm. . . . Insofar as expressivism also objects to the very proclamation implicit in PND and PGD, it is making . . . a claim about non-consequentialist, representational or symbolic harm . . . that attaches to the meaning of acts or practices rather than to their effects. The symbolic harm alleged to attach to PND and PGD is that it devalues persons with disabilities by seeking to identify "healthy" embryos.[1] We can unpack this claim as follows: PND and PGD devalue persons with disabilities (1) by depicting them in a way that is inconsistent with their proper moral status, and/or (2) by unjustly positioning them as subordinate.

Devaluation and Proper Moral Status

What is it to be represented consistently with our proper moral status? Jean Harvey (1999, pp. 105-9) offers a useful distinction between the proper moral status of members of the moral community and our de facto status. Our proper moral status is the status we carry as human persons, and it should elicit "recognition respect;" our *de facto* status reflects the recognition we actually receive and the degree of empowerment that we, as moral agents, enjoy. Although our proper moral status (deriving from our worth as human beings and our equal membership in the moral community) cannot be increased or diminished, our *de facto* status clearly can. . . . One's public persona can be degraded by embedded bias directed (consciously or not) towards oneself or the group with which one is identified. Stereotypes of female irrationality, timidity or excessive emotionality persist, as do stereotypes of gay promiscuity. The disabled bear, and are perceived to be, "burdens." How we, or the group with which we are identified, are represented both reflects and shapes our standing in the moral and cultural imaginary. . . .

To understand the conceptual dynamics of identity construction and their relation to devaluation, we need an account of dualistic logic. As Taylor and Mykitiuk (2001) argue, genetic discourse has come to dominate the language of health and to divide us into "healthy" and "unhealthy" according to our relation to a norm of genetic health. This form of relational categorization follows a familiar pattern of dualistic and hierarchical thinking, thoroughly expounded by Val Plumwood (1993). The logic of negation, . . . she argues, sets up a conceptual world in which the positive defines and inferiorizes the negative. . . . Exploiting existing patterns of difference, the dualistic conceptual world solidifies difference into . . . hierarchical and linked pairs of properties, . . . attached to asymmetrically positioned groups. Common to our received cultural understanding, for instance, are the following contrasts: mind/body; reason/nature; reason/matter; human/non-human; male/female; civilized/primitive. . . . Although useful as distinctions,

> **De facto**
> A Latin term meaning "in fact." The author is concerned with the actual moral status of the disabled as opposed to the status they ought to be accorded.

under the logic of domination, these descriptors act as implicit norms, in each case situating the contrasting property or party as an inferior Other. Collections of such inferiorized descriptors cluster around certain groups (women, non-human animals, persons of colour, slaves, the environment) and, with the aid of five identity-constructing devices, define and solidify the self-understandings of both the dominant and the inferiorized Other. The conceptual devices, which serve to deny continuity between the polarized groups and to obscure any distinctiveness within the inferiorized, are backgrounding, hyperseparation, incorporation, instrumentalism and stereotyping. . . .

It is instructive to consider how the non-disabled/disabled distinction can be unpacked using Plumwood's model. . . . "Genohype" . . . constructs disability as deviance from a supposed norm of health and humanness. . . . Under "genohype," disability is inferiorized to non-disability. Once a genetic paradigm of disability is accepted, descriptors of inferiority cluster around the notion of disability. So, physicality . . . becomes a defining feature of persons with disabilities and carries with it the oppositional feature . . . primitivity (because the physical is contrasted to the cultural). Defined materially, disability is then conceived as hostile to mind, to freedom and to civilization. . . . Inferiorizing strategies follow readily. Backgrounding is . . . evident in the discourse of "accommodation," which assumes the priority of the non-disabled and discounts the ubiquity of vulnerability and dependency. . . . The paradigm of the non-disabled, adult, independent, rational citizen is at the core of hypothetical models of political negotiation, as though we were not all thoroughly dependent

> **Discourse of "accommodation"**
> The political and legal language employed in attempting to make provisions for the disabled in a society like ours that caters primarily to the needs and desires of the non-disabled.

as children and destined most likely to be so again in old age, if disease or accident does not hasten it. Hyperseparation essentializes and magnifies the differences between disabled and non-disabled, locating the site of difference as the gene or body of the Other, thus obscuring any continuity (for instance, common difficulties with itinerant pain or weakness or with obstacles in the physical or social world) and offering only a technological fix (the erasure of the Other) as the remedy. The disabled Other is incorporated by being defined in terms of her lack of ability and is simultaneously stereotyped because what is important is that she and other members of her group are not like the non-disabled. . . . Finally, instrumentalism allows us to deny disabled Others the status of independent centres of desires and needs. . . . Situating "genohype" in a framework of dualistic logic shows how the message of PGD can be inferiorizing, and how it can readily find uptake in a disableist cultural environment. For rather than offering a conceptual model within which persons are represented as Kantian "ends in themselves," "genohype" thoroughly constructs the identities of persons with disabilities by their problematic relation to the norm of genetic health, which can be considered a symbolic harm.

> **Kantian "ends in themselves"**
> The idea found in the ethical philosophy of Immanuel Kant (1724–1804), according to which each human being has a special status by virtue of possessing the capacity for rational choice. Proper respect of this value involves treating each human as an end and never as a means only.

Expressivist Claims

Placing "genohype" in the dualistic logic of domination not only supports the expressivist claim that PND and PGD devalue persons with disabilities through the message they send about "unhealthy" embryos but also strengthens the plausibility of the claim that such practices can, indeed, send a message. Expressivism has been given two different articulations: the individual act version, and the social practice version.[2] According to the individual act version, deciding to terminate a pregnancy or finding a particular embryo "unhealthy" and unacceptable because of disability sends a message that persons with disabilities are inferior, unworthy of life or unwelcome. According to the social practice version, which is the focus in what follows, it is the practice — the funding, development and expansion of tests for disability and the routinization of such testing — that sends the message. . . .

The Meaning and the Message

Alternative accounts of the meaning of PND and PGD have been offered, and they are initially plausible. For instance, James Nelson (2000) suggests that the purpose of the practice is the expansion of women's reproductive choices, and Nancy Press (2000) directs attention to what she calls the "official view" of the purpose of PND: that it aims to reassure or psychologically prepare women and to allow for in utero or early therapeutic intervention. As accounts of the meaning of PND or PGD, expressivism must address these claims. . . .

PND and PGD . . . are socially established and orchestrated practices, organized within the institutions of scientific funding and research, population and prenatal health, and the provision of medical care. . . . PND and PGD have an underlying ideology — a set of rules, principles and value judgments framed in a particular normative understanding of health. . . . What do PND and PGD, as practices, amount to? . . . Where the structures, procedures and outcomes exhibit values and purposes at odds with those that are alleged, practice meaning can be questioned.

Is the purpose of PND or PGD the enhancement of reproductive choice, the reassurance of women and couples, or the expansion of therapeutic possibilities as the official story suggests? . . . The problems of false positives and negatives, and the impossibility of predicting severity of outcome in the case of many conditions tested for suggest that the aims of maternal reassurance and therapeutic preparation are questionable (Carroll et al., 1997). Reassurance is tainted by diagnostic uncertainty and the anxiety associated with the outcome of tests, and choice is problematic because of the normalization of testing and its construction as "doing what's best for the baby. . . ."

From an analysis of her research on California's maternal serum alpha fetoprotein screening policy, Nancy Press (2000) argues that the official goals of enhanced choice and therapy rest on a normative subtext that emphasizes benefit to families or individuals rather than society; that assumes the joint good of mother and fetus; and that is broadly "for life" (p. 222). Yet a close examination of the practice, argues Press (2000), reveals instead controversial goals: the ability to terminate pregnancy for fetal disability . . . and the concomitant cost savings to society. As she points out, PND serves population health primarily by precluding disabled persons from the population. The subtext of the controversial goals . . . is that "not all life is worthwhile, and that the interests of society may conflict with those of the fetus" (p. 221). Scepticism over the official story about the meaning of PND is further strengthened by . . . the type of language used in genetic counselling (e.g., the language of "risk"), the routinization of maternal testing without sufficient statistical justification, the asymmetries of epistemic and social authority between clients and physicians . . . and the background attitudes of all participants towards disabilities (Press 2000). (For instance, Press found that although only 15 per cent of women interviewed in her study said they would terminate on a positive finding, the rate of terminations after testing was 85 per cent (p. 221).) . . .

We might argue, then, that the subtext . . . of PND and PGD and the preoccupation with identifying "healthy embryos" is that of "serving" society by reducing the number of disabled in the population. The supporting ideology, the rules, purposes, and values encompassed by these practices, are discernible in the linkage between testing and negative selection or termination, in the conditions tested for, and in the conceptual location of testing within the geneticized, reductionist model of health and human identity. The severe dissonance between the alleged ideology and the structural and institutional manifestations of PND and PGD cast doubt on alternative accounts, and increase the plausibility of the expressivist claim. . . .

Devaluation and Subordination

Genetic testing for disability is supported by an authoritative medical discourse, whose pronouncements may elicit widespread uptake (Sherwin 1992). Because physicians and geneticists have authority in the domain of reproductive and population health, the practice of genetic testing reflects a relevant body of authoritative speakers and a body of hearers for whom they are authoritative. And, further, a culture of disableism supports a dominant discourse of parental and social responsibility that militates against any countervailing desires or perspectives. . . . Can we then say that the socially endorsed practices of PND and PGD subordinate, that their routinization in prenatal care, the massive share of healthcare and research funding they receive, their institutionalized affiliation with termination services, and their overall embeddedness in the "genohype ideology" function . . . [to] rank persons with disabilities as inferior, legitimize discrimination against them and deprive

them of recourse available to others? If so, we could argue that these practices influence negatively on the *de facto* moral status of persons with disabilities. . . .

Two arguments may be presented to support the view that the offer of PND and PGD does, indeed, function in that way. . . . First, we might argue that the conceptual positioning within dualistic identity construction that devalues representationally at the same time functions to rank persons with disabilities as inferior. As Plumwood's analysis (1993) of social categorization shows, difference is essentialized and hierarchized in the logic of domination, which constitutes representational devaluation. Does this process, and its concretization in the message of genetic testing, also legitimize discrimination against persons with disabilities? This question has been a matter of hot debate, with opponents of expressivism . . . pointing to the coincidence between enhanced support for persons with disabilities and the rise of PND and PGD. For instance, argues Steinbock, "the rise of prenatal screening has coincided with more progressive attitudes toward the inclusion of people with disabilities, as evidenced in the United States by the passage of the Americans with Disabilities Act." However, according to Nancy Press, attitudes towards disability are ambivalent and often shrouded in positive discourse. Under these conditions, legal protections and economic gains for persons with disabilities (though vitally important) are likely to be unstable. Furthermore, where social attitudes are discriminatory, formal protections do little to ensure lives of security and respect. . . .

The second line of argument supporting the claim that PND and PGD deprive persons with disabilities of rights and privileges is an argument by analogy. Although . . . significant differences exist between disability and race, class or gender, it is useful to consider whether testing for sex or race, with an institutionalized connection to termination or negative selection for a positive finding, would effect a reduction in the rights and privileges of women or racialized groups (Scully 2005). This question is hardly hypothetical; prenatal testing for sex is commonplace, is accompanied by what some have called femicide, and coexists with women's inferiorized status and diminished enjoyment of rights in contexts where such testing is widely practiced (Hoskins and Holmes 1984; Alexander 2001).

One might object that the analogy is faulty on the grounds either that the objective of testing for disability is beneficent, or that (Scully 2005) it is false that the disadvantages of disability could all be removed in some possible world. Does this perspective show that the analogy with sex and race fails? I think not. First, we have seen reason to question whether the objective of the practice of testing for disability is beneficent. Nancy Press (2000) argues persuasively that, in the case of PND, the "societally accepted" beneficent goals cannot account adequately for the way the practice is structured, whereas the "controversial" goals of termination and cost containment can. But what about the claim that the practice reflects the truth that certain conditions simply are incompatible with an acceptable quality of life, and no amount of social readjustment would alter that fact? Does this claim not show that the analogy with sex and race fails? To answer, we need only attend to the fact that testing is not limited to fully predictable conditions known to be incompatible with an acceptable quality of life, and that the genetic imaginary, by homogenization, fails to acknowledge the relevant distinctions among disabilities and lives lived with them. . . .

Conclusion

I have argued that the practice of testing for the "healthy" embryo is symbolically harmful insofar as it represents persons with disabilities as inferior and its message may also subordinate. Insofar as the message is authoritative and is taken up as such, it may rank persons with disabilities as inferior, legitimize discrimination against them and deprive them of rights and privileges. . . .

If we judge a social practice to function so as to violate the proper moral status of citizens, . . . should such practices be prohibited? . . . There are sound reasons against such a draconian approach. . . . The message sent by a practice is only one of its moral features. The undesirability of the message must be balanced against the importance of respecting reproductive choice, reducing future suffering, and advancing medical knowledge. Preferable is an approach that alters the devaluing message while preserving these attendant goods, if possible. . . .

> **Draconian**
> Especially or unduly harsh.

Because the "remedy" of prohibiting or even limiting genetic testing for disability in the context of reproduction is unhelpful in altering its message and would compromise reproductive autonomy and medical advances, other means of addressing the message of testing must be sought. Here, attention to the discursive context is key. A corrective to the message of genetic testing for disability will involve making adequate space for the dissenting discourses from disabilities theory and empowering persons who speak from that position. Because discourses, even when framed dualistically, are logically unstable, apertures for counter-discourses are available and can be exploited. At the level of cultural imagery, foregrounding narratives and performances of rich lives lived in the absence of "goods" such as sight and hearing undermines the normative construction of health. And at the political level, a good first step towards broadening and democratizing reproductive policy-making would be . . . expanded public debate on our aims in proceeding down the path of PND and PGD.

Study Questions

1. How does Gedge distinguish between consequentialist and symbolic harm?

2. What is the difference between Gedge's conclusion that PGD undermines the proper moral status of the disabled and the conclusion that it subordinates them?

3. What is Gedge's reason for not advocating a prohibition on PGD?

Notes

1. Symbolic harm has intermittently been featured in ethical debates over our reproductive practices. For instance, as early as 1988, George Annas argued that by enforcing pregnancy contracts, we are *proclaiming* that women (unequivocal holders of legal and moral rights) are less important than the fetuses they are carrying. Furthermore, argued Annas (1986), when women are required to forfeit their autonomy and submit to intrusive procedures "for the sake of the fetus" and according to the terms of their gestational contracts, sexual equality is violated because such restrictions can apply only to women. Sex selection as well as contract pregnancy was challenged on non-consequentialist ethical grounds, as Tabitha Powledge (1981), Michael Bayles (1984) and Christine Overall (1987) alerted us to the possibility of its inherent sexism. A sexist practice, whatever its consequences, is *prima facie* open to moral disapproval, as they observed, in part because it *pronounces* persons inferior on the basis of sex. These objections concern the ethical appropriateness of how certain acts and practices represent members of the moral community and the messages they send about the moral status of those represented, rather than their material or social consequences.

2. The distinction between the "individual" account and the "social practice" version of expressivism is first made by James Lindemann Nelson (2000).

References

Alexander, W. (2001). Fatal daughter syndrome. In *Globalizing Feminist Bioethics*, ed. R. Tong. Boulder, CO: Westview Press, pp.179–97.

Carroll, J.C., Reid, A., Woodward, C.A., Permaul-Woods, J.A., Domb, S., Ryan, G. et al. (1997). Ontario Maternal Serum Screening Program: Practices, knowledge and opinions of healthcare providers. *Canadian Medical Association Journal*, 156, 775–84.

Caulfield, T., Burgess, M.M., Williams-Jones, B., Baily, M.-A., Chadwick, R., Cho, M. *et al.* (2001). Providing genetic testing through the private sector: a view from Canada. *Canadian Journal of Policy Research*, 2, 72–81.

Harvey, J. (1999). *Civilized Oppression*. Lanham, MD: Rowman and Littlefield.

Hoskins, B. and Holmes, H.B. (1984). Technology and prenatal femicide. In *Test-Tube Women: What Future for Motherhood*, eds. R. Arditti, R. Duelli-Klein, and S. Minden. London: Pandora Press, pp. 237–55.

Langton, R. (1993). Speech acts and unspeakable acts. *Philosophy and Public Affairs*, 22, 293–330.

Nelson, J. (2000). The meaning of the act: reflections on the expressive force of reproductive decision making and policies. In *Prenatal Testing and Disability Rights*, eds. E. Parens and A. Asch. Washington, DC: Georgetown University Press, pp.196–213.

Plumwood, V. (1993). *Feminism and the Mastery of Nature*. London: Routledge.

Press, N. (2000). Assessing the expressive character of prenatal testing: the choices made or the choices made available? In *Prenatal Testing and Disability Rights*, eds. E. Parens and A. Asch. Washington, DC: Georgetown University Press, pp.214–33.

Saxton, M. (2000). Why members of the disability community oppose prenatal diagnosis and selective abortion. In *Prenatal Testing and Disability Rights*, eds. E. Parens and A. Asch. Washington, DC: Georgetown University Press, pp. 147–64.

Scully, J. (2005). Admitting all variations? Postmodernism and genetic normality. In *Ethics of the Body: Postconventional Challenges*, eds. M. Shildrik and R. Mykitiuk. Cambridge. MA: MIT Press, pp.49–68.

Sherwin, S. (1992). *No Longer Patient: Feminist Ethics and Health Care*. Philadelphia, PA: Temple University Press.

Steinbock, B. (2000). Disability, prenatal testing, and selective abortion. In *Prenatal Testing and Disability Rights*, eds. E. Parens and A. Asch. Washington, DC: Georgetown University Press, pp. l09–23.

Taylor, K. and Mykitiuk, R. (2001). Genetics, normalcy and disability. *Canadian Journal of Policy Research*, 2(3), 65–71.

Wates, M. (2005). Qualifying for the right to die—a dubious privilege: assisted dying for the terminally ill. In *Making Sense Of Health, Illness, and Disease*, eds. I. Lange and Z. Norridge. Available at Inter-Disciplinary. Net. Http://www.inter-disciplinary.netlmso/hid/hid41 cc.htm.

THREE Measuring Mothering

Rebecca Kukla | *International Journal of Feminist Approaches to Bioethics* 2008; 1: 67-90.

. . . Aristotle (1941) said that a man's happiness could be measured only once he was dead; happiness and unhappiness reside in his life narrative only taken as a whole. Similarly, good mothering can be constituted only through an entire parenting narrative. . . .

Yet as a society we have a tendency to measure motherhood, not in extended narratives, but by a set of signal moments that we interpret as emblematic tests and summations of women's mothering abilities. . . . Mothers often internalize these measures and evaluate their own mothering in terms of them. These "defining moments" tend to come very early in the mothering narrative—indeed, several of them come during pregnancy or even before conception.

Consider how the phrase *reproductive ethics* has come to refer almost exclusively to ethical analyses of discrete choices faced during pregnancy or even earlier. Key topics in reproductive ethics include abortion, pre-implantation genetic diagnosis, and fertility medicine. This ought to strike us as strange. Reproduction is the process of creating new people and building families and communities. Reproductive ethics ought to refer to the ethics of creating and caring for new generations. This is a process that extends across the life span. . . . Yet mainstream bioethicists consistently lose interest in mothers once the beginning of their narrative is over. We give little or no bioethical attention to the ethics of mothering children after infancy. I claim that this reductive understanding of mothering has had counterproductive effects upon health care practice and policy, encouraging measures that penalize mothers who do not live up to cultural norms during signal moments while failing to encourage extended narratives of healthy mothering.[1]

One of the important tasks for feminist bioethics is to turn the bioethical spotlight upon the fact that reproduction not only happens in women's bodies, but through women's ongoing, richly textured labour—labour that, after all, does not escape a complicated relationship with medical institutions and spaces after pregnancy ends. . . . Mothers bear a disproportionate responsibility for managing their children's contact with professional health institutions, maintaining their health at the domestic level (through feeding and hygiene practices), and training them in safety and self-care. Correspondingly, mothers are held disproportionately responsible for their children's physical and mental health imperfections.[2] Just as bioethics misrepresents pregnancy and conception when it severs them from the rest of mothering, likewise accounts of the ethics of family relationships miss a pressing dimension of mothering if they fail to bring the tools of medical ethics to bear.

In the following, I explore two examples of signal moments that we interpret as displays and tests of women's maternal adequacy; I then turn to the larger cultural and ethical impact of measuring mothering in these ways. . . .

Birth as a Maternal Achievement Test

Labour and delivery typically take less than a day, some women labour for as long as a few days. Mothering, however, typically lasts for many decades. . . . Yet we have elevated the symbolic importance of birth to the point where it appears to serve as a make-or-break test of a woman's mothering abilities. . . .

According to our cultural mythos, "good" mothers deliver vaginally without pain medication, after advance planning and appropriate prenatal education. Second-best mothers submit regretfully but docilely to whatever medical interventions the doctors recommend. "Bad" mothers make "selfish" choices, such as giving birth at home, seeking out an epidural or a caesarean section, or attempting a vaginal birth after a previous c-section. . . . In some hospitals, women that end up receiving caesarean sections resulting in healthy babies are routinely given unsolicited literature on grieving to help them through their feelings of failure and loss at not having successfully achieved a normative birth.[3]

> **Cultural mythos**
> Prevailing or common-sense evaluative attitudes.

> **Epidural**
> The injection of an analgesic into the epidural area of the spine during labour. This is done to provide pain relief.

When women were first encouraged to draw up birth plans in which they specified their preferences concerning pain medication, who would be allowed in their rooms during labour, and other basic aspects of their care, the laudable idea was to help women become at least partial agents of their own births, rather than passively submitting to medical management. However, over time, formulating a birth plan has moved from an empowering option to a social duty. . . . Contemporary North American pregnant women are expected to plan out their births with the elaborate precision and care of a traditional bride planning her wedding day, and they are expected to do it early. . . . We can push the analogy between birth planning and wedding planning farther: as women are called upon to plan and design their births, they are invited to think of birth, not primarily as the first day of the rest of their children's lives, but as their "special day," during which their tenure as mothers will be symbolically foreshadowed and put on display, just as weddings are often framed as the bride's special day and as the symbolic moment at which the perfection (or imperfection) of the marriage is performed as a spectacle.

Such elaborate birth plans set up completely unrealistic expectations concerning how much control one can possibly have over the labouring process, thereby setting women up for feelings of failure, lack of confidence, disappointment, and maternal inadequacy when things do not go according to plan, even when mother and baby end up healthy. . . . Furthermore, although the entire phenomenon of the "birth plan" is pervaded by the rhetoric of choice and autonomy, all women know that good mothers make some choices but not others. For instance, indicating that one wants pain medication at the earliest medically possible moment is not a socially acceptable choice, even though it is a choice available on the form. . . .

In popular culture, the distaste for mothers who do not behave properly during their births is strong and explicit, as is the implication that this bad behaviour reflects upon the entirety of their mothering. . . . Mothers who choose elective caesareans for non-medical reasons are vilified by the media and in online discussions. In an article entitled "Too Posh to Push Moms Set Bad Example for Society," the *Vancouver Sun* editorializes, "Pity poor Sean Preston Spears Federline . . . His mom couldn't even be bothered to suffer a little pain for a lot of gain on the day of his celebrated birth. Yes, giving birth the old-fashioned way hurts. *Welcome to motherhood*" (Fralic 2005). Here, Britney Spears' elective c-section is taken as reflecting directly upon her entire relationship to motherhood, whereas proper maternity is associated with self-sacrifice and a willingness to bear pain. . . .

Part of what interests me about comments like this is the complete vagueness concerning what sorts of gains and harms are at stake. What exactly would Britney gain by attempting a vaginal birth, and exactly how are mothers who elect c-sections putting their babies "in harm's way"? . . . This is a complex scientific question. . . . What we do know is that, in comparison with a host of other mundane activities, and in comparison to all previous moments in history, *all* of the standard options for birth in developed nations (caesarean sections, vaginal births after

caesarean, home births) are extremely safe for mother and baby alike. Britney surely takes fewer chances with her baby by scheduling a c-section than does a mother who chooses a preschool that is a car ride rather than a walk away from her home.[4]

In fact, whether we cast caesarean sections or vaginal births as the risky, selfish option varies in accordance with context, not in accordance with actual risks. Some women who have resisted medically recommended caesarean sections have been served with court orders, or in the case of Melissa Rowland in Salt Lake City in 2004, with homicide charges, while women who wish to attempt vaginal birth after a previous caesarean section are increasingly faced with draconian hospital restrictions (Schneider 2005; Grady 2004) and the same charges of selfishness and risk-taking that their peers who seek elective caesarean sections face. The standard justification for preventing women from attempting vaginal births after a caesarean is based on the risk of catastrophic outcomes due to uterine rupture. Not only is the risk of uterine rupture tiny, but—ironically—this risk turns out to be roughly equivalent to the risk of uterine rupture during *primary* vaginal delivery (Smith et al. 2002). Meanwhile, repeat caesareans are no safer than primary caesareans; indeed, quite the opposite. In other words, whether a scheduled caesarean or an attempted vaginal birth is the socially sanctioned, "properly maternal" choice depends on whether or not the mother had a previous caesarean or not. But the fact of a previous caesarean in no way reverses the relative risk of these two options. Therefore, here our social attitudes toward proper maternal choice are cut free of any basis in objective relative risks.[5]

But in any case, the real risks and their sizes do not seem to be of interest to the lay critics of mothers' birth choices, who appear quite content with hand-waving references to gains and harms. Especially because these critiques are not responsive to any specific, sizable risks, it is hard not to conclude that the main normative standards at play are ideological, not medical: Our cultural insistence that women make "proper" birth choices and maintain control over their birth narratives is not about minimizing real risks; rather, it supports our desire to measure mothering in terms of women's choices and self-discipline exercised during signal moments. What is at stake is not the health of babies but an image of proper motherhood, combined with the idea that birth should function as a symbolic spectacle of such motherhood. . . .

You Are What Your Child Eats

Providing high-quality early nutrition to children and eating well during pregnancy are undeniably important components of good mothering. Children's nutritional status depends on eating habits that are established over time. However, our culture is replete with images of feeding *moments* that purportedly corrupt both children and mothers in some permanent way.

The logic of the single corrupting bite shows vividly in a recent article by Jodi Kantor in the *New York Times* entitled "Memo to Nanny: No Juice Boxes." Kantor writes, . . . "The current nutritional wisdom says that what children eat may set their tastes in place permanently. In this view, a hot dog is *never just a single tube of meat*." Here the seemingly single hot dog is pictured as extending beyond itself, determining and encapsulating a lifetime of poor eating habits rather than remaining singular. By allowing a hot dog to slip into her child in a moment of weakness, a mother can pervert the child's tastes and eating practices forever, thereby undoing months or years of devotion to . . . planning and preparing balanced meals for her child out of fresh ingredients. . . .

Birth is an idiosyncratic event, and I have argued that mothers are measured by their performance during this event. The logic of feeding is slightly different: one must feed one's child over and over again, and there is no discrete moment at which one can prove one's *proper* maternality through feeding. On the other hand, at any moment a mother may prove herself an *improper* mother through an act of feeding. Hence this is a test that one can never pass but is always at risk of failing. . . .

Indeed, one can fail the feeding test very early on. Many parenting guides claim outright that allowing her baby *one single* suck on an artificial nipple may destroy a mother's chances for a successful breast-feeding relationship forever (and . . . that a baby who is not breast-fed is at high risk for failure to bond with its mother, low IQ, and multiple behavioural and health problems).[6] North American breast-feeding promotional materials consistently emphasize *exclusive* breast-feeding, as opposed to the more productive message that the more breast milk babies receive, the better. . . . According to the La Leche League a single bottle of formula can trigger life-threatening allergies, and any contact with artificial nipples (bottles or pacifiers) can cause nipple confusion, wherein the baby is no longer willing or able to latch onto a breast. In fact, although it is true that a baby who is regularly fed from a bottle may reject the breast or lose the skill of latching onto it, there is no evidence for nipple confusion resulting from the occasional use of artificial nipples (cf. Fisher and Inch 1996 and Neifert, Lawrence and Seacat 1995). A 1992 study found no difference in breast-feeding outcomes between newborn infants who were exclusively breast-fed and those who received one bottle daily (Cronenwett, Stukel and Kearney 1992). The pervasive fear of instant nipple confusion among new mothers, cultivated by the medical establishment, the World Health Organization (WHO) and the United Nations Children's Fund (UNICEF), among others, is itself indicative of the power of the logic of the single corrupting moment. . . .[7]

> **La Leche League**
> An organization that started in the US in 1956 with the intention of promoting and educating mothers and families about the benefits of breast-feeding.

The idea that each feeding moment presents a pivotal choice between risk and maternal responsibility extends backwards into pregnancy. *What to Expect When You're Expecting* warns, "Every bite counts: Before you close your mouth on a forkful of food, consider, 'Is this the best bite I can give my baby?' If it will benefit your baby, chew away. If it'll only benefit your sweet tooth or appease your appetite, put your fork down." (Murkoff, Eisenberg and Hathaway 2002) This passage . . . demands that mothers discipline their eating with literally every bite of food, avoiding the corrupting, selfish bite that is not baby-directed. Here, eating simply because one is hungry ("to appease your appetite") is akin to maternal betrayal.

The risks and benefits that arise from mothers' ongoing lifestyle, economic security, and access to high-quality foods far outweigh the risks and benefits that attach to any single forkful or suck. Our focus on the importance of feeding moments rather than on long-term eating patterns betrays an ideological picture of normative maternal performance, rather than a reasonable concern with children's well-being.

The Effects of Measuring Mothering in Moments

I have described two maternal activities . . . that . . . serve as cultural tests during which women's maternal bona fides are measured. . . . The rhetoric surrounding these moments suggests, on the one hand, that they will *determine* the success of the future mothering narrative . . . and on the other hand, that they *reveal* the truth about a woman's fitness to mother. . . .

> **Bona fides**
> A Latin phrase meaning good faith.

Our cultural images of proper maternal behaviour during these tests are not politically neutral. Rather, a woman's ability to perform "properly" with respect to prenatal care, birth, and feeding are marked by socio-economic status and ethnic identity. Consider: . . .

(1) A woman's chances of having an unmedicated vaginal birth that goes according to a predetermined birth plan . . . depend heavily upon her own health, her access to high quality, continuous health care with a provider who is familiar with her preferences, her ability to articulate her wishes in a way that health professionals will understand, . . . her ability to hire an advocate such as a doula or midwife, and her level of support from family members who can speak for her during the birth. The ability to insist that a birth plan be respected by the hospital staff normally requires a high degree of education, confidence, and perceived social authority. Every one of these factors varies by socioeconomic position. Women who manage to have a "natural" birth may feel that they are somehow communing with their mythical pre-industrial sisters, but in fact, they normally draw heavily upon their social privilege and their immediate access to state-of-the-art technological interventions in enacting their birth narratives.

> **Doula**
> A birth coach providing emotional and other support to a woman during labour and the initial stages of childcare, but who usually possesses no medical expertise.

(2) Poor women have less access to high-quality, diverse foods, and less time to prepare meals for themselves and their children. Poor and minority women have lower rates of breast-feeding than financially secure white women. . . .[8] Among other determining factors, poor and minority women are less likely to have jobs that provide enough maternity leave to establish breast-feeding or private spaces in which to nurse. They are more likely to be single parents and to work long hours.[9]

Thus to the extent that we take "proper" maternal performance during key moments as a measure of mothering as a whole, we will re-inscribe social privilege. We will read a deficient maternal character into the bodies and actions of underprivileged and socially marginalized women, whereas privileged women with socially normative home and work lives will tend to serve as our models of proper maternal character. Yet it is likely that women pass these mothering tests less by dint of their inherently maternal character and their responsible commitment to their children than because they have the right kind of education, financial resources, health insurance plans, family structure, and jobs.

Our focus on how mothers perform at signal moments is part of a larger cultural sensibility: in North America and Britain, at least, public ethical discourse focuses heavily on personal responsibility and willpower as it is displayed (or fails to be displayed) at discrete choice-points, rather than on the structural conditions that enable or undermine people's ability to make good choices over the long term. It is difficult to turn public attention to the environmental, economic, and social conditions that can make various choices and behaviours difficult or easy; instead we tend to employ a conceptual repertoire— . . . of character, will-power, choice, and responsibility— that inherently isolates individuals as ethical agents and occludes such contextual determinants.

This individualist logic encourages policies and initiatives that focus on influencing the choices that mothers make at particular moments, rather than on creating structural conditions that foster extended narratives of healthy mothering. . . .

As a culture, then, we privilege early, discrete moments of choice as the measures of mothers, as opposed to ongoing patterns and developing relationships—as if we can bond in a moment, destroy or secure our child's chances at well-being in a moment, or fail at mothering in a moment. And yet, while there is always the possibility that a poor decision will turn out to have tragic consequences, . . . single events rarely play a large role in determining how a child will turn out, or how healthy and successful a mothering narrative will be. My suggestion is that we need to view mothering as a work in progress until the very end. When it comes to health promotion and policy, we should shift our attention away from mothers' performances at key moments, and onto providing families with the systematic support that would enable women to engage in ongoing narratives of good mothering. Such support would include food and job security; decent maternity leave; full access to family planning; a cleaner environment; universal access to decent education and health care; workplaces and labour laws that are structured around the assumption that many workers will have substantial parental commitments, including commitments to breast-feeding and to fathering; accessible interventions for women struggling with addiction, mental illness, or other social stresses; and a safe, competent, junk-food-free public school system for all children.

If we take seriously the idea that reproduction is typically a decades-long social and material labour of love, and never merely a biological event involving eggs, sperm, and wombs; then these are all *reproductive* rights, and the bioethical consideration of their contours and limits is *reproductive ethics*. Hence the reorientation of attention that I have been urging would dramatically change the scope and methods of reproductive ethics. In the first instance, reproductive ethics would no longer concern particular medical choices made before conception and during pregnancy. Its primary subject matter would be larger questions of social, economic, and environmental justice, and inevitably—rather than just as an afterthought—gender equity. . . . As feminists, we must insist that bioethicists take mothers to be whole, socially situated people with entire life narratives, typically including several decades of mothering.

Study Questions

1. Describe the two signal moments in a woman's life that Kukla discusses.

2. What does Kukla believe is the proper scope of reproductive ethics?

3. Kukla contends that "we need to view mothering as a work in progress until the very end." What does this involve? Why is this important?

Notes

1. As an anonymous referee rightly pointed out, I do not make any serious attempt to define good or healthy mothering in this paper. Surely women can be better or worse mothers. However, my interest here is in gaining critical distance from (what I see as) one problematic, hegemonic way of measuring mothering, rather than with forging and defending a specific alternative picture of the ethics of mothering. Mothering is serious moral work, and hence we do need to consider what it takes to mother well; hopefully, however, we can transcend the idea that mothering can be measured in any uniform way.

2. I elaborate and defend the claim that mothers play such a crucial role in the health care system in Kukla (2006).

3. This was the practice at Ottawa Civic Hospital, where I gave birth to my perfectly healthy son by caesarean section. I do not know how many hospitals do this, however it is easy to find pamphlets designed for this purpose online. See for instance www.birthrites.org/BookletIndex.html (accessed 12 November 2007). See www.plus-size-pregnancy.org/CSANDVBAC/csemotionalrecov.htm#References (accessed 12 November 2007) for a large clearinghouse of literature designed to aid emotional recovery after cesarean section.

4. I could not possibly document or compare all the possible risks of routine driving and of being born by scheduled caesarean section. But for purposes of illustration, consider that according to the National Center for Statistics, the 2003 rate of automobile accident-related fatalities in the United States was 8.34/1000 population, whereas the rate of perinatal death associated with scheduled caesarean sections in the United States is 1.3/1000 population (Landon et al. 2004).

5. The argument of this paragraph, differently worded, appeared previously in Lyerly et al. (2007).

6. Cf., e.g., La Leche (1997) and Tamaro (1998), as well as the standard lactation nursing textbook, Lawrence 1994, which recommends giving new mothers this advice.

7. Cf., e.g., American Academy of Family Physicians 2000. UNICEF and the WHO jointly sponsor the Baby Friendly Hospitals Initiative, which explicitly promotes the total avoidance of artificial nipples in order to prevent

nipple confusion. Cf. www. babyfriendlyusa.org (accessed 13 November 2007).

8. www.cdc.gov/MMWR/preview/mmwrhtml/mm5512a3.htm, accessed 13 November 2007.

9. For detailed discussions of why poor and minority women breast-feed at lower rates, cf. Blum (2000), and Kukla (2006).

References

American Academy of Family Physicians. 2000. Promoting and supporting breast-feeding. *American Family Physician* 61(7). Available atwww.aafp.org/afp/ 20000401/2093. html. Accessed 13 November 2007.

Aristotle. 1941. *Nicomachean ethics*. Trans. W. D. Ross. In *The basic works of Aristotle*. Ed. R. McKeon. New York: Random House.

Blum, L. 2000. *At the breast: Ideologies of breastfeeding and motherhood in the contemporary United States*. Boston: Beacon Press

Cronenwett, L., T. Stukel, and M. Kearney. 1992. Single daily bottle use in the early weeks post-partum and breast-feeding outcomes. *Pediatrics* 63: 760.

Grady, D. 2004. Trying to avoid a second cesarean: Many women find choice isn't theirs. *New York Times*. 29 November, Al.

Kukla, Rebecca. 2006. Ethics and ideology in breastfeeding advocacy campaigns. *Hypatia: A Journal of Feminist Philosophy* 21(1): 157-80.

La Leche League International. 1997. *The womanly art of breastfeeding*. 6th ed. New York: Plume Books.

Lawrence, R. 1994. *Breastfeeding: A guide for the medical profession*. 4th ed. New York: Mosby Inc.

Murkoff, H., A. Eisenberg, and S. Hathaway. 2002. *What to expect when you're expecting*. 3rd ed. New York: Workman Publishing

Schneider, M. E. 2005. Insurers set criteria for VBAC coverage. *OB GYN News*. 1 February.

Smith, G. C, J.P. Pell, A.D. Cameron, and R. Dobbie. 2002. Risk of perinatal death associated with labor after previous cesarean delivery in uncomplicated term pregnancies. *JAMA* 287: 2684-90

Tamaro, J. 1998. *So that's what they're for! Breastfeeding basics*. Avon, MA: Adams Media.

Chapter Study Questions

1. What are the chief differences between Kukla and Savulescu in terms of their approach to reproductive ethics?

2. To what extent do Savulescu and Gedge agree about the importance of reproductive freedom? To what extent do they disagree?

3. Does Kukla's claim that it is wrong for reproductive ethics to focus on the early stages of pregnancy and child-rearing apply with equal force to Gedge and Savulescu?

Critical Analysis

Consider the following from the article by Gedge:

"The second line of argument supporting the claim that PND and PGD deprive persons with disabilities of rights and privileges is an argument by analogy. Although significant differences exist between disability and race, class or gender, it is useful to consider whether testing for sex or race, with an institutionalized connection to termination or negative selection for a positive finding would effect a reduction in the rights and privileges of women or racialized groups. This question is hardly hypothetical; prenatal testing for sex is commonplace, is accompanied by what some have called femicide, and coexists with women's inferiorized status and diminished enjoyment of rights in contexts where such testing is widely practiced."

Outline Gedge's argument in your own words, paying particular attention to the premises that she relies on to support her main conclusion. Choose one of the premises for evaluation. Try to think of at least one objection to this premise.

Case Study

Barb and Ginny are in a loving, committed relationship. They would like to start a family together. Since they are a lesbian couple, to conceive one of them will have to be artificially inseminated using the sperm of a donor. Ginny is younger and healthier than Barb and seems the better candidate for pregnancy. Before embarking on donor sperm insemination, the fertility clinic treating Ginny runs a few tests to determine whether she has any fertility problems. She learns that she has obstructions in both fallopian tubes. She is a resident of Ontario, so she is eligible for up to three rounds of provincially-funded in vitro fertilization.

Both Barb and Ginny are deaf. They take a great degree of joy in participating in the deaf community, and they would be unable to live the meaningful lives that they now live without participating in this community. They think of themselves as belonging to a unique culture, in the same way that many belonging to a religion do. They would very much like it to be the case that their child be part of this community and have the same sense of belonging that they have. It would also make their lives easier. Of course, it is not certain that any of the implanted embryos created using IVF would be deaf.

Luckily, the clinic treating Ginny offers pre-implantation genetic diagnosis. The clinic is able to run genetic tests on the embryos created in order to determine whether any of them has a high probability of being deaf. Barb and Ginny would like to use this technique to select only embryos that are likely to be deaf, provided they have no other serious genetic disorders. They learn that of the embryos they have created, all of them are healthy and are plausible candidates for implantation. Some of them are likely to be deaf. They want only these implanted.

The clinic is reluctant to honour this wish since it means that they would not be implanting the healthiest embryos that have been created. In their view deafness is a disability. Barb and Ginny argue that they have strong moral reasons in favour of their decision. In addition, there is no law in Canada for forbidding them from doing what they would like the clinic to do.

1. Are the values discussed in Savulescu and Gedge represented in this case? What other values might be at play in this case?

2. Is it right to think that deafness is a disability? Think about this question in terms of how disability is understood in the readings by Gedge and Savulescu.

3. What reasons might one provide for refusing to honour Barb's and Ginny's request? Is there a conflict here in terms of what it is legitimate for a parent to want for his or her child? How might Kukla's feminist view of measuring mothering illuminate this issue?

Further Reading

Brake E. Millum J. Parenthood and procreation. In: Zalta EN, editor. Stanford Encyclopedia of Philosophy [Internet]. 2012. Available from: http://plato.stanford.edu/entries/parenthood/. Date Accessed: 7 June 2012.

Glover J. *Choosing children: The ethical dilemmas of genetic intervention*. Oxford: Oxford University Press; 2006.

Nisker J, Baylis F, Karpin I, McLeod C, Mykitiuk R, editors. *The healthy embryo: social, biomedical, legal and philosophical perspectives*. Cambridge: Cambridge University Press; 2010.

Parens E, Asch A, editors. *Prenatal testing and disability rights*. Washington, DC: Georgetown University Press; 2000.

Speechley K, Nisker J. Preimplantation genetic diagnosis in Canada: a survey of Canadian IVF units. *J Obstet Gynaecol Can* 2010 32:341–347.

Adults and Decision-making

In this chapter, we examine the respect owed to autonomous moral agents in the health care setting. People who are capable of making decisions for themselves have a right of self-determination. That is, they have a right to determine what will and what will not be done to them, consistent with their own set of values. In the health care context, the right of self-determination is the foundation of the doctrine of informed consent, which obligates a physician to discuss treatment options with his patient and obtain the patient's consent before initiating any treatment. While a physician is an expert on the diagnosis and treatment of disease, most medical conditions have a variety of treatment options and treatments differ in important ways in terms of their costs and benefits. For instance, moderate depression can be treated with talk therapy, exercise, or medication. The choice as to which treatment is best—if any—depends on the values and life goals of the patient.

But who shall we regard as an autonomous moral agent? The question is tied to whether a patient is competent, that is, whether she is capable of making a decision for which she may be held responsible. In this chapter's first article, Allan Buchanan and Dan Brock argue that the determination of competence ought to be made on a decision-by-decision basis. Competence depends both on the complexity of the decision and the degree to which the patient possesses the requisite cognitive capacities, including the ability to understand the consequences of the decision, the ability to reason soundly about the various alternatives, and possession of a "reasonably consistent and stable" set of values. Setting the standard for competence involves an inevitable trade-off between respecting the patient's self-determination and promoting her well-being. According to Buchanan and Brock, where we draw the line ought to depend on the consequences of respecting a particular choice. Thus, when treatment is potentially life-saving and relatively free of risk, a patient may be deemed competent to accept the treatment but incompetent to reject it.

In this chapter's second article, Benjamin Freedman disagrees with Buchanan and Brock, and begins by examining what it means for a choice to be responsible. He asks:

> "Does this entail that the physician may at any time override a patient's judgment on the basis that, in the physician's view, the patient has not chosen responsibly? Surely not; to adopt such a criterion would defeat the purpose embodied in the doctrine of consent. It would mean that a person's exercise of autonomy is always subject to review."

For Freedman, a responsible choice is one made by a person who is generally disposed to act responsibly. To regard someone as responsible is just to say that she generally takes into account the consequences of her actions and that she is open to rational arguments that a different course of action may be preferred. Someone who is responsible is capable of living with her life plan and takes responsibility for her actions. Shifting the question of responsibility from the particular choice to the person who is making the choice has important consequences. It avoids the risk of affirming a patient's right to choose only when we agree with the particular decision made.

Respect for autonomy is commonly taken to require a presumption of decision-making competency; that is, a person is held to be competent unless there is evidence to the contrary. In the third reading, Cheryl Misak draws on her own horrific experience as a patient in an intensive care unit to challenge the presumption of decision-making competency in this setting. A substantial proportion—perhaps a majority—of patients in ICUs suffer from moderate to severe psychiatric symptoms as a result of pain, stress, sleep deprivation, medications, and serious illness. As Misak vividly describes, patients can lose touch with reality and develop paranoid delusions, in which health care workers are seen as tormentors rather than healers. In some cases, patients are obviously incompetent; in others, including Misak's own case, cognitive impairments may be more subtle. The ICU is a challenging setting in which to assess decision-making competency. Most patients are intubated (and hence unable to talk) and too sick to write, so questions are limited to "yes or no" responses. Further, being on a ventilator is an unpleasant experience, and patients may, in their rush to be rid of the breathing tube, make decisions that are contrary to their interests. In these circumstances, it may be better to presume that patients are incompetent to make their own decisions unless there is evidence to the contrary. In the ICU, a "policy of doing what is in the patient's best interests, despite the fact that this will be viewed as highly paternalistic by the patient herself and by many health care professionals and ethicists" may be the best course of action.

ONE Deciding for Others: Competence

Allan Buchanan and Dan W. Brock | *The Milbank Quarterly* 1986; 64.2: 17-94.

The Concept of Competence

Competence as Decision-relative

. . . The statement that a particular individual is (or is not) competent is incomplete. Competence is always competence *for some task*—competence to do something. The concern here is with competence to perform the task of making a decision. Hence, competence is to be understood as *decision-making capacity*. But the notion of decision-making capacity is itself incomplete until the nature of the choice as well as the conditions under which it is to be made are specified. Thus competence is decision-relative, not global (President's Commission for the Study of Ethical Problems in Medicine and Biomedical and Behavioural Research 1982, 1983a). A person may be competent to make a particular decision at a particular time, under certain circumstances, but

> **Competence**
> The ability of a person to make a decision for which she will be held responsible; the capacity to perform a particular decision making task at a particular time and under specified conditions.

incompetent to make another decision, or even the same decision under different conditions. A competency determination, then, is a determination of a particular person's capacity to perform a particular decision-making task at a particular time and under specified conditions. . . .

Decision-making tasks vary substantially in the capacities they require for performance at an appropriate level of adequacy. For example, even restricted to medical treatment decisions, there is substantial variation in the complexity of information that is relevant to a particular treatment decision and that, consequently, must be understood by the decision maker. There is, therefore, variation in what might be called the *objective demands* of the task in question—here, the level of abilities to understand, reason, and decide about the options in question. But there is also variation of several sorts in a subject's ability to meet the demands of a particular decision. Many factors that diminish or eliminate competence altogether vary over time in their presence or severity in a particular person. For example, the effects of dementia on a person's cognitive capacities is at some stages commonly not constant, particularly in cases of borderline competence. Instead, mental confusion may come and go; periods of great confusion are sometimes followed by comparative lucidity.

In other cases, the environment and the behavior of others may affect the relative level of decision-making competence. For example, side effects of medications often impair competence, but a change of medication may reduce those effects. Behavior of others may create stresses for a person that diminish decision-making capacities, but that behavior can often be altered, or the situations in which it occurs can be avoided. Further, cognitive functioning can sometimes be enhanced by familiar surroundings and diminished by unfamiliar ones. A person may be competent to make a decision about whether to have an elective surgical procedure if the choice is presented in the familiar surroundings of home by someone known and trusted, but may be incompetent to make that same choice in what is found to be the intimidating, confusing, and unfamiliar environment of a hospital. . . .

Capacities Needed for Competence

What capacities are necessary for a person competently to decide about such matters as health care, living arrangements, financial affairs, and so forth? As already noted, the demands of these different decisions will vary, but it is nevertheless possible to generalize about the necessary abilities. Two may be distinguished: the capacity for communication and understanding, and the capacity for reasoning and deliberation (President's Commission for the Study of Ethical Problems in Medicine and Biomedical and Behavioural Research 1982). Although these capacities are not entirely distinct, significant deficiencies in any of them can result in diminished decision-making competence. A third important element of competence is that the individual must have a set of values or conception of the good.

> **Dementia**
> A mental disorder characterized by memory loss, personality change, and impaired reasoning that may be the result of a variety of different underlying causes.

> **Cognitive capacities**
> Mental abilities, including the abilities to understand, to rationally manipulate information, and to communicate.

Under *communication and understanding* are included the various capacities that allow a person to take part in the process of becoming informed of and expressing a choice about a given decision. These include the ability to communicate and the possession of various linguistic, conceptual, and cognitive abilities necessary for an understanding of the particular information relevant to the decision at hand. The relevant cognitive abilities, in particular, are often impaired by disease processes to which the elderly are especially subject, including most obviously various forms of dementia, but also aphasia due to stroke and, in some cases, reduced intellectual performance associated with depression. . . . Even where cognitive function is only minimally impaired, ability to express desires and beliefs may be greatly diminished or absent. . . .

> **Aphasia**
> The inability to speak either temporarily or permanently, often as a result of a stroke or blockage in the blood flow to the area of the brain controlling speech.

Understanding also requires the ability to appreciate the nature and meaning of potential alternatives—what it would be and "feel" like to be in possible future states and to undergo various experiences. In young children this is often prevented by the lack of sufficient life experience. In the case of elderly persons facing diseases with progressive and extremely debilitating deterioration, it is hindered by people's generally limited ability to understand a kind of experience radically different from their own and by the inability of severely impaired individuals to communicate the character of their own experience to others. Major psychological blocks—such as fear, denial, and depression—can also significantly impair the appreciation of information about an unwanted or dreaded alternative. In general, communication and understanding require the capacities to receive, process, and make available for use the information relevant to particular decisions.

Competence also requires *capacities for reasoning and deliberation*. These include capacities to draw inferences about the consequences of making a certain choice and to compare alternative outcomes based on how they further one's good or promote one's ends. Some capacity to employ rudimentary probabilistic reasoning about uncertain outcomes will commonly be necessary, as well as the capacity to give due consideration to potential future outcomes in a present decision. Reasoning and deliberation obviously make use of both capacities mentioned earlier: understanding the information and applying the decision maker's values.

Finally, a competent decision maker also requires *a set of values or conception of what is good* that is reasonably consistent and stable. This is needed in order to be able to evaluate particular outcomes as benefits or harms, goods or evils, and to assign different relative weight or importance to them. Often what will be needed is the capacity to decide on the import and relative weight to be accorded different values, since that may not have been fully determined before a particular choice must be made. Competence does not require a fully consistent set of goals, much less a detailed "life plan" to cover all contingencies. Sufficient internal consistency and stability over time in the values relative to a particular decision, however, are needed to yield a decision outcome. Although values change over time and although ambivalence is inevitable in the difficult choices faced by many persons of questionable competence concerning their medical care, living arrangements, and personal affairs, sufficient value stability is needed to permit, at the very least, a decision that can be stated and adhered to over the course of its discussion, initiation, and implementation. . . .

Competence as a Threshold Concept, Not a Comparative One

Sometimes incompetence will be uncontroversially complete, as with patients who are in a persistent vegetative state or who are in a very advanced state of dementia, unable to communicate coherently at all. Often, however, defects in the capacities and skills noted above as necessary to competence will be partial and a matter of degree, just as whether a patient's decision is voluntary or involuntary, informed or uninformed, is also often a matter of degree. Does this mean that competence itself should be thought of as sometimes partial and possessed in different degrees? It is certainly the case that persons are commonly

> **Persistent vegetative state**
> A state of "eyes-open unconsciousness" resulting from catastrophic injury to the brain in which the capacity for consciousness is lost but sleep-wake cycles and non-voluntary movements remain.

thought of and said to be more or less competent to perform many tasks, not just decision-making. Nevertheless, because of the role competency determinations play in health care generally, and in the legal process in particular, it is important to resist the notion that persons can be determined to be more or less competent, or competent to some degree. . . .

The central purpose of assessing competence is to determine whether a patient may assert his or her right to decide to accept or refuse a particular medical procedure, or whether that right shall be transferred to a surrogate. We must, therefore, ask what values are at stake in whether people are allowed to make such decisions for themselves. The informed consent doctrine assigns the decision-making right to patients themselves; but what fundamental values are served by the practice of informed consent? In the literature dealing with informed consent, many different answers—and ways of formulating answers—to that question have been proposed, but we believe the most important values at stake are: (1) promoting and protecting the patient's well-being, and (2) respecting the patient's self-determination. It is in examining the effect on these two values that the answer to the proper standard of decision-making competence will be found.

> **Informed consent doctrine**
> An implication of the principle of self-determination that requires physicians to discuss treatment options with their patients and obtain their permission before initiating treatment; it is well accepted that a patient may choose from available treatment options or refuse all treatment.

> **Well-being**
> How well an individual's life is going from that individual's perspective; broadly speaking, what is good for an individual or what is in an individual's self-interest.

> **Self-determination**
> The principle that people have a right to determine what will and what will not be done to them; the idea that each of us, to the extent that it is possible, ought to have control over our own lives.

Standards of Competence: Underlying Values

Promotion of Individual Well-Being

There is a long tradition in medicine that the physician's first and most important commitment should be to serve the well-being of the patient. The more recent doctrine of informed consent is consistent with that tradition, if it is assumed that, at least in general, competent individuals are better judges of their own good than others are.

The doctrine recognizes that while the physician commonly brings to the physician-patient encounter medical training that the patient lacks, the patient brings knowledge that the physician lacks: knowledge of particular subjective aims and values that are likely to be affected by whatever decision is made. . . .

In the exercise of their right to give informed consent, then, patients often decide in ways that they believe will best promote their own well-being as they conceive it. As is well known, and as physicians are frequently quick to point out, however, the complexity of many treatment decisions—together with the stresses of illness with its attendant fear, anxiety, dependency, and regression, not to mention the physical effects of illness itself—means that a patient's ordinary decision-making abilities are often significantly diminished. Thus, a patient's treatment choices may fail to serve his or her good or well-being, even as that person conceives it. Although one important value requiring patient participation in their own health care decision-making is the promotion of patient well-being, that same value sometimes also requires persons to be protected from the harmful consequences to them of their own choices.

Respect for Individual Self-determination

The other principal value underlying the informed-consent doctrine is respect for a patient's self-determination, understood here as a person's interest in making important decisions about his or her own life. . . . No attempt will be made here to analyze the complex of ideas giving context to the concept of individual self-determination, nor of the various values that support its importance. But it is essential to underline that many persons commonly want to make important decisions about their life for themselves, and that desire is in part independent of whether they believe that they are always in a position to make the best choice. Even when we believe that others may be able to decide for us better than we ourselves can, we sometimes prefer to decide for ourselves so as to be in charge of and responsible for our lives.

The interest in self-determination should not be overstated, however. People often wish to make such decisions for themselves simply because they believe that, at least in most cases, they are in a better position to decide what is best for themselves than others are. Thus, when in a particular case others are demonstrably in a better position to decide for us than we ourselves are, a part, but not all, of our interest in deciding for ourselves is absent. . . .

Conflict between the Values of Self-determination and Well-being

In the conflict between the values of self-determination and patient well-being, a tradeoff between avoiding two kinds of errors should be sought. The first error is that of failing to protect a person from the harmful consequences of his or her decision when the decision is the result of serious defects in the capacity to decide. The second error is failing to permit someone to make a decision and turning the decision over to another, when the patient is able to make the decision him- or herself. With a stricter or higher standard for competence, more people will be found incompetent, and the first error will be minimized at the cost of increasing the second sort of error. With a looser or more minimal standard for competence, fewer persons will be found incompetent, and the second sort of error is more likely to be minimized at the cost of increasing the first.

Evidence regarding a person's competence to make a particular decision is often uncertain, incomplete, and conflicting. Thus, no conceivable set of procedures and standards for judging competence could guarantee the elimination of all error. Instead, the challenge is to strike the appropriate balance and thereby minimize the incidence of either of the errors noted above. No set of procedures will guarantee that all and only the incompetent are judged to be incompetent.

But procedures and standards for competence are not merely inevitably imperfect. They are inevitably *controversial* as well. In the determination of competence, there is disagreement not only about which procedures will minimize errors, but also about the proper standard that the procedures should be designed to approximate. The core of the controversy derives from the different values that different persons assign to protecting individuals' well-being as against respecting their self- determination. We believe there is no uniquely "correct" answer to the relative weight that should be assigned to these two values, and in any event it is simply a fact that different persons do assign them different weight. . . .

Deciding on Standards of Competence

There is no reason to believe that there is one and only one optimal tradeoff to be struck between the competing values of well-being and self-determination, nor, hence, any one uniquely correct level of capacity at which to set the threshold of competence—even for a particular decision under specified circumstances. In this sense, setting a standard for competence is a value choice, not a scientific or factual matter. . . .

Relation of the Standard of Competence to Expected Harms and Benefits

Because the competency evaluation requires setting a balance between the two values of respecting patients' rights to decide for themselves and protecting them from the harmful consequences of their own choices, it should be clear that no single standard of competence . . . can be adequate. That is simply because the degree of expected harm from choices made at a given level of understanding and reasoning can vary from virtually none to the most serious, including major disability or death.

There is an important implication of this view that the standard of competence ought to vary with the expected harms or benefits to the patient of acting in accordance with a choice—namely, that just because a patient is competent to consent to a treatment, it does not follow that the patient is competent to refuse it, and vice versa. For example, consent to a low-risk life-saving procedure by an otherwise healthy individual should require a minimal level of competence, but refusal of that same procedure by such an individual should require the highest level of competence.

Because the appropriate level of competence properly required for a particular decision must be adjusted to the consequences of acting on that decision, no single standard of decision-making competence is adequate. Instead, the level of competence appropriately required for decision-making varies along a full range from low to high. . . . When the patient's level of decision-making competence is only at the low level, the grounds derive only minimally from the fact that the patient has chosen the option in question; they principally stem from others' positive assessment of the choice's expected effects for life and health. . . .

At the other extreme, when the expected effects of the patient's choice for life and health appear to be substantially worse than available alternatives, the requirement of a high . . . level of competence provides grounds for relying on the patient's decision as itself establishing that the choice best fits the patient's good (his or her own particular aims and ends). That highest level of competence is required to rebut the presumption that if the choice seems not best to promote life and health, then that choice is not, in fact, reasonably related to the patient's interests.

When the expected effects for life and health of the patient's choice are approximately comparable to those of alternatives, a moderate level of competence is sufficient to provide reasonable grounds that the choice promotes the patient's good and that his or her well-being is adequately protected. It is also reasonable to assume that as the level of competence increases (from low to high), the value or importance of respecting the patient's self-determination increases as well, since a part of the value of self-determination rests on the assumption that persons will secure their good when they choose for themselves. As competence increases, the likelihood of this happening increases.

Thus, according to the concept of competence endorsed here, a particular individual's decision-making capacity at a given time may be sufficient for making a decision to refuse a diagnostic procedure when forgoing the procedure does not carry a significant risk, although it would not necessarily be sufficient for refusing a surgical procedure that would correct a life-threatening condition. The greater the risk—where risk is a function of the severity of the expected harm and the probability of its occurrence—the greater the level of communication, understanding, and reasoning skills required for competence to make that decision. It is not always true, however, that if a person is competent to make one decision, then he or she is competent to make another decision so long as it involves equal risk. Even if this risk is the same, one decision may be more complex, and hence require a higher level of capacity for understanding options and reasoning about consequences. . . .

Study Questions

1. How do Buchanan and Brock define competence? Can a patient be competent to make one decision but not competent to make another? Why?

2. What are the three main capacities that someone must have in order to be competent? For each, give an example of how someone might lack it in a way that undermines her decisional competence.

3. According to Buchanan and Brock, what is the relationship between the level of expected harms and benefits from a particular procedure, and the standard that should be used to assess competence?

References

Anderson, C.G., P.M. Pierce, and M.A. Walker. 1984. Have Nurses and Physicians Signed Living Wills? [letter] *New England Journal of Medicine* 311:678.

Angell, M. 1984. Respecting Autonomy of Competent Patients. *New England Journal of Medicine* 310:1115–16.

Baron, C. 1979. Medical Paternalism and the Rule of Law: A Reply to Dr. Relman. *American Journal of Law and Medicine* 8:37.

Beauchamp, T.L., and J.F. Childress. 1983. *Principles of Biomedical Ethics*. New York: Oxford University Press.

Beauchamp, T.L., and R. Faden. 1987. *A Theory of Informed Consent*. New York: Oxford University Press.

Bedell, S., and T. Delbanco. 1984. Choices about Cardiopulmonary Resuscitation in the Hospital. *New England Journal of Medicine* 310:1089–93.

Brock, D.W. 1983. Paternalism and Promoting the Good. In *Paternalism*, ed. R.E. Sartorius, 237–60. St. Paul: University of Minnesota Press.

Buchanan, A.E. 1979. Medical Paternalism or Legal Imperialism: Not the Only Alternatives for Handling Saikewicz-type Cases. *American Journal of Law and Medicine* 5 :103–4.

———. 1983. Medical Paternalism. In *Paternalism*, ed. R.E. Sartorius, 61–82. St. Paul: University of Minnesota Press.

———. 1984. The Right to a "Decent Minimum" of Health Care. *Philosophy and Public Affairs* 13(11):55–78.

———. 1985. *Ethics, Efficiency and the Market*. Tocowa, N.J.: Rowman and Allanheld.

Calabresi, G., and P. Bobbitt. 1978. *Tragic Choices*. New York: W. W. Norton.

Callahan, D. 1985. What Do Children Owe Their Elderly Parents? *Hastings Center Report* 15(2):32–37.

Cope, L. 1980. Doctors Think Mack in Vegetative State. *Minneapolis Tribune*, 20 March.

Cranford, R.E., and A.E. Doudera. 1984. *Institutional Ethics Committees and Health Care Decision Making*. Ann Arbor: Health Administration Press.

Daniels, N. 1985. *Just Health Care*. New York: Cambridge University Press.

English, J. 1975. Abortion and the Conception of a Person. *Canadian Journal of Philosophy* 5:112–24.

Evans, A., and B. Brody. 1985. The Do Not Resuscitate Order in Teaching Hospitals. *Journal of the American Medical Association* 253:2236–45.

Feinberg, J. 1984. *The Moral Limits of the Criminal Law. Volume I: Harm to Others*. New York: Oxford University Press.

Frontline. 1985. What About Mom and Dad? Public Broadcasting System, 21 May.

Gaylin, W. 1982. Competence: No Longer All or None. In *Who Speaks for the Child?*, ed. W. Gaylin and R. Macklin, 32–41. New York: Plenum Press.

Horstman, P. 1975. Protective Services for the Elderly: The Limits of Parens Patriae. *Missouri Law Review* 40:215–78.

Jarvik, L. 1980. Diagnosis of Demention in the Elderly: A 1980 Perspective. *Annual Review of Gerontology and Geriatrics* 1:252–61.

Katz, J. 1977. Informed Consent: A Fairy Tale? *University of Pittsburgh Law Review* 39:137–74.

Lidz, C.W., A. Meisel, E. Zerubavel, M. Carter, R.M. Sestak, and L.H. Roth. 1984. *Informed Consent: A Study of Decision Making in Psychiatry*. New York: Guilford Press.

Lynn, J., and J.F. Childress. 1983. Must Patients Always Be Given Food and Water? *Hastings Center Report* 13(5):21–3.

Meisel, A. 1979. The "Exceptions" to the Informed Consent Doctrine: Striking a Balance between Competing Values in Medical Decision Making. *Wisconsin Law Review* 2:413–88.

National Institute on Aging. 1977. *Our Future Selves: A Research Plan toward Understanding Aging*. Washington: National Institutes of Health.

———. 1978. *Our Future Selves: A Research Plan toward Understanding Aging*. Washington: National Institutes of Health.

Peterson, D. 1980. Shooting Case Turns into Vigil. *Minneapolis Tribune*, 7 March.

President's Commission for the Study of Ethical Problems in Medicine and Biomedical and Behavioural Research. 1982. *Making Health Care Decisions. Volume One: Report*. Washington.

———. 1983a. *Deciding to Forego Life-sustaining Treatment*. Washington.

———. 1983b. *Securing Access to Health Care. Volume One: Report*. Washington.

Relman, R. 1978. The Saikewicz Decision: A Medical Viewpoint. *American Journal of Law and Medicine* 4 :233–7.

Robertson, J. 1976. Organ Donations by Incompetents and the Substituted Judgment Doctrine. *Columbia Law Review* 76:48–68.

Rosenberg, G.A., S.F. Johnson, and R.P. Brenner. 1977. Recovery of Cognition after Prolonged Vegetative State. *Annuals of Neurology* 2:167–75.

Roth, M. 1983. Senile Dementia and Related Disorders. In *Senile Dementia: Outlook for the Future*, ed. J. Wertheimer and M. Marais. New York: Alan R. Liss.

Sartorius, R.E. 1983. *Paternalism*. St. Paul: University of Minnesota Press.

Steinbock, B. 1983. The Removal of Mr. Herbert's Feeding Tube. *Hastings Center Report* 13(5):12–15.

Tooley, M. 1972. Abortion and Infanticide. *Philosophy and Public Affairs* 2:37–65.

Warren, M.A. 1973. On the Moral and Legal Status of Abortion. *Monist* 57:43–61.

Wikler, D. 1983. Paternalism and the Mildly Retarded. In *Paternalism*, ed. R.E. Sartorius. St. Paul: University of Minnesota Press.

TWO   A Moral Theory of Informed Consent

Benjamin Freedman | *Hastings Center Report* 1975; 5.4: 32-9.

Consent and the Competent

. . . A person who has the capacity to give valid consent, and who has in fact consented to the procedure in question, has a right to have that fact recognized by us. We all have a duty to recognize a valid consent when confronted with it. From whence derives this right? It arises from the right which each of us possesses to be treated as a person, and in the duty which all of us have, to have respect for persons, to treat a person as such, and not as an object. For this entails that our capacities for personhood ought to be recognized by all—these capacities including the capacity for rational decision, and for action consequent upon rational decision. Perhaps the worst which we may do to a man is to deny him his humanity, for example, by classifying him as mentally incompetent when he is, in fact, sane. It is a terrible thing to be hated or persecuted; it is far worse to be ignored, to be notified that you "don't count."

> **Personhood**
> Possessing the qualities that make one a moral agent, including, in this context, rationality and the capacity to make responsible choices.

If an individual is capable of and has given valid consent, I would argue that he has a right, as against the world but more particularly as against his physician, to have it recognized that valid consent has been given. (The same applies, of course, with still greater force, with regard to *refusals* to consent to medical procedures.) The limited force of this claim must be emphasized: it does not entail a right to be treated, or to be experimented upon. It is a most innocuous right, one which most of us would have little hesitation about granting. . . .

From the patient's point of view, he has a right to have his health protected by the physician, and a mere liberty to be experimented upon. From the physician-investigator's point of view, he has a duty to protect the subject's health, and a mere liberty to experiment upon the subject (contingent, of course, upon obtaining the subject's consent). A recognition of the claims of personhood and autonomy, however, reveals this to be a conflict between rights and duties. The physician-investigator has a duty to recognize consent when validly offered. When the consent is of doubtful validity, therefore, the physician experiences a conflict between two duties. He will not be ethically well-protected by choosing not to experiment, for there exists the possibility—which, as cases are multiplied, becomes a probability—that he is violating a duty in so choosing. Problems in informed consent present us with a dilemma. It is no longer the case that the burden of proof devolves upon the would-be experimenter. The would-be abstainer from experiments may have to prove his case as well.

> **Autonomy**
> Possessing autonomy involves possessing the capacity to decide for oneself in light of one's sober, reflective values; literally "self-rule."

These considerations give us a new point of departure in investigating problems of informed consent. They show us that there is no "fail-safe" procedure which we can fall back upon in cases of doubt. Rather, what is required is an exhaustive examination of each case and issue, to see whether or not a valid consent has in fact been obtained. . . .

The Requirement of Information

The most common locution for the requirement which

> **Liberty to be experimented upon**
> Freedman is interested in both the issue of consent to medical treatment and consent to medical experimentation. He believes the patient possesses a right to have her health protected by her physician, but she does not have a right to be included in a medical experiment. To be included in a medical experiment, there must exist a study that is suitable for the patient and the investigator must be willing to include her in the study. Thus, the patient has a mere liberty to be included in an experiment, and the exercise of this liberty is contingent on other factors.

I am discussing is "informed consent"—we require "informed consent" to protect a doctor from legal liability resultant from his therapeutic endeavors, or to ensure the ethical permissibility of an experiment. But I believe "informed consent" to be a serious misnomer for what we do, in fact, want medical practice to conform to. . . .

The basic mistake which is committed by those who harp upon the difficulties in obtaining informed consent (and by critics of the doctrine) is in believing that we can talk about information in the abstract, without reference to any human purpose. It is very likely impossible to talk about "information" in this way; but impossible or not, when we do in fact talk about, or request, information, we do not mean "information in the abstract." If I ask someone to "tell me about those clouds" he will, ordinarily, know what I mean; and he will answer me, in the spirit in which he was asked, by virtue of his professional expertise as an artist, meteorologist, astronomer, soothsayer, or what-have-you. The meteorologist will not object that he cannot tell you the optical refraction index of the clouds, and therefore that he cannot "fully answer" your question. He knows that you are asking him with a given end in mind, and that much information about the cloud is irrelevant *relative to that purpose.*

> **Soothsayer**
> A person in many traditions, including the Classical Western tradition, who is said to be able to predict the future.

That this "abstract information" requirement is not in question in obtaining valid consent is hardly an original point, but it is worth repeating. One of the leading court opinions on human experimentation puts it like this: " . . . the patient's interest in information does not extend to a lengthy polysyllabic discourse on all possible complications. A mini-course in medical science is not required ."[1] . . .

The proper question to ask, then, is not "What information must be given?" That would be premature: we must first know for what purpose information is needed. *Why* must the patient be informed? Put that way, the answer is immediately forthcoming. The patient must be informed so that he will know what he is getting into, what he may expect from the procedure, what his likely alternatives are—in short, what the procedure (and forbearance from it) will mean, so that a responsible decision on the matter may be made. This is the legal stance, as well as, I think, a "commonsensical" stance; as Alexander

Capron writes, the information component in valid consent derives in law from the recognition that information is "necessary to make meaningful the power to decide."[2] The proper test of whether a given piece of information needs to be given is, then, whether the physician, knowing what he does about the patient/subject, feels that that patient/subject would want to know this before making up his mind. Outré, improbable consequences would not ordinarily, therefore, be relevant information. Exceptionally, they will be: for example, when there is a small risk of impotence consequent upon the procedure which the physician proposes to perform upon a man with a great stake in his sexual prowess. This is only sensible. . . .

> **Outré**
> Highly unusual or atypical to a degree that evokes surprise.

Our conclusion, then, is that the informing of the patient/subject is not a fundamental requirement of valid consent. It is, rather, derivative from the requirement that the consent be the expression a responsible choice. The two requirements which I do see as fundamental in this doctrine are that the choice be responsible and that it be voluntary.

The Requirement of Responsibility

What is meant by saying that the choice must be "responsible"? Does this entail that the physician may at any time override a patient's judgment on the basis that, in the physician's view, the patient has not chosen responsibly? Surely not; to adopt such a criterion would defeat the purpose embodied in the doctrine of consent. It would mean that a person's exercise of autonomy is always subject to review.

Still, some such requirement would appear to be necessary. A small child can certainly make choices.[3] Small children can also be intelligent enough to understand the necessary information. Yet surely we would not want to say that a small child can give valid consent to a serious medical procedure.[4] The reason for this is that the child cannot choose *responsibly.*

We are faced with a dilemma. On the one hand, it appears that we must require that the choice be responsible. To require only that the choice be free would yield counterintuitive results. On the other hand, if we do require that the choice made be a responsible one, we seem to presuppose somebody which shall judge the reasonableness of choices; this represents a

Paternalism
Restricting the patient's freedom to choose in the name of his or her best interests.

Antithetical
For one thing to be sharply contrasted or mutually incompatible with another. For instance, "slavery is antithetical to basic human freedoms."

paternalism which is antithetical to the doctrine of consent. An elderly patient chooses to forgo further life-saving measures. How are we to judge whether or not this choice is a responsible one?

The path between the horns of this dilemma involves saying that the "responsibility" which we require is to be predicated not on the nature of the particular choice, but on the nature of the patient/subject. What we need to know is whether *he* is a responsible man ("in general," so to speak), not whether the choice which has been made is responsible. In this way, we avoid the danger of upholding as "responsible" only those choices which we ourselves feel are good choices. We can and do admit into the community of responsible persons individuals who make choices with which we do not agree.

In this sense, responsibility is a dispositional characteristic. To say that someone is a responsible individual means that he makes choices, typically, on the basis of reasons, arguments, or beliefs—and that he remains open to the claims of reason, so that further rational argument might lead him to change his mind. It is to say that a person is capable of making and carrying through a life-plan—that he is prepared to act on the basis of his choices. It is to say that a person is capable of living with his life-plan; he can live with the consequences of his choices, he *takes responsibility* for his choices.[5] Of course, none of these are absolutes: all responsible people are at times pigheaded, at times short-sighted, at times flighty. That is to say, all responsible men at times act irresponsibly. Should the lack of responsibility persist, of course, to an extreme degree, we may say that the person has left the community of responsible folk.

Voluntarism and Reward

The other requirement of valid consent is that it be given voluntarily. The choice which the consent expresses must be freely made. We all know some conditions which, if satisfied, make us say that a consent has been given involuntarily. The case which immediately springs to mind occurs when an individual succumbs under a threat: we call this duress or coercion. But the threat need not be overt; and perhaps there need not be a threat at all to render consent involuntary. Hence, the major problem currently engendered by the requirement of voluntariness. It is typified by the prisoner who "volunteers" for an experiment in the hope or expectation of a reward: significantly higher wages, an opportunity for job training, better health care while involved in the experiment, a favorable report to his parole board. Is the consent which the prisoner offers a voluntary consent? The problem may be stated more generally thus: At what point does reward render consent involuntary? . . .

Voluntariness
The ethical requirement that consent be freely given; consent that is obtained under threat or coercion is generally regarded as invalid.

This problem may be clarified by the following examples. Imagine an upper middle class individual, who can provide for his family all of their needs and most of the amenities of civilized life. Let us say that this person is offered one hundred dollars to cross the street—if you like, make it one thousand or ten thousand dollars? He chooses to cross the street. Is his choice *involuntary*? Despite the substantial reward, I think most of us would agree that the consent was freely offered (and would that we should have such problems!).

Consider a person who deeply wants to be an astronaut. He is told that as part of the program he must participate in experiments to determine resistance to high-G conditions. Is his consent to this invalid, involuntary? I think not. We would say, this is part of his job; he should have expected it; and if he can't stand the heat, he should get out of the kitchen. In this vein, consider Evel Knievel, a financially prosperous man, who is offered millions of dollars to perform daredevil stunts. His choice may be bizarre, even crazy: but has his reward rendered it unfree?

Finally, consider a man who is informed by his doctor that he will most likely die unless he has open-heart surgery. His "reward" for consenting is his life; the penalty for not consenting is death. Does this mean this man cannot give the doctor valid consent—morally valid consent—to proceed?

Evel Knievel
Robert Craig Knievel (1938-1997) was a daredevil motorcyclist and entertainer who rose to prominence from the late 1960s to early 1980s. Perhaps his most famous stunt involved an unsuccessful attempt to jump a rocket powered motorcycle across the Snake River Canyon in 1974.

There are two distinctions which, I think, go a long way towards dispelling these problems. First, I think it must be granted that natural contingencies ("acts of God," things which come to pass naturally, those contingencies which we cannot hold anyone responsible for) do not render a person unfree, nor do they render unfree the choices which a person makes in light of those contingencies.[6]

That natural contingencies do not render a man unfree is a point which is apt to be forgotten in the present context. I am not—in the morally relevant sense—lacking in freedom because I cannot, unaided, fly through the air, or live on grass. Nor am I unfree because my heart is about to give out. Nor am I unfree when, recognizing that my heart may give out, I choose to undergo surgery. I may, of course, be so crazed by knowing that I am near death's door that I am in a state of general incompetence, and hence must have the choice made for me; but general incompetence is not in question here. The distinction between choices forced by man, and choices forced by nature, is, then, of importance.

The second distinction is between those pressures which are, and those which are not, in Daube's words, "consonant with the dignity and responsibility of free life."[7] I would explain this as follows: there are certain basic freedoms and rights which we possess which *entitle* us (morally) to certain things (or states of affairs). We would all, no doubt, draw up different lists of these rights and freedoms; but included in them would be safety of person, freedom of conscience and religion, a right to a certain level of education, and, for some of us, a right to some level of health care. When the "reward" is such as only to give us the necessary conditions of these rights and freedoms—when all that the reward does is to bring us up to a level of living to which we are entitled, and of which we have been deprived by man—then the "reward," I think, constitutes duress. A reward which accrues to one who has achieved this level, or who can easily achieve it (other than by taking the reward option), and which hence serves only to grant us "luxury" items, does not constitute duress, and hence does not render choice unfree, no matter how great this reward may be.

The rewards above the moral subsistence level are true rewards. In contrast, we may say (with some touch of metaphor) that the "rewards" which only bring us up to the level to which we were in any event entitled are properly viewed as functioning as *threats*: "Do this, or stay where you are:"—when you should not have been "where you are" in the first place. The astronaut, Evel Knievel, and the upper-middle-class street-crosser are being granted "luxury" items, and hence are capable of giving free consent. But consider a man who will not be admitted to the hospital for treatment unless he agrees to be a subject in an experiment (unrelated to his treatment). Those who feel, as I do, that we are, here and now, morally entitled to medical treatment would agree, I trust, that this illegitimate option coerces the man into agreeing. Or consider a man who has religious scruples against donating blood, who takes his daughter to a hospital for treatment. He is told that the doctors will not treat her unless the family donates a certain amount of blood. His freedom has been nullified; his "consent" to donating blood is morally invalid. Similarly, the college student whose grade is contingent upon his participation in the instructor's psychological experiments is not validly consenting to serve. He is entitled to have his grade based upon his classroom work. . . .

Study Questions

1. According to Freedman, what are the three elements that are necessary in order for consent to be valid? Which two are "fundamental?" Why?

2. What according to Freedman is a "responsible choice?" How does this position avoid paternalism?

3. What does it mean for consent to be voluntary? Does an offer of money invalidate consent?

Notes

1. *Cobbs v. Grant*, 502 P. 2d 1, 11.
2. Alexander M. Capron, "Legal Rights and Moral Rights," in Hilton, et al., eds., *Ethical Issues in Human Genetics* (Plenum Press, 1973), 228.
3. The counter-suggestion may be made that children cannot *really* make choices. This would, I think, put too great a weight upon the requirement of voluntarism. We would be recruiting the concepts of choice and volition to do a job which they have not been designed for.
4. I am speaking of course in the moral, not the legal, context. It may be that in an emergency a child may, in the absence of his parents, give legally valid consent.
5. This gives us the link between "responsible" in the dispositional sense explained here, and "responsible" in the blame-sense of the word ("I'll hold you responsible for that.").
6. The *caveat* must be added: natural contingencies do not have, as their *sole* result, the rendering of a person unfree, in the sense which vitiates consent: a man's brain tumor can make the man an idiot, schizophrenia can make a man insane, but these do not so much affect a person's volition as they do disturb his entire psychic structure.
7. David Daube, quoted in Henry K. Beecher, *Research and the Individual: Human Studies* (Boston: Little, Brown, 1970), p. 146.

THREE ICU Psychosis and Patient Autonomy: Some Thoughts from the Inside

Cheryl Misak | *Journal of Medicine and Philosophy* 2005; 30(4): 411-30.

Introduction

. . . In this paper I draw on my rather grim experience of septic shock, ARDS (acute respiratory distress syndrome), and multiple organ failure. . . . ARDS is a severe lung injury caused by one of a number of things: sepsis, trauma, burns, and so on. It is usually accompanied by multiple organ failure: mechanical ventilation and other forms of life-support are required. It is thus a wide-ranging descriptor, catching a significant proportion of long-stay patients in a medical-surgical intensive care unit (ICU). By the time I reached the hospital, I was already on death's door. I was put on a ventilator and spent the next few weeks in multiple organ failure and a drug-induced paralytic coma, with minimal chances of survival. When I eventually resurfaced, I was emaciated, virtually lungless, and incredibly weak. . . .

From my reflections on this set of experiences, . . . I will argue that the principle of patient autonomy—that physicians must respect the intrinsic value of people's capacity to run their lives for themselves, even if there is reason to think that they are making a mistake—needs to be rethought in the critical care context.[1] . . .

> **Septic shock**
> A life-threatening condition in which an overwhelming systemic infection leads to low blood pressure and multiple organ failure. Septic shock requires treatment in an intensive care unit and, despite treatment, has a mortality rate of 30 per cent or greater.

ICU Psychosis

There are two sorts of awfulness involved in what the medical profession charmingly calls a serious "insult." One sort arises from what is physically going on: the pain, the extreme discomfort that comes with mechanical ventilation, and the physical panic induced by the suctioning process and the attendant inability to breathe. . . .

But there is a second, perhaps even worse, sort of awfulness: that of stepping well over the fuzzy line that separates sanity from madness. Numerous studies have looked at the mental distress experienced by ICU patients with ARDS. Of those surviving patients who remember anything at all, many report harrowing psychotic episodes. These are usually "nightmares

> **ICU psychosis**
> Patients in intensive care units can experience a range of psychiatric symptoms due to pain, stress, sleep deprivation, medication, and serious illness. Thought processes become abnormal and lose contact with reality. Symptoms may include agitation, disorientation, hallucinations, and paranoia.

often of a bizarre and extremely terrifying nature," hallucinations, and paranoid delusions—typically of a nurse or a doctor trying to rape, murder, or otherwise harm the patient.[2]. . .

> **Delusion**
> A false belief that is strongly held despite evidence to the contrary. Delusions may be a prominent feature of a variety of mental illnesses, including schizophrenia, bipolar affective disorder ("manic depression"), and psychotic depression.

The thing that makes these phenomena especially terrifying and insidious is that unlike ordinary nightmares and more like paranoid delusions, they tend to occur in real time and to hook onto slices of external reality. One takes an actual physician or nurse in the ICU, whips up a violent conspiracy theory around that person, and then has the conspiracy play itself out in the midst of actual conversations and medical procedures. . . . One quite literally loses one's grip on what is true and what is false. . . .

For weeks after coming to consciousness, my central preoccupation was the attempt to sort out which memories were of actual events and which were imagined. . . . But much of the required sorting had to wait until I was extubated, when I could question others. I asked my husband whether there really was a Christmas party (this was in April), at which the ICU physicians drank copious quantities of alcohol and proceeded to parade, ridicule, and humiliate the most pathetic patients, myself included, much to the mirth of all. Part of me knew that this could not have happened, but it seemed so real that part of me could not believe that it did not happen. I think that I will never quite shake that "memory" of being completely wretched, physically restrained, unable to speak, and at the mercy of that band of cruel sadists . . . who, in reality, selflessly fought night and day to save my life.

The most persistent delusion began as I first struggled into consciousness. . . . The pain and discomfort were unspeakable and certain of the medical staff were standing over me with the police, trying to bully me to lay charges against a . . . student. . . . The delusion involving the bullying was so convincing that, once I had properly resurfaced, it was almost impossible for me to discard the belief that a certain physician had tried to make me lay the charge. Again, what is unusual about these delusions is that they are a mix of fact and fiction: I didn't imagine the distinctive thump of the machines, the pain, the background context, the physicians and nurses, . . .

and the struggle into consciousness, but I certainly imagined the police and the bullying.

It thus strikes me as right when I read that these traumatic experiences in the ICU "may be as emotionally devastating as intra-operative awareness during anaesthesia." (Schelling et al. 1998, p. 658) Both are associated with a highly elevated incidence of post-traumatic stress disorder in the weeks and even years after discharge. . . . Indeed, as the clear-headed thoughts started . . . after I came round, the following struck me forcibly. Dying is easy: it is the coming back that is unimaginably difficult.

It ought to be clear that mental distress of this sort . . . has . . . severe consequences for the patient-physician

> **Post-traumatic stress disorder**
> A psychiatric syndrome that may occur days, months, or years after an event involving the threat of injury or death. Individuals may experience repeated upsetting memories of the event, feel detached, and have difficulty concentrating.

relationship. Most importantly, I shall argue, it brings into question just how seriously we ought to take the principle that the competent-seeming patient ought to take part in decisions about his or her care or be part of the decision-making "team."

Extubation

A second kind of mental distress in the ICU contributes to the problematic status of the principle of patient autonomy: the incredibly intense and single-minded desire to be extubated and then released, whatever the costs. . . . Trying to rip out the tube lodged in one's throat is a frequent phenomenon: the technical term is the brilliantly understated "unplanned extubation."

> **Extubated**
> The removal of the breathing tube from the patient's trachea.

I was so desperate that I had a series of hallucinations in which "the team" went round to each bed and merrily extubated patient after patient, bypassing my bed altogether, despite my imagined frantic waving and pleading.

I managed to communicate this desperation to the nurses and physicians, notwithstanding the fact that I could not speak and was too weak to write. I did not want my already-traumatized small children to visit until . . . I was off the ventilator and . . . I was ferocious in my desire to see them. Various physicians would come round, show me X-rays of my lungs, and explain how they were not ready. My glares, however, were eventually persuasive and I was extubated a day or two before it was thought maximally desirable. More seriously, once I was moved to the ward I managed to get released after just two nights, despite all the excellent reasons offered to the contrary.

I was of course most grateful for both of these things. But even at the time I wondered why my desires were being taken into consideration: could they not tell, I wondered, that I was a lunatic? And once I was at home, in an alarmingly fragile state, it was not clear to me or to my family that this was the best outcome.

Autonomy in the ICU

Consequences of Irrational Decisions

While the principle of respect for patient autonomy has it that health care professionals . . . should always treat . . . the patient who passes tests of competency as a full participant on the decision-making team, it seems clear that this principle should not always be upheld in critical care medicine. It may well be a trumping principle with respect to end-of-life decision-making, resuscitation and continuation of life-support, but . . . not . . . for more routine treatment matters. To make this suggestion plausible, I will offer three arguments. The first is, as Franklin and Rosenbloom (2000) pointed out, . . . that an irrational decision taken by a critically ill patient is likely to be catastrophic.

Seeming to be Competent

The other two arguments note that it is far from clear that ICU patients are competent, even when they seem to be. The first of these . . . is an anecdotal appeal to my own experience and cannot be generalized in an unproblematic way. I appeared competent—I was appropriately responsive to questions and propped up in bed reading . . . a biography of Walter Benjamin. The medical personnel seemed impressed and expressed their

Walter Benjamin
(1892–1940) A German literary critic and philosopher. His writings include works on 19th century life in Paris, German theatre, and Marxist philosophy. After the fall of France, he eluded an arrest warrant from the Gestapo, only to be captured by Spanish authorities in September 1940. Rather than be turned over to Nazi custody, he committed suicide on 26 September 1940.

surprise at how quickly I was rebounding. I was in fact a psychological mess and should not have been taken to be fit to participate in decisions. I was filled with what I took to be well-concealed fear and loathing for most of my lifesavers and caregivers. And I was overwhelmed by the determination to be extubated and to get out of there.

It is not clear that competency can be measured only by taking into account present abilities and capacities. It might well be that difficulties in the past are affecting, under the radar screen of the tests, one's functioning in the present. One might be able to complete all the tests with the required accuracy and yet be haunted by what has recently happened. . . .

Difficulties in Assessing Psychological Status

The last argument . . . has to do with the testing for psychological well-being in the ICU: . . . most patients are ventilated and this renders concurrent assessment of psychological status very difficult (Turnock 1997). It is . . . easy to see when a patient is in an agitated or hyperactive . . . mental state. . . . It is also relatively easy to assess a patient who can in some way communicate and who cannot remember the names of her children, does not know that she is in a hospital, and so on. Patients in these states would never be taken to be psychologically sound or competent.

But assessments of psychological status are much more difficult in the face of quiet or hypoactive malfunctioning, especially when the patient is having trouble with communication. And they are even more difficult when the quiet malfunctioning is subtle, but nonetheless devastating. Indeed, I want to argue that assessments of this kind of change in mental status are pretty much impossible. Given the prevalence of these kinds of situations, my suggestion is that the principle of patient autonomy in the ICU needs to be rethought.

To appreciate the point I am trying to make, look at the current methods of assessment of psychological status. . . . E.W. Ely's . . . Confusion Assessment Method for the Intensive Care Unit (CAM-ICU) is a method for measuring *delirium*, especially the most commonly missed subtype: hypoactive or non-agitated delirium. He argues that it is unrecognized in 66 to 84 per cent of patients.[3]

In many ICUs the test for quiet mental distress is informal: finding out whether patients can obey commands and whether they know who they are talking to, the names of their children, and so on. CAM-ICU allows for a more precise and standardized measure. It is based on the DSM-IV—modified for non-verbal (i.e., intubated) patients—and is conducted in less than two minutes. . . . The tester asks the patient to do such things as squeeze his or her hand whenever he recites, say, the letter "A" in a list of 10 recited letters and to indicate which 5 of 10 pictures (of common objects) has been shown earlier in a series.

> **DSM-IV**
> The fourth edition of the Diagnostic and Statistical Manual of Mental Disorders, the standard text for the classification and diagnosis of psychiatric disease published by the American Psychiatric Association.

Like the less formal ways of assessing confusion, the CAM-ICU tests for some minimal degree of clear thinking, recognition, and memory. Indeed, the characterization given of delirium is that a patient's "ability to receive, process, store, and recall information is *strikingly impaired*." (Ely, Inouye et al. 2001b, p. 2793) Most of the work on delirium . . . is aimed at identifying it with the goal to discovering whether delirium contributes to poor outcomes[4] and whether it can be reduced and treated. . . . But . . . whether or not a patient is delirious will inevitably be a part of any discussion of competency. That is, despite the fact that the CAM-ICU was not developed as a competency instrument, it will be hijacked for this purpose. And it will not serve well. . . .

The problem is this: how can you know when you are accurately measuring quiet and *subtle* mental distress and malfunctioning? . . . The only possibility is to look at the way that mental state is manifesting itself in behavior. Given that you cannot ask complex questions of an intubated patient and get suitably complex answers, the range of behavior available is minimal: only gross behavior ("squeeze my hand, indicate which pictures . . .") is possible. And only simple questions can be answered. Quiet and subtle mental malfunctioning in intubated patients is extremely difficult to measure. . . .

A patient might have a subsyndromal amount of brain dysfunction that could be completely missed by the CAM-ICU and by any other test that could be administered to intubated patients. . . . In order to assess competency, the phenomenon which needs studying is not merely over-arching delusional and disorganized states in which the patient is so confused that he or she is unable to respond appropriately to very simple questions, but the whole phenomenon of mental failings caused by critical illness. . . .

> **Subsyndromal**
> Exhibiting symptoms that are not sufficiently severe to meet the requirements of a particular diagnosis.

The anecdotal argument can be joined to the better argument. . . . I would have often scored very well on tests such as the CAM-ICU. . . . I cannot remember being tested when I was in the grip of a *quiet* delusion, but . . . the very nature of ICU delusions is that they are a mix of fact and fiction and it may be possible to respond accurately to simple questions in the midst of such a mixed state. During my non-delusional states, when I was trying to sort out what had been real and what had not been real and to determine whether the physicians and nurses were on my side or not, I easily passed the tests. . . . My mental malfunctioning was such that I appeared perfectly fine, but nonetheless I still had roving bouts of overwhelming suspicions, conspiracy theories, etc.

The tests . . . are not fine-grained enough to be sensitive to those quiet mixed states and they are not fine-grained enough to be sensitive to those patients who are sane enough to be trying to sort out their confused mental states while trying to maximize their chances of being extubated and then released. Disturbed mental states need not be marked by agitation or even by current hallucination and inattention. . . . The available tests are tests for minimal mental capacity. A patient might pass them but nonetheless not be competent because he or she is afraid, desperate, tired and traumatized.

My anecdotal observations are supported by the recent literature. Ely, Inouye and colleagues (2001b) reported that between 39 to 42 per cent of alert or easily aroused patients who could make eye contact and follow commands were found to be delirious, using the tests for striking delusional and disorganized states. . . . These are patients "who are usually assumed to be cognitively intact by ICU personnel." Imagine how many would be found to be cognitively impaired if we could test for more subtle (i.e., non-striking) impairment. . . .

Implications for Autonomy

Let us return to the principle of patient autonomy: . . . we are to assume competence when no explicit evidence to the contrary exists. And when we assume competence, we are to take the person in question as having the capacity to make his or her own choices. Given what we know about the prevalence of quiet delirium in ICU settings, how hard it is to detect subtle mental weakness relevant to competence, and the reasonable desire to mask mental weakness by under-reporting it (in order to be extubated and then released), this presumption seems out of place in the ICU. . . .

My suggestion is that it is better to go on the policy of doing what is in the patient's best interests, despite the fact that this will be viewed as highly paternalistic by the patient herself and by many health care professionals and ethicists. Perhaps this kind of suggestion can be made only in those societies, in which paternalism in the medical profession has been significantly eroded. . . . The suggestion is, therefore, that we . . . find a reasonable middle position between patient autonomy and paternalism.

Atul Gawande, a surgeon who has written extensively on his profession, is of the same view. He has said . . . that "the new orthodoxy about patient autonomy has a hard time acknowledging an awkward truth: patients frequently don't want the freedom that we've given them." (2002, p. 219) I want to add a twist to this claim: patients may clearly want that freedom at the actual decision-making time. But on reflection, patients often see that it is better to be steered or overruled. . . . The point is that patients find themselves in extraordinarily difficult and complex predicaments. Our principles must be subtle enough to account for those predicaments.

Perhaps we ought to recognize that physicians . . . must, on the one hand, see the patient as an autonomous person who ought to be in control of his or her life and they must, on the other, see the patient as a medical problem in need of the best solution. . . . They must see the patient as a person, but also as a physical body on which they need to act, often in horrific ways that are in tension with seeing the patient as an individual with desires, needs, family, and friends. . . . This is difficult. . . . But its problematic nature should be reflected in our thoughts about how physicians should treat their patients, . . . not hidden or simplified by a presumption that is too crude an instrument for the subtle phenomenon in question.

Study questions

1. What is ICU psychosis? How does it interfere with a patient's decision-making capacity?

2. Describe the challenges in assessing decision-making competency in an ICU patient.

3. Why does Misak believe that the presumption of decision-making competency should not apply in the ICU context? Do you agree?

Notes

1. I make this point, in an abbreviated way, in Misak (2004b).
2. See, for instance, Schelling et al. (1998) and the testimonials on the ARDS support website: www.ARDS.org.
3. See also: http://www.ICUdelirium.org.
4. It does: see Ely, Shintani et al. (2004).

References

Ely, E.W., Gautem, S., Margolin, R., Francis, J., May, L., Speroff, T., Truman, B., Dittus, R., Bernard, R., & Inouye, S.K. (2001). The impact of delirium in the intensive care unit on hospital length of stay. *Intensive Care Medicine*, 27(12), 1892–900.

Ely, E.W., Inouye, S.K, Bernard, R., Gordon, S., Francis, J., May, L., Truman, B., Speroff, T., Gautam, S., Margolin, R., Hart, R.P., & Dittus, R. (2001b). Delirium in mechanically ventilated patients: Validity and reliability of the confusion assessment method for the intensive care unit (CAM-ICU). *Journal of the American Medical Association*, 21(286), 2703–10.

Ely, E.W., Shintani, A., Truman, B., Speroff, T., Gordon, S.M., Harrell, F.E., Inouye, S.K., Bernard, G.R., & Dittus, R.S. (2004). Delirium as a predictor of mortality in mechanically ventilated patients in the intensive care unit. *Journal of the American Medical Association*, 291(14), 1753–62.

Franklin, C., & Rosenbloom, B. (2000). Proposing a new standard to establish medical competence for the purpose of critical care intervention. *Critical Care Medicine*, 28(8), 3035–8.

Gawande, A. (2002). *Complications: A surgeon's notes on an imperfect science*. New York: Henry Holt.

Misak, C. (2004). The critical care experience: A patient's view. *American Journal of Respiratory and Critical Care Medicine*, 170(4), 357–9.

Schelling, G., Stoll, C., Haller, M., Briegel, J., Manert, W., Hummel, T., Lenhart, A., Heyduck, M., Polasek, J., Meier, M., Preuss, U., Bullinger, M., Schuffel, W., & Peter, K. (1998). Heath-related quality of life and post-traumatic stress disorder in survivors of the acute respiratory distress syndrome. *Critical Care Medicine*, 26(4), 651–9.

Chapter Study Questions

1. Buchanan and Brock argue that the standard for competence should vary in accord with the consequences of the particular decision. Using Freedman's notion of "responsible choice," critique this view. Who do you think is right and why?

2. Buchanan and Brock argue that the standard of competence ought to vary with consequences of the choice. Is this compatible with Misak's argument against the presumption of decision-making competency in the ICU setting? Why?

3. Can voluntary choices be made by patients in the ICU setting? Why?

Critical Analysis

Consider the following from the article by Freedman:

"When the 'reward' is such as only to give us the necessary conditions of these rights and freedoms—when all that the reward does is to bring us up to a level of living to which we are entitled, and of which we have been deprived by man—then the 'reward,' I think, constitutes duress. A reward which accrues to one who has achieved this level, or who can easily achieve it (other than by taking the reward-option), and which hence serves only to grant us 'luxury' items, does not constitute duress, and hence does not render choice unfree, no matter how great this reward may be."

Outline Freedman's argument in your own words, paying particular attention to the premises that he relies on to support his main conclusion. Choose one of the premises for evaluation. Try to think of at least one objection to this premise.

Case Study

Scott Starson is a self-taught physicist with a long history of mental illness. Since 1985, he has been in and out of psychiatric facilities and is diagnosed with schizoaffective disorder, a disease characterized by distortions of reality and elevated or depressed mood. In 1998, when he was 42 years old, he was arrested for threatening to kill fellow residents of a Toronto townhouse and a police officer. When a court found him not responsible for his actions due to mental illness, he was transferred to a psychiatric hospital where he adamantly refused antipsychotic medication prescribed by his physicians.

Mr. Starson, who insists on being called "Professor Starson," has no formal training in physics, but has published several papers with Pierre Noyes, a physics professor at Stanford University. He disagrees with the diagnosis made by his psychiatrists. Furthermore, having taken antipsychotic medication in the past, he believes that it slows his mental abilities and hinders his ability to do creative work in physics. He describes his work in physics as the most important source of meaning in his life. Being deprived of the ability to continue his work would, in his words, "be like death."

His treating physicians believe that his condition is deteriorating. They point to the fact that he has been unable to publish since the mid-1980s, in their view, due to his illness. They also point to a variety of delusional beliefs held by the patient, including that he continues to work from his hospital room with an international network of scientists, even though his room has no phone or computer. Antipsychotic medication, they believe, represents his best chance for recovery. Due to his aggressive and threatening behaviour when untreated, he is unlikely to be released from the psychiatric hospital without treatment with medication.

1. Does the fact that Mr. Starson disagrees with his physicians about his diagnosis mean he is incompetent?

2. Does he understand the consequences of treatment with antipsychotic medication and the refusal of treatment?

3. Do you think he is competent to refuse treatment? Why?

Further Reading

Buchanan AE, Brock DW. *Deciding for others: the ethics of surrogate decision making.* Cambridge, UK: Cambridge University Press; 1990.

College of Physicians and Surgeons of Ontario. Consent to Medical Treatment [Internet]. Available from: http://www.cpso.on.ca/policies/policies/default.aspx?ID=1544. Date accessed: 6 June 2012.

Doig C, Burgess E. Withholding life-sustaining treatment: are adolescents competent to make these decisions? CMAJ [Internet], 2000;162:1585–8. Available from: http://www.cmaj.ca/content/162/11/1585.full.pdf+html. Date accessed: 6 June 2012.

Evans KG, Henderson GL. Consent: a guide for Canadian physicians [Internet]. Available from: http://www.cmpaacpm.ca/cmpapd04/docs/resource_files/ml_guides/consent_guide/com_cg_informedconsent-e.cfm. Date accessed: 6 June 2012.

Faden RR, Beauchamp TL. *A history and theory of informed consent.* New York: Oxford University Press; 1995.

5

Conflict about Appropriate Treatment

I n this chapter, we explore the limits of the right of self-determination. If autonomous moral agents have the right to refuse unwanted treatment, do they have the right to demand wanted treatment? A patient demand for a particular treatment might arise in any aspect of health care. For instance, a patient with an upper respiratory tract infection might demand a prescription for an antibiotic. His primary care physician, believing the infection to be caused by a virus, thinks that antibiotics are not indicated. While good communication and patient education are the first lines of response, if the patient persists in his demand must the physician accede to his request on grounds of patient self-determination? Or may the physician say "no"? If so, on what ethical grounds may the physician refuse a treatment demand?

No set of circumstances is more challenging than conflicts at the end-of-life in the intensive care unit. Conflicts in the intensive care unit are not uncommon for many reasons: first, the treatments used are complex and are rapidly evolving, making them more difficult to explain to patients and families. Also, there may be disagreement among expert physicians as to preferred treatments. Second, the patient's prognosis or likelihood of recovery may be difficult to assess with accuracy. Third, the consequences of treatment decisions in the intensive care unit are weighty; withdrawing a ventilator or other life-supporting treatment often means the death of the patient. Fourth, beds in the intensive care unit are a scarce resource. Thus, a decision to continue to treat a patient with a very poor prognosis may mean that a patient with a better chance of benefiting from intensive care treatment is denied access to it.

The concept of medical futility has been proposed as a way to limit the demands of patients and their families for treatment, often treatment in the intensive care unit. In the first reading, Lawrence Schneiderman and colleagues understand futility as treatment that "cannot achieve the goals of the action" and explain that it is designed to take "precedence over patient autonomy and [permit] physicians to withhold or withdraw care deemed to be inappropriate without subjecting such a decision to patient approval." They distinguish between two types of futility. A treatment is quantitatively futile "when physicians conclude (either through personal experience, experiences shared with colleagues, or consideration of reported empiric data) that in the last 100 cases, [it] . . . has been useless." In other instances, a treatment may have an effect, but the ends supported are unreasonable. "[A]ny treatment that merely preserves permanent unconsciousness or that fails to end total dependence on intensive medical care should be regarded" as qualitatively futile. While medical futility provides grounds for physicians to refuse patient demands for treatment, Schneiderman and colleagues do permit exceptions when providing treatment is in the patient's best interests.

Can the concept of medical futility stand up to close scrutiny? In the second reading, Robert Truog and colleagues lay out three major criticisms of futility. First, the notion of quantitative futility relies on setting a cut-off in the probability of a treatment's success. But drawing the line at no success in the last 100 cases seems arbitrary. Why not draw the line at no success in the last 1000 cases? Second, qualitative futility seems not to be about futility at all but about values. Families who want to continue treatment in the face of a coma from which a loved one is unlikely to recover often do so on the basis of deeply held cultural or religious beliefs. For instance, physicians may consider treatment of a patient who is permanently unconscious to be futile, but a religious family may believe that they have an obligation to God to preserve the life, even the unconscious life, of a loved one. Third, futility cases in the intensive care unit are inescapably, at least in part, about the allocation of scarce resources. Acknowledging the resource allocation dimension to these cases broadens the scope of considerations from a narrow focus on the treatment of the patient in question to include whether other patients might be more likely to benefit from that patient's bed in the intensive care unit.

In the third reading, Charles Weijer and colleagues cast further doubt on the notion of futility, and they echo the concerns raised by Truog and colleagues. Additionally, they argue that the concept of futility is unnecessary. Patient demands for ineffective or potentially harmful treatment can be rejected on the basis of the widely accepted legal concept of standard of care, and without appeal to medical futility. The standard of care is "understood as treatment that falls within the bounds of standard medical practice, that is, medical interventions used by at least a 'respectable minority' of expert practitioners." Many cases, however—and likely the most difficult ones—are not about ineffective treatment but center their disputes on moral/personal/religious values. These cases call for skilled communication and not unilateral decision-making. Physicians should seek to understand the patient's beliefs and values in such cases and educate when there is misunderstanding about the diagnosis or prognosis. "When disagreement among health care providers, patients and family persists, the physician should conceptualize this as a situation of conflict in which the goal is to seek a negotiated solution." When negotiation fails, the physician should involve a third party to help mediate or arbitrate the situation.

ONE Medical Futility: Its Meaning and Ethical Implications
Lawrence J. Schneiderman, Nancy S. Jecker, and Albert R. Jonsen | *Annals of Internal Medicine* 1990; 112: 949-54

. . . In our view, judgments of futility emerge from either quantitative or qualitative evaluations of clinical situations. Such evaluations determine whether physicians are obligated to offer an intervention. If an intervention is judged to be futile, the duty to present the intervention as an option to the patient or the patient's family is mitigated or eliminated. We recognize—indeed invite—examination and challenge of our proposal. . . .

> **Futility**
> A medical judgment that the administration of a particular treatment or plan of treatment is very unlikely to achieve the goals of patient care.

The Glare of Autonomy
Ethics and the law give primacy to patient autonomy, defined as the right to be a fully informed participant in all aspects of medical decision-making and the right to refuse unwanted, even recommended and life-saving, medical care. So powerful has this notion of autonomy become that its glare often blinds physicians (and ethicists) to the validity of earlier maxims that had long defined the range of physicians' moral obligations toward patients. Among these was the maxim, respected in ethics and law, that futile treatments are not obligatory. No ethical principle or law has ever required physicians to offer or accede to demands for

treatments that are futile.[1,2] Even when this maxim is accepted in theory, however, physicians frequently practice as though every available medical measure, including absurd and overzealous interventions, must be used to prolong life unless patients give definitive directions to the contrary.[3,4] Some physicians allow patients (or surrogates) to decide when a treatment is futile, thereby overriding medical judgment and potentially allowing the patient (or their surrogate) to demand treatment that offers no benefit.[5]

Comparison of Effect and Benefit

One advance of modern medicine, particularly with the introduction of controlled clinical trials, was to clarify by empiric methods the important distinction between effect and benefit. In examining the notion of futility, physicians sometimes fail to keep this distinction in mind.

For example, a recent discussion of futility includes the following: "[Physicians] may acknowledge that therapy is effective, in a limited sense, but believe that the goals that can be achieved are not desirable, as when considering prolonged nutritional support for patients in a persistent vegetative state. Physicians should acknowledge that, in such situations, potentially achievable goals exist. Therapy is not, strictly speaking, futile."[6] On the contrary, we believe that the goal of medical treatment is not merely to cause an effect on some portion of the patient's anatomy, physiology, or chemistry, but to benefit the patient as a whole. . . . Nutritional support could effectively preserve a host of organ systems in a patient in persistent vegetative state, but fail to restore a conscious and sapient life. Is such nutritional treatment futile or not? We argue that it is futile for the simple reason that the ultimate goal of any treatment should be improvement of the patient's prognosis, comfort, well-being, or general state of health. A treatment that fails to provide such a benefit—even though it produces a measurable effect—should be considered futile. . . .

Approaching a Definition

A futile action is one that cannot achieve the goals of the action, no matter how often repeated. The likelihood of failure may be predictable because it is inherent in the nature of the action proposed, and it may become immediately obvious or may become apparent only after many failed attempts. This concept should be distinguished from etymologic neighbours. Futility should not be used to refer to an act that is, in fact, impossible to do. . . . Nor should futility be confused with acts that are so complex that, although theoretically possible, they are implausible. . . .

Futility should also be distinguished from hopelessness. Futility refers to the objective quality of an action; hopelessness describes a subjective attitude. Hope and hopelessness bear more relation to desire, faith, denial, and other psychological responses than to the objective possibility or probability that the actions being contemplated will be successful. . . . It is possible then to say in the same breath, "I know this is futile, but I have hope." Such a statement expresses two facts, one about the objective properties of the situation, the other about the speaker's psychological state.

Futility refers to an expectation of success that is either predictably or empirically so unlikely that its exact probability is often incalculable. Without specific data, one might predict futility from closely analogous experience. (For example, one might avoid a trial of a particular chemotherapy for one type of cancer based on failures seen when used for treating similar forms of cancer.) Or one may have accumulated empiric experience insufficient to state precisely the likelihood of success, but sufficient to doubt the likelihood of success. . . .

Reports of one or two "miraculous" successes do not counter the notion of futility, if these successes were achieved against a background of hundreds or thousands of failures. Such rare exceptions are causally inexplicable, because any clinical situation contains a multitude of factors—in addition to treatment—that might affect outcome. As Wanzer and colleagues stated, "The rare report of a patient with a similar condition who survived is not an overriding reason to continue aggressive treatment."[7]

Quantitative and Qualitative Aspects

The futility of a particular treatment may be evident in either quantitative or qualitative terms. That is, futility may refer to an improbability or unlikelihood of an event happening, an expression that is quasi-numeric, or to the quality of the event that treatment would produce. Thus, determining futility resembles using decision analysis—with one important distinction. In decision analysis, the decision to use a procedure is based on the joint product of the probability of success and the quality (utility) of the outcome.[8] Thus, very low probability might be balanced by very high utility. In our proposal of futility, however, we treat the quantitative and qualitative aspects as independent thresholds, or minimal cutoff levels, either of which frees the physician from the obligation to offer a medical treatment. . . .

Both quantitative and qualitative aspects relate to a single underlying notion: The result is not commensurate to the effort. The effort is, on the part of the agent, a repeated expenditure of energy that is consistently non-productive or, if productive, its outcome is far inferior to that intended.

Defining Futility

We propose that, on the basis of these considerations, the noun "futility" and the adjective "futile" be used to describe any effort to achieve a result that is possible but that reasoning or experience suggests is highly improbable and that cannot be systematically produced. The phrase, "highly improbable," implies that a statistical statement about probability might be applicable. In the strict sense, such a statement cannot be made, as proper conditions for determining probability (that is, prospective comparisons of precisely controlled treatment and nontreatment on identically matched subjects) will never be present. We introduce the concept of "systematic" to point out that if a rare "success" is not explicable or cannot be predictably repeated, its causality is dubious, because it is uncertain whether treatment, some extraneous influence, or random variation caused the result.

Quantitative Aspects

In keeping with the quantitative approach to futility, we propose that when physicians conclude (either through personal experience, experiences shared with colleagues, or consideration of reported empiric data) that in the last 100 cases, a medical treatment has been useless, they should regard that treatment as futile. Technically, we cannot say that observing

> **Quantitative approach to futility**
> A means of assessing treatment that is very unlikely to produce the intended effect; according to the authors, a treatment that has failed to produce the intended effect in the last 100 cases.

no successes in 100 trials means that the treatment never works. However, such an observation serves as a point estimate of the probability of treatment success. Although we cannot say with certainty that the point estimate is correct, statistical methods can be used to estimate a range of values that include the true success rate with a specified probability. For example, if there have been no successes in 100 consecutive cases, the clinician can be 95 per cent confident that no more than 3 successes would occur in each 100 comparable trials (3 successes per 100 trials is the upper limit of the 95 per cent confidence interval [CI]). This confidence range would narrow as the number of observations increased. If no successes were seen in 200 cases, the upper limit of the 95 per cent CI would be 1.5 successes per 100 cases and, for no successes in 1000 observations, the upper limit would be approximately 0.3 successes per 100 cases. In practical terms, because data from controlled clinical trials can only rarely be called on and applied to a specific case, practitioners usually use their extended experience as the source of their conclusions. Here, specialty practice contributes an essential element; for example, an intensive care pulmonary specialist who sees several hundred patients who have similar disease conditions and receive similar therapy can often group together "futility characteristics" better than a generalist who does not see cases in so focused a manner.

Without systematic knowledge of the various factors that cause a therapy to have less than a 1 per cent chance of success—knowledge that would allow the physician to address these factors—we regard it as unreasonable to require that the physicians offer such therapy. To do so forces the physician to offer any therapy that may have seemed to work or that may conceivably work. In effect, it obligates the physician to offer a placebo. Only when empirically observed (though not understood) outcomes rise to a level higher than that expected by any placebo effect,[9] can a specific therapy be considered to be "possibly helpful" in rare or occasional cases and its appropriateness evaluated according to rules of decision analysis. In the clinical setting, such judgments also would be influenced, of course, by considering such tradeoffs as how cheap and simple the intervention is and how serious or potentially fatal the disease (see "Exceptions and Cautions"). . . .

Obviously, as medical data on specific situations are gathered under appropriate experimental conditions, empiric uncertainty can be replaced with empiric confidence.[10] Admittedly, some disorders may be too rare to provide sufficient experience for a confident judgment of futility, even when efforts are made to pool data. We acknowledge this difficulty but adhere to our conservative standard to prevent arbitrary abuse of power. In judging futility, as in other matters, physicians should admit uncertainty rather than impose unsubstantiated claims of certainty. Therefore, our view of futility should be considered as encouraging rather than opposing well-conducted clinical trials. . . .

Already, data on burn patients[11] and on patients in persistent vegetative state with abnormal neuroophthalamic signs[12] are sufficient to help with decision-making. The latter group of patients present a particular challenge to presently confused notions of futility, perhaps accounting in part for why an estimated 5000 to 10,000 patients in persistent vegetative state are now being maintained in medical institutions.[13] The mythologic power of the coma patient who "wakes up" apparently overrides the rarity of documented confirmation of such miraculous recoveries (which have resulted, moreover, in incapacitating mental impairment or total dependence).[14] This point bears on the frequently heard excuse for pushing ahead with futile therapies: "It is only by so doing that progress is made and the once futile becomes efficacious. Remember the futility of treating childhood leukemia or Hodgkin lymphoma." These statements hide a fallacy. It is not through repeated futility that progress is made, but through careful analysis of the elements of the "futile case," followed by well-designed studies, that advances knowledge. . . .

> **Abnormal neuroophthalamic signs**
> Clinical evidence of damage to the "lower" centres of the brain that is associated with very poor patient outcomes.

Qualitative Aspects

In keeping with the qualitative notion of futility we propose that any treatment that merely preserves permanent unconsciousness or that fails to end total dependence on intensive medical care should be regarded as non-beneficial and, therefore, futile. . . . Here is the crux of the matter.

> **Qualitative notion of futility**
> Treatment that can work in some limited sense but has no practical prospect of achieving reasonable medical goals, such as restoring consciousness or the capacity to survive outside of an intensive care unit.

If futility is qualitative, why should the patient not always decide whether the quality achieved is satisfactory or not? Why should qualitatively "futile" results not be offered to the patient as an option? We believe a distinction is in order. Some qualitatively poor results should indeed be the patient's option, and the patient should know that they may be attainable. We believe, however, that other sorts of qualitatively poor results fall outside the range of the patient's autonomy and need not be offered as options. The clearest of these qualitatively poor results is continued biologic life without conscious autonomy. The patient has no right to be sustained in a state in which he or she has no purpose other than mere vegetative survival; the physician has no obligation to offer this option or services to achieve it. Other qualitatively poor results are conditions requiring constant monitoring, ventilatory support, and intensive care nursing (such as in the example at the beginning of our paper) or conditions associated with overwhelmingly suffering for a predictably brief time. Admittedly, these kinds of cases fall along a continuum, and there are well-known examples of the most remarkable achievements of life goals despite the most burdensome handicaps. However, if survival requires the patient's entire preoccupation with intensive medical treatment, to the extent that he or she cannot achieve any other life goals (thus obviating the goal of medical care), the treatment is effective but not beneficial; it need not be offered to the patient, and the patient's family has no right to demand it.

Specifically excluded from our concept of futility is medical care for patients for whom such care offers the opportunity to achieve life goals, however limited. Thus, patients whose illnesses are severe enough to require frequent hospitalization, patients confined to nursing homes, or patients with severe physical or mental handicaps are not, in themselves, objects of futile treatments. Such patients (or their surrogates) have the right to receive or reject any medical treatment according to their own perceptions of benefits compared with burdens.

Some observers might object, as a matter of principle, to excluding patient input from assessments of qualitative futility. Others might be concerned that such exclusion invites abuse, neglect, and a retreat to the paternalistic "silent world" of the past in which doctors avoided communication with their patients.[15] In response to the latter objection, we acknowledge that the potential for abuse is present and share this concern. We would deplore the use of our proposal to excuse physicians from engaging patients in ongoing informed dialogue. Nonetheless, the alternative is also subject to abuse (for example, when legal threats made by patients and surrogates cow hospitals into providing excessive care). We reiterate that the distinction between medical benefit and effect justifies excluding patients from determination of qualitative futility. Physicians are required only to provide medical benefits to patients. Physicians are permitted, but not obligated, to offer other, non-medical benefits. . . .

Exceptions and Cautions

We have attempted to provide a working definition of futility. We also have drawn attention to the ethical notion that futility is a professional judgment that takes precedence over patient autonomy and permits physicians to withhold or withdraw care deemed to be inappropriate without subjecting such a decision to patient approval. Thus, we regard our proposal as representing the ordinary duties of physicians, duties that are applicable where there is medical agreement that the described standards of futility are met. We recognize, however, that the physician's duty to serve the best interests of the patient may require that exceptions to our approaches be made under special circumstances.

An exception could well be made out of compassion for the patient with terminal metastatic cancer who requests resuscitation in the event of cardiac arrest to survive long enough to see a son or daughter who has not yet arrived from afar to pay last respects. Such an exception could also be justified to facilitate coping and grieving by family members, a goal the patient might support.[16-20] Although resuscitation may be clearly futile (that is, would keep the patient alive in the intensive care unit for only one or two more days), complying with the patient's wishes would be appropriate, provided such exceptions do not impose undue burdens on other patients, health care providers, and the institution, by directly threatening the health care of others. We hasten to add, however, that our notion of futility does not arise from considerations of scarce resources. Arguments for limiting treatments on grounds of resource allocation should proceed by an entirely different route and with great caution in our present open system of medical care, as there is no universally accepted value system for allocation[21] and no guarantee that any limits a physician imposes on his or her patients will be equitably shared by other physicians and patients in the same circumstances.[22,23] . . .

> **Scarce resources**
> Restricted availability of key materials or services for patient care such that demand is greater than supply. In such cases, some form of rationing is required to fairly allocate resources to patients.

What if a hospitalized patient with advanced cancer demands a certain medication (for example, a particular vitamin), a treatment that the physician believes to be futile? Several aspects of this demand support its overriding the physician's invocation of futility. Certain death is expected and, although an objective goal such as saving the patient's life or even releasing the patient from the hospital might be unachievable, the subjective goal of patient well-being might be enhanced (a placebo-induced benefit). In this particular situation, the effort and resources invested to achieve this goal impose a negligible burden on the health care system and do not threaten the health care of others. Thus, although physicians are not obligated to offer a placebo, they occasionally do. For example, Imbus and Zawacki[24] allowed burn patients to opt for treatment even when survival was unprecedented. In this clinical situation, compassionate yielding imposes no undue burden, because survival with or without treatment is measured in days. In contrast, yielding to a surrogate's demand for unlimited life-support for a patient in a persistent vegetative state may lead to decades of institutional care.

Study Questions

1. According to the authors, why do we need a concept of medical futility?

2. Who decides whether a treatment is futile and on what authority may they do so?

3. What is the difference between quantitative and qualitative futility?

Notes

1. President's Commission for the Study of Ethical Problems in Medicine and Biomedical and Behavioral Research. *Deciding to Forego Life-Sustaining Treatment*: A *Report on the Ethical, Medical, and Legal Issues in Treatment Decisions*. Washington DC: US Government Printing Office; 1983:60–89.

2. Jonsen AR. What does life support support? *Pharos.* 1987;50(1):4–7.

3. Blackhall LJ. Must we always use CPR? *N Engl J Med.* 1987; 317:1281–5.

4. Tomlinson T, Brody H. Ethics and communication in do-not-resuscitate orders. *N Engl J Med.* 1988;318:43–6.

5. Lo B. Life-sustaining treatment in patients with AIDS: challenge to traditional decision-making. In: Juengst ET, Koenig BA, eds. *The Meaning of AIDS.* v 1. New York: Praeger; 1989:86–93.

6. Lantos JD, Singer PA, Walker RM, et al. The illusion of futility in clinical practice. *Am J Med.* 1989;87:81–4.

7. Wanzer SH, Adelstein SJ, Cranford RE, et al. The physician's responsibility toward hopelessly ill patients. *N Engl J Med.* 1984; 310:955–9.

8. Weinstein MC, Fineberg HV. *Clinical Decision Analysis.* Philadelphia: W.B. Saunders; 1980.

9. Beecher HK. The powerful placebo. *JAMA.* 1955;159:1602–6.

10. Freiman JA, Chalmers TC, Smith H Jr, Kuebler RR. The importance of beta, the type II error and sample size in the design and interpretation of the randomized control trial. Survey of 71 "negative" trials. *N Engl J Med.* 1978;299:690–4.

11. Imbus SH, Zawacki BE. Autonomy for burned patients when survival is unprecedented. *N Engl J Med.* 1977;297:308–11.

12. Plum F, Posner JB. *The Diagnosis of Stupor and Coma.* 3d ed. Philadelphia: F.A . Davis ; 1980.

13. Cranford RE. The persistent vegetative state: the medical reality (getting the facts straight). *Hastings Cent Rep.* 1988;18:27–32.

14. Plum and Posner, *The Diagnosis of Stupor and Coma.*

15. Katz J. *The Silent World of Doctor and Patient.* New York: Free Press; 1984.

16. Yarborough M. Continued treatment of the fatally ill for the benefit of others. *J Am Geriatr Soc.* 1988;36:63–7.

17. Perkins HS. Ethics at the end of life: practical principles for making resuscitation decisions. *J Gen Intern Med.* 1986;1:170–6.

18. Miles SH. Futile feeding at the end of life: family virtues and treatment decisions. *Theor Med.* 1987;8:293–302.

19. Jecker NS. Anencephalic infants and special relationships. *Theor Med.* 1990 11(4): 333-42.

20. Jecker NS. The moral status of patients who are not strict persons. *J Clin Med.* 1990 1(1): 35-8.

21. Emery DD, Schneiderman W. Cost-effectiveness analysis in health care. *Hastings Cent Rep.* 1989;19:8–13.

22. Schneiderman LJ, Spragg RG. Ethical decisions in discontinuing mechanical ventilation. *N Engl J Med.* 1988;318:984–8.

23. Daniels N. Why saying no to patients in the United States is so hard: cost containment justice, and provider autonomy. *N Engl J Med.* 1986;314:1380–3.

24. Imbus and Zawacki, Autonomy for burned patients (see Note 11).

TWO The Problem with Futility

Robert D. Truog, Allan S. Brett, and Joel Frader | *New England Journal of Medicine* 1992; 326: 1560-4

"Futility" is one of the newest additions to the lexicon of bioethics. Physicians, ethicists, and members of the media are increasingly concerned about patients and families who insist on receiving life-sustaining treatment that others judge to be futile. A clear understanding of futility has proved to be elusive, however. . . .

The concept has appeared frequently in court decisions and policy statements.[1-4] The so-called Baby Doe law exempts physicians from providing treatment that would be "virtually futile."[5] The Council on Ethical and Judicial Affairs of the American Medical Association (AMA) recently concluded that physicians have no obligation to obtain consent for a do-not-resuscitate (DNR) order when cardiopulmonary resuscitation (CPR) is deemed futile.[6] The fact that this concept has appeared in law and policy may seem to indicate that it is clearly understood and widely accepted. In reality, however, the notion of futility hides many deep and serious ambiguities that threaten its legitimacy as a rationale for limiting treatment.

> **Cardiopulmonary resuscitation**
> A complex set of physical, electrical, and pharmacological interventions that attempt to restore a patient's heart and lungs when they cease to function properly.

Paradigms of Futility

Contemporary discussions of futility have centered primarily on cases involving patients in a persistent vegetative state and those involving the use of CPR. A third type of case, involving organ-replacement technology,

> **Do-not-resuscitate order**
> An instruction written by a patient's physician directing the health care team not to intervene if the patient's heart stops or the patient stops breathing.

> **Organ-replacement technology**
> A machine that can assist a failing organ—such as the kidney, liver, heart, or lungs—in performing its function or that can be used to replace it entirely on a temporary basis while a patient awaits an organ transplant.

has received little attention but is helpful to our understanding of futility.

Futility and the Persistent Vegetative State

The first type of scenario involving the question of futility is represented by the recent Minnesota case of Helga Wanglie.[7] Mrs Wanglie was an 86-year-old woman who had been dependent on mechanical ventilation and in a persistent vegetative state for more than a year. Her husband insisted that she believed in maintaining life at all cost, and that "when she was ready to go . . . the good Lord would call her."[8] Her physicians, on the other hand, believed that the continued use of mechanical ventilation and intensive care was futile. When attempts to transfer her elsewhere failed, they sought to have a court appoint an independent conservator with responsibility for making medical decisions on her behalf. The judge denied this petition and reaffirmed the authority of her husband as legal surrogate. Three days later, Mrs Wanglie died. Cases like that of Mrs Wanglie seldom reach the courts, but they are probably not rare. . . .

Futility in Cases Involving CPR

The second prototypical scenario involves the use of DNR orders. Although the techniques of CPR were originally intended only for use after acute, reversible cardiac arrests, the current practice is to use CPR in all situations unless there is a direct order to the contrary. . . . DNR orders were developed to spare patients from aggressive attempts at revival when imminent death is anticipated and inevitable. Nevertheless, patients or families sometimes request CPR even when caregivers believe such attempts would be futile. Some have argued that in these circumstances a physician should be able to enact a DNR order without the consent of the patient or family.[9-11]

Futility and Organ-Replacement Technology

Although the bioethical debate over the question of futility has been most concerned with cases involving CPR and the treatment of patients in a persistent vegetative state, a third type of futility-related judgment has gone essentially unchallenged. It involves the increasingly large number of interventions that could possibly prolong the life of virtually any dying patient. For example, extracorporeal membrane oxygenation can replace heart and lung function for up to several weeks. Physicians now use this intervention when they expect organ systems eventually

to recover or while they await organs for transplantation. However, it could prolong the life of almost anyone with cardiorespiratory failure, reversible or not. Patients thus kept alive may remain conscious and capable of communicating. Caregivers do not now offer this therapy to terminally ill patients, presumably because it would be futile. This judgment has gone largely unchallenged, yet it is not obvious why a clinician's unilateral decision not to use "futile" extracorporeal membrane oxygenation is inherently different from a decision not to use "futile" CPR or "futile" intensive care. If all three treatments can be characterized as objectively futile, then unilateral decisions not to offer them should be equally justified.

As it is used in these three cases, the concept of futility obscures many ambiguities and assumptions. These can be usefully grouped into two categories: problems of value, and problems of probability.

Futility and Values

It is meaningless simply to say that an intervention is futile; one must always ask, "Futile in relation to what?" The medical literature provides many examples in which the importance of identifying the goals of treatment has not been fully appreciated. The effectiveness of CPR, for example, is often discussed in terms of whether patients who require the procedure can survive long enough to be discharged from the hospital.[12] This definition of success usually implies that short-term survival is a goal not worth pursuing. Patients or family members may value the additional hours of life differently, however. Indeed, physicians and other caregivers have repeatedly been shown to be poor judges of patients' preferences with regard to intensive care.[13-15]

Schneiderman and colleagues have argued that treatments that merely preserve permanent unconsciousness or that cannot end dependence on intensive medical care should be considered futile.[16] Although society may eventually endorse decisions to override the previously expressed wishes of patients or the desires of surrogates who demand such treatments, it does not follow that the treatments are futile. Mr Wanglie would have rejected this conclusion, and there is no reason to dismiss his view out of hand. The decision that certain goals are

> **Extracorporeal membrane oxygenation**
> A kind of organ replacement technology in which a patient's blood is circulated through an "artificial lung" that removes carbon dioxide from the blood and adds oxygen.

not worth pursuing is best seen as involving a conflict of values rather than a question of futility.

Certainly in this context, the plurality of values in our society makes agreement on the concept of futility difficult if not impossible. Several groups have therefore attempted to arrive at a value-free understanding of the concept.[17,18] The most promising candidate thus far is the notion of "physiologic futility." As the guidelines on the termination of life-sustaining treatment prepared by the Hastings Center state, if a treatment is "clearly futile in achieving its physiological objective and so offer[s] no physiological benefit to the patient, the professional has no obligation to provide it.". . .

> **Physiologic futility**
> A set of circumstances involving a treatment that is very unlikely to achieve its intended effect understood narrowly in terms of the proper functioning of the body, for example, when putting a patient on a ventilator will not restore sufficient lung function because of massive tumour infiltration of the lungs.

Physiologic futility, understood in narrow terms, comes close to providing a value-free understanding of futility. Unfortunately, it applies to a very small number of real cases. . . . Since in the case of Mrs Wanglie mechanical ventilation could maintain adequate oxygenation and ventilation, her treatment could not be considered futile in the physiologic sense. Even the use of extracorporeal membrane oxygenation in terminally ill patients cannot be considered physiologically futile, since it can maintain circulation and ventilation. The concept of physiologic futility therefore falls short of providing guidance in most cases resembling those described above.

Futility and Statistical Uncertainty

In most medical situations, there is no such thing as never. Futility is almost always a matter of probability. But what statistical cutoff point should be chosen as the threshold for determining futility? The statement from the Council on Ethical and Judicial Affairs of the AMA concludes that physicians have no obligation to provide futile CPR, but it fails to specify any level of statistical certainty at which the judgment is warranted.[20] The AMA statement fails to acknowledge that this is even an issue. Should each physician decide independently what probability of success should be considered to indicate futility?

Even if we could agree on a statistical cutoff point for determining futility, physicians are often highly unreliable in estimating the likelihood of success of a therapeutic intervention. Psychological research[21,22] has shown that estimates of probability are susceptible to "severe and systematic errors."[23] Empirical studies have corroborated the limitations of clinical assessment in estimating both prognosis[24] and diagnosis.[25] Even in theory, statistical inferences about what might happen to groups of patients do not permit accurate predictions of what will happen to the next such patient. . . .

Schneiderman and colleagues recently argued that a treatment should be considered futile when 100 consecutive patients do not respond to it.[26] But how similar must the patients be? In assessing the efficacy of mechanical ventilation to treat pneumonia, for example, is it sufficient simply to recall the 100 most recent patients who received artificial ventilation for pneumonia? Or must this group be stratified according to age, etiologic organism, or coexisting illness? Clearly, many of these factors will make an important difference.

Futility and Resource Allocation

Although medical practice has increasingly emphasized patients' autonomy, there is growing pressure on physicians to slow the increase in health care costs by foreclosing some options. Thus, we have a tension between the value of autonomy, exercised in the form of consent to use or omit various interventions, and the desirability of a more Spartan approach to the consumption of medical resources. . . . Unfortunately, there is no consensus about what constitutes a just method of balancing the preferences of individual patients against the diverse needs of society.

To some, the concept of futility provides at least a partial solution to this dilemma: it offers a reason to limit therapy without the need to define a fair procedure for allocating resources. This approach allows treatments to be denied on the grounds that they are simply not indicated, apart from the matter of cost. Despite its attractions, there are good reasons why we should not use this concept to solve problems of allocation.

First, arguments based on the futility concept conceal many statistical and value-laden assumptions, whereas strategies based on resource allocation force these assumptions to be stated explicitly. Societies

> **Resource allocation**
> Approaches to the fair distribution of scarce medical materials and services based on explicit consideration of their benefits, harms, costs, and social value.

may choose to limit the use of therapies that may be of value and have a reasonable likelihood of success in some cases. For example, the much discussed Oregon plan for allocating Medicaid funds[27] seeks to reflect community values in ranking various health care goals (placing preventive care ahead of cosmetic surgery, for example). Since rationing policies make explicit the values and probabilities that futility-based arguments leave implicit, it is clearly preferable to develop and adopt them rather than use futility arguments as a cover for limiting the availability of scarce and expensive resources.

Another problem with invoking the idea of futility in the debate over allocation is that we have no reason to believe that it is applicable in enough cases to make a difference in the scarcity of medical resources. Although it may be true that beds in the intensive care unit (especially those used for extracorporeal membrane oxygenation) are relatively scarce, it seems unlikely that patients similar to Helga Wanglie occupy an important fraction of those beds, let alone account for a major proportion of the cost of medical care in the United States. From a macroeconomic perspective at least, we must remain skeptical that an appeal to the idea of futility will get us very far.

Moving Beyond Futility

Our rejection of futility as a useful concept does not imply that we endorse patients' unrestricted demands for interventions such as those described in our prototypical scenarios. On the contrary, when providers oppose such demands they are usually acting from a profound sense that further treatment would be fundamentally wrong. Our task is to take account of that sense of wrongness without resorting to unilateral, provider-initiated declarations of futility.

In many of the situations in which questions of futility arise, providers believe that the treatment in question would not be in the patient's interests, even from the patient's perspective, and that any insistence by the patient (or surrogate) on further interventions is based on faulty reasoning, unrealistic expectations, or psychological factors, such as denial or guilt. In these circumstances, providers are obligated to make every effort to clarify precisely what the patient intends to achieve with continued treatment. If the patient's goals appear to reflect unrealistic expectations about the probable course of the underlying illness or the probable effect of medical interventions, providers should attempt to correct those impressions. Because inadequate or insensitive communication by providers probably accounts for a substantial proportion of unrealistic requests, such discussions will successfully resolve many conflicts.[28,29] Empirical studies of ethics consultations have demonstrated precisely this point.[30,31] . . .

Judgments about what is in the patient's interest are properly grounded in the patient's perspective, whereas judgments cast in the language of futility falsely assume that there is an objective and dispassionate standard for determining benefits and burdens. Nevertheless, even after providers make sustained attempts to clarify patients' preferences, some patients or surrogates will continue to demand life-sustaining interventions when the caregivers feel deeply troubled about providing them. In many such cases, unrestrained deference to the wishes of the patient or surrogate conflicts with two other values that do not require a unilateral judgment of the futility of treatment: professional ideals, and social consensus.

The ideals of medical professionals include respect for patients' wishes, to be sure, but they also include other values, such as compassionate action and the minimization of suffering. Consider, for example, a bedridden victim of multiple strokes who has contractures and bedsores and who "communicates" only by moaning or grimacing when she is touched. Physicians asked to perform chest compressions, institute mechanical ventilation, or use other life-sustaining interventions in such a patient may regard these actions as cruel and inhumane.[32] Moreover, physicians and other caregivers have a legitimate interest in seeing that their knowledge and skills are used wisely and effectively. For example, if surgeons were repeatedly pressured to perform operations that they believed to be inappropriate, they would certainly suffer a loss of dignity and sense of purpose. Although appealing to professional ideals can serve as a convenient means of protecting the interests of physicians at the expense of patients' values, these ideals are legitimate factors to weigh against other values. To dismiss this perspective as irrelevant in decision-making is to deny an essential part of what it means to practice medicine. . . .

Finally, social consensus is yet another expression of the values at stake in some medical decisions. In a pluralistic society, differences in personal values and interests occasionally run so deep that they cannot be resolved by the introduction of additional facts or by further private debate. At certain critical junctures, the resolution of these conflicts may require an explicit public process of social decision-making.[33] Social consensus has been sought, for example, to address the issue of fair allocation of resources.[34] The involvement of society is also essential when the most highly charged questions of morality are at stake, as in the increasingly heated debate over euthanasia.[35]

In the prototypical scenarios described at the outset of this article, an ongoing attempt to achieve social consensus is perhaps most conspicuous with regard to the prolongation of life for patients in a persistent vegetative state. From a legal perspective, the relevant decisions began with the case of Karen Quinlan[36] and have extended through that of Nancy Cruzan.[37] These cases have increased awareness of the ethical issues raised by the situation of patients in a persistent vegetative state and have helped to consolidate the view that it is acceptable to withdraw life-sustaining treatment from patients in such a state. Controversy does remain about who has the ultimate authority to make these decisions. Some hold that the choice must remain with the patient or surrogate, whereas others believe that under some circumstances this prerogative may be overridden. For example, the Hastings Center[38] and the Society of Critical Care Medicine[39] have concluded that providing intensive care to patients in a persistent vegetative state is generally a misuse of resources, and the President's Commission stated that such patients should be removed from life support if such action is necessary to benefit another patient who is not in a persistent vegetative state.[40] It is unclear how this debate will conclude, but the confluence of medical, legal, and ethical thinking about the persistent vegetative state is an example of how social consensus may evolve.

In summary, the Wanglie case demonstrates how the resolution of these conflicts must proceed on many levels. Most such cases will benefit from sustained attempts to clarify the patient's values and the likelihood of the various relevant outcomes, and to improve communication with patients or their surrogates. When this approach fails, physicians and other caregivers should ask themselves whether the care requested is consistent with their professional ethics and ideals. When these ideals appear to be violated, either alternative venues for such care should be found or the conflict should be addressed in a public forum. This broader review could be provided through institutional mechanisms, such as the hospital's ethics committee, or by the courts. The public scrutiny that attends such cases will further the debate over the appropriate use of medical resources and foster the development of consensus through legislation and public policy.

Karen Quinlan

Karen Quinlan (1954-85) fell unconscious at the age of 21 years after drinking alcohol and taking sedative drugs at a party. While unconscious, she stopped breathing and suffered a severe brain injury resulting in a persistent vegetative state. Her parents' appeal to the courts to withdraw a ventilator that was assisting her breathing was ultimately granted. After the ventilator was removed she survived another nine years and never regained consciousness.

Nancy Cruzan

Nancy Cruzan suffered injuries in a car crash at the age of 25 years that resulted in a persistent vegetative state. Her parents fought a lengthy battle in the courts to have a tube removed that provided her with food and fluids. The US Supreme Court ultimately both upheld the patient's right to refuse unwanted treatment and the State's right to impose a high standard of evidence for prior expressed wishes regarding care. Her grave marker reads: "Born July 20, 1957; Departed January 11, 1983; At Peace December 26, 1990."

Ethics committee

A body within a hospital or other health care institution that is usually composed of health care workers, an ethicist, a lawyer, and community representatives and that provides advice on matters of policy and patient care including end-of-life issues.

Conclusion

In outlining the perspectives of the principal stakeholder —patients and their surrogates, physicians, and society—we have avoided the construction of a rigid formula for resolving conflicts over interventions frequently regarded as futile. Because of clinical heterogeneity, pluralistic values, and the evolutionary nature of social consensus, most clinical decision-making on behalf of critically ill patients defies reduction to universally applicable principles.

The notion of futility generally fails to provide an ethically coherent ground for limiting life-sustaining treatment, except in circumstances in which narrowly defined physiologic futility can be plausibly invoked. Futility has been conceptualized as an objective entity independent of the patient's or surrogate's perspective, but differences in values and the variable probabilities of clinical outcomes undermine its basis.

Furthermore, assertions of futility may camouflage judgments of comparative worth that are implicit in debates about the allocation of resources. In short, the problem with futility is that its promise of objectivity can rarely be fulfilled. The rapid advance of the language of futility into the jargon of bioethics should be followed by an equally rapid retreat.

Study Questions

1. According to the authors, how does futility obscure disagreements about values?

2. In what ways can scientific evidence fail to tell us which treatments are futile?

3. How can communication failures lead to futility cases? How should physicians respond to demands to treatment thought to be inappropriate in such cases?

Notes

1. Capron AM . In re Helga Wanglie. *Hastings Cent Rep* 1991;21(5):26–8.

2. Lantos JD, Singer PA, Walker RM. et al. The illusion of futility in clinical practice. *Am J Med* 1989;87:81–4.

3. Standards for cardiopulmonary resuscitation (CPR) and emergency cardiac care (ECC). V. Medicolegal considerations and recommendations. *JAMA* 1974;227:Suppl:864–6.

4. Appendix A: the proposed legislation. In: *Do not resuscitate orders: the proposed legislation and report of the New York State Task Force on Life and the Law.* 2nd ed. New York: The Task Force. 1986:83.

5. 1984 Amendments to the Child Abuse Prevention and Treatment Act. Pub Law 98–457. 1984.

6. Council on Ethical and Judicial Affairs, American Medical Association. Guidelines for the appropriate use of do-not-resuscitate orders. *JAMA* 1991;265:1868–71.

7. Miles SH. Informed demand for "non-beneficial" medical treatment. *N Engl J Med* 1991;325:512–5.

8. Brain-damaged woman at center of lawsuit over life-support dies. *New York Times.* 5 July 1991:A8.

9. Blackhall LJ. Must we always use CPR? *N Engl J Med* 1987;317:1281–5.

10. Hackler JC, Hiller FC. Family consent to orders not to resuscitate: reconsidering hospital policy. *JAMA* 1990;264:1281–3.

11. Murphy DJ. Do-not-resuscitate orders: time for reappraisal in long-term-care institutions. *JAMA* 1988;260:2098–101.

12. Bedell SE, Delbanco TL, Cook EF, Epstein FH. Survival after cardiopulmonary resuscitation in the hospital. *N Engl J Med* 1983;309:569–76.

13. Danis M, Gerrity MS, Southerland L1, Patrick DL. A comparison of patient, family, and physician assessments of the value of medical intensive care. *Crit Care Med* 1988;16:594-600.

14. Danis M, Jarr SL, Southerland LI , Nocella RS, Patrick DL. A comparison of patient, family, and nurse evaluations of the usefulness of intensive care. *Crit Care Med* 1987;15:138–43.

15. Danis M, Patrick DL, Southerland LI, Green ML. Patients' and families' preferences for medical intensive care. *JAMA* 1988;260:797–802.

16. Schneiderman LJ, Jeeker NS, Jonsen AR. Medical futility: its meaning and ethical implications. *Ann Intern Med* 1990;112:949–54.

17. The Hastings Center. *Guidelines on the termination of life-sustaining treatment and the care of the dying.* Bloomington: Indiana University Press, 1987:32.

18. Appendix C: New York Public Health Law Article 29-B—orders not to resuscitate. In: *Do not resuscitate orders: the proposed legislation and report of the New York State Task Force on Life and the Law.* 2nd ed. New York: The Task Force, 1986:96.

19. The Hastings Center. *Guidelines on the termination of life-sustaining treatment and the care of the dying.* 1987.

20. Council on Ethical and Judicial Affairs, American Medical Association. Guidelines for the appropriate use of do-not-resuscitate orders. *JAMA* 1991.

21. Tversky A, Kahneman D. Judgment under uncertainty: heuristics and biases. *Science* 1974;185:1124–31.

22. Elstein AS. Clinical judgment: psychological research and medical practice . *Science* 1976; 194:696–700.

23. Tversky and Kahneman. Judgment under uncertainty. *Science.* 1974.

24. Poses RM , Bekes C, Copare FJ, Scott WE . The answer to "What are my chances, doctor?" depends on whom is asked: prognostic disagreement and inaccuracy for critically ill patients. *Crit Care Med* 1989;17:827–33.

25. Poses RM, Cebul RD. Collins M, Fager SS. The accuracy of experienced physicians' probability estimates for patients with sore throats: implications for decision making. *JAMA* 1985;254:925–9.

26. Schneiderman, Jeeker, and Jonsen. Medical Futility. *Ann Intern Med.* 1990.

27. Eddy OM . What's going on in Oregon? *JAMA* 1991;266:417–20.
28. Murphy DJ. Do-not-resuscitate orders. *JAMA* 1988.
29. Youngner SJ. Who defines futility? *JAMA* 1988;260:2094–5.
30. Brennan TA. Ethics committees and decisions to limit care: the experience at the Massachusetts General Hospital. *JAMA* 1988;260:803–7.
31. La Puma J. Consultations in clinical ethics—issues and questions in 27 cases. *West J Med* 1987;146:633–7.
32. Braithwaite S. Thomasma DC. New guidelines on foregoing life-sustaining treatment in incompetent patients: an anti-cruelty policy. *Ann Intern Med* 1986; 104:711–5.
33. Callahan D. Medical futility, medical necessity: the-problem-without-a-name. *Hastings Cent Rep* 1991;21(4):30–5.
34. Eddy OM . What's going on in Oregon? *JAMA* 1991.
35. Misbin RI. Physicians' aid in dying. *N Engl J Med* 1991;325:1307–11.

36. In the Matter of Karen Ann Quinlan, an alleged incompetent. 355 A.2d 647; or 70 NJ 10. 31 March 1976.
37. Annas GJ. Nancy Cruzan and the right to die. *N Engl J Med* 1990;323:670–3.
38. The Hastings Center. *Guidelines on the termination of life-sustaining treatment and the care of the dying.* Bloomington: Indiana University Press. 1987:112.
39. Task Force on Ethics of the Society of Critical Care Medicine. Consensus report on the ethics of foregoing life-sustaining treatments in the critically ill. *Crit Care Med* 1990;18:1435–9.
40. President's Commission for the Study of Ethical Problems in Medicine and Biomedical and Behavioral Research. *Deciding to forego life-sustaining treatment: ethical, medical, and legal issues in treatment decisions.* Washington. D.C.: Government Printing Office, 1983: 188–9.

THREE Dealing with Demands for Inappropriate Treatment

Charles Weijer, Peter A. Singer, Bernard M. Dickens, and Stephen Workman | *Canadian Medical Association Journal* 1998; 159: 817-21

What Are Demands for Inappropriate Treatment?

. . . The right of the patient to refuse an unwanted medical intervention, even a life-saving treatment, is a well-established ethical and legal dictum in medicine. The limits of patient autonomy, however, have been challenged recently by demands from patients and families for medical interventions felt by the health care team to be inappropriate. Although treatment demanded by patients runs the gamut of medical interventions, the most pressing cases involve appeals for life-sustaining treatment. Must clinicians always accede to the wishes of patients and families? Are all such cases more or less similar, or are important moral distinctions among cases to be drawn?

A number of approaches to the problem have been proposed. Perhaps best known is that of "medical futility." The concept was devised to take "precedence over patient autonomy and [permit] physicians to withhold or withdraw care deemed to be inappropriate without subjecting such a decision to patient approval."[1] According to this view, a treatment is quantitatively futile "when physicians conclude (either through personal experience, experiences shared with colleagues, or consideration of reported empiric data) that in the last 100 cases, a medical treatment has been useless."[2] A treatment is qualitatively futile if it "merely preserves permanent unconsciousness or . . . fails to end total dependence on intensive medical care."[3] Futile treatment need neither be offered to patients nor be provided if demanded.

Critics of medical futility have argued that it confounds morally distinct cases: demand for treatment unlikely to work, and demand for effective treatment supporting a controversial end (e.g., permanent unconsciousness). They point out that the concept of medical futility is unnecessary in the first case and harmful in the second. Appeals for ineffective treatment can be dismissed because such treatment falls outside the bounds of standard medical care.[4] Cases in which care is effective but the end supported is controversial typically involve substantial value disagreements. An optimal approach to such cases will rest on open communication and negotiation between the health care team and the patient or family.

Why Are Demands for Inappropriate Treatment Important?

Demands for inappropriate treatment, although infrequent, cause substantial emotional and moral distress for patients, families and health care workers. In a few cases conflict may be so severe that legal action is taken by either the hospital or the patient.

Ethics

Medical care is governed by a number of ethical principles, including respect for persons, beneficence, non-maleficence and justice.[5] These principles find expression in the Canadian Medical Association's *Code of Ethics*.[6] When caring for patients, including those who are receiving (or who may receive) life-prolonging treatments, physicians have an obligation to "[a]scertain wherever possible and recognize [the] patient's wishes about the initiation, continuation or cessation of life-sustaining treatment" and, if the patient is unable to speak for herself, to respect wishes expressed in an advance directive or by a proxy decision maker (usually a family member).[7] Obligations to respect the wishes of patients, however, must be tempered by duties to "consider first the well-being of the patient" and to provide "appropriate care."[8] Finally, physicians must not discriminate against patients on such grounds as medical condition, disability or religion.[9] Demands for ineffective treatment and demands for effective treatment that supports a controversial end must be considered separately.[10]

> **Respect for persons**
> An ethical principle that obliges physicians to take seriously the choices of people who can decide for themselves and to protect those who cannot decide for themselves.
>
> **Beneficence**
> An ethical principle that requires that the physician promote their patient's welfare.
>
> **Non-maleficence**
> An ethical principle which claims that physicians must, in so far as is possible, protect patients from harm.
>
> **Justice**
> An ethical principle requiring physicians to treat patients without discrimination and manage scarce resources responsibly.

> **Advance directive**
> A legal document setting out one's wishes for treatment in the event that one can no longer speak for oneself.

> **Proxy decision maker**
> A person, often the next-of-kin, who has the legal authority to make medical decisions on behalf of a patient who cannot make decisions for him- or herself.

Demands for Ineffective Treatment

It is uncontroversial that clinicians have no obligation to provide a treatment that cannot work or is very unlikely to work (e.g., an antibiotic to treat a common cold, or mechanical ventilation in the presence of massive tumor deposits in the chest).[11,12] Such treatment falls outside the bounds of "appropriate care." But what of demands for experimental treatment (treatment with an unknown chance of success) when proven treatment exists or treatment is effective but outdated (the success rate is known to be less than that of standard treatment but greater than 1 per cent)? Medical futility provides no basis to refuse these *prima facie* unreasonable requests from patients. Clearly, then, we require a more robust ethical concept.

"Appropriate care" is most productively understood as treatment that falls within the bounds of standard medical practice, that is, medical interventions used by at least a "respectable minority" of expert practitioners.[13,14] Standard of care is a well-established concept rooted in the physician-patient relationship:

> **Standard of care**
> Medically validated treatment; more formally, treatment that is endorsed by at least a respectable minority of expert physicians.

> *[The] health care professional has an obligation to allow a patient to choose from among medically acceptable treatment options . . . or to reject all options. No one, however, has an obligation to provide interventions that would, in his or her judgment, be countertherapeutic.*[15]

Thus, on the basis of standard of care alone, and without appeal to medical futility, clinicians have a sound basis for refusing to provide ineffective, experimental, or outdated treatment.

Demands for Inappropriate Treatment

Disagreements about so-called qualitatively futile treatment are not about probabilities—they are about values. Often the question "What sort of life is worth preserving?" is at their core. Although most patients and their families would not choose to prolong life in a profoundly diminished state, some have very good reasons for doing so. For example, members of a variety of religions, including Orthodox Judaism, fundamentalist Protestantism, fundamentalist Islam and conservative Catholicism, believe that the sanctity of human life implies a religious obligation to seek out and obtain life-prolonging medical treatment.[16] The concept of medical futility wrongly tries to redefine a debate about conflicting values as a debate about medical probabilities. And given that physicians are generally the sole arbiters of medical probability, this amounts to saying to families, "Your values don't count."[17]

A unilateral decision to withhold or withdraw care in such cases violates the obligation to respect the wishes and values of the patient and may constitute discrimination on grounds of physical or mental disability, or religion. Within the constraints of available resources, clinicians must try to deal with such conflicts through open communication and negotiation.

Cases at the Boundary

Our analysis implicitly rests on the determination of whether a particular treatment falls within the bounds of standard medical care. A variety of factors may be used to argue for a treatment being considered appropriate: the prevalence of its use by expert clinicians (the threshold being its use by at least a "respectable minority"), licensure by Health Canada's Therapeutic Products Directorate for a specific use, and the existence of high-quality scientific evidence of its safety and efficacy.

The gap between scientific evidence and clinical practice is closing because of initiatives in evidence-based medicine, including clinical practice guidelines. Although the correspondence between evidence and practice is currently less than perfect, high-quality evidence of the effectiveness of a treatment may be sufficient to establish that it falls within the bounds of standard care, assuming adequate resources. *A fortiori*, clear evidence that a prevalent treatment is positively harmful or ineffective establishes that the treatment is not appropriate medical care.

Law

Although the physician has a legal duty to treat a patient once the physician–patient relationship has been established,[18] this does not imply that the physician must provide any treatment demanded by the patient. Picard and Robertson,[19] in their authoritative book *Legal Liability of Doctors and Hospitals in Canada*, conclude that there is no obligation to inform patients of or to provide them with treatment that is completely ineffective.

Nor is there a duty to provide treatment contrary to the patient's best interests. Manitoba's Court of Appeal recently ruled on a case involving a do-not-resuscitate (DNR) order being challenged by the parents of a one-year-old child in a persistent vegetative state.[20] The child had been savagely attacked at three months of age and afterward had been taken by the Child and Family Services of Central Manitoba. Justice J.A. Twaddle, upholding the lower court's decision to grant the DNR order, commented:

> "[I]t is in no one's interest to artificially maintain the life of a . . . patient who is in an irreversible vegetative state. That is unless those responsible for the patient being in that state have an interest in prolonging life to avoid criminal responsibility for the death."[21]

That is, the judge found that the parents were not deciding in the best interests of the child.

A case involving demand for life-prolonging treatment based on deeply rooted cultural or religious beliefs has yet to be considered by Canadian courts, and so the issue remains undecided. Defendant doctors and hospitals are likely to be confronted with a number of well-known cases in the US courts that have sided with families and supported the provision of life-sustaining treatment. . . . The US cases of Helga Wanglie and Baby K are particularly well-known. Both cases involved demands for continued life-prolonging treatments for patients in a persistent vegetative state. In the Wanglie case, the court refused an attempt to have the husband replaced as the decision-maker for his wife.[22,23] In the Baby K case, the court ordered physicians to provide life-prolonging interventions to the child.[24]

In other US cases courts have sided with clinicians. In the Gilgunn case, a jury found that

---

Baby K

Baby K was born in 1992 with a serious congenital malformation called anencephaly in which most of brain fails to develop. Children born with this condition usually die within the first week of life. Baby K's mother, a devout Christian, insisted that physicians provide her daughter with all necessary treatment, including mechanical ventilation. The physicians refused and a court ordered them to provide life-sustaining treatment. Baby K died in 1995, at the age of 29 months.

Gilgunn

In May 1989, Catherine Gilgunn, 71 years of age, fell in her home and broke her hip. She delayed seeking medical treatment and when she was finally admitted to the Massachusetts General Hospital she suffered multiple seizures, brain damage, and coma. Overriding her daughter's demands for continued treatment, physicians unilaterally wrote a do-not-resuscitate order and withdrew the ventilator that was helping her breathe. She died three days after the ventilator was removed.

clinicians were not negligent for the death of a patient when they removed mechanical ventilation despite the objections of the patient's daughter.[25] Commentators have questioned whether the court would have sided against the family if the patient were still alive and the continued provision of life-sustaining care were at issue.[26] These conjectures notwithstanding, the decision in the Gilgunn case is consistent with many others in common-law jurisdictions. In a leading English case, for instance, Lord Keith noted the following:

> "[A] medical practitioner is under no duty to continue to treat . . . a patient where a large body of informed and responsible medical opinion is to the effect that no benefit would be conferred by continuance."[27]

Issues raised by demands for inappropriate treatment have been dealt with in a number of policy statements.[28-32] All of these policies acknowledge the patient's right to refuse unwanted medical treatment, even life-prolonging treatment. Some of these policies assert that the physician has a right to unilaterally withhold or withdraw treatment that she or he deems futile. For example, the Canadian Medical Association's "Joint statement on resuscitative interventions (update 1995)" states that "[t]here is no obligation to offer a person futile or nonbeneficial treatment;" that is, the treatment "offers no reasonable hope of recovery or improvement or . . . the person is permanently unable to experience any benefit."[33] The policy was recently criticized on the basis that families of people in a persistent vegetative state may have morally and legally enforceable reasons to demand CPR.[34]

At least one recent policy initiative has shifted away from attempts to define "futility" and has instead focused on the establishment of fair procedures for dealing with demands for inappropriate treatment. This initiative involves a staged approach to such conflicts currently in use in a number of hospitals in Texas.[35] The procedure emphasizes clear communication, negotiation and, if needed, impartial arbitration. The University of Toronto Critical Care Program and Joint Centre for Bioethics have developed a model policy on appropriate use of life-sustaining treatment. . . .

Empirical Studies

Decisions to withhold or withdraw life-sustaining treatment are common in modern health care.[36-38] Disagreements over withdrawing life-support, a kind of demand for inappropriate treatment, are relatively uncommon and many resolve over time.[39-41] Demands for inappropriate treatment are nonetheless a source of substantial moral and emotional distress for health care workers and patients' families.[42,43] Such requests and the distress they incite arise from a variety of causes, including unrealistic expectations of the family, failure of the clinician to be realistic, lack of clear explanation of the implications of continued treatment and fear of litigation.[44]

How Should I Approach Demands for Inappropriate Treatment in Practice?

If the proposed treatment clearly falls outside the bounds of standard medical care, the physician has no obligation to offer or provide it. However, if substantial medical controversy as to the beneficial effect of the treatment exists, the law on this issue is unclear. Furthermore, this assertion does not address the emotions surrounding a case, so a clinician should proceed with caution.

Some of the most difficult cases occur at the boundary of appropriate medical care, when it is unclear whether demanded treatment falls within the standard of care. A treatment may have little evidence to support its safety and efficacy, it may be advocated by a very small group of physicians, or new evidence may have arisen questioning established use. Because patients and their families have increased access to uncontrolled sources of medical information on the Internet, demands for treatment of this sort may increase. In such cases, the physician ought to consult with colleagues within and outside of her institution: How prevalent is the treatment? How respected are those advocating it? Is there evidence for efficacy and safety? Beyond these obvious questions, others will need to be asked by the physician: Am I competent to administer the treatment? Does its provision violate my own conscience or the mission of my institution? A negative response to these last two questions calls for the patient to be transferred to the care of another physician or another institution.

Misunderstandings, emotional anguish, and disagreements about fundamental values often lie at the heart of cases in which seemingly inappropriate care is demanded. Therefore, the health care team should take a patient, supportive, empathic, and open approach in attempting to resolve these cases. Effective communication skills are essential. The physician should ask: Why has the conflict over treatment arisen? What are the deeper issues at stake (e.g., a need for more information, denial, trust, differing values)? Such cases often also lead to conflicts among members of the health care team, and these too should be addressed in an open and constructive manner.

When disagreement among health care providers, patient, and family persists, the physician should conceptualize this as a situation of conflict in which the goal is to seek a negotiated solution.[45] If necessary, the physician should seek the services of someone trained in conflict mediation, such as a clinical bioethicist, psychiatrist, psychologist, or social worker.

If the conflict cannot be resolved through mediation, arbitration may be necessary. Consultation with a lawyer is important at this stage. Some provinces have provisions in their consent laws for arbitration through boards. For example, the Consent and Capacity Board in Ontario has the power to replace a substitute decision maker who is not making decisions according to the patient's wishes or best interests.[46] As a final recourse, the courts may be appealed to by either party, but this step runs the risk of increasing both the emotional anguish of patients, family, and health care providers, and the conflict among them. Ideally, the health care institution will have a policy on dealing with demands for inappropriate treatment. The policy should describe a clear and nonarbitrary process to address such cases in the institution.[47]. . .

Study Questions

1. What is implied in the concept "standard of care?" How does it help determine whether demanded treatments ought to be provided?

2. How should physicians proceed if it is unclear whether demanded treatment falls within the standard of care?

3. How are value disputes best resolved? Why is this approach superior to unilateral decision-making?

Notes

1. Schneiderman LJ, Jecker NS, Jonsen AR. Medical futility: its meaning and ethical implications. *Ann Intern Med* 1990;112:949–54.
2. Ibid.
3. Ibid.
4. Weijer C, Elliott C. Pulling the plug on futility. *BMJ* 1995;310:683–4.
5. Beauchamp TL, Childress JF. *Principles of biomedical ethics.* 4th ed. New York: Oxford University Press; 1994.
6. Canadian Medical Association. *Code of ethics.* Ottawa: The Association; 1996.
7. Ibid.
8. Ibid.
9. Ibid.
10. Truog RD, Brett AS, Frader J. The problem with futility. *N Engl J Med* 1992;326:1560–4.
11. Ibid.
12. *Of life and death. Report of the Special Senate Committee on Euthanasia and Assisted Suicide.* Ottawa: Supply and Services Canada; 1995. Cat no YC2-351/1-OIE.
13. Freedman B, McGill/Boston Research Group. Nonvalidated therapies and HIV disease. *Hastings Cent Rep* 1989;19(3):14–20.
14. Brett AS, McCullough LB. When patients request specific interventions: defining the limits of the physician's obligation. *N Engl J Med* 1986;315:1347–51.
15. US President's Commission for the Study of Ethical Problems in Medicine and Biomedical Research. *Deciding to forgo life-sustaining treatment: a report on the ethical, medical and legal issues in treatment decisions.* Washington: The Commission; 1983.
16. Post SG. Baby K: medical futility and the free exercise of religion. *J Law Med Ethics* 1995;23:20–6.
17. Weijer C. Cardiopulmonary resuscitation for patients in a persistent vegetative state: Futile or acceptable? *CMAJ* 1998;158(4):491–3.
18. Picard EI, Robertson GB. *Legal liability of doctors and hospitals in Canada.* 3rd ed. Scarborough (ON): Carswell; 1996. p. 235–69.
19. Picard EI, Robertson GB. *Legal liability of doctors and hospitals in Canada.* 3rd ed. Scarborough (ON): Carswell; 1996. p. 264–5.
20. *Child and Family Services of Central Manitoba v. Lavallee* (14 Nov 1997), (Man. C.A.) [unreported].
21. Ibid.
22. Angell M. The case of Helga Wanglie: a new kind of "right to die" case. *N Engl J Med* 1991;325:511–2.
23. Capron AM. In re Helga Wanglie. *Hastings Cent Rep* 1991;21(5):26–8.
24. Annas GJ. Asking the courts to set the standard of emergency care—the case of Baby K. *N Engl J Med* 1994;330:1542–5.

25. *Gilgunn v. Massachusetts General Hospital.* No 92-4820 (Mass. Sup. Ct. Civ. Action Suffolk Co. 22 Apr 1995).

26. Prip W, Moretti A. Medical futility: a legal perspective. In: Zucker MB, Zucker HD, editors. *Medical futility and the evaluation of life-sustaining interventions.* Cambridge (MA): Cambridge University Press; 1997. p. 136–54.

27. *Airedale N.H.S. Trust v. Bland* [1993] 1 All E.R. 821 at 861.

28. American Thoracic Society Bioethics Task Force. Withholding and withdrawing life-sustaining therapy. *Am Rev Respir Dis* 1991;144:726–31.

29. Society of Critical Care Medicine Ethics Committee. Consensus statement on the triage of critically ill patients. *JAMA* 1994;271:1200–3.

30. Joint statement on resuscitative interventions (update 1995). *CMAJ* 1995;153 (11):1652A–C.

31. Murphy DJ, Barbour E. GUIDe (Guidelines for the Use of Intensive care in Denver): a community effort to define futile and inappropriate care. *New Horiz* 1994;2:326–30.

32. Task Force on Ethics of the Society of Critical Care Medicine. Consensus on the ethics of forgoing life-sustaining treatments in the critically ill. *Crit Care Med* 1990;18:1435–9.

33. Joint statement on resuscitative interventions (update 1995). *CMAJ* 1995.

34. Weijer C. Cardiopulmonary resuscitation for patients in a persistent vegetative state. *CMAJ* 1998.

35. Halevy A, Brody BA. A multi-institution collaborative policy on medical futility. *JAMA* 1996;276:571–4.

36. Wood GG, Martin E. Withholding and withdrawing life-sustaining therapy in a Canadian intensive care unit. *Can J Anaesth* 1995;42:186–91.

37. Prendergast TJ, Luce JM. Increasing incidence of withholding and withdrawal of life support from the critically ill. *Am J Respir Crit Care Med* 1997;155:15–20.

38. Corley MC. Moral distress of critical care nurses. *Am J Crit Care* 1995;4:280–5.

39. Wood, Martin. Witholding and withdrawing life-sustaining therapy. *Can J Anaesth* 1995.

40. Prendergast, Luce. Increasing incidence of withholding and withdrawal of life support. *Am J Respir Crit Care Med* 1997.

41. Corley. Moral distress of critical care nurses. *Am J Crit Care* 1995.

42. Solomon MZ. How physicians talk about futility: making words mean too many things. *J Clin Ethics* 1993;21:231–7.

43. Simmonds A. Decision-making by default: experiences of physicians and nurses with dying patients in intensive care. *Humane Health Care Int* 1996;12: 168–72.

44. McCrary SV, Swanson JW, Younger SJ, Perkins HS, Winslade WJ. Physicians' quantitative assessments of medical futility. *J Clin Ethics* 1994;5:100–5.

45. Fisher R, Ury W. *Getting to yes: negotiating agreement without giving in.* New York: Penguin; 1991.

46. *Health Care Consent Act,* SO 1996, c 2, sch A.

47. Halevy, Brody. A multi-institution collaborative policy. *JAMA* 1996.

Chapter Study Questions

1. According to each of the articles, what limits may be set on patient autonomy?

2. Truog and colleagues are critical of futility generally, but endorse the notion of physiological futility. Is physiological futility the same as Schneiderman and colleagues' concept of quantitative futility? Is this a position that Truog and colleagues can reasonably sustain?

3. Weijer and colleagues think that treatments outside of the medical standard of care need neither be offered nor provided if demanded. Is this position vulnerable to the criticisms of unilateral decision-making raised by Truog and colleagues?

Critical Analysis

Consider the following from the article by Schneiderman and colleagues:

"Admittedly, these kinds of cases fall along a continuum, and there are well known examples of the most remarkable achievements of life goals despite the most burdensome handicaps. However, if survival requires the patient's entire preoccupation with intensive medical treatment, to the extent that he or she cannot achieve any other life goals (thus obviating the goal of medical care), the treatment is effective but not beneficial; it need not be offered to the patient, and the patient's family has no right to demand it."

Outline Schneiderman and colleagues' argument in your own words, paying particular attention to the premises that they rely on to support their main conclusion. Choose one of the premises for evaluation. Try to think of at least one objection to this premise.

Case Study

Samuel Golubchuk, an 84-year-old Orthodox Jewish man, was admitted to Winnipeg's Grace Hospital on 26 October 2007 with pneumonia and an irregular heartbeat. Prior to his admission to hospital he had numerous medical problems. Golubchuk was very badly injured in a fall in 2003, that left him with brain damage and the inability to care for himself. After his head injury, physicians predicted that he would have no quality of life. While Golubchuk needed constant care, his family recalled fondly being able to take him bowling and to play bingo, and they believe he had a good quality of life.

In the current admission, however, his very poor condition did not improve after a week in the intensive care unit. Golubchuk's physicians felt that he was no longer self-aware and that his chances of meaningful recovery were slim to none. Physicians were worried that continued treatment would cause him to suffer needlessly. They further believed that such treatment was inconsistent with their duties as physicians.

The family demanded that intensive medical measures to keep Golubchuk alive be continued.

They argued that as an Orthodox Jew, he would have wanted the treatments continued so long as he had a heartbeat. Withdrawing treatment now would, in the family's view, amount to the physicians "playing God."

Once dialogue reached an impasse, communication between the family and physicians stopped. No effort was made to bring in an ethicist or a neutral third party to attempt to arbitrate the conflict. When physicians sought to unilaterally remove life-support, the family obtained a court injunction to stop them from doing so.

1. According to the physicians in this case, is continued treatment an instance of quantitative or qualitative futility? Do you agree?

2. What reasons does the family have for demanding continued treatment? Do you think they are good reasons?

3. Were the physicians right to try and unilaterally stop treatment? Was the family right to seek a court injunction?

Further Reading

Canadian Medical Association. Joint Statement on Preventing and Resolving Ethical Conflicts Involving Health Care Providers and Persons Receiving Care [Internet]. 1998. Available from: http://www.cma.ca/index.php?ci_id=3217&la_id=1. Date Accessed: 5 June 2012.

Council on Ethical and Judicial Affairs, American Medical Association. Medical futility in end-of-life care. JAMA [Internet]. 1999; 281:937–41. Available from: http://www.ama-assn.org/ama1/pub/upload/mm/code-medical-ethics/2037a.pdf. Date Accessed: 5 June 2012.

Helft PR, Siegler M, Lantos J. The rise and fall of the futility movement. *N Eng J Med* 2000; 343:293–6.

Moratti S. The development of "medical futility": towards a procedural approach based on the role of the medical profession. *J Med Ethics* 2009; 35: 369–72.

Singer PA, Barker G, Bowman KW, Harrison C, Kernerman P, Kopelow J, Lazar N, Weijer C, Workman S for the University of Toronto Joint Centre for Bioethics/Critical Care Medicine Program Task Force. Hospital policy on appropriate use of life-sustaining treatment. Crit Care Med [Internet]. 2001; 29:187–91. Available from: http://www.jointcentreforbioethics.ca/publications/documents/ccm2001.pdf. Date Accessed: 5 June 2012.

6

Equipoise and Clinical Research

In this chapter, our focus is the physician's obligations to her patient in the context of clinical research. Specifically, we ask, may the physician, consistent with her duty to provide competent medical care, invite her patient to participate in a clinical trial? Clinical trials form the foundation of contemporary scientific medicine in which novel treatments are tested rigorously to ensure that they are safe and effective. Novel treatments, identified on the basis of theoretical considerations and animal testing, typically undergo testing in human beings in phase I, phase II, and phase III clinical trials before being adopted in clinical practice. In a phase I clinical trial, the treatment is administered to healthy volunteers to determine the dosage for subsequent testing and to assess any adverse effects. In a phase II clinical trial, the treatment is given to a small group of patients to gather preliminary evidence of an effect on a particular disease. If evidence from early phase clinical trials is sufficiently promising, the novel treatment may be compared with a treatment used in clinical practice in a phase III trial. In a phase III randomized clinical trial (RCT), patients are allocated by chance to receive the novel treatment or the standard treatment (or placebo) and are followed for a period of time to document the outcome. The results of phase III RCTs form the basis for applications to license new drugs and provide evidence that may lead to changes in clinical practice. The articles in this chapter focus on the ethical challenges of RCTs.

The central moral challenge of the RCT emerges from a conflict between the goals of medical practice and the goals of research. The doctor-patient relationship is widely regarded as a fiduciary relationship—a legally-recognized trust relationship—in which the physician has a moral duty to act and advise to promote the best medical interests of the patient. This duty of care obliges the physician to prescribe only treatment that is consistent with the medical standard of care (discussed in chapter 5). But how can the physician, consistent with her duty of care to the patient, offer enrollment in an RCT? Allocating the patient to one or another treatment *randomly* seems to run counter to the physician's duty to promote the patient's best medical interests. Further, all RCTs involve non-therapeutic procedures—be they additional blood draws, an added X-ray, or a questionnaire—that expose patient-subjects to risk solely for the scientific ends of the study.

In the first article, Benjamin Freedman examines the adequacy of "equipoise" as a solution to the RCT dilemma. According to the theory of "clinical equipoise," a physician may offer RCT enrollment to her patient when she is genuinely uncertain of the preferred treatment. Equipoise has been criticized in the literature on the grounds that it seems too fragile to sustain or even initiate a clinical trial—the slightest accumulation of evidence in favour of the new treatment will throw the physician out of equipoise. Freedman traces the difficulty to an understanding of equipoise as requiring that the evidence supporting the treatments be exactly balanced—a concept he calls "theoretical equipoise." Freedman believes theoretical equipoise to be "both conceptually odd and ethically irrelevant." In its place, he proposes "clinical equipoise," according to which a physician may offer his patient enrollment in an RCT when there is a state of honest, professional disagreement in the community of expert practitioners as to the preferred treatment. Clinical equipoise is based on the recognition that the physician's duty of care to the patient is essentially a social norm determined by the community of expert practitioners. Thus understood, it is consistent with an imbalance in evidence where one treatment is favoured over the other so long as insufficient evidence has accumulated to settle the controversy in the medical community.

In the second article, Franklin Miller and Howard Brody argue that clinical equipoise is based on a therapeutic misconception—that is, a conflation of the ethics of clinical practice with the ethics of research. The goals of clinical practice and clinical research differ: clinical practice aims to improve the health of the patient; clinical research aims to produce knowledge that will benefit future patients. Miller and Brody claim that activities with different ends cannot share the same moral rules. While physicians in clinical practice are rightly viewed as owing a duty of care to their patients, it is a mistake to think that physician-investigators owe a duty of care to patient-subjects. Rather, the ethics of research needs to be built anew on the recognition of the "frankly utilitarian purpose" of clinical research. According to their view, the physician-investigator has obligations not to exploit patient-subjects unduly and to seek their informed consent for research participation. Miller and Brody believe informed consent should emphasize that research is not another mode of therapy, but they recognize that this may dissuade some from participating in clinical research. If need be, they suggest that recruitment rates for RCTs may be enhanced by offering prospective subjects money to enroll in a study. While this may drive up the cost of doing research, payment is a tangible way of underscoring to prospective patient-subjects that the research is not intended to be beneficial.

In the third article, Paul B. Miller and Charles Weijer disagree with Miller and Brody's claim that activities with different ends cannot share moral rules and explore the implications of trust relationships for the ethics of clinical research. Trust relationships are relationships of inequality in which the weaker party entrusts control of significant practical interests to the more powerful party. The more powerful party assumes a variety of obligations to the weaker party, including a duty of care—that is, a duty to act and advise in such a way as to promote the significant practical interests of the weaker party. Some of the most important relationships in our society are trust relationships—doctor-patient; lawyer-client; corporate executive-share holder—and all, despite the differing aims of the activities involved, involve a duty of care. Miller and Weijer see two trust relationships at the heart of the ethics of research. The first is a little-recognized trust relationship between the State and the research subject. The research ethics board (REB) is best understood as an arm of the State that ensures that the liberty and welfare interests of research subjects are protected. In requiring that therapeutic procedures in research meet the clinical equipoise requirement, the REB ensures that the patient-subject's interest to receive competent medical care is protected. The second trust relationship is that between the physician-researcher and patient-subject. Knowing that a study has been approved by a REB (and therefore, that a state of clinical equipoise exists), the physician-researcher fulfills the duty of care by ensuring that nothing in the particular patient-subject's circumstances would require that she be excluded from the study. This is known as the "clinical judgment principle."

ONE Equipoise and the Ethics of Clinical Research

Benjamin Freedman | *New England Journal of Medicine* 1987; 317: 141-5.

The Problems of Equipoise

There is widespread agreement that ethics requires that each clinical trial begin with an honest null hypothesis.[1,2] In the simplest model, testing a new treatment B on a defined patient population P for which the current accepted treatment is A, it is necessary that the clinical investigator be in a state of genuine uncertainty regarding the comparative merits of treatments A and B for population P. If a physician knows that these treatments are not equivalent, ethics requires that the superior treatment be recommended. Following Fried, I call this state of uncertainty about the relative merits of A and B "equipoise."[3]

Equipoise is an ethically necessary condition in all cases of clinical research. In trials with several arms, equipoise must exist between all arms of the trial; otherwise the trial design should be modified to exclude the inferior treatment. If equipoise is disturbed during the course of a trial, the trial may need to be terminated and all subjects previously enrolled (as well as other patients within the relevant population) may have to be offered the superior treatment. It has been rigorously argued that a trial with a placebo is ethical only in investigating conditions for which there is no known treatment;[4] this argument reflects a special application of the requirement for equipoise. Although equipoise has commonly been discussed in the special context of the ethics of randomized clinical trials,[5,6] it is important to recognize it as an ethical condition of all controlled clinical trials, whether or not they are randomized, placebo-controlled, or blinded. . . .

Many of the problems raised by the requirement for equipoise are familiar. Shaw and Chalmers have written that a clinician who "knows, or has good reason to believe," that one arm of the trial is superior may not ethically participate.[7] But the reasoning or preliminary results that prompt the trial (and that may themselves be ethically mandatory)[8] may jolt the investigator (if not his or her colleagues) out of equipoise before the trial begins. Even if the investigator is undecided between A and B in terms of gross measures such as mortality and morbidity, equipoise may be disturbed because evident differences in the quality of life (as in the case of two surgical approaches) tip the balance.[9-12] . . .

Late in the study—when p-values are between 0.05 and 0.06—the moral issue of equipoise is most readily apparent,[13,14] but the same problem arises when the earliest comparative results are analyzed.[15] Within the closed statistical universe of the clinical trial, each result that demonstrates a difference between the arms of the trial contributes exactly as much to the statistical conclusion that a difference exists as does any other. The contribution of the last pair of cases in the trial is no greater than that of the first. If, therefore, equipoise is a condition that reflects equivalent evidence for

> **Clinical trial**
> An experiment involving healthy people or patients to test the safety or efficacy of a medical treatment.

> **Null hypothesis**
> The supposition, at the start of a study, that the experimental treatment (in this case treatment B) is no better than the comparator treatment (or placebo; in this case treatment A). If a study finds evidence that the new treatment is superior to the comparator (or control) treatment, the null hypothesis may be rejected.

> **Placebo**
> In a clinical trial with a no treatment comparator or control, a placebo is a physiologically inert version of the active treatment (e.g., a small blue pill) that is administered to research subjects in the control arm so that they do not know whether they are receiving active treatment or not.

> **Randomized clinical trial**
> A clinical trial in which patients are allocated by chance to the one of the various treatments being tested in the study. Randomized clinical trials are generally thought to produce the most reliable evidence of the efficacy of a new treatment.

> **Morbidity**
> A deviation from a state of health caused by illness or injury.

> **P-value**
> A standard statistical measure of evidence in favour of the hypothesis being tested in a study. By convention, a p-value of less than 0.05 is considered "statistically significant," that is, the point at which the null hypotheses is rejected.

> **Closed statistical universe**
> An analysis of the study per se, without appeal to conditions outside of the study.

alternative hypotheses, it is jeopardized by the first pair of cases as much as by the last. The investigator who is concerned about the ethics of recruitment after the penultimate pair must logically be concerned after the first pair as well. . . .

Finally, these issues are more than a philosopher's nightmare. Considerable interest has been generated by a paper in which Taylor et al.[16] describe the termination of a trial of alternative treatments for breast cancer. The trial foundered on the problem of patient recruitment, and the investigators trace much of the difficulty in enrolling patients to the fact that the investigators were not in a state of equipoise regarding the arms of the trial. With the increase in concern about the ethics of research and with the increasing presence of this topic in the curricula of medical and graduate schools, instances of the type that Taylor and her colleagues describe are likely to become more common. The requirement for equipoise thus poses a practical threat to clinical research.

> **Alternative hypotheses**
> The supposition, at the start of a study, that the experimental treatment is better than (or different from) the comparator treatment (or placebo). The alternative hypothesis is contrasted with the null hypothesis.

> **Trial of alternative treatments for breast cancer**
> Freedman here refers to a very well-known clinical trial called "NSABP B-06" conducted in the early 1980s that compared the standard surgical approach for breast cancer involving removal of the entire breast, with an experimental approach that combined breast-conserving surgery with radiation therapy. At the time the clinical trial was enrolling patients, many surgeons had already switched—in advance of definitive evidence—to the breast-conserving approach.

Theoretical Equipoise versus Clinical Equipoise

The problems of equipoise examined above arise from a particular understanding of that concept, which I will term "theoretical equipoise." It is an understanding that is both conceptually odd and ethically irrelevant. Theoretical equipoise exists when, overall, the evidence on behalf of two alternative treatment regimens is exactly balanced. This evidence may be derived from a variety of sources, including data from the literature, uncontrolled experience, considerations of basic science and

> **Theoretical equipoise**
> A state of uncertainty about the relative merits of two (or more) treatments being tested in which the evidence supporting each is precisely balanced.

fundamental physiologic processes, and perhaps a "gut feeling" or "instinct" resulting from (or superimposed on) other considerations. The problems examined above arise from the principle that if theoretical equipoise is disturbed, the physician has . . . a treatment preference—let us say, favouring experimental treatment B. A trial testing A against B requires that some patients be enrolled in violation of this treatment preference.

Theoretical equipoise is overwhelmingly fragile; that is, it is disturbed by a slight accretion of evidence favouring one arm of the trial. According to one view, equipoise is disturbed when the odds that A will be more successful than B are anything other than 50 per cent, it is therefore necessary to randomize treatment assignments beginning with the very first patient, lest equipoise be disturbed. We may say that theoretical equipoise is balanced on a knife's edge.

Theoretical equipoise is most appropriate to one-dimensional hypotheses and causes us to think in those terms. The null hypothesis must be sufficiently simple and "clean" to be finely balanced; will A or B be superior in reducing mortality or shrinking tumours or lowering fevers in population P? Clinical choice is commonly more complex.

> **One-dimensional hypothesis**
> A supposition regarding the comparative merits of two treatments that can be expressed as a single, simple variable, such as tumour size or blood pressure.

The choice of A or B depends on some combination of effectiveness, consistency, minimal or relievable side effects, and other factors. On close examination, for example, it sometimes appears that even trials that purport to test a single hypothesis in fact involve a more complicated, portmanteau measure—e.g., the "therapeutic index" of A versus B. The formulation of the conditions of theoretical equipoise for such complex, multi-dimensional clinical hypotheses is tantamount to the formulation of a rigorous calculus of apples and oranges.

> **Portmanteau measure**
> A combination of two or more single, simple variables—a compound variable, such as a treatment's therapeutic index (a measure of a treatment's benefits minus its risks).

Theoretical equipoise is also highly sensitive to the vagaries of the investigator's attention and perception. Because of its fragility, theoretical equipoise is disturbed as soon as the investigator perceives a difference between the alternatives—whether or not any genuine difference exists. Prescott writes, for example, "It will be common at some stage in most trials for the survival curves to show visually different survivals," short of significance but "sufficient to raise ethical difficulties for the participants."[17] A visual difference, however, is purely an artifact of the research methods employed: when and by what means data are assembled and analyzed and what scale is adopted for the graphic presentation of data. Similarly, it is common for researchers to employ interval scales for phenomena that are recognized to be continuous by nature—e.g., five-point scales of pain or stages of tumour progression. These interval scales, which represent an arbitrary distortion of the available evidence to simplify research, may magnify the differences actually found, with a resulting disturbance of theoretical equipoise.

> **Survival curves**
> A graphical plot of the proportion of patients alive (y-axis) versus time (x-axis).

Finally, . . . theoretical equipoise is personal and idiosyncratic. It is disturbed when the clinician has . . . what might even be labelled a bias or a hunch, a preference of a merely intuitive nature.[18] The investigator who ignores such a hunch, by failing to advise the patient that because of it the investigator prefers B to A or by recommending A (or a chance of random assignment to A) to the patient, has violated the requirement for equipoise and its companion requirement to recommend the best medical treatment.

The problems with theoretical equipoise should be evident. To understand the alternative, preferable interpretation of equipoise, we need to recall the basic reason for conducting clinical trials: there is a current or imminent conflict in the clinical community over what treatment is preferred for patients in a defined population. The standard treatment is A, but some evidence suggests that B will be superior because of its effectiveness or its reduction of undesirable side effects, or for some other reason. . . Or there is a split in the clinical community, with some clinicians favouring A and others favouring B. Each side recognizes that the opposing side has evidence to support its position, yet each still thinks that overall its own view is correct. There exists or, in the case of a novel therapy, there may soon exist an honest, professional disagreement among expert clinicians about the preferred treatment. A clinical trial is instituted with the aim of resolving this dispute.

At this point, a state of "clinical equipoise" exists. There is no consensus within the expert clinical community about the comparative merits of the alternatives to be tested. We may state the formal conditions under which such a trial would be ethical as follows: at the start of the trial, there must be a state of clinical equipoise regarding the merits of the regimens to be tested, and the trial must be designed in such a way as to make it reasonable to expect that, if it is successfully concluded, clinical equipoise will be disturbed. In other words, the results of a successful clinical trial should be convincing enough to resolve the dispute among clinicians.

> **Clinical equipoise**
> A state of uncertainty about the relative merits of two (or more) treatments being tested characterized by honest, professional disagreement in the community of expert practitioners as to the preferred treatment. Clinical equipoise does not require that the evidence regarding the two treatments be precisely balanced; nor does it require that individual practitioners be uncertain about the preferred treatment.

A state of clinical equipoise is consistent with a decided treatment preference on the part of the investigators. They must simply recognize that their less-favoured treatment is preferred by colleagues whom they consider to be responsible and competent. Even if the interim results favour the preference of the investigators, treatment B, clinical equipoise persists as long as those results are too weak to influence the judgment of the community of clinicians, because of limited sample size, unresolved possibilities of side effects, or other factors. This judgment can necessarily be made only by those who know the interim results—whether a data-monitoring committee or the investigators.

At the point when the accumulated evidence in favour of B is so strong that the committee or investigators believe no open-minded clinician informed of the results would still favour A, clinical equipoise has been disturbed. This may occur well short of the original schedule for the termination of the trial, for

> **Data monitoring committee**
> A group of experts, including physicians, a statistician, and an ethicist, who review the accumulating data in a clinical trial to protect the welfare of trial participants. A clinical trial may be stopped early due to the proven superiority of one of the treatments, serious safety concerns, or a low probability of achieving the trial's objectives.

unexpected reasons. Therapeutic effects or side effects may be much stronger than anticipated, for example, or a definable subgroup within population P may be recognized for which the results demonstrably disturb clinical equipoise. Because of the arbitrary character of human judgment and persuasion, some ethical problems regarding the termination of a trial will remain. Clinical equipoise will confine these problems to unusual or extreme cases, however, and will allow us to cast persistent problems in the proper terms. For example, in the face of a strong established trend, must we continue the trial because of others' blind fealty to an arbitrary statistical benchmark?

Clearly, clinical equipoise is a far weaker—and more common—condition than theoretical equipoise. Is it ethical to conduct a trial on the basis of clinical equipoise, when theoretical equipoise is disturbed? Or, . . . is doing so a violation of the physician's obligation to provide patients with the best medical treatment?[19-21] Let us assume that the investigators have a decided preference for B but wish to conduct a trial on the grounds that clinical (not theoretical) equipoise exists. The ethics committee asks the investigators whether, if they or members of their families were within population P, they would not want to be treated with their preference, B? An affirmative answer is often thought to be fatal to the prospects for such a trial, yet the investigators answer in the affirmative. Would a trial satisfying this weaker form of equipoise be ethical?

I believe that it clearly is ethical. As Fried has emphasized,[22] competent (hence, ethical) medicine is social rather than individual in nature. Progress in medicine relies on progressive consensus within the medical and research communities. The ethics of medical practice grants no ethical or normative meaning to a treatment preference, however powerful, that is based on a hunch or on anything less than evidence publicly presented and convincing to the clinical community. Persons are licensed as physicians after they demonstrate the acquisition of this professionally validated knowledge, not after they reveal a superior capacity for guessing. Normative judgments of their behaviour—e.g., malpractice actions—rely on a comparison with what is done by the community of medical practitioners. Failure to follow a "treatment preference" not shared by this community and not based on information that would convince it could not be the basis for an allegation of legal or ethical malpractice, As Fried states: "[T]he conception of what is good medicine is the product of a professional consensus." By definition, in a state of clinical equipoise, "good medicine" finds the choice between A and B indifferent.

In contrast to theoretical equipoise, clinical equipoise is robust. The ethical difficulties at the beginning and end of a trial are therefore largely alleviated. There remain difficulties about consent, but these too may be diminished. Instead of emphasizing the lack of evidence favouring one arm over another that is required by theoretical equipoise, clinical equipoise places the emphasis on informing the patient of the honest disagreement among expert clinicians. The fact that the investigator has a "treatment preference," if he or she does, could be disclosed; indeed, if the preference is a decided one, and based on something more than a hunch, it could be ethically mandatory to disclose it. At the same time, it would be emphasized that this preference is not shared by others. It is likely to be a matter of chance that the patient is being seen by a clinician with a preference for B over A, rather than by an equally competent clinician with the opposite preference.

Clinical equipoise does not depend on concealing relevant information from researchers and subjects, as does the use of independent data-monitoring committees. Rather, it allows investigators, in informing subjects, to distinguish appropriately among validated knowledge accepted by the clinical community, data on treatments that are promising but are not (or, for novel therapies, would not be) generally convincing, and mere hunches. Should informed patients decline to participate because they have chosen a specific clinician and trust his or her judgment—over and above the consensus in the professional community—that is no more than the patients' right. We do not conscript patients to serve as subjects in clinical trials.

The Implications of Clinical Equipoise

The theory of clinical equipoise has been formulated as an alternative to some current views on the ethics of human research. At the same time, it corresponds closely to a preanalytic concept held by many in the research and regulatory communities. Clinical equipoise serves, then, as a rational formulation of the approach of many toward

> **Malpractice actions**
> Legal proceedings undertaken in which one party claims that the actions of a physician have been negligent, illegal, or otherwise improper.

> **Preanalytic concept**
> An intuition; an idea that has not yet been exposed to rigorous rational analysis.

research ethics; it does not so much change things as explain why they are the way they are. Nevertheless, the precision afforded by the theory of clinical equipoise does help to clarify or reformulate some aspects of research ethics; I will mention only two.

First, there is a recurrent debate about the ethical propriety of conducting clinical trials of discredited treatments, such as Laetrile.[23] Often, substantial political pressure to conduct such tests is brought to bear by adherents of quack therapies. The theory of clinical equipoise suggests that when there is no support for a treatment regimen within the expert clinical community, the first ethical requirement of a trial—clinical equipoise—is lacking; it would therefore be unethical to conduct such a trial.

> **Laetrile**
> A compound extracted from apricot pits that was purported to have anticancer effects.

Second, Feinstein has criticized the tendency of clinical investigators to narrow excessively the conditions and hypotheses of a trial in order to ensure the validity of its results.[24] This "fastidious" approach purchases scientific manageability at the expense of an inability to apply the results to the "messy" conditions of clinical practice. The theory of clinical equipoise adds some strength to this criticism. Overly "fastidious" trials, designed to resolve some theoretical question, fail to satisfy the second ethical requirement of clinical research, since the special conditions of the trial will render it useless for influencing clinical decisions, even if it is successfully completed.

The most important result of the concept of clinical equipoise, however, might be to relieve the current crisis of confidence in the ethics of clinical trials. Equipoise, properly understood, remains an ethical condition for clinical trials. It is consistent with much current practice. Clinicians and philosophers alike have been premature in calling for desperate measures to resolve problems of equipoise.

Study Questions

1. What is theoretical equipoise? Why, according to Freedman, is it a problematic concept for the ethics of clinical trials?

2. What is clinical equipoise? How does it avoid the pitfalls of theoretical equipoise?

3. If a physician believes that one of the treatments in a clinical trial is superior, may she recommend trial participation to one of her patients? Why?

Notes

1. Levine RJ. *Ethics and regulation of clinical research*. 2nd ed. Baltimore: Urban & Schwarzenberg, 1986.
2. Levine RJ. The use of placebos in randomized clinical trials. *IRB: Rev Hum Subj Res* 1985; 7(2):1–4.
3. Fried C. *Medical experimentation: personal integrity and social policy*. Amsterdam: North-Holland Publishing, 1974.
4. Levine. The use of placebos. 1985.
5. Marquis D. Leaving therapy to chance. *Hastings Cent Rep* 1983; 13(4):407.
6. Schafer A. The ethics of the randomized clinical trial. *N Engl J Med* 1982; 307:719–24.
7. Shaw LW, Chalmers TC. Ethics in cooperative clinical trials. *Ann NY Acad Sci* 1970; 169:487–95.
8. Hollenberg NK, Dzau VJ, Williams GH. Are uncontrolled clinical studies ever justified? *N Engl J Med* 1980; 303:1067.
9. Fried. *Medical experimentation*. 1974.
10. Marquis. Leaving therapy to chance. 1983.
11. Schafer. The ethics of the randomized clinical trials. 1970.
12. Levine RJ, Lebacqz K. Some ethical considerations in clinical trials. *Clin Pharmacol Ther* 1979; 25:728–41.
13. Klimt CR, Canner PL. Terminating a long-term clinical trial. *Clin Pharmacol Ther* 1979; 25:641–6.
14. Veatch RM. Longitudinal studies, sequential designs and grant renewals: what to do with preliminary data. *IRB: Rev Hum Subj Res* 1979; 1(4): 1–3.
15. Chalmers T. The ethics of randomization as a decision-making technique and the problem of informed consent. In: Beauchamp TL, Walters L, eds. *Contemporary issues in bioethics*. Encino, Calif.: Dickenson, 1978:426–9.
16. Taylor KM, Margolese RC, Soskolne CL. Physicians' reasons for not entering eligible patients in a randomized clinical trial of surgery for breast cancer. *N Engl J Med* 1984; 310:1363–7.
17. Prescott RJ. Feedback of data to participants during clinical trials. In: Tagnon HJ, Staquet MJ, eds. *Controversies in cancer: design of trials and treatment*. New York: Masson Publishing, 1979:55–61.
18. Schafer A. The randomized clinical trial: for whose benefit? *IRB: Rev Hum Subj Res* 1985; 7(2):4–6.
19. Marquis. Leaving therapy to chance. 1983.
20. Schafer. The ethics of the randomized clinical trials. 1970.

21. Schafer. The randomized clinical trial. 1985.
22. Fried. *Medical experimentation.* 1974.
23. Cowan DH. The ethics of clinical trials of ineffective therapy. *IRB: Rev Hum Subj Res* 1981; 3(5):10–1.

24. Feinstein AR. An additional basic science for clinical medicine. II. The limitations of randomized trials. *Ann Intern Med* 1983; 99:544–50.

TWO   A Critique of Clinical Equipoise: Therapeutic Misconception in the Ethics of Clinical Trials

Franklin G. Miller and Howard Brody | *Hastings Center Report* 2003; 33(3): 19-28.

Therapeutic Misconceptions

. . . The prevailing ethical perspective on clinical trials holds that physician-investigators can discharge their "therapeutic obligation" to patients in the context of randomized clinical trials (RCTs) as long as treatments being tested scientifically satisfy clinical equipoise. We contend that this ethical perspective is fundamentally flawed.

> **Therapeutic obligation**
> The physician's duty to act and to advise the patient in accord with the patient's best medical interests.

An ethical framework that provides normative guidance about a practice should accurately characterize the practice. The prevailing ethical perspective fails this test: All sound ethical thinking about clinical research, and the regulatory framework for review of protocols for clinical investigation, depends on a basic distinction between research and therapy. But the claims in the prevailing ethical perspective on clinical trials conflate research and therapy. These claims are that the ethics of the physician-patient relationship must govern RCTs, that physicians who conduct these trials have a "therapeutic obligation" to patients enrolled in them, and that RCTs must be compatible with some form of equipoise. . . .

The therapeutic misconception about the ethics of clinical trials has emerged from the "similarity position," which argues that ultimately, the ethics of clinical trials rest on the same moral considerations that underlie the ethics of therapeutic medicine. The "difference position" argues that the ethics of clinical trials must start with the realization that

> **Therapeutic misconception**
> The mistaken belief said to be common among research subjects that purely scientific elements of a clinical trial are designed to benefit the research subject. For instance, a research subject who believes that randomization means that a computer picks the best treatment for her is suffering from a therapeutic misconception. Here the authors extend the scope of this term to include the belief common amongst ethicists that medical research and medical practice share at least some common ethical principles.

medical research and medical treatment are two distinct forms of activity, governed by different ethical principles. . . .

The Distinction between Research and Therapy

Clinical medicine aims at providing optimal medical care for individual patients. Ethically, it is governed by the principles of therapeutic beneficence and therapeutic non-maleficence. Therapeutic beneficence directs physicians to practice medicine with primary fidelity to promoting the health of particular patients. According to therapeutic non-maleficence, the risks of medical care to which a patient is exposed are to be justified by the prospect of compensating medical benefits for that patient. The physician uses scientific knowledge to care for the patient and engages in therapeutic experimentation with the aim only of finding optimal treatment. It is not part of the role of the physician in providing medical care to develop scientific knowledge that can help future patients.

> **Therapeutic beneficence**
> A physician's obligation to promote his or her patient's well-being.
>
> **Therapeutic non-maleficence**
> A physician's obligation not to expose his patient to the possibility of harm without the prospect of direct and counterbalancing benefit to the patient.

Clinical research, in contrast, is not a therapeutic activity devoted to the personal care of patients. It is designed for answering a scientific question, with the aim of producing "generalizable knowledge." The investigator seeks

> **Generalizable knowledge**
> Reliable information that may be used outside of the experimental context. Clinical trials are generally regarded as a source of generalizable knowledge in that information on the safety and efficacy of a treatment in a trial reliably informs the treatment of similar patients in medical practice.

to learn about disease and its treatment in *groups* of patients, with the ultimate aim of improving medical care. Scientific interest in any particular patient concerns what can be learned that is applicable to other patients. In view of the nature and purpose of clinical research, the principles of beneficence and non-maleficence applicable to clinical research lack the therapeutic meaning that guides their application to medical care. Clinical research is dedicated primarily to promoting the medical good of future patients by means of scientific knowledge derived from experimentation with current research participants—a frankly utilitarian purpose.

A major reason for distinguishing research from therapy is to underscore that clinical research has an inherent potential for exploiting research participants.[1] Exploitation also may occur in clinical medicine—venal physicians sometimes perform medically unnecessary procedures for the sake of profit, for example. Yet when physicians of integrity practice medicine, physicians' and patients' interests converge. The patient desires to regain or maintain health or to relieve suffering; the physician is dedicated to providing the medical help that the patient needs.

> **Exploitation**
> The unfair use of another person or her labour for one's own benefit or some other end. Just what counts—and what does not count—as an instance of exploitation is contested.

> **Venal**
> Susceptible to bribery; corrupt.

In clinical research, by contrast, the interests of investigators and patient volunteers are likely to diverge, even when the investigator acts with complete integrity. Patient volunteers, especially in clinical trials, typically seek therapeutic benefit, though they also may be motivated by altruism.[2] Investigators are interested primarily in developing scientific knowledge about groups of patients. Regardless of investigators' motivations, patient volunteers are at risk of having their well-being compromised in the course of scientific investigation. Clinical research involves an inherent tension between pursuing rigorous science and protecting research participants from harm.[3]

Historically, the ethical distinction between research and therapy emerged out of concern about exploitive abuses of patients in clinical research. Reflection on this dark history gave rise to a major development in the ethics of clinical research: the requirement for independent, prospective review and approval of research protocols.[4] Prior independent review was considered necessary for clinical research because of the divergence between the interests of the investigator and the research participant. Self-regulation by physician-investigators could not be trusted in the research context to the same extent that self-regulation by physicians was appropriate in the therapeutic context. The basic rationale for prospective, independent research review depends on the distinction between research and therapy. . . .

Abandoning the Distinction

The distinction between research and therapy is most likely to be obfuscated in the context of clinical trials, which test the safety or efficacy of investigational and standard treatments. Since patients may derive medical benefit from trial participation, especially in phase III RCTs (the final stage of testing, which many investigational drugs never even reach), clinical trials are often characterized as "therapeutic research."

Nonetheless, the process of treatment in RCTs differs radically from routine clinical practice.[5] Consider the contrast between the hypericum-sertraline trial and routine medical care for depression. If a physician treated 340 patients for major depression, she would not decide which drug to administer by flipping a coin. If the physician elected to use sertraline, she would judge each case individually to determine dose, when to change the dose, and whether to prescribe a second antidepressant or recommend other treatment. We would expect to find considerable variation in the treatment administered to those 340 patients after eight weeks or so. From the vantage point of therapy, this is what it means to provide care to patients.

> **Hypericum-sertraline trial**
> A controversial clinical trial funded by the US National Institutes of Health in which 340 patients with depression—a psychiatric disease for which there exists proven, effective treatment—were randomly assigned to receive hypericum (St. John's Wort; an herbal remedy), sertraline (a standard treatment for depression), or placebo.

From the vantage point of research, such variation would wreak havoc on experimental design and the validity and generalizability of findings. So when patients are randomized to one or another experimental drug, and are treated according to relatively inflexible protocols, the activity is very different from therapeutic medicine.

In many other ways, too, routine aspects of research deviate from what would be required by the duties of therapeutic beneficence and non-maleficence. Volunteer patients and physician investigators are often ignorant of assignment to the experimental or control treatment, which may be a placebo. Trials often include interventions such as blood draws, lumbar punctures, radiation imaging, or biopsies that measure trial outcomes but in no way benefit participants. RCTs often contain a drug "washout" phase before randomization to avoid confounding the evaluation of the investigational treatment with the effects of medication that patients were receiving prior to the trial. These various features of research design promote scientific validity; they carry risks to participants without the prospect of compensating therapeutic benefit. . . .

Once one understands the distinction between research and therapy, one realizes that "therapeutic" research is still research, and that the ethical rules appropriate to it are those appropriate for clinical research generally. Even though the patient may derive benefit from the treatment being evaluated, the basic goal of the activity is not personal therapy, but rather the acquisition of generally applicable scientific knowledge. The basic goal and nature of the activity determines the ethical standards that ought to apply. . . .

Charles Fried and the Similarity Position

In 1974, Fried published *Medical Experimentation: Personal Integrity and Social Policy*, which launched the similarity position within bioethics.[6] Fried assumed that answers to ethical dilemmas in research would have to be found within the ethics of therapeutic medicine. He defended fidelity to the interests of the individual patient against a model in which "medicine is to be viewed as caring for populations."[7] What made the RCT ethically suspect was that it seemed to him a prime example of population-focused—rather than individualized—and utilitarian medicine.

Fried devoted most of his book to defending patients' "rights in personal care."[8] Returning to medical research, he took issue with trials in which patients were randomized to receive either the experimental intervention or standard care. Fried coined the term "equipoise" to describe the ethically necessary condition for conducting an RCT: physician-investigators

must be indifferent to the therapeutic value of the experimental and control treatments evaluated in the trial. The basic idea of equipoise had previously been articulated by Bradford Hill, a pioneer in the development of RCTs.[9] But what Fried objected to primarily in RCTs was not randomization per se, but the fact that no informed consent had been obtained. Fried saw the threat of "care for groups" (instead of "care for individuals") as residing primarily in the idea that it was legitimate to enroll subjects in an RCT without explicit, informed consent because the results of the trial would provide new medical knowledge that would improve the lot of future patients.[10] Because Fried was concerned chiefly about informed consent, an essential ingredient of both medical research and therapeutic medicine, he saw no problem in applying the ethics of medical therapy to medical research. . . .

The Emergence of Clinical Equipoise

The similarity position and clinical equipoise have been popular not only among bioethicists, but also among investigators. We speculate that this ethical perspective helps to address investigators' psychological needs. Physician-investigators, after all, went to medical school, not investigator school. To think of research with patients outside the ethical framework of the physician-patient relationship, as the difference position requires, may be difficult and threatening to them. Clinical equipoise offers a formula that seems to allow them to mix both physician and investigator roles—even if the psychological comfort is purchased at the price of ethical obfuscation. . . .

Critique of the Similarity Position and Clinical Equipoise

We contend that clinical equipoise is fundamentally mistaken because "the RCT dilemma," for which it was proposed as a solution, is false. Clinical equipoise and all other forms of equipoise make sense as a normative requirement for clinical trials only on the assumption that investigators have a therapeutic obligation to the research participants. The "therapeutic obligation" of

> **RCT dilemma**
> The question that Freedman took himself to be addressing: How can the physician, consistent with his duties to the patient, offer the patient participation in a randomized controlled trial in which the treatment the patient received will be determined by chance?

investigators, forming one horn of the RCT dilemma, constitutes a therapeutic misconception about the ethics of clinical trials. The presumption that RCTs must be compatible with the ethics of the physician-patient relationship assumes erroneously that the RCT is a form of therapy, thus inappropriately applying the principles of therapeutic beneficence and non-maleficence that govern clinical medicine to the fundamentally different practice of clinical research. It is impossible to maintain fidelity to doing what is best medically for patients in the context of RCTs because these are not designed for, and may conflict with, personalized care. Although ethically appealing, the project of bridging the gap between therapy and research via the doctrine of clinical equipoise is doomed to fail. . . .

By conflating the ethics of clinical trials with the ethics of therapeutic medicine, proponents of the similarity position may also contribute to the lack of adequate informed consent. If investigators view the ethics of clinical trials through a therapeutic lens, they may explicitly or implicitly foster the therapeutic misconception among research participants—that is, the tendency of participants in trials to confuse clinical trials with medical care. Research participants need to know that the overall activity is aimed not at their own ultimate benefit, but at discovering new knowledge to help future patients. If they think that clinical trial participation is a form of therapy, then they cannot give informed consent. Moreover, unlike the therapeutic context, the patient-subject cannot delegate the decision to the physician-researcher. In the therapeutic setting, a patient can decide to trust the physician to choose the best treatment because the physician has the patient's best interests at heart. The investigator has the interests of future patients at heart, and so cannot decide for the subject whether or not to participate in the research. To be trustworthy, investigators must themselves understand clearly the ways in which clinical research differs from clinical practice and convey this forthrightly to potential research subjects.

It is worth pondering, however, the practical consequences that might ensue if physicians, investigators, patients, and ethicists understood clinical trials without distortion by therapeutic misconceptions. Would recruitment of participants for valuable clinical trials become substantially more difficult, slowing progress in medical care? The fact that clinical trials are no longer seen as a mode of therapy leaves unchanged the real prospect of therapeutic benefits offered to patients from trial participation, including the opportunity to receive promising investigational agents, ancillary medical care, expert diagnostic evaluations, and education about their disorder. Nonetheless, some patients might be less inclined to participate in clinical trials when they appreciate the differences between these scientific experiments and medical care.

To attract enough subjects, researchers might have to pay people for their participation, as researchers in industry-sponsored clinical trials already do with increasing frequency. Payments would add to the cost of conducting clinical trials, but it might help prevent the therapeutic misconception among trial participants.[11] To be paid signifies that the trial participant is not merely a patient seeking therapy. If additional expenditure is necessary to motivate clinical trial participation, then this is a price worth paying for enhanced professional integrity and informed consent. . . .

Study Questions

1. How, according to Miller and Brody, does clinical equipoise "conflate research and therapy"?

2. What is the difference between research and therapy? What does this imply for the ethics of research?

3. How might clinical equipoise impede valid informed consent? Will Miller and Brody's proposal of paying research subjects promote valid informed consent?

Notes

1. E.J. Emanuel, D. Wendler, and C. Grady, "What Makes Clinical Research Ethical?" *JAMA* 283 (2000):2701–11.

2. J. Sugarman, N.E. Kass, S.N. Goodman, P. Perentesis, P. Fernandes, and R.R. Faden, "What Patients Say About Medical Research," *IRB* 20, no. 4 (1998):1–7.

3.   FG. Miller, D.L.Rosenstein, and E.G. DeRenzo, "Professional integrity in Clinical Research," *JAMA* 280 (1998):1449–54.

4.   R.R.Faden and T.L.Beauchamp, *A History and Theory of Informed Consent* (New York: Oxford University Press, 1986):200–2.

5.   J.W. Berg, P.S. Appelbaum, C.W.Lidz, and L.S. Parker, *Informed Consent: Legal Theory and Clinical Practice*, 2nd edition (New York: Oxford University Press, 2001):280–3.

6.   C. Fried, *Medical Experimentation: Personal Integrity and Social Policy* (New York: American Elsevier, 1974).

7.   Ibid., 5

8.   Ibid., 94.

9.   A.B.Hill, "Medical ethics and controlled trials," *British Medical Journal* 1 (1963):1043–9.

10. C. Fried, *Medical Experimentation: Personal Integrity and Social Policy* (New York: American Elsevier, 1974): 8.

11. N. Dickert and C. Grady, "What's the Price of a Research Subject? Approaches to Payment for Research Participation" *New England Journal of Medicine* 341 (1999): 198–203.

THREE Trust-based Obligations of the State and Physician-Researchers to Patient-Subjects

Paul B. Miller and Charles Weijer | *Journal of Medical Ethics* 2006; 32: 542-7.

. . . The solution given by Miller and Brody (pp. 100–3 in this collection) is unsatisfactory. It has been noted that an implausible form of moral dissociation is required, whereby doctors engaging in research must willfully ignore the professional obligations they have as physicians.[1] Further, the assertion that activities themselves generate norms is counterintuitive and requires argument. Finally, the additional assertion that the norms governing activities with differing ends are non-overlapping is obviously false. Norms prohibiting fraud and murder are universal and thus apply across diverse activities. Worse still, Miller and Brody's view is internally inconsistent on this very point. They recognize a duty to obtain informed consent applicable to clinical practice and clinical research. Thus, at least one norm in their schema is overlapping, refuting a central premise of their argument.

Given this, we think physician-researchers will rightly continue to wonder about the implications of their duty of care to patient-subjects when conducting clinical research. When, consistent with this obligation, can a physician offer a patient enrolment in an RCT? Is approval by the research ethics board (REB) sufficient? Is there a role for clinical judgment when doctors act as physician-researchers?

> **Moral dissociation**
>
> A separation of normally related roles and obligations; in this case, a person who is both a physician and an investigator who ignores her professional obligations as a physician to a patient-subject. In psychiatry, moral dissociation is a precursor to multiple personality disorder.

> **Research ethics board**
>
> A committee comprising health professionals, researchers, an ethicist, a lawyer, and one or more community representatives that provide local peer review of the ethical acceptability of human subjects research protocols.

To consider these questions and the broader dilemma satisfactorily, in our view, requires recognition and elucidation of the independent obligations of the state and the physician-researcher to protect the interests of patient-subjects. These obligations are understood to be derived from the trust-based relationship between the patient-subject and the state and the physician-researcher, respectively.

Obligations of the State

Clinical research is the source of a critical public benefit: it aims to place medical practice on a foundation of scientific evidence. Without the voluntary participation of patient-subjects, clinical research cannot proceed and the public will be deprived of an important good. Patient-subjects reasonably trust that the state will protect them in exchange for their contribution to the public good of science. As a result of the trust shown by patient-subjects, and the public benefit derived from their participation in clinical research, the state is morally obliged to exercise its powers to protect their interests. The state fulfils its trust-based obligation to protect the interests of patient-subjects through promulgating regulations with adequate substantive and procedural safeguards for subjects and by ensuring adequate enforcement of these regulations. National regulations and guidelines define standards for scientific and ethical acceptability of clinical research. REBs and national oversight authorities provide an arms-length review of clinical

> **Trust-based obligation**
>
> A moral duty that stems from a trust relationship.

National regulations and guidelines
Most countries have national statements setting out ethical standards for human subjects research. National regulations and guidelines vary in terms of legal force and content from one country to the next. Canada's Tri-Council Policy Statement is a set of guidelines for research ethics boards that does not have the force of law; the US' Common Rule, on the other hand, sets out legally binding standards.

research to ensure its compliance with national standards. The REB, therefore, is best understood as an arm of the state that ensures protection of the liberty and welfare of citizens who give of themselves to further medical knowledge.

Clinical research is reviewed prospectively by the REB. Before potential patient-subjects may be approached regarding study participation, an REB review ensures that protocols meet general ethical and scientific standards.[2] In carrying out this prospective review, REBs scrutinize several key aspects of the research protocol. The study must be scientifically valid—that is, the methods must be appropriate to answer the study question. The study question posed must be of sufficient value to science and society to justify non-therapeutic risks to patient-subjects. Procedures to enroll patient-subjects in the study must be fair and neither exclude those who may benefit from participation nor enroll those who may be unduly susceptible to harm. The benefits and harms of study participation for patient-subjects must stand in reasonable relation. Adequate procedures must be in place to secure valid informed consent. Finally, sufficient safeguards must be in place to protect the confidentiality of private health information.

In making judgments pertaining to liberty and welfare, the REB does not take into account the agent-relative interests of patient-subjects. Review of clinical research by REBs is prospective

Non-therapeutic risks
Potential physical, psychological, social or economic harms associated with procedures in a study that are administered solely to answer the scientific question at hand and that do not hold out a reasonable prospect of direct benefit for the research subject.

Agent-relative interests
The morally relevant concerns of people as individuals in a research study, as distinguished from their concerns as members of a group or population of similar individuals. An assessment of agent-relative interests requires specific knowledge of the individual including his or her particular medical history and circumstances.

and, as such, particular patient-subjects and their particular interests are not yet in view. Rather, REB review is aimed at protecting the agent-neutral interests of patient-subjects. It ensures that patient-subjects are not exposed needlessly to the risks of a study that cannot answer the scientific question posed, or one that deals with a trivial question. It checks procedures for patient-subject selection, but does not check that each enrolled patient-subject is in fact eligible for study participation. It assesses the benefits and harms of the study in the light of existing data on the treatments and characteristics of the study population, not in light of the medical history of particular patient-subjects. The REB scrutinizes consent procedures and documents, not processes of obtaining informed consent from particular patient-subjects. It requires that adequate procedures are in place for protecting the privacy and confidentiality of the personal information of patient-subjects, but does not supervise the handling of information of particular patient-subjects.

Of all of the norms used by the REB in protecting the agent-neutral interests of patient-subjects, the least understood are the substantive and procedural norms through which REBs ensure that benefits and harms of study participation stand in reasonable relation. Existing regulatory norms relating to the evaluation of research benefits and harms are typically vague and disconnected. Interpretations of key concepts vary widely.[3] REBs are thus left to make intuitive assessments on the acceptability of benefits and harms of the research, contributing to inconsistent decision-making processes and results. Elsewhere, we have worked to remedy this problem by providing a structured set of norms and procedures for benefit-harm evaluation by the REB. . . .

We have named our approach component analysis, for it rests on the insight that clinical research often contains a mixture of study procedures.[4] Some procedures

Agent-neutral interests
The morally relevant concerns of people as members of a group or population of similar individuals in a research study, as distinguished from their concerns as individuals. An assessment of agent-neutral interests requires knowledge of only group characteristics, such as the disease under study, and does not require specific knowledge of the individual including her particular medical history and circumstances.

Component analysis
A systematic and comprehensive approach to the ethical analysis of benefits and harms in clinical research that involves the separate consideration of therapeutic and non-therapeutic procedures in a study.

in clinical trials are administered with therapeutic warrant ("therapeutic procedures"), whereas others in the absence of therapeutic warrant are administered purely to answer the scientific question at hand ("non-therapeutic procedures"). The distinction in terms of the presence of therapeutic warrant is morally relevant. Only procedures administered with therapeutic warrant can reasonably be said to advance the welfare interests of patient-subjects in receiving treatment. The benefits and harms associated with therapeutic procedures may therefore be justified through a comparative assessment of the benefits and harms of available treatments. Non-therapeutic procedures cannot reasonably be said to advance the welfare interests of patient-subjects. The risks associated with non-therapeutic procedures must therefore be justified by standards that weigh the welfare interests of patient-subjects in protection from harms of research against the interests of the public and others in the benefits of research. The moral condition imposed on the use of therapeutic procedures is intended to protect their welfare interests in receiving competent medical treatment. By contrast, moral conditions imposed on the use of non-therapeutic procedures are intended to secure their welfare interests in protection from unreasonable risks solely in the interests of others.

On the basis of this distinction, component analysis provides separate substantive moral standards for REB evaluation of the benefits and harms of therapeutic and non-therapeutic procedures. . . . When protocols provide for both therapeutic and non-therapeutic procedures, an REB may deem that a study poses an acceptable balance of benefits and harms only if both sets of moral standards are fulfilled. Obviously, when protocols provide only for non-therapeutic procedures (e.g., interview studies or phase I drug trials in healthy people), this determination is contingent only on satisfaction of standards applicable to non-therapeutic procedures.

Therapeutic procedures must satisfy the clinical equipoise requirement.[5] That is, to approve randomization of subjects to the therapeutic procedures to be studied in the trial, the REB must find that there is a state of honest, professional disagreement in the community of expert practitioners as to the preferred treatment. The prospective and general nature of REB review, combined with the inherently social nature of the establishment of treatment standards, make it appropriate for the REB to evaluate therapeutic procedures in the light of the state of community opinion on the comparative merits of available treatments. In ensuring that the expert community is at odds regarding the comparative merits of treatments available to patient-subjects, the REB ensures that they will not be asked to accept substandard treatment to participate in clinical research. Procedurally, to make this determination, the REB does not survey practitioners. Rather, it scrutinizes the justification for the study, the relevant literature and, where needed, the opinion of impartial clinical experts. Therapeutic procedures are acceptable when the REB judges that, were the evidence supporting the various therapeutic procedures widely known, expert clinicians would disagree as to the preferred treatment.

As non-therapeutic procedures are not administered with therapeutic warrant, differing moral standards apply to their evaluation. In general, risks associated with non-therapeutic procedures must be minimized, consistent with sound scientific design, and must be reasonable in relation to the knowledge to be gained. . . . Procedurally, the REB ensures that all proposed procedures are actually required to meet the scientific ends of the study. At times, non-therapeutic risks may be minimized by piggybacking on routine clinical procedures—for example, extra blood for research purposes may be taken at the time of a clinically indicated blood draw, thereby saving the patient-subject an additional venepuncture. Whether non-therapeutic risks are reasonable in relation to the knowledge to be gained requires a judgment that draws on both scientific expertise on the REB and the opinion of community representatives on the social value of the scientific ends pursued. . . .

Component analysis provides REBs with a comprehensive and systematic framework for evaluating

---

Therapeutic warrant
Evidence that makes it reasonable to believe that a procedure is likely to directly benefit a research subject.

Therapeutic procedure
A study intervention administered on the basis of therapeutic warrant. Therapeutic procedures in research may involve pharmacological, surgical, or psychological interventions.

Non-therapeutic procedure
A study intervention administered solely to answer the scientific question at hand and not on the basis of therapeutic warrant.

Phase I drug trials
Early studies of a new drug in human beings that seek to establish, among other things, a safe dose at which the drug may be administered in further studies. Phase I drug studies often involve healthy volunteers rather than patients as research subjects.

Venepuncture
Piercing a vein, usually in the arm, with a needle and syringe to withdraw blood for testing.

the acceptability of benefits and harms in research. It thereby offers the prospect of improving the quality and consistency of REB review, enabling REBs to better meet the trust patient-subjects repose in the state. However, it is important that we realize the limitations of REB approval. As with its enforcement of other norms, so in its enforcement of the norms related to benefits and harms in component analysis, REB approval signifies only that a protocol meets general standards mandated by the state. The scope of REB review is limited to protection of the agent-neutral interests of patient-subjects, and hence the moral and legal significance of REB approval is circumscribed. REB approval does not entail the moral or legal acceptability of enrolling particular patient-subjects in research, nor does it entail the acceptability of their continued participation in the study, as these acts engage the agent-relative interests of patient-subjects. It is the physician-researcher who retains the independent moral and legal obligation to protect the agent-relative interests of the patient-subject in clinical research.

Obligations of the Physician-Researcher

Miller and Brody deny that the physician-researcher is bound by a duty of care to protect the agent-relative welfare interests of the patient-subject in clinical research. Their position is without persuasive moral or legal foundation. Their account of the obligations of the physician-researcher to the patient-subject has the hallmarks of contractualism. Most notable is the overriding emphasis on informed consent and the negative obligation to avoid exploitation. Although the norms of contractual relationships have an essential role in the social and economic order, they are unsuited to the relationship between a physician-researcher and patient-subject. We leave open the question of whether the contractual model is an appropriate one for relationships between healthy participants and researchers.

It has long been recognized that trust forms the foundation of the relationship between a physician and a patient. The central normative importance of trust to the relationship has been recognized by physicians and protected by fiduciary law for several important reasons. First and foremost, the physician-patient relationship is rooted in the frailty of the human condition. People are vulnerable to sickness and disease, and are often made vulnerable by illness when entering into relationships with physicians. Furthermore, the state vests exclusively in physicians the authority to receive, diagnose and treat patients. By virtue of this grant of exclusive professional license, coupled with disparities in knowledge and power, patients must depend on physicians for the beneficial exercise of clinical judgment in maintaining and improving their health.

Coming to a relationship often prefigured by circumstantial inequality of power and dependence, patients are doubly vulnerable on account of the structural inequality of power and dependence generated by the very act of entrusting power over one person's interests to another—namely, the physician. Circumstantial and structural inequality of power and dependence give rise to a heightened vulnerability to exploitation on the part of the patient-subject. In short, in entrusting power to physicians, patients necessarily face the risk that this power will be misused to their detriment by physicians in pursuit of their own interests or those of others. Precisely because of the vulnerability that prefigures and is generated by it, the relationship between a physician and a patient is closely monitored and policed by the profession and the state.

The trust model is the appropriate one for the relationship between physician-researcher and patient-subject. The relationship bears all the hallmarks of a trust relationship. The patient-subject cannot reasonably be expected to act as a shrewd, independent party to a contract, enjoying an arms-length relationship with the physician-researcher in which both fend for their own interests. Many patients considering participation in research continue to be made vulnerable by illness. They usually agree to participate in research hoping thereby to receive improved treatment. Through consent, the physician-researcher is authorized to exercise most, if not all, of the discretionary powers enjoyed by the physician, including powers of diagnosis and treatment. Similar to other trust relationships, the relationship between physician-research and patient-subject is characterized by circumstantial and structural inequality of

---

Contractualism
A moral view that defines what people owe one another based on the agreements reached between them.

Trust
A relationship of structural inequality in which the more powerful party (e.g., the physician or physician-researcher) is given control over significant practical interests of the less powerful party (e.g., the patient or patient-subject), engendering dependence and vulnerability.

power and dependence relating to authorization of the exercise of power. By virtue of their illness and their desire to overcome it, patient-subjects authorize physician-researchers to exercise discretionary powers, and trust and rely on them to do so in their interests to the greatest extent possible given the inherent demands of research design.

If the relationship between a physician-researcher and a patient-subject is properly theorized as one of trust, what obligations accrue thereby to the physician-researcher? We suggest that trust relationships of this kind—that is, in which one party entrusts another with power over significant practical interests—give rise to a range of obligations reflecting the structure of the relationship. They include a duty of loyalty and a duty of care. We do not explore all trust-based obligations presently, as we are here interested only in the manner in which one of them—the duty of care— is to be specified in consideration of a particular trust relationship— namely, that between physician-researcher and patient-subject.

The specification of the duty of care will vary among relationships depending on the scope of power wielded by the stronger party and how the interests of the weaker party are defined. Patient-subjects in clinical research by definition are ill and have an interest in receiving competent medical care. Physician-researchers by virtue of their professional license have the power to provide such care. The duty of care under which physician-researchers operate may thus be specified as follows. The physician-researcher is trusted to exercise clinical judgment in protecting the medical interests of the patient-subject and has an obligation to act in a manner that meets this trust.

This simple statement of the duty of care belies considerable difficulty and disagreement over its precise specification. Just how are physician-researchers to meet their obligation to exercise judgment in the interests of patient-subjects, given the restrictions trial design places on treatment? . . . A novel specification of the physician-researcher's duty of care to the patient-subject is required that keeps the individual patient-subject in view. Given the requirement for

review and approval of RCTs by REBs, this specification should also be temporally situated.

The physician-researcher may approach a patient for enrollment in an RCT only after REB approval is obtained. As such, when it is based on appropriate implementation of component analysis, REB approval provides the physician-researcher with a reasonable basis for believing that the enrolment of patients in the RCT is provisionally consistent with their duty of care to the patients. This is because clinical equipoise protects the agent-neutral welfare interests of patient-subjects in receiving competent care. Nevertheless, the use of clinical judgment by the physician-researcher is essential to ensuring that the agent-relative welfare interests of the patient-subject are protected. Accordingly, to satisfy their duty of care to the patient-subjects, the conduct of the physician-researchers is subject to what we call the clinical judgment principle. Under the clinical judgment principle, knowing that an RCT has been approved by an REB under component analysis, the physician may offer patients enrolment in a trial unless (1) they believe that it would be medically irresponsible to do so, and (2) this belief is supported by evidence that ought to be convincing to colleagues.

Physician-researchers meet their duty of care through making expert judgments, taking account of evidence on treatment alternatives and the circumstances of the patient-subject. In fulfilling the duty, the physician-researcher will decline to offer enrolment to a patient who meets eligibility criteria, but whose medical history suggests that participation may be unduly harmful. The physician-researcher must also recommend that a patient-subject withdraw from an RCT regardless of protocol requirements in the case of an unexpected adverse event that would, in clinical practice, require cessation of treatment or adoption of an alternate course of treatment.

The clinical judgment principle has at least four advantages over previous specifications of the physician-researcher's duty of care. Firstly, it recognizes and defines the place for the clinical judgment of the physician-researcher in protecting the agent-relative

> **Duty of loyalty**
> Moral obligation of the physician-researcher to be faithful in protecting the interests of the patient-subject.

> **Duty of care**
> Moral obligation of the physician-researcher to act and to advise in accord with the patient-subject's best medical interests.

> **Clinical judgment principle**
> A specification of a physician-researcher's duty of care according to which the physician-researcher, knowing that an RCT was reviewed by an REB using component analysis, may offer a patient enrollment in a study unless he believes that doing so is medically irresponsible and this belief is supported by evidence that ought to be convincing to colleagues.

welfare interests of the patient-subject. Clinical equipoise does not leave room for such judgment. Secondly, it situates the exercise of clinical judgment temporally, recognizing that the physician-researcher may not approach a patient for enrolment in an RCT until after the study has been approved by an REB. The uncertainty principle does not speak to REB approval or the relationship between judgments made by the REB and physician-researcher. Thirdly, it provides a reasonable epistemic basis for physician-researcher judgment, avoiding the undue restrictiveness of clinical equipoise (i.e., only RCT results count as evidence) and the undue laxity of the uncertainty principle (i.e., anything counts as evidence). The clinical judgment principle allows judgments to be based on many sources of evidence, including the physician's experience, the patient-subject's history or novel findings in the literature, provided that such evidence ought to be deemed convincing by colleagues. Finally, the clinical judgment principle specifies a duty of care that is, in turn, firmly rooted in the moral and legal theory of trust relationships. . . .

> **Uncertainty principle**
> A moral requirement according to which a physician must be genuinely uncertain as to the preferred treatment for a particular patient before she may offer RCT enrollment to the patient. Any treatment preference—even one based on anecdotal information or a hunch—is thought, according to this view, to make trial enrollment unethical.

Study Questions

1. What is a research ethics board? How does it function to protect research subjects?

2. What is the clinical judgment principle? How does it function to protect research subjects?

3. What is the trust-model used by Miller and Weijer? How does it operate at the level of the state and the physician-researcher?

Notes

1. Lemmens T, Miller PB. Avoiding a Jekyll-and-Hyde approach to the ethics of clinical research and practice. *Am J Bioethics* 2002;2:14–17.
2. Emanuel EJ, Wendler D, Grady C. What makes clinical research ethical? *JAMA* 2000;283:2701–11.
3. Shah S, Whittle A, Wilfond B, et al. How do institutional review boards apply the federal risk and benefit standards for pediatric research? *JAMA* 2004;291:476–82.
4. Weijer C, Miller PB. When are research risks reasonable in relation to anticipated benefits? *Nat Med* 2004;10:570–3.
5. Freedman B. Equipoise and the ethics of clinical research. *N Engl J Med* 1987;317:141–5.

Chapter Study Questions

1. Miller and Brody claim that Freedman's view is based on a therapeutic misconception. What do they mean by this and how might Freedman respond?

2. Miller and Brody's view can be understood as rooted in contract, while Miller and Weijer's view is grounded in a trust model. Describe and critically assess each view.

3. Miller and Weijer do not believe that Freedman solved the "RCT dilemma." Are they right?

Critical Analysis

Consider the following from the article by Miller and Brody:

> "Once one understands the distinction between research and therapy, one realizes that 'therapeutic' research is still research, and that the ethical rules appropriate to it are those appropriate for clinical research generally. Even though the patient may derive benefit from treatment being evaluated, the basic goal of the activity is not personal therapy, but rather the acquisition of generally applicable scientific knowledge. The basic goal and nature of the activity determines the ethical standards that ought to apply."

Outline Miller and Brody's argument in your own words, paying particular attention to the premises that they rely on to support their main conclusion. Choose one of the premises for evaluation. Try to think of at least one objection to this premise.

Case Study

Brandon was originally referred to Dr Johnston's practice by Student Health during his first year of university for treatment of depression. After discussing his symptoms of insomnia, fatigue, and weight loss Dr Johnston prescribed the first of what, over the next three years, would be several antidepressants. While Brandon would have periods of stability lasting from a few months to a year, eventually either the medication stopped working or the side effects became too bothersome. Despite his chronic depression, Brandon continues to function at a high level, and is now in the final semester of his undergraduate degree.

Today Brandon arrives at Dr Johnston's office complaining about worsening symptoms. He says, "I'm starting to feel tired again, like I have no energy, and my motivation to do things is slipping." Brandon goes on to describe a worsening of his depressive symptoms as well as a growing dissatisfaction with the current antidepressant's side effects. Then, he mentions a recent conversation with one of his cousins, who also has a history of depression, in which she enthusiastically relayed her experience in a clinical trial for Serenil, a new lithium-based antidepressant.

Ordinarily in these circumstances, Dr Johnston would consider either increasing the dose of the antidepressant Brandon is taking or switching him to a different antidepressant. Dr Johnston is familiar with Serenil and believes that it shows promise for the treatment of chronic depression, especially in younger adults. However, ongoing clinical trials for the medication utilize a placebo control, meaning that half the patients enrolled in the study will receive no treatment. In addition, data is not yet available concerning the follow-up treatment of patients who withdrew from the trials. Brandon is anxious to participate. "I've tried so many older drugs. I mean, what have I got to lose? How do I sign up for the trial?"

1. What are the potential benefits and harms for Brandon in participating in the RCT of Serenil?

2. How would the authors of the three articles in this chapter characterize Dr Johnston's obligations to Brandon in this case?

3. What should Dr Johnston do? Why?

Further Reading

Canada National Placebo Working Committee on the Appropriate Use of Placebos in Clinical Trials in Canada. Final report [Internet]. Ottawa: Canadian Institute of Health Research; 2004. Available from: http://www.cihr-irsc.gc.ca/e/25139.html. Date Accessed: 7 June 2012.

Canadian Institutes of Health Research, Natural Sciences and Engineering Research Council of Canada, and Social Sciences and Humanities Research Council of Canada. Tri-council policy statement: ethical conduct for research involving humans [Internet]. December, 2010. Available from: http://www.pre.ethics.gc.ca/eng/policy-politique/initiatives/tcps2-eptc2/Default/. Date Accessed: 7 June 2012.

Kimmelman J. The therapeutic misconception at 25: treatment, research, and confusion. *Hastings Center Report* 2007; 37(6):36–42.

Miller PB, Weijer C. Fiduciary obligations in clinical research. *J Law Med Ethic* 2006;34 (2):424–40.

Miller PB, Weijer C. Rehabilitating equipoise. *Kennedy Inst Ethic J* 2003;13 (2):93–118.

Justice and Access to Health Care

I n this chapter, we explore the role of justice in determining access to health care. Clearly, health is important. Without a reasonable degree of health, mental and physical, one cannot live well or enjoy life's essential goods, and if one suffers from poor health, it is not possible for one to exercise one's autonomy fully or execute one's choices. It is extraordinarily difficult to predict the loss of health or injury even for the most prescient individual, and when one is struck down by disease or injury the remedy can be costly. The centrality of health to well-being and autonomy, and the unpredictability of disease and loss of health, are what explain the fact that the acquisition of health care is a high priority for most individuals. That most individuals assign health a high priority is reflected in the fact that in almost all countries in which it is financially possible, the state plays some role in the provision of health care.

Our political rhetoric often speaks of health care and its provision as a right. However, in Canada it is not the case that citizens have a constitutional right to health care insurance. It would not be a violation of Canada's *Charter of Rights and Freedoms* if governments simply ceased to provide it. Instead, it is offered to a citizen as a matter of social policy; it is a privilege that people have as citizens of Canada. Canada has developed a unique system of health care delivery. The government, whether federal, provincial or territorial, is the only insurance provider for those procedures that are considered by the *Canada Health Act* to be medically necessary. When you visit a doctor for a check-up or you get your hip replaced in a hospital, the procedures are billed to the government. For other services not deemed to be medically necessary by the *Canada Health Act*, Canadians must purchase private insurance or pay out of pocket for the expenses incurred. This is the way in which most people pay for dental care and vision care, and for prescription drugs that are not provided in a hospital setting.

This system strikes many as a plausible means by which to satisfy the need for health care, consistent with the promotion of other social goods (e.g., education, environmental protection, and so on). It is, however, essential to ask what might justify this particular system of health care insurance and whether it can be improved upon. This requires dealing with a deeper question. What is the basis for the claim that the state ought in some way to provide health care insurance to its citizens? This is particularly important in light of the fact that it is not entirely obvious that the state ought to play any positive role whatever in the provision of health care.

In "An Ethical Framework for Access to Health Care," the members of the US President's Commission for the Study of Ethical Problems in Medicine and Biomedical and Behavioral Research argue that there is a social obligation to provide everyone with an adequate standard of care without excessive burden. The ground of this obligation is not a right. Rather, the ground rests on the special nature of health care. The authors argue that what makes health care special is its impact on well-being and opportunity, the kind of information it supplies, and the interpersonal significance of that with which it deals, namely, birth, illness, and death. The fact that it produces various goods generates an obligation to provide an adequate standard of health care, which means a level of care sufficient to produce the goods to the point that they "facilitate a reasonably full and satisfying life." The obligation to make health care available is social rather than individual in nature because: (1) it is usually impossible for an individual to obtain it by him- or herself; (2) an individual's health status is largely undeserved; and (3) there is a marked difficulty associated with predicting health care needs. The authors move some way towards specifying the notion of adequacy, though the details are left to policy makers. They remain open-minded about the specific institutions that should assume the primary role for making health care insurance available. Indeed, the authors do not think that the government should be the institution that is primarily responsible for providing health care insurance.

In "The Medical Minimum: Zero", Jan Narveson argues that there is no obligation for the state to provide or mandate others to provide universal health care or health insurance. His argument rests on the distinction between two kinds of rights: negative and positive. He thinks that everyone agrees that there is a negative right to health care or health insurance, which entails that others have a duty not to interfere with legitimate and voluntary attempts to obtain it. This right is justified by the fact that it answers to our common interest in securing what is agreed to be a precondition to living the lives we choose to live. However, no such justification is available for a positive right to health care or health insurance, which entails that others have a duty to provide such care or insurance. No justification exists for forcing others to pay for health care or insurance for all, since there is no common interest that this right serves. We have no common interest in satisfying the health needs of others, and, moreover, there are good reasons not to: we are not our brothers' keeper and we do not want to provide health care to the feckless.

In "Health Care as a Commodity," Joseph Heath attacks some of the arguments commonly relied on in defending Canada's socialized health care insurance scheme. In particular, he maintains that the argument according to which only a system like Canada's is consistent with not treating health care as a commodity is bad and obscures the most plausible rationale for it. Heath thinks that it is important to note that provincial and other governments are in the business of providing universal health care insurance, not health care. The main rationale for this is that health care costs are unpredictable, making simple markets for its delivery inefficient. Furthermore, private insurers tend to avoid insuring certain high-risk groups and they find it difficult to control costs. Heath argues that the universal public insurance scheme in Canada solves both of these worries, and is therefore more efficient. He goes on to suggest that not all forms of two-tiered medicine are inconsistent with this system.

`ONE` An Ethical Framework for Access to Health Care

President's Commission for the Study of Ethical Problems in Medicine and Biomedical and Behavioral Research | *Securing Access to Health Care*. **Washington, DC: US Government Printing Office 1983: 11-47.**

The Special Importance of Health Care

Although the importance of health care may, at first blush, appear obvious, . . . it is possible to step back and examine those properties of health care that lead to the ethical conclusion that it ought to be distributed equitably.

Well-Being

Ethical concern about the distribution of health care derives from the special importance of health care in promoting personal well-being by preventing or relieving pain, suffering, and disability and by avoiding loss of life. . . .

Opportunity

Health care can also broaden a person's range of opportunities, that is, the array of life plans that is reasonable to pursue within the conditions obtaining in society.[1] . . . Health is comparable in importance to education in determining the opportunities available to people to pursue different life plans.

> **Range of opportunities**
> The members of the commission maintain that health is what the American political philosopher John Rawls called a primary good: something that every rational person is assumed to want and something that is of use regardless of one's particular desires or life plans. In addition to health, primary goods include income, wealth, rights, liberties, opportunities, and powers.

Information

The special importance of health care stems in part from its ability to relieve worry and to enable patients to adjust to their situation by supplying reliable information about their health. Most people do not understand the true nature of a health problem when it first develops. Health professionals can then perform the worthwhile function of informing people about their conditions and about the expected prognoses with or without various treatments. Though information sometimes creates concern, often it reassures patients either by ruling out a feared disease or by revealing the self-limiting nature of a condition and, thus, the lack of need for further treatment. . . .

The Interpersonal Significance of Illness, Birth, and Death

Since all human beings are vulnerable to disease and all die, health care has a special interpersonal significance: it expresses and nurtures bonds of empathy and compassion. The depth of a society's concern about health care can be seen as a measure of its sense of solidarity in the face of suffering and death. Moreover, health care takes on special meaning because of its role in the beginning of a human being's life as well as the end. In spite of all the advances in the scientific understanding of birth, disease, and death, these profound and universal experiences remain shared mysteries that touch the spiritual side of human nature. For these reasons a society's commitment to health care reflects some of its most basic attitudes about what it is to be a member of the human community.

The Concept of Equitable Access to Health Care

The special nature of health care helps to explain why it ought to be accessible, in a fair (and equitable) fashion, to all. . . .

Access to What?

"Equitable access" could be interpreted in a number of ways: equality of access, access to whatever an individual needs or would benefit from, or access to an adequate level of care.

Equity as Equality

It has been suggested that equity is achieved either when everyone is assured of receiving an equal quantity of health care dollars or when people enjoy equal health. The most common characterization of equity as equality, however, is as providing everyone with the same level of health care. In this view, it follows that if a given level of care is available to one individual it must be available to all. If the initial standard is set high, by reference to the highest level of care presently received, an enormous drain would result on the resources needed to provide other goods. Alternatively, if the standard is set low in order to avoid an excessive use of resources, some beneficial services would have to be withheld from people who wished to purchase them. In other words, no one would be allowed access to more services or services of higher quality than those available to everyone else, even if he or she were willing to pay for those services from his or her personal resources.

As long as significant inequalities in income and wealth persist, inequalities in the use of health care can be expected beyond those created by differences in need. Given people with the same pattern of preferences and equal health care needs, those with greater financial resources will purchase more health care. Conversely, given equal financial resources, the different patterns of health care preferences that typically exist in any population will result in a different use of health services by people with equal health care needs. Trying to prevent such inequalities would require interfering with people's liberty to use their income to purchase an important good like health care while leaving them free to use it for frivolous or inessential ends. Prohibiting people with higher incomes or stronger preferences for health care from purchasing more care than everyone else gets would not be feasible, and would probably result in a black market for health care. . . .

Equity as Access Solely According to Benefit or Need

Interpreting equitable access to mean that everyone must receive all health care that is of any benefit to them also has unacceptable implications. Unless health is the only good or resources are unlimited, it would be irrational for a society—as for an individual—to make a commitment to provide whatever health care might be beneficial regardless of cost. Although health care is of special importance, it is surely not all that is important to people. Pushed to an extreme, this criterion might swallow up all of society's resources, since there is virtually no end to the funds that could be devoted to possibly beneficial care for diseases and disabilities and to their prevention.

Equitable access to health care must take into account not only the benefits of care but also the cost in comparison with other goods and services to which those resources might be allocated. Society will reasonably devote some resources to health care but reserve most resources for other goals. This, in turn, will mean that some health services (even of a life-saving sort) will not be developed or employed because they would produce too few benefits in relation to their costs and to the other ways the resources for them might be used. . . .

Equity as an Adequate Level of Health Care

The special nature of health care dictates that everyone have access to *some* level of care: enough care to achieve sufficient welfare, opportunity, information, and evidence of interpersonal concern to facilitate a reasonably full and satisfying life. That level can be termed "an adequate level of health care." The difficulty of sharpening this amorphous notion into a workable foundation for health policy is a major problem in the United States today. This concept is not new; it is implicit in the public debate over health policy and has manifested itself in the history of public policy in this country. . . .

Understanding equitable access to health care to mean that everyone should be able to secure an adequate level of care has several strengths. Because an adequate level of care may be less than "all beneficial care" and because it does not require that all needs be satisfied, it acknowledges the need for setting priorities within health care and signals a clear recognition that society's resources are limited and that there are other goods besides health. Thus, interpreting equity as access to adequate care does not generate an open-ended obligation. One of the chief dangers of interpretations of equity that require virtually unlimited resources for health care is that they encourage the view that equitable access is an impossible ideal. Defining equity as an adequate level of care for all avoids an impossible commitment of resources without falling into the opposite error of abandoning the enterprise of seeking to ensure that health care is in fact available for everyone.

In addition, since providing an adequate level of care is a limited moral requirement, this definition also avoids the unacceptable restriction on individual liberty entailed by the view that equity requires equality. Provided that an adequate level is available to all, those who prefer to use their resources to obtain care that exceeds that level do not offend any ethical principle in doing so. . . .

> **Equity as an adequate level of care for all**
> The idea that justice requires that people have access to some reasonable level of care without excessive burden and without forbidding some from acquiring more care if they choose to do so.

With What Burdens?

It is not enough to focus on the care that individuals receive; attention must be paid to the burdens they must bear in order to obtain it—waiting and travel time, the cost and availability of transport, the financial cost of the care itself. Equity requires not only that adequate care be available to all, but also that these burdens not be excessive.

If individuals must travel unreasonably long distances, wait for unreasonably long hours, or spend most of their financial resources to obtain care, some will be deterred from obtaining adequate care, with adverse effects on their health and well-being. Others may bear the burdens, but only at the expense of their ability to meet other important needs. If one of the main reasons for providing adequate care is that health care increases welfare and opportunity, then a system that required large numbers of individuals to forego food, shelter, or educational advancement in order to obtain care would be self-defeating and irrational.

The concept of acceptable burdens in obtaining care, as opposed to excessive ones, parallels in some respects the concept of adequacy. Just as equity does not require equal access, neither must the burdens of obtaining adequate care be equal for all persons. What is crucial is that the variations in burdens fall within an acceptable range. As in determining an adequate level of care, there is no simple formula for ascertaining when the burdens of obtaining care fall within such a range. Yet some guidelines can be formulated. To illustrate, since a given financial outlay represents a greater sacrifice to a poor person than to a rich person, "excessive" must be understood in relation to income. . . .

A Societal Obligation

Society has a moral obligation to ensure that everyone has access to adequate care without being subject to excessive burdens. In speaking of a societal obligation the Commission makes reference to society in the broadest sense—the collective American community. . .

The Commission believes it is important to distinguish between society, in this inclusive sense, and government as one institution among others in society. Thus the recognition of a collective or societal obligation does not imply that government should be the only or even the primary institution involved in the complex enterprise of making health care available. . . .

Securing equitable access is a societal rather than a merely private or individual responsibility for several reasons. First, while health is of special importance for human beings, health care—especially scientific health care—is a social product requiring the skills and efforts of many individuals; it is not something that individuals can provide for themselves solely through their own efforts. Second, because the need for health care is both unevenly distributed among persons and highly unpredictable and because the cost of securing care may be great, few individuals could secure adequate care without relying on some social mechanism for sharing the costs. Third, if persons generally deserved their health conditions or if the need for health care were fully within the individual's control, the fact that some lack adequate care would not be viewed as an inequity. But differences in health status, and hence differences in health care needs, are largely undeserved because they are, for the most part, not within the individual's control.

Uneven and Unpredictable Health Needs

While requirements for other basic necessities, such as adequate food and shelter, vary among people within a relatively limited range, the need for health care is distributed very unevenly and its occurrence at any particular time is highly unpredictable. . . .

Responsibility for Differences in Health Status

Were someone responsible for (and hence deserving of) his or her need for health care, then access to the necessary health care might be viewed as merely an individual concern. But the differences among people's needs for health care are for the most part not within their control, and thus are not something for which they should be held accountable. Different needs for care are largely a matter of good or bad fortune—that is, a consequence of a natural and social lottery that no one chooses to play.

In a very real sense, people pay for the consequences of the actions that cause them illness or disability—through the suffering and loss of opportunity they experience. The issue here is a narrower one: to what extent is the societal responsibility to secure health care for the sick and injured limited by personal responsibility for the need for health care? It seems reasonable for people to bear the foreseeable consequences (in terms of health care needs) of their informed and voluntary choices. Indeed, as an ethical matter, the principle of self-determination implies as a corollary the responsibility of individuals for their choices.

However, to apply the notion of personal responsibility in a fair way in setting health care policy would be a complex and perhaps impossible task. First, identifying those people whose informed, voluntary choices have caused them foreseeable harm would be practically as well as theoretically very difficult. It is often not possible to determine the degree to which an individual's behaviour is fully informed regarding the health consequences of the behaviour.

> **Natural and social lottery**
> The metaphors of the natural and social lotteries attempt to capture the thought that one's natural capacities (e.g., one's intelligence) and one's social standing (e.g., one's political and economic power) are a matter of chance and luck, just like the winnings in a regular lottery. For many, these benefits and burdens are seen as undeserved or arbitrary from the moral point of view, requiring that justice in part nullify their effects.

Efforts to educate the public about the effects of life-style on health status are desirable, but it must also be acknowledged that today people who conscientiously strive to adopt a healthy lifestyle find themselves inundated with an enormous amount of sometimes contradictory information about what is healthful. Voluntariness is also especially problematic regarding certain behaviours that cause some people ill health, such as smoking and alcohol abuse.[2]

Moreover, there are great difficulties in determining the extent of the causal role of particular behaviour on an individual's health status. For many behaviours, consequences appear only over long periods of time, during which many other elements besides the particular behaviour have entered into the causal process that produces a disease or disability. For example, the largely unknown role of genetic predispositions for many diseases makes it difficult to designate particular behaviours as their "cause."

Second, even if one knew who should be held responsible for what aspects of their own ill health, policies aimed at institutionalizing financial accountability for "unhealthy behaviour" or at denying the necessary

> **Genetic predisposition to disease**
> The likelihood of contracting a disease or developing a medical condition because of one's genetic composition, which in part determines one's chances of becoming diseased.

health care for those who have "misbehaved" are likely to involve significant injustices and other undesirable consequences. Leaving people free to engage in health-risky behaviour only if they can afford to pay for its consequences is fair only if the existing patterns of income distribution are fair, and if the payment required fully accounts for all the costs to society of the ill health and its treatment. . . .

However, even if it is inappropriate to hold people responsible for their health status, it is appropriate to hold them responsible for a fair share of the cost of their own health care. Society's moral obligation to provide equitable access for all and the individual responsibility for bearing a share of the costs of achieving equity rest on the same considerations of fairness. Individuals who—because they know that others will come to their aid—fail to take reasonable steps to provide for their own health care when they could do so without excessive burdens would be guilty of exploiting the generosity of their fellow citizens. The societal obligation is therefore balanced by corresponding individual obligations.

In light of the special importance of health care, the largely undeserved character of differences in health status, and the uneven distribution and unpredictability of health care needs, society has a moral obligation to ensure adequate care for all. . . .

Approximating Adequacy

The intention of the Commission is to provide a frame of reference for policymakers, not to resolve these complex questions. Nevertheless, it is possible to raise some of the specific issues that should be considered in determining what constitutes adequate care. It is important, for example, to gather accurate information about and compare the costs and effects, both favourable and unfavourable, of various treatment or management options. The options that better serve the goals that make health care of special importance should be assigned a higher value. The assessment of costs must take two factors into account: the cost of a proposed option in relation to alternative forms of care that would achieve the same goal of enhancing the welfare and opportunities of the patient, and the cost of each proposed option in terms of foregone opportunities to apply the same resources to social goals other than that of ensuring equitable access.

Furthermore, a reasonable specification of adequate care must reflect an assessment of the relative importance of many different characteristics of a given form of care for a particular condition. Sometimes the problem is posed as: What *amounts* of care and what *quality* of care? Such a formulation reduces a complex problem to only two dimensions, implying that all care can readily be ranked as better or worse. Because two alternative forms of care may vary along a number of dimensions, there may be no consensus among reasonable and informed individuals about which form is of higher overall quality. It is worth bearing in mind that adequacy does not mean the highest possible level of quality or strictly equal quality any more than it requires equal amounts of care; of course, adequacy does require that everyone receive care that meets standards of sound medical practice.

Any combination of arrangements for achieving adequacy will presumably include some health care delivery settings that mainly serve certain groups, such as the poor or those covered by public programs. The fact that patients receive care in different settings or from different providers does not itself show that some are receiving inadequate care. The Commission believes that there is no moral objection to such a system so long as all receive care that is adequate in amount and quality and all patients are treated with concern and respect.

At this point, the complexity of the problem of deciding what constitutes adequate care is apparent. However, clear and useful conclusions can emerge even when there is no agreement on the details of adequacy. In the case of pregnant women, for example, there is a consensus in the United States that some prenatal care, the attention of a trained health professional during labour and delivery, and some continuity between the two are all essential for an adequate level of care. . . .

Study Questions

1. What are the four characteristics of health care that make it special?

2. What reasons do the authors provide for thinking that there is a social rather than an individual obligation to provide health care?

3. To specify the idea of an "adequate level of health care," the authors appear to appeal to the notion of consensus. Is this a plausible tool on which to rely in this context?

Notes

1. Norman Daniels, Health Care Needs and Distributive Justice, *Philosophy and Public Affairs,* 10, 2, p. 146 (1981).

2. Daniel Wikler, Persuasion and Coercion for Health, *The Milbank Memorial Fund Quarterly. Health and Society*, 56, 3, p. 303 (1978).

TWO The Medical Minimum: Zero

Jan Narveson | *Journal of Medicine and Philosophy* 2011; 36: 558-71.

The Issue

. . . In 1983, the President's Commission released a report entitled "Securing Access to Health Care," which concluded that there were normative reasons for ensuring access to an "adequate level of care" for all Americans. . . . But . . . is there a natural or moral right to health care access or does the government have a moral duty to provide it? . . . The answer to this question is: No.

Let us begin with some important definitions. When there is talk of the government, or perhaps "society," "securing access" to this "adequate level of health care," the most obvious interpretation of those words is that the government will tax people to fund the supply of that level of care to *all Americans* (or, if it is some other country, then *all citizens of that country*). In the current terminology of political philosophy, this is equivalent to proclaiming that all Americans have the right against their government—which means all their fellow Americans, since that is where the money comes from—to that level of care.

Those sorts of rights—rights that others, on pain of punishment, are to provide to the right holder with something in the way of a good or service that is advantageous to the recipient—are what we nowadays called "positive rights." The use of the term "right" is in fact systematically ambiguous, for in addition to positive rights there are *negative* rights. These are rights that others not do certain things to the right holder: especially, that those other people refrain from damaging, injuring, or depriving the person in question of what he or she has a right to. That we have a negative right to our health is something no one would surely deny: for to say this is simply to say that others *may not damage our health*—make us sick, injure us, or, at the extreme, kill us. . . .

This distinction is not a distinction between two kinds of goods *supplied by governments*. It is a purely moral distinction between two sorts of actions/

> **Right**
> A particular kind of moral constraint on what it is permissible to do or refrain from doing to the entity possessing the right.

inactions that our fellow men may be claimed to owe us: namely, between their doing things for us, for example, supplying things to us, which requires cost and exertion on their part, and their not doing things to us, especially not *harming* us, which normally and in principle requires nothing from them. . . .

The doing of nothing, just as such, requires no output and no expense from us, normally. . . . If some people will not refrain, on their own initiative, from theft and assault then it may be helpful for others to assemble forces to prevent them from doing such or perhaps to punish them, . . . which requires expense, effort, or both. . . . However, to have a negative right is not as such to have a *positive* right to *the provision* of that effort or expense by our fellows. . . .

Of course, the important question is whether anything *morally* important hangs on this distinction. Are there good arguments why we should think that our fellows should have negative rights and similarly good ones against crediting them with a significant array of positive rights? . . .

To say that someone has a right is to say that someone else has a duty. . . . If it is a general proclamation of rights, notionally of all humans in relation to all humans, then it is to say that everyone has a duty. When we talk rights talk, we are claiming that there is something about the putative right holders, which is such that, somehow, it constitutes reason to impose something on others. With negative rights, it is the duty to refrain; with positive rights, it is the duty to provide the help needed, when and if it is needed and we are able to make the provision in question. Rights are what we morally are allowed to *compel* each other to respect if compulsion should be needed to elicit the respect in question. . . .

All that is merely analysis in hopes of clarifying what is at issue. The question now is, what are rights or more generally moral claims based on—or are there any at all? . . . What there is to go on is individuals and their interests—their wants, their desires, their satisfactions, their goals—plus the fact of there being a great many others, each with their various interests, etc., and yet each of them with a unique bundle of interests, at least some of which bring them into conflict with their fellows. There is also the fact of our abilities, skills, and talents, which vary enormously.

What each of us simply wants of our fellows is of little interest as such. (Why one's fellows ought to be disposed to satisfy one's desires, after all, is a bit of a puzzler.) What we collectively want, however, would be of great interest if we can manage to say what that is. But one thing it is not is something like the general welfare. Some of us want that, some do not; many are indifferent. . . . We do not unite behind things like that. We can, however, unite behind what is in the *common* interest and especially behind any general requirements that can be seen to be what we need to impose on each other if we are to live the satisfactory lives we are each variously trying to live.

> **The general welfare**
> What is best for society as a whole considering the interests of all those who make it up.

Now, the case for a general and generous allotment of negative rights is . . . clear. . . . If I propose to get my way by force, then you will be rational to resist, especially because . . . we are probably not much different in strength and especially in our ability to rally others around to help if it comes to that. Nobody wants to be injured, killed, or robbed. We all do well both to disapprove of such actions and also to take measures to deal with those who would do such things. . . .

We are, in short, safe in asserting the Humean natural rights: security of persons and possessions, recognition of transfers by consent (only), and reliability of contracts. None of these assures or even makes it particularly plausible that we should impose on all who can pay the duty of providing these various goods and services to persons who cannot produce enough to pay for them themselves. Charitable assistance to our fellows in time of need, yes. But compulsory assistance, as with taxation? Not obviously. . . .

Now we can get back to proposals about positive rights. Minimal income, minimal education, minimal medical care? Is there a real claim that we will all rationally unite behind the proposal to *require* contributions from all—and specifically all our fellow countrypersons in the particular nation-state we happen to live in—for those purposes? . . .

When people talk of a right to a decent minimum, etc., what do they have in mind? In context, it is clear that current discussions among academics in the United States in particular have in mind the "amount" of health care that your fellow citizens may be *required*, in the form of taxation, to purchase for you. It is presumed, in brief, that we have what is now known as a "positive right" against our fellow citizens to some amount of health care—the only real question being, how much? (That is certainly the standard assumption in Canada, where I live.) But the presumption has to be challenged. We may insist that to that particular question, there is only one plausible answer: None. . . . Any other answer needs to tell us why people should be compelled to pay for other people's health care at the proposed level. . . A positive right to medical care in today's world would be a right to something that can indeed be supplied. The question is whether that supply may properly be *compelled*. . . .

Rights: The Bearing of the Negative-Positive Distinction

The distinction of negative and positive rights . . . makes all the difference, in this case, . . . between self-administered charity or voluntary insurance on the one hand and centrally enforced supposed entitlement on the other. . . . Appeals . . . to the latter . . . are question-begging: few nowadays ask whether; they ask only how much. But surely the first thing to settle should be whether we have the entitlement in question at all. In the absence of a good case for the latter, the default, surely, is the former. Voluntary actions, so long as they are peaceable, need no justification. Compulsory impositions do. . . .

Insurance

Among those voluntary actions needing no justification would, of course, be contributions toward the care of others and, for that matter, toward research aimed at discovering cures or preventions of various diseases and other afflictions. The remaining possibility is, of course, formation of an insurance group, whose members pay an agreed fee in return for a range of services if those should be required.

Thus, our first question might be: would a free person choose to impose on himself a regime of health insurance, with regular payments due? Answer: in most cases, yes—though definitely not in all. But this does not bridge the gap between that choice and *requirements*, to pay, mandatorily, for health care for *everyone else*. . . .

An argument is needed for any such program. What might it be? Some assert . . . that there is a positive *human right* to health care. . . . They perhaps have not appreciated the implication of that view: namely, that we are all responsible for the health care of everyone—all seven billion of us. . . . Most of them are quite unable to pay. . . . The implication looms large

that America would be stuck with a health care bill considerably in excess of its gross national product. Very few advocates of government-provided health care are ready to swallow that implication. Their proposals tend to be confined in their reach to citizens or residents of their own country: people on the other side of the national boundary are not covered, despite being at least equally in need of care. Thus, the proposal that there is a positive human right to such care does not, at least, reflect the realistic spectrum of political opinion. Nor of any other kind of opinion short of the slightly lunatic, one would think. . . .

The main point is that on the most reasonable view of people, such a supposed right is not justifiable. We are not our brothers' keepers (especially when they are altogether unrelated). We are, of course, responsible for injury to others . . . but this does not easily extend to being responsible for the care of their health.

All that said, the plausibility of health insurance, for many people, is clear enough. What kind of insurance? . . . Whatever they choose. But not a type that is thrust upon them by somebody else. . . . Let us imagine our way into a regime of health insurance—what might it best be like?

First, it should be very sensitive to its status as *insurance*. In principle, and normally, insurance is voluntary: you decide whether to buy it and how much, in negotiation with providers or fellow members of insurance groups. . . . Second, . . . insurance is best understood as insuring against the risk that unforeseeable or uncontrollable external factors present, such as ambient viruses or subtle genetic environmental features that affect the human genome. Thus, the bad habits of many people that leave them with heart disease, lung cancer, and so on should not obviously be insurable or, perhaps better, should be insurable only at actuarially derived higher premiums. No one should be in the position that his fellows can exact payments from others for avoidable, voluntarily imposed risks. Thus, smokers, persons with dangerous lifestyles, or persons with bad diets should pay more. Those who cannot afford this cannot afford their lifestyles—so why, then, should others be paying for them?

The force of this restriction should not be underestimated. It has been plausibly claimed that by far the majority of major causes of death currently—heart attacks, diabetes, stroke, and many cancers—would be avoided by modest attention to exercise and diet and avoidance of smoking (and a few other things).

An insurance policy that provided cover for emergencies but greatly increased costs for those who insist on being overweight, smoking, or prolonged inactivity would be rational. Those who adhere to known guidelines in respect of a healthy lifestyle can have modest health care costs even in today's expensive world. But involuntary, collective health care systems provide little or no incentive for such savings. So the question is: why should those who take reasonable care be stuck with the costs of those who do not? Others may, of course, take pity on them, but the *exaction* of charity is a contradiction in terms, as well as bad social policy. Normal people have considerable reserves of charitable sentiment, and those sentiments do impel them to philanthropy if they can afford it. . . . But why should other people in general be saddled with expensive mandatory "health plans" for their irresponsible neighbors? . . ..

Those who participate in current discussions of "health care policy" assume, on the contrary, that it does not matter how or why people came to be in whatever unfortunate medical condition they are in—the government has the right, and of course the duty, given that right—to impose taxes on all of us to relieve those conditions to some level or other. And then it is just a question of how much the taxpayer can be expected to be willing to part with, as measured by who will win which elections in which this has become a major issue.

Those assumptions are obviously wrong. First, many people care little about their health: drug users, people who eat huge amounts of foods known to be likely to shorten their life expectancy significantly, etc. Second, all of us have interests such that we are willing, with perfect rationality, to expend less of our time, energy, and money on trying to maintain an advanced state of physical health than we are in promoting those interests. And third, both of the first two are clearly the subject of huge variation among people. It is absurd and fascist to force higher levels of health care on all than are called for by their particular profiles of interest and resources.

So the correct answer to the question addressed, to repeat, is: None. There is no level of health such that governments have any business compelling anyone to bring it about that everyone enjoys at least that level of health and certainly that they have access to a given level of "health care." Nor is there one standard health insurance policy that would plainly be best for everyone. If we were all rich, we would need no health insurance and therefore no health care legislation. We are not, but that does not mean that we therefore do need such legislation, beyond the usual requisites of civilized society—that people who misuse their medical (or whatever) knowledge to do harm to others can be brought to account and forced to make restitution where possible. . . .

Study Questions

1. What is the basis of the distinction that Narveson draws between positive and negative rights?

2. What reason does Narveson supply for the claim that certain negative rights are justified?

3. What does Narveson mean when he says that we are not our brothers' keeper?

THREE Health Care as a Commodity
Joseph Heath | *Éthique publique* 2003; 5: 84-89

One of the arguments that is often advanced in defense of the public health care system in Canada appeals to the idea that medical care should not be treated as a "commodity." The recent *Romanow Report on the Future of Health Care in Canada*, for instance, says that, "Canadians view medicare as a moral enterprise, not a business venture."[1] . . . This is . . . a bad argument, and it is one that actually obscures the rationale for the current public system. . . .

Consider one argument that might be advanced by those wanting to highlight the downsides of commodifying medical care. It has been observed that in

Pecuniary
Relating to money; monetary incentives or interests.

Collective action problem
A situation in which the uncoordinated actions of individuals each pursuing their own interests leads to an outcome that is worse for all. For example, each person buys a car, since travelling by car is the easiest way to get to work. However, since everyone does the same thing, we end up in traffic jams, which make us all worse off.

Efficiency
Pareto efficiency means that situation A is more efficient than situation B when, by moving from A to B, at least one person is made better off without making anyone else worse off.

Duty of rescue
The moral obligation to aid someone in certain or imminent peril.

Capitation
A system in which physicians are paid a fixed amount per patient per year, rather than a fee for a particular service.

some cases, moral incentives are able to secure a superior level of provision of a particular good than pecuniary ones. Since the creation of a market tends to encourage self-interested behaviour, commodification can have the perverse effect of provoking collective action problems, and thus reducing the efficiency of a particular sector. This dynamic is best-known from Richard Titmuss' study of blood supply, and his argument that a system of voluntary donation will secure higher quality donors than one in which people are paid for their blood. [2]. . .

One can imagine a similar set of motives structuring the delivery of health care. Doctors, for example, generally feel bound by a duty of rescue, which leads them to provide medical services without compensation when there is an emergency on an airplane. Airlines often provide some consideration for doctors who have had to attend to inflight emergencies, but this is widely understood to be a gift, not a payment. If instead airlines developed a formal compensation arrangement, so that doctors signaled their availability when embarking upon the craft (becoming, in effect, "on call" to the flight crew), in return for a flat payment, one could predict an overall decline in the health and safety of passengers. If regarded as a voluntary transaction, rather than a moral obligation, many doctors would decline to participate in such an arrangement (e.g. preferring to start their vacations the moment they get on the airplane, rather than the moment they get off).

It seems clear to me, however, that this argument cannot be extended to cover the health care system in general. One might imagine a system in which all doctors were salaried employees of the state, and dispensed care out of a sense of moral obligation. Under such a system, health care would not be a commodity, in the sense that doctors would not receive pecuniary compensation for the particular services delivered, and choice of treatment options would not be affected by such considerations. One might draw an analogy between the role of doctors under such a system and the way that the police force currently operates in our society. Personal security is a basic right, not a commodity. When someone feels threatened, they call the police, who then intervene in order to restore that person's security (or initiate criminal charges in the event that they are too late, etc.). The police do not charge per house call, nor do they receive pecuniary compensation for the number of interventions that they make. They act out of an obligation "to serve and to protect."

Certain advocates would like to see health care as a basic right, along the lines of personal security. When they are sick, citizens would have the right to pick up the phone and call a doctor, in much the same way that they currently are entitled to pick up a phone and call the police in the event that they are attacked. However, there are three things worth noting about this proposal. First, this is clearly not how our health care system currently works. Although our system does generate a universal entitlement (so that every citizen has guaranteed access to medical care regardless of ability to pay), it does not rely upon moral incentives to motivate physicians. It is almost entirely run on a fee-for-service basis. Even doctors who are paid through capitation arrangements are still being paid for the quantity of services that they provide (it is just that the primary unit used to calculate compensation is the number of patients, rather than the number of procedures). So if there is something wrong with treating health care as a commodity, then there is something gravely wrong with the organization of our present health care system.

Second, it is highly doubtful that a system based purely on moral incentives would be more effective at delivering health care to the population than the current one. Above all, there is no evidence that the current system is crowding out moral incentives. The conduct of doctors is still governed by a very strong sense of professional obligation. A doctor who dropped everything at 5 pm and went home would find it very difficult to find a job at any hospital in Canada. The fact that doctors are paid per procedure would appear to be encouraging them to do more work, not less. A system in which all doctors were salaried might therefore be less efficient, and would be unlikely to generate improvements in patient care.

Finally, turning back momentarily to the analogy with the police force, while no one doubts that personal security is a basic human right in our society, not a commodity, no one has ever suggested that this should prevent people from purchasing more of it, above and beyond the baseline established by the state. There is in fact a thriving market for private security services, alongside the public. Thus the mere fact that something is a right does not mean that it cannot *also* be a commodity, especially when some people have a strong desire to consume more of it than the community at large is willing to provide through the public sector. Thus the commodification argument does nothing to justify a state monopoly of the health sector, nor does it show that there is anything wrong with a two-tiered health care system.

Distribution According to Need

When taken literally, the claim that health care should not be a commodity is extremely weak. This suggests that people who use this argument understand it in a slightly different fashion. In fact, one often finds the claim about commodification made as a somewhat oblique way of introducing a concern over distributive justice. Consider, for example, recent statements by British Chancellor Gordon Brown, concerning the original mission statement of the NHS: "The NHS was built around the cornerstone of universal access to health services, regardless of ability to pay. And at its core is the recognition of health care as a fundamental human right, not a consumer commodity."

These two phrases often occur together. People identify the idea that health care should not be a commodity with the suggestion that it should be distributed in accordance with need, and not ability to pay.[3] Thus the claim is not that there is something intrinsic to health care that means it is unsuitable for purchase and sale. What underlies the argument instead is a set of fundamentally distributive concerns.

Yet if distributive justice is the concern, then there is something vaguely

demagogic about the commodification argument. There is no reason why the to-each-according-to-need principle has to be in tension with the use of a market to provide the goods. After all, people tend to spend their money on things that they *need*. Food, clothing and shelter should also be distributed in accordance with need—but this is precisely why we have a *market* for these goods. "But what about the needs of people with no money?" comes the natural reply. Here we must tread carefully. The mere existence of poverty is not an argument for socialized medicine, any more than it is an argument for socialized food. It is an argument for income supports and poverty relief. It's why Americans have food stamps. Thus the argument from poverty clearly fails to capture what is distinctive about health care, what justifies public provision.

It is at this point that we can start to see how the anti-commodification argument obscures the genuine rationale for the public health care system. The important difference between food and clothing, on the one hand, and medical care, on the other, is not that the latter is a "human right" and the former are not. The difference is that it is extremely easy for individuals to predict their need for food and clothing, and to budget accordingly. Medical expenses, on the other hand, are extremely unpredictable. Disaster can strike at any time, and even the most prudent individual may not be able to set aside an appropriate amount to pay for care. As a result, a simple market for health care would be extremely inefficient. This is why health care, unlike food and clothing, is paid for almost exclusively through insurance systems (or, as is increasing the case in the United States, through large, highly diversified health management organizations). It is the uncertainty that attaches to the consumption of medical care that constitutes the dominant characteristic of these markets. It is also what provides the primary rationale for public provision.

Markets for private health insurance are subject to extremely severe information asymmetries. This leads to serious adverse selection problems (insurers attract bad risks, forcing firms to refuse insurance to certain groups, and institute

---

Demagogic
Resembling a demagogue or rabble-rouser. A demagogue gains the support of the people by appealing to their emotions, not their rational capacities.

Information asymmetries
These occur when one party (e.g., people seeking insurance) possesses more information than another party (e.g., insurers) about a matter relevant to their interactions (e.g., their current state of health).

Moral hazard
This occurs when insurance or social welfare provisions operate in such a way that they erode people's incentives to take care to avoid accidents or unemployment.

costly underwriting practices for others), and moral hazard (cost control is difficult, because it is very expensive for insurers to determine whether claims that they receive are justified). Both of these problems generate enormous transaction costs at best, complete market failure at worst. The Canadian "single-payer" system eliminates the adverse selection problem in one fell swoop, by creating a single mandatory universal plan. It also minimizes moral hazard, by centralizing negotiations over fee structures, and eliminating the collective action problem in enforcement. However, it is extremely important to the structure of the Canadian system that the government delivers health *insurance* as a public good, not health *care*. And the reason that government provides insurance of this type is not that there is something intrinsically wrong with buying and selling health insurance, it is that markets fail to do so efficiently.

It is also worth noting that unless one is clear about the fact that government in Canada provides health insurance, not health care, it is impossible to justify the monopoly that it exercises in this sector. Government provides roads, but there is no reason why people should not be able to build their own roads as well. But in the case of health care, it is important to recognize that the efficiency gains that justify the public-sector role arise primarily through the elimination of an adverse selection problem. In other words, it is the mandatory pooling of the entire population into one insurance scheme that generates the efficiency gain. Thus the rationale for government monopoly is precisely that it prevents "cream skimming" among private insurers—which is to say, it prevents the state from becoming itself the victim of an adverse selection problem.

Finally, focusing on the role of insurance shows how misleading it is to put emphasis on the principle of distribution according to "need" rather than "ability to pay." All insurance systems, whether public or private, distribute resources according to need. Car insurance provides new cars to people who "need" them, i.e. those who just crashed their old ones. Fire insurance provides new houses to people whose old ones burned down. But in neither case is state intervention necessary. Thus it does not help the case for *public* provision of health care to appeal to the principle of distribution according to need. It merely distracts from the more powerful arguments that are available.

Two-Tiered Medicine

The suggestion that health care should be distributed in accordance with need, not ability to pay, is also sometimes accompanied by the suggestion that there is something wrong with the thought that the rich might be able to purchase a superior level of care. Many people object to private clinics on the grounds that they would permit "queue-jumping." Because there are some waiting lists, the concern is that people who are willing to pay out of their own pocket will be able to buy their way to the front of the line, and will therefore receive better quality care.

This is an argument that needs to be formulated extremely carefully, in order to avoid the charge of "levelling down." One way of achieving greater equality is to improve the condition of those who are at the bottom. But it is just as easy—and in many cases easier—to achieve equality by worsening the condition of those who are at the top. When this is done without improving anyone else's condition, it is referred to as levelling down. It amounts to cutting down all the tall poppies, while leaving the rest of the field intact.

Most people agree that levelling down is unattractive. If we are going to tax the rich, for example, we should be able to show that doing so generates some benefit for the poor. Otherwise it's just punitive. Unfortunately, people who care about equality are not always as careful as they should be to avoid the charge of levelling down. Recent debates over two-tier medicine provide some uncomfortable examples of this.

Part of the problem stems from an ambiguity in the term "queue-jumping." There is no question that, if there is a line-up, and some people are allowed to buy their way to the front of the line, then that worsens the condition of everyone else in the line, because it bumps them all back. That is genuinely objectionable. The case is quite different when people are able to jump the queue by leaving it entirely. Suppose someone who is on the waiting list for an MRI gets impatient and goes to the United States to have the test done. This person has "jumped the queue," and so will probably wind up with better health care. But this sort of queue-jumping in itself does not harm anyone. In fact, all of the people on the waiting list behind that person are better off, since they all get bumped forward.

> **MRI**
> Magnetic resonance imagining is an expensive form of medical imaging technology used to view internal structures.

There is no question that when people jump the queue in this way it exacerbates inequality. However, if we look carefully, we can see that prohibiting this sort of queue-jumping is levelling down. We are promoting equality, not by improving the quality of anyone's health care, but simply by preventing the rich person from acquiring higher quality care. . . .

The concept of medical "need" is always structured by budgetary considerations. The government could choose to vaccinate the entire population against hepatitis B. It chooses not to do so, simply because hepatitis B is not very common in Canada, and the vaccine is expensive (about $100 retail). Thus the ratio of expense to medical benefit does not support universal inoculation. Nevertheless, any citizen who, for one reason or another, is at high risk of contracting hepatitis B, is perfectly free to go to the doctor and request it. But they must purchase the vaccine, or else charge it to a private prescription-drug plan.

This is the current situation in Canada, and there is no question that it is a form of two-tiered medicine. People who are willing and able to spend $100 for this vaccine will enjoy superior health (i.e. at very least in the form of reduced risk of illness). But is this an objectionable form of two-tiered medicine? People have different levels of tolerance for risk, and have different attitudes towards health. Some people are willing to pay an enormous amount to protect themselves from disability and disease, whereas others have a positively cavalier attitude (smoking, driving motorcycles, etc.) A universal insurance system, while attractive from an efficiency perspective, does have the disadvantage of imposing a "one-size-fits-all" package upon citizens. When individuals are prohibited from purchasing supplementary private insurance, or additional health care, outside the system, it imposes a tangible loss of welfare upon those who have an above-average level of risk-aversion or health-consciousness. In order to justify the imposition of such losses, very substantive moral considerations must be brought to bear upon the issue. One must demonstrate that such choices would generate significant harm to others—merely appealing to the principle of equality will not suffice.

Thus it seems to me that, unless one is willing to subscribe to "levelling down" egalitarianism there is nothing wrong with the two-tier vaccine program. Two-tier systems are objectionable, in my view, only insofar as they undermine the integrity of the public *insurance mechanism*. For example, the problem with proposals that recommend individual "medical savings accounts" is not that they would permit the rich to purchase a superior quality of care; the problem is that they eliminate or scale back the insurance mechanism that is at the core of the present system. [4] . . .

Study Questions

1. What are Heath's reasons for thinking that the "commodification argument does nothing to justify a state monopoly of the health sector"?

2. What is the "levelling down" objection? Why, in Heath's view, is it important?

3. What does Heath mean to suggest by claiming that "two-tier systems are objectionable ... only insofar as they undermine the integrity of the public *insurance mechanism*"?

Notes

1. Commission on the Future of Heath Care in Canada, *Building on Values: The Future of Health Care in Canada*, (Ottawa: Government of Canada: 2002). CP32-85/2002E-IN, p. xx. The implications of this phrase were made clear in Romanow's speech at Yale University, just prior to the release of the report, when he claimed that health care was a moral venture, and "not a commodity." See "In Canada, publicly-funded health care is 'moral enterprise', says official," *Yale Bulletin & Calendar*, 31:8 (25 October 2002).

2. Richard M. Titmuss, *The Gift Relationship* (London: Allen & Unwin, 1970).

3. Similar arguments can be found in the Romanow report, *Building on Values*, p. xx.

4. For a proposal of this type, see David Gratzer, *Code Blue* (Toronto: ECW Press, 1999).

Chapter Study Questions

1. To what extent are the arguments provided by the members of the President's Commission compatible with the arguments that Heath offers for Canada's public health care insurance scheme?

2. Neither Heath nor the members of the President's Commission appeal to the notion of a right to health care insurance in their arguments.

Is there a role for rights in their arguments? What might that role be?

3. Compare and contrast the claims made by the members of the President's Commission about the responsibility people bear for their health outcomes with those made by Narveson. Who has the more persuasive view? Why?

Critical Analysis

Consider the following from the article by the members of the President's Commission:

"As long as significant inequalities in income and wealth persist, inequalities in the use of health care can be expected beyond those created by differences in need. Given people with the same pattern of preferences and equal health care needs, those with greater financial resources will purchase more health care. Conversely, given equal financial resources, the different patterns of health care preferences that typically exist in any population will result in a different use of health services by people with equal health care needs. Trying to prevent such inequalities would require

interfering with people's liberty to use their income to purchase an important good like health care while leaving them free to use it for frivolous or inessential ends. Prohibiting people with higher incomes or stronger preferences for health care from purchasing more care than everyone else gets would not be feasible, and would probably result in a black market for health care."

Outline this argument in your own words, paying particular attention to the premises that the members of the President's Commission rely on to support their main conclusion. Choose one of the premises for evaluation. Try to think of at least one objection to this premise.

Case Study

Canada has an advanced health care system. It provides some of the most sophisticated treatment of illness and disease and some of the most unique and technically advanced forms of surgery in the world. In particular, Canada boasts a full complement of surgeons who work in cardiac care. In February 2010, however, Danny Williams, the Premier of Newfoundland and Labrador, decided that he would exercise his option to have surgery on his heart performed in the United States of America. Premier Williams needed to have the mitral valve in his heart repaired; this valve functions to regulate blood flow in the heart. This surgery is offered in Canada (though not in the Province of Newfoundland and Labrador), and Canadian physicians have been at the forefront of developing forms of this surgery. It is therefore far from clear that Premier Williams would have substantially increased his chances of receiving better care by going to the US. It is not clear from media reports that he would have had to wait for an inordinate amount of time to receive the surgery in Canada. The form of

the procedure that Williams did receive seems to have had one benefit: it would leave a smaller, less noticeable scar. When Williams was challenged to explain why he opted to have his surgery performed outside of Canada he claimed that "This is my heart, it's my health and it's my choice." In short, Premier Williams stated that it was his right to seek what he thought was the best care available. Premier Williams is a very prominent Canadian politician. He has spoken in favour of the public system of health care insurance as it exists in Canada, which covers the sort of surgery that he sought. In the Federal election of 2008, he adopted an anything-but-Stephen-Harper stance. In specific, he argued that Stephen Harper's Conservatives were an inappropriate choice for the electorate because the Conservatives would threaten the Canadian health care insurance system. He suggested that they would not uphold the universality and accessibility of health care in Canada. He is quoted as saying "Nothing would be safe . . . when it comes to going after sacrosanct principles [such as these]."

1. What, if anything, is wrong with a wealthy individual seeking the best treatment available to him or her in the US? What sort of impact does this have on the perception of the health care system in Canada?

2. Does Premier Williams have a special obligation not to seek health care in the US, when he has spoken in favour of the Canadian public health care insurance system?

3. Premier Williams' physicians recommended that he leave the Province of Newfoundland and Labrador in order to undergo surgery. Would it be unfair for them to recommend that Premier Williams seek treatment in the US when they would not recommend this same route to a person without means?

Further Reading

Canada Health Act (R.S.C., 1985, c. C-6) [Internet]. Available from: http://laws.justice.gc.ca/eng/C-6/FullText.html. Date Accessed: 8 June 2012.

Daniels N. Justice and access to health care. In: Zalta EN, editor. Stanford encyclopedia of philosophy [Internet]. 2008. Available from: http://plato.stanford.edu/entries/justice-healthcareaccess/. Date Accessed: 10 June 2012.

Gratzer D. *Code blue: reviving Canada's health care system*. Toronto: ECW Press; 1999.

Romanow RJ. Building on values: the future of health care in Canada [Internet]. Canada: Commission on the Future of Health Care in Canada; 2002. Available from: http://publications.gc.ca/site/eng/237274/publication.html. Date Accessed: 8 June 2012.

Steinbrook R. Private health care in Canada. *N Eng J Med.* 2006;354:1661–4.

Obligations to the Global Poor

In this chapter, we focus on the following question: What do those who are more than able to provide for their own health care owe to those in other countries who are unable to meet their most basic health needs? There are, among others, two groups inhabiting the world: the absolutely wealthy, and the absolutely poor. The billion people in the former group have more than enough to satisfy their most basic needs. Indeed, a sizable proportion of what they earn is spent in pursuit of the clearly unnecessary: designer clothes, electronics, and fancy automobiles. The roughly 1.4 billion in the latter group rely each day on less than what $1.29 can buy in major Canadian cities. They do not have enough to satisfy even their most basic needs. They have no access to basic health care, clean water, or sanitation. Twenty-two thousand children under the age of five from this group die every day from preventable causes, including dehydration and malnourishment.

How do Canadians respond to the plight of those living in absolute poverty? The Canadian government typically spends about 0.3 per cent of Gross Domestic Product (GDP) per year in the form of Official Development Assistance, which is designed in part to help the world's most needy citizens. This amount is as a proportion more than is spent by, for example, the United States, but still well below the suggested target of 0.7 per cent of GDP developed by the United Nations with the help of former Canadian Prime Minister Lester B. Pearson. In addition, this money is often spent to facilitate Canada's strategic and economic goals rather than to alleviate the suffering of the most impoverished. Therefore, not all of this development assistance goes to where it is most needed.

What is the morality of Canada's response to the plight of the absolutely poor? To answer this question we must confront a more basic issue. What, morally speaking, do the absolutely rich owe the absolutely poor? In particular, what ought the absolutely rich to do to facilitate the health and related ambitions of the absolutely poor? The articles in this chapter aim to specify answers to this question. Each provides an account of the content and justification of the obligation to the absolutely poor.

In his article "Health and Justice in our Non-ideal World," Gopal Sreenivasan defends a non-ideal theory of justice. He calls this theory an anticipatory theory, since it anticipates what an acceptable theory of international justice would involve. He argues that among other things such a theory would include a provision obliging the world's wealthiest nations to devote one per cent of their GDP to the world's absolutely poor. He contends that by focusing on health we are able to vindicate this obligation. His position is that by directing this transfer to the health of the world's poorest citizens we deflect the worry that the provision is not strong enough and the complaint that we ought to concentrate on other elements of well-being. He maintains that a one per cent transfer would have a significant impact on life expectancy and that aiming at health involves focusing on other important elements of well-being that might seem to compete with it (e.g., income, education, basic nutrition, and so on).

Gross Domestic Product
The total value of all goods and services developed within a country's boundaries during a specific time period.

Official Development Assistance
The loans or grants provided by a government like Canada's to developing nations or multilateral organizations active in development. It is designed to boost economic growth and quality of life.

In the excerpt reproduced from his book *The Life You Can Save*, Peter Singer argues that an important principle governs our obligations to the absolutely poor. He maintains that this principle is the best explanation of our intuitions about the following kind of scenario. Imagine that you are on your way to work in the morning. You are passing by a shallow pond that is close to a local school. You notice that a child is playing on the edge of the pond, and that she is steadily wading deeper into its middle. As you approach the pond you see the child slip under the water, at which point she instantly begins to give you every sign that she will drown unless you assist her. No one else is around but you. You have a meeting to get to and you are dressed in your finest clothing. The pond is dirty and you will surely ruin your outfit if you save the child. It is therefore either your outfit or the child's life. It seems obvious that your outfit is not nearly as important as the life of a child. Therefore, it seems wrong not to save the child's life. Singer argues that this intuition is correct, and that the following principle explains why it is correct. If you can prevent something bad from happening without sacrificing anything of comparable moral importance, then you ought, morally speaking, to do it. In addition to explaining why we ought to save the drowning child, this principle entails that we ought to do a lot more for the absolutely poor. It is at present true that we can prevent a lot of their suffering without thereby sacrificing anything of comparable moral significance. In his defence of this principle, Singer replies to two worries: (1) that his view is hard to execute in practice, since we often lack knowledge of the best ways to reduce poverty; and (2) that his principle is more demanding than certain rivals. In response he presents information regarding the efficacy of various charitable organizations and an argument to the effect that (certain) rival positions generate counter-intuitive implications.

Singer appeals to our intuitions about benefiting others in his argument for greater duties to those in desperate need. However, this may not be the only basis for such duties. In her article "Domination and Destitution in an Unjust World," Ryoa Chung argues that our duties are based on the fact that the absolutely wealthy bear some responsibility for the plight of the absolutely poor. In particular, through their financial and economic institutions, the major industrialized nations of the world have produced inequities which have exposed the absolutely poor to extreme vulnerability. She illustrates this by focusing on the HIV/AIDS epidemic. Her argument rests on a number of claims. The first is that the countries of the world form a system of social cooperation. The second is that the poorest countries are dominated by Western-run institutions and that these have produced inequalities that exacerbate disease and related ills. This leaves the absolutely rich partly responsible for this situation, placing us under an obligation of justice to these populations. We have a specific duty to uphold basic subsistence rights on a global scale.

ONE Health and Justice in our Non-ideal World
Gopal Sreenivasan | *Politics, Philosophy & Economics* 2007; 6: 218-36.

Most readers are familiar with the dismal statistics on the severity and extent of global poverty and inequality. The number of human beings whose daily existence must be sustained on a miserable pittance (as officially defined, the equivalent of US$1 or US$2 per day) is truly staggering. Equally familiar is a philosophical appeal to these statistics designed to establish that we rich inhabitants of the globe have weighty obligations to improve the well-being of the global poor. . . .

Often, this appeal highlights not simply the very low incomes of the global poor, but also their appalling *health*. In Malawi, for example, life expectancy at birth is a mere 41 years for men and 42 years for women.[1] Twenty-seven countries, all but one in sub-Saharan Africa, have both male and female life expectancies at birth (at or) below 50 years. By contrast, global life expectancy at birth, combining male and female rates, is 66.75 years. In the US, life expectancy at birth is considerably higher still, nearly *double* that in Malawi, at 75 years for men and 80 years for women. . . .

No doubt the plight of the global poor strikes us both more vividly and as more urgent when it is framed in terms of their reduced health. While this observation likely informs the rhetorical strategy of the familiar appeal, it does not fundamentally alter the role the surface picture assigns to income and health. In that picture, income and health are simply alternative indicators of well-being. However, the relationship between income and health is actually considerably more complicated than this. Within a given society, an individual's health is highly positively correlated with her income; and, in comparisons between developed societies and developing ones, there is also a strong correlation between average national income and national life expectancy.

In this article, I shall argue that the advantages of framing the shortfall in well-being suffered by the global poor in terms of their *health* are more than merely rhetorical. . . . I begin . . . with a brief analysis of the category of "non-ideal theory."[2] In the course of this analysis, I propose that we minimally have an obligation to transfer 1 per cent of our income to the globally worst off. The central aim of my article is to show, more specifically, how the vindication of this minimum obligation is facilitated by considering individual well-being through the lens of health in particular. To appreciate what there is to gain from adopting this perspective, we shall need a better understanding of the underlying determinants of health. . . . I then draw on this material to explain . . . how a focus on the health of the worst off helps to vindicate the 1 per cent obligation as a non-ideal requirement of justice.

On Rawls' conception, ideal theory describes a well-ordered institutional arrangement: institutions are well-ordered when they are both just and known to be just; and when individuals both accept and comply fully with the requirements these institutions impose on them.[3] This suggests two rather different ways in which circumstances may fail to be ideal. On the one hand, background institutions may not be just and, on the other hand, individuals may not fully comply with the standing requirements placed on them. . . . For each kind of defective case, there is a corresponding branch of non-ideal theory. . . .

I propose to understand "non-ideal theory" more expansively than . . . Rawls. To see what I mean, we should notice an assumption . . . that ideal theory is *prior to* non-ideal theory. . . .

The rough idea is that before we can take any steps forward, we need to know where we are supposed to end up. Otherwise, we cannot know whether any given step is a step in the right direction. . . .

Of course, I do not deny that non-ideal theory *can* work like this. But I want to suggest that it need not. More strongly, there exists a kind of non-ideal theory for which the priority assumption fails. On this conception, non-ideal theory functions as an anticipation of ideal theory. Its prescriptions anticipate the ideal requirements of justice rather than presupposing them. To do so, non-ideal theory has to make assumptions about the minimum requirements that *any plausible and complete* ideal theory of justice will include. In this vein, it can define targets for practical action *before* a complete ideal has been worked out, even in outline. Furthermore, if our assumptions about the minimum demands of justice are defensible, we can be confident that steps towards these targets are steps in the right direction.

Let us call this non-ideal theory as *anticipatory* theory. . . .

I take it that non-ideal theory so conceived is coherent and distinctive. What remains to be seen is whether it has any significant instantiations. Let me therefore propose an anticipatory theory of international distributive justice: any plausible and complete ideal theory of international distributive justice will minimally include an obligation on the richest nations to transfer *1 per cent* of their GDP to the poorest nations. [4]. . . To establish the 1 per cent proposal as an instance of anticipatory theory, then, we would have to show that it can be secured *without* having to resolve various debates in ideal theory. . . .

I shall not attempt to discharge that burden comprehensively here. My present aim is more limited: to show how focusing on the health of the worst off helps to vindicate this minimum obligation. To make this focus explicit in the proposal, let us understand the obligation as requiring 1 per cent of GDP to be spent specifically on improving the health of the globally worst off.

A background review of the underlying determinants of health will put us in a better position to see the advantages of framing the obligation in these terms. . . .

At the outset I mentioned some of the correlations between income and health. Evidence on these correlations is the stock in trade of a well-established, and still rapidly growing, literature in the field of population health. A central lesson of this literature is that there are important social determinants of health. In this context, a *social determinant* of health is a socially controllable factor outside the health care system (medical care and public health) that is an independent partial cause of an individual's health status. Candidate examples include income, education, occupational rank, and social or occupational class. To recognize that there are social determinants of health is not to deny the importance of health care as another partial cause, but it is to place other socially controllable factors at least *on a par* with health care as determinants of health.[5]

While income dominates the literature, it is by no means the only relevant social factor. In fact, it may not even be the most important social determinant of health. We should begin, in any case, with a more general focus, since the literature's most significant and powerful finding can actually be replicated with *any* of the listed candidate social determinants: this is the existence, within a given society, of a *social gradient* in health.

To illustrate, take occupational class as the candidate determinant. Figure 8.1 exhibits the differences in life expectancy by occupational class in England and Wales for men and women in the period 1997–99. At *each* step up the class ladder, from "Unskilled Manual" through to "Professional," there is a clear improvement in individual life expectancy. This stepwise gradient holds for both sexes, with the cumulative life expectancy gap between bottom and top being more than seven years for men and almost six years for women. Notice, moreover, that this gradient emerges against a background of free universal access to health care.

Similar domestic gradients in individual life expectancy can be found when the social variable is *income*,[6] when it is *education*,[7] and when it is *occupational rank*.[8] . . .

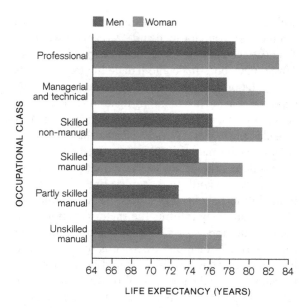

FIGURE 8.1   Occupational class differences in life expectancy, England and Wales (1997–9)

Wilkinson and M. Marmot, *Social Determinants of Health: The Solid Facts*, 2nd edn (Copenhagen: WHO, 2003), p. 10.

This certainly suggests that *something* in addition to health care exercises a powerful influence on individual health. . . .

Since we are particularly interested in improvements in the health of the globally worst off, we should also briefly review the fundamental determinants of health specifically in developing countries. . . .

Recognizing the role of the social determinants of health should not, of course, obscure the significance of health care as a determinant of health. In particular, public health and primary health care systems are important determinants of health, especially in developing countries. For example, the significant contribution made by immunization, vector control, clean water, and sanitation to reducing mortality in the developing world has been well documented.[9] Preston estimated that at least 50 per cent of the mortality gains by developing nations between 1940 and 1970 were due to factors *other than* income, literacy, and nutrition.[10] . . .

In the context of the developed world, there is an ongoing debate about

> **Vector control**
>
> A vector is an insect or an animal that is capable of carrying a disease pathogen from one animal or human to another. The purpose of a vector control is to manage the population size of a vector. Insecticide is a common way to control mosquitoes, which are a malaria vector.

precisely which definition of "income" is adequate to capture the contribution that individual income makes to individual life expectancy.[11] However, when attention is restricted to developing countries, this controversy dissipates. All sides agree that, at very low levels of income, an individual's *non*-comparative income makes a significant contribution to his or her life expectancy.[12] In addition, there is general agreement on the causal pathways through which non-comparative income contributes to life expectancy, namely, via the material risk factors of inadequate nutrition, lack of clean water and sanitation, and poor housing, *inter alia*. . . .

Anand and Ravallion argue that the entire relationship between per capita GDP and life expectancy can be explained in terms of two factors: per capita public spending on health, and the proportion of the population in extreme poverty.[13] On their analysis, in other words, the relevance of national income to life expectancy is entirely mediated by the extent to which it funds *public spending* on our first determinant;[14] and by the extent to which it (that is, our second determinant) is distributed to the poorest inhabitants. Anand and Ravallion calculate that roughly two-thirds of their explanation is due to the first factor and one-third to the second.

A final fundamental determinant of health is education. In developing countries, *female* education in particular correlates very highly with infant and child (under five) life expectancy, even after controlling for income and other factors.[15] Thus, mothers with primary schooling have child mortality rates 26 per cent lower than mothers with no schooling, while mothers with secondary schooling have rates 36 per cent lower again than mothers with only primary schooling.[16] . . . Caldwell describes several pathways through which greater female education contributes to improved health, both a woman's own health and that of her children.[17] These include not only improvements in (health and general) knowledge, but also the empowerment of women. Indeed, Caldwell emphasizes the important role of female *autonomy* in the most impressive cases of health gains by developing countries (on which, more below). A further pathway, which combines the previous ones, works through an increased demand for health services. In addition to better access to care, increased demand contributes to improvements in the efficiency of local health services. Caldwell thereby suggests several possible interactions between education and health services as determinants of health. Filmer

and Pritchett dispute the claim that *public* spending on health contributes significantly to life expectancy.[18] They find that 95 per cent of the cross-national variation in child mortality can be explained in terms of the level and distribution of income, the extent of female education, and two other social factors,[19] while adding public spending on health to their equation improves the explanation only trivially. By their estimate, each additional year of female schooling yields roughly a 10 per cent decrease in child mortality.

We can now return to the proposed 1 per cent obligation. . . . Two serious objections of principle may spring to mind. First, it may be objected that 1 per cent of GDP is too small a transfer to qualify as a minimum obligation. To describe an obligation as the "minimum" implies that the moral performance of those who discharge it is, in some sense, "satisfactory." It draws a significant distinction between them and those who do less. No rich nation that only transfers 1 per cent of its GDP, it may be felt, should be shielded from full moral censure in this way. Second, whatever its magnitude, there are, naturally, different ways to allocate a given resource transfer. Even from the standpoint of concern for the well-being of the worst off, various alternative expenditures can plausibly claim top priority. An obligation to spend the 1 per cent specifically on improving the health of the worst off may thus be found objectionable independently of its magnitude.

A proper understanding of the fundamental determinants of health allows us to pre-empt both of these objections. We should begin by recognizing that proposals to improve the health of the globally worst off actually require improving the *determinants* of health in developing countries. As we can now appreciate, this means that the transfers should therefore be targeted at (1) primary health care and public health, (2) basic nutrition and income support, and (3) education (especially for girls and women). If we allocate a quarter per cent to each of these fundamental determinants, that leaves a quarter per cent to cover existing development commitments. It turns out that 0.75 per cent of GDP from the G7 will fund a per capita package of US$144 for 1.26 billion people, which covers the world's bottom quintile.

G7

Group of Seven; a meeting of the seven finance ministers of the world's seven leading industrialized nations, including Canada.

This refined proposal is immune to the objection from alternative priorities. From the standpoint of individual well-being, nutrition, shelter, basic income, and education are reasonably conceived as instrumental priorities on a par with health care. For on any plausible theory of well-being, knowledge and autonomy, to which education is instrumental, will count as basic intrinsic components. In this respect, they are comparable to health. Income is not itself an intrinsic component. But it is the primary all-purpose means to well-being, while nutrition is simply an indispensable means.[20] Still, important as they are, these priorities cannot possibly compete with the social determinants of health because they are identical to them. Moreover, nothing else plausibly has a similar priority for individual well-being.

In this light, we can see more precisely how health functions as a notably effective summary measure of well-being. Not only is health itself a basic intrinsic component, but its social determinants comprehend all of the plausible instrumental competitors to health *care* for priority in improving well-being. . . . By likewise comprehending all of the fundamental determinants of health within its spending target, the refined proposal also pre-empts the pittance objection. We will be able to see this better if we first notice some of the practical advantages of its "comprehensive approach." To begin with, the relative strength of the causal contributions made by the respective determinants of health remains disputed, as we have seen. Not only is this true as between the traditional health-sector determinants and the social determinants, but also within the social determinants, that is, between income and education. However, by spreading the US$144 per capita over all three, the refined proposal maintains a bet, as it were, on all the principal horses in the race. It thereby mitigates the uncertainty concerning the precise causal strengths at work.[21] . . .

Finally, 0.75 per cent of GDP from the G7 is enough to fund this comprehensive package for the world's bottom quintile at levels comparable to those actually employed by the high achievers. That is because US$144 per capita is a real dollar figure, whereas cross-national comparisons should be made in purchasing power parity (PPP) equivalents. Since the relevant PPP multiplier can be conservatively set at 3,[22] US$144 PPP can be spent per capita on *each* of the three fundamental determinants. In Sri Lanka, for comparison, total health expenditure in 2002 was US$131 (PPP) per capita and public educational expenditure in 1995–7 was US$111 (PPP) per capita.[23] Hence, there is no "budgetary" need to forgo the advantages of the comprehensive approach.

To fix ideas, then, let us say that spending US$432 (PPP) annually per capita on the comprehensive package in jurisdictions where life expectancy is 15 years or more below the global average (this includes not only many countries of sub-Saharan Africa, but also the worst-off Indian states and Chinese provinces) would raise life expectancy there by 10 years. While by no means guaranteed, the evidence we have reviewed makes this entirely plausible.[24] In that case, the objection that 1 per cent of GDP is *too small* to qualify as a minimum obligation simply cannot be sustained. Far from being a pittance, a 10-year improvement in life expectancy represents a huge gain in well-being for the world's worst-off inhabitants.

A 1 per cent obligation is light enough in its burden on the G7, so I have assumed, to pre-empt the objection that it is too demanding. Yet its effects on the well-being of the globally worst off, it now turns out, are nevertheless also bountiful enough to make 1 per cent worthy of the status of "minimum obligation." What reconciles these claims is the fact that targeting the 1 per cent at the fundamental determinants of health in developing countries produces a disproportionate "bang for the buck" in terms of individual well-being. . . .

The addition of 10 years to these people's lives . . . highlights a compelling advantage of focusing on the health of the globally worst off, an advantage that helps to secure recognition of the 1 per cent obligation as a vital step towards justice in our non-ideal world.

> **Purchasing power parity**
> A tool used to determine the relative value of two different currencies. This is determined by seeing what the very same item or bundle of goods costs in each currency. It provides a common measure for comparing living standards across distinct countries.

Study Questions

1. Sreenivasan defends a non-ideal theory of international justice. What are the main features of such a theory?

2. What is a social gradient of health? Why is it important to Sreenivasan's argument?

3. Why does Sreenivasan focus on health?

Notes

1. Unless otherwise noted, the life-expectancy figures cited are for 2003. World Health Organization, *World Health Report 2005* (Geneva: WHO, 2005), Annex Table 1.

2. For a fuller analysis, see G. Sreenivasan, "What is Non-Ideal Theory?," in *Transitional Justice*, NOMOS L, edited by M. Williams and J. Elster (New York: New York University Press, 2012, pp. 233-256).

3. J. Rawls, *A Theory of Justice*, revised edn. (Cambridge, MA: Harvard University Press, 1999 [1971]), Sections 2, 39, 69.

4. I have elaborated on this proposal in G. Sreenivasan, "International Justice and Health: A Proposal," *Ethics and International Affairs* 16 (2002): 81–90. Parts of the present discussion extend that article and others abbreviate it. The formulation in the text presupposes a certain degree of inequality between nations. I omit to specify the degree because, on any plausible specification, current international inequalities clearly satisfy it and because we should, anyhow, begin by regarding the 1 percent obligation as temporary.

5. For a brief corrective against the tendency to reserve a privileged position for health care, see M. Marmot and R. Wilkinson (eds), *Social Determinants of Health* (Oxford: Oxford University Press, 1999), Ch. 1.

6. P. McDonough, G. Duncan, D. Williams and J. House, "Income Dynamics and Adult Mortality in the United States, 1972 through 1989," *American Journal of Public Health* 87 (1997): 1476–83.

7. M. Huisman et al., "Educational Inequalities in Cause-Specific Mortality in Middle-Aged and Older Men and Women in Eight Western European Populations," *Lancet* 365 (2005): 493–500; E. Crimmins and Y. Saito, "Trends in Healthy Life Expectancy in the United States, 1970–1990: Gender, Racial, and Educational Differences," *Social Science and Medicine* 52 (2001): 1629–41; I. Elo and S. Preston, "Educational Differences in Mortality: United States, 1975–1989," *Social Science and Medicine* 42 (1996): 47–57; A. Kunst and J. Mackenbach, "The Size of Mortality Differences Associated with Educational Level in Nine Industrialized Countries," *American Journal of Public Health* 84 (1994): 932–7.

8. M.G. Marmot, G. Rose, M.J. Shipley and P.J.S. Hamilton, "Employment Grade and Coronary Heart Disease in British Civil Servants," *Journal of Epidemiology and Community Health* 32 (1978): 244–9. Twenty-five-year follow-up data are given in C. van Rossum et al., "Employment Grade Differences in Cause Specific Mortality," *Journal of Epidemiology and Community Health* 54 (2000): 178–84.

9. J. Caldwell, "Routes to Low Mortality in Poor Countries," *Population and Development Review* 12 (1986): 171–220.

10. S.H. Preston, "Causes and Consequences of Mortality Declines in Less Developed Countries During the Twentieth Century," in *Population and Economic Change in Developing Countries*, edited by R. Easterlin (Chicago, IL: University of Chicago Press, 1980), pp. 289–360.

11. I survey this debate in a forthcoming entry in the *Stanford Encyclopedia of Philosophy*. For a more technical account, see A. Deaton, "Health, Inequality, and Economic Development," *Journal of Economic Literature* 41 (2003): 113–58.

12. Compare Richard Wilkinson, the foremost proponent of the "relative income" hypothesis: "we should probably interpret the leveling off of the curve of rising life expectancy with increasing GNP per capita as the attainment among the majority of the population of a minimum real material standard of living, above which *further* increases in personal subsistence *no longer* provide the key to *further* increases in health." See R. Wilkinson, *Unhealthy Societies: The Afflictions of Inequality* (London: Routledge and Kegan Paul, 1996), p. 45 (emphases added).

13. S. Anand and M. Ravallion, "Human Development in Poor Countries: On the Role of Private Incomes and Public Services," *Journal of Economic Perspectives* 7 (1993): 133–50. But they caution that their results are based solely on their sample of 22 countries.

14. Note that this is a narrower interpretation of "health care" than we specified, since it excludes private spending on health care. Like that on clean water and sanitation, private spending on health care doubles as a material pathway through which our second determinant (individual income) contributes to health.

15. J. Hobcraft, "Women's Education, Child Welfare, and Child Survival: A Review of the Evidence," *Health Transition Review* 3 (1993): 159–75.

16. D. Filmer and L. Pritchett, "The Impact of Public Spending on Health: Does Money Matter?," *Social Science and Medicine* 49 (1999): 1309–23.

17. Caldwell, "Routes to Low Mortality in Poor Countries."

18. Filmer and Pritchett, "The Impact of Public Spending on Health: Does Money Matter?"

19. The additional factors are the extent of ethnolinguistic fragmentation and whether a country is predominantly Muslim.

20. I am taking shelter to be covered in the proposal under "income."

21. The sub-allocations can obviously be adjusted, once the relative causal contributions of the three determinants become more reliably known.

22. In 2003, the World Bank's multiplier ranged from an average of 4.49 for low-income countries to 3.03 for middle-income countries. See UNDP, *Human Development Report 2005* (New York: Oxford University Press, 2005), p. 269. For Sri Lanka, it was 3.99. Ibid., p. 267.

23. Health expenditures come from ibid., p. 237. Educational expenditures come from UNDP, *Human Development Report*

2001 (New York: Oxford University Press, 2001), pp. 171, 179. More recent educational expenditure has been lower.

24. Compare Caldwell's conclusion: "These findings . . . show that low mortality is indeed within the reach of all countries." Caldwell, "Routes to Low Mortality in Poor Countries," p. 209.

TWO   The Life You Can Save

Peter Singer | *The Life You Can Save*. New York: Random House, 2009: 13-19, 81-104, 140-150.

Bob is close to retirement. He has invested most of his savings in a very rare and valuable old car, a Bugatti, which he has not been able to insure. The Bugatti is his pride and joy. Not only does Bob get pleasure from driving and caring for his car, he also knows that its rising market value means that he will be able to sell it and live comfortably after retirement. One day when Bob is out for a drive, he parks the Bugatti near the end of a railway siding and goes for a walk up the track. As he does so, he sees that a runaway train, with no one aboard, is rolling down the railway track. Looking farther down the track, he sees the small figure of a child who appears to be absorbed in playing on the tracks. Oblivious to the runaway train, the child is in great danger. Bob can't stop the train, and the child is too far away to hear his warning shout, but Bob can throw a switch that will divert the train down the siding where his Bugatti is parked. If he does so, nobody will be killed, but the train will crash through the decaying barrier at the end of the siding and destroy his Bugatti. Thinking of his joy in owning the car and the financial security it represents, Bob decides not to throw the switch. . . .

In my experience, people almost always respond that Bob acted badly when he did not throw the switch and destroy his most cherished and valuable possession, thereby sacrificing his hope of a financially secure retirement. . . .

The above example reveals our intuitive belief that we ought to help others in need, at least when we can see them and when we are the only person in a position to save them. But our moral intuitions are not always reliable. The case for helping those in extreme poverty will be stronger if it does not rest solely on our intuitions. Here is a logical argument from plausible premises to the same conclusion.

First premise:	Suffering and death from lack of food, shelter, and medical care are bad.
Second premise:	If it is in your power to prevent something bad from happening, without sacrificing anything nearly as important, it is wrong not to do so.
Third premise:	By donating to aid agencies, you can prevent suffering and death from lack of food, shelter, and medical care, without sacrificing anything nearly as important.
Conclusion:	Therefore, if you do not donate to aid agencies, you are doing something wrong. . . .

Ask yourself if you can deny the premises of the argument. How could suffering and death from lack of food, shelter, and medical care not be really, really bad? . . .

The second premise is also very difficult to reject, because it leaves us some wiggle room when it comes to situations in which, to prevent something bad, we would have to risk something *nearly* as important as the bad thing we are preventing. Consider, for example, a situation in which you can only prevent the deaths of other children by neglecting your own children. This standard does not require you to prevent the deaths of the other children.

"Nearly as important" is a vague term. That's deliberate, because I'm confident that you can do without plenty of things that are clearly and inarguably not as valuable as saving a child's life. I don't know what *you* might think is as important, or nearly as important, as saving a life. By leaving it up to you to decide what those things are, I can avoid the need to find out. I'll trust you to be honest with yourself about it. . . .

You might now be thinking to yourself that the basic argument—that we should donate to aid agencies when by doing so we can prevent suffering and death without giving up anything nearly as important—isn't all that controversial. Yet if we were to take it seriously, our lives would be changed dramatically. For while the cost of saving one child's life by a donation to an aid organization may not be great, after you have donated that sum, there remain more children in need of saving, each one of whom can be saved at a relatively small additional cost. Suppose you have just sent $200 to an agency that can, for that amount, save the life of a child in a developing country who would otherwise have died. You've done something really good, and all it has cost you is the price of some new clothes you didn't really need anyway. Congratulations! But don't celebrate your good deed by opening a bottle of champagne, or even going to a movie. The cost of that bottle or movie, added to what you could save by cutting down on a few other extravagances, would save the life of another child. After you forgo those items, and give another $200, though, is everything else you are spending on as important, or nearly as important, as the life of a child? Not likely! So you must keep cutting back on unnecessary spending, and donating what you save, until you have reduced yourself to the point where if you give any more, you will be sacrificing something nearly as important as a child's life—like giving so much that you can no longer afford to give your children an adequate education. . . .

If the basic argument presented above is right, then what many of us consider acceptable behavior must be viewed in a new, more ominous light. When we spend our surplus on concerts or fashionable shoes, on fine dining and good wines, or on holidays in faraway lands, we are doing something wrong.

Suddenly the three premises laid out above are much harder to swallow. You may now be questioning whether a moral argument that has such radically demanding implications can possibly be sound. . . .

The argument that we ought to be doing more to save the lives of people living in extreme poverty presupposes that we can do it, and at a moderate cost.

But can we? If so, to which organizations should we donate? Holden Karnofsky and Elie Hassenfeld began to tackle these questions a few years ago. . . . You have probably heard questions raised about various charities' use of funds—in particular, about how much of the money they raise actually goes to helping the people it's intended to help, rather than to cover the administrative costs of the home office. . . .

Karnofsky and Hassenfeld were astonished by how unprepared charities were for questions that went beyond superficial and potentially misleading indicators of efficacy. Eventually, they realized something that seemed to them quite extraordinary: the reason they were not getting the information they wanted from the charities was that the charities themselves didn't have it. . . . If the information didn't exist, then both individual donors and major foundations were giving away huge sums with little idea what effect their gifts were having. How could hundreds of billions of dollars be spent without some evidence that the money is doing good?

Having identified the problem, Karnofsky and Hassenfeld decided to do something about it. In 2007 they founded GiveWell, a non-profit dedicated to improving the transparency and effectiveness of charities. . . . They invited charities to apply for grants of $25,000 in five broad humanitarian categories, with the application process asking the charities to provide information demonstrating that they were making measurable progress toward achieving their goals, and indicating the cost of their achievements. In this way, the money GiveWell raises is effective in two distinct ways. A substantial part of it—the $25,000 grants—goes to the most effective charity in each category, thus supporting its work. At the same time, the existence of the grants encourages charities to do more to evaluate the effectiveness of what they are doing. Of the five categories, the one most relevant to our concerns was "Saving Lives in Africa." Since Africa has one-third of the world's extremely poor people, with some of the world's highest rates of childhood mortality and shortest overall life expectancy, the information GiveWell seeks is just the information we need to answer the questions posed by the argument set out in this book: Is it true that a relatively modest donation to an aid agency can save a life? And if so, which agencies do this best? . . .

In 2007, GiveWell published the results of its investigation into charities working to save lives and improve health in Africa. The investigation covered only the 59 organizations that applied for a GiveWell grant; of these, only 15 provided adequate information. . . .

GiveWell gave top rating to an organization based in Washington, D.C., called Population Services International (PSI). PSI sells condoms, bed nets, water purification treatment, and treatment for malaria and diarrhea, and educates people on their uses. It sells the items at a nominal cost because evidence suggests that people are more likely to use things properly if they have paid for them. In 2005, PSI sold 8.2 million nets at a cost of $56 million. Using a conservative estimate of the number of children sleeping under each net, and allowing that the nets may be used only 50 to 80 per cent of the time, GiveWell gives a range of $623 to $2367 for the cost per life saved by preventing malaria. PSI's own estimate is $820, a figure that falls between GiveWell's high and low estimates. . . .

As for PSI's other major activity, promoting and distributing condoms, GiveWell estimates that each HIV infection averted costs between $200 and $700. (In poor countries where antiretroviral drugs are not available, HIV is a great deal more likely to kill.)

PSI's program to save lives from diarrhea is a relatively minor part of its budget, so GiveWell did not study it as fully as other parts of PSI's operations, but it may be the most cost-effective. PSI distributes products that can be mixed into water to make it safe to drink and to prevent diarrhea. It also distributes oral rehydration treatment. GiveWell's rough estimate is that this program costs $250 per life saved. Since the program plays only a small part in PSI's activities, however, GiveWell estimates that across the organization as a whole, PSI saves lives for between $650 and $1000 each. In addition, it prevents non-fatal malaria attacks, non-fatal sexually transmitted diseases, unwanted pregnancies, and non-fatal attacks of diarrhea. . . .

Another of GiveWell's most effective organizations was Partners in Health. . . . From its modest beginnings in Haiti and then Peru, it has now expanded to Rwanda, Lesotho, and Russia, providing free health care to some of the world's poorest people. Although the cost per life saved by its provision of basic health services in impoverished rural areas is relatively high—estimated at $3500—Partners provides many other health benefits to those it serves. . . .

According to Richard Miller, a philosopher who has written widely about global justice, we ought to give to the point at which, if we were to give more, we would run a "significant" risk of worsening our lives—but we do not need to go beyond this point. Miller's idea is that morality allows us to pursue "the underlying goals to which we are securely attached" but that, when others are in need, it does not allow us to spend more than we need to achieve those goals.[1] Garrett Cullity, author of *The Moral Demands of Affluence*, believes that we should give to the point at which further contributions would undermine our pursuit of "intrinsically life-enhancing goods" such as friendship, developing one's musical talents, and being involved in the life of one's community.[2] In his book *Ideal Code, Real World*, Brad Hooker argues that we should try to live according to the code that, if widely accepted, would lead to the best outcome. Hooker asserts that we are morally required to help those in

---

Bed nets
Insecticide-treated nets which are placed over a bed, and which function as a protection against disease vectors (especially mosquitoes).

Malaria
A life-threatening disease that is caused by parasites that are transmitted to humans via the bites of mosquitoes that are themselves infected. It kills nearly a million people a year, most of whom are children born in Africa.

Diarrhea
The passage of three or more loose stools per day; it is often caused by a bacteria, virus, or parasite found in unclean drinking water. It kills about 1.5 million children per year, and it is one of the leading causes of death amongst children under the age of five.

HIV infection
Human immunodeficiency virus is a retrovirus that infects the cells of the immune system, wholly or partially undermining its ability to fight disease and infection. Its most advanced state is known as AIDS or acquired immunodeficiency disease syndrome. It is transmitted via unprotected sex, and the transfusion of contaminated blood, among other means. Approximately 33 million people in the world are infected with HIV, two-thirds of whom live in sub-Saharan Africa.

Antiretroviral drugs
A cocktail of drugs used to suppress the HIV virus and retard or stop the progress of the HIV disease. Slightly fewer than four million people in sub-Saharan Africa receive antiretroviral drugs.

Oral rehydration treatment
A therapy used to treat dehydration due to diarrhea; it is a sugar and salt solution that is administered orally. It is responsible for saving the lives of many living in developing nations.

Non-fatal sexually transmitted disease
An infection that is typically spread from one person to another through sexual contact, e.g., chlamydia, herpes, gonorrhea.

greater need "even if the personal sacrifices involved in helping them add up to a significant cost," but that we are not required to go beyond this threshold.[3]

Miller's standard is the least demanding. If it is important to you to express your sense of who you are by occasionally buying clothes or accessories that are stylish or fun, rather than something more basic, you are permitted to buy those items. The same is true of eating: If we never ate in good restaurants we could not pursue our "worthwhile" goal of eating "in a way that explores a variety of interesting aesthetic and cultural possibilities." Similarly, enjoying "the capacity of great composers and performers to exploit nuances of timbre and texture to powerful aesthetic effect" is a worthwhile goal, and one that justifies buying "more than minimal" stereo equipment.

Cullity's standard is more demanding. His "intrinsically life-enhancing goods" don't appear to include things like stylish clothes, though they do include whatever is necessary to enjoy music, since he regards that as an intrinsically life-enhancing good. But for most goods, if there is a cheaper alternative I can pursue that is not substantially worse for me, that is what I should go for. Only goods like friendship and integrity, which involve our deepest commitments, should not be judged on the basis of how much they cost.

Hooker acknowledges that his criterion is vague, but says it would be met by a person who regularly gives a little money or time to charities. He stresses that the test is whether all of the time or money given adds up to a significant cost, not whether the sacrifice involved on any particular occasion of helping someone in greater need is significant. Hence giving to this level would not require forgoing, Hooker says, one's personal projects.

So our obligations to the poor do not, in Miller, Cullity, and Hooker's views, go as far as to say that you must give to the point where if you give any more, you will be sacrificing something nearly as important as a child's life. However, it's important not to lose sight of the fact that these three philosophers agree that if you fail to give anything, or give only trivial sums to aid the world's poorest people, you are acting wrongly. Depending on the facts about how much it would take to overcome widespread extreme poverty, the obligations Miller, Cullity, and Hooker posit may be demanding. Miller, for example, would allow us to purchase a luxury item of attire "only occasionally." The stereo that the music lover may buy can be "more than minimal," but that implies that we are not justified in buying at the top of the line, even if we can afford it. Cullity allows us to spend money on significant activities that will enhance our lives, but spending on trivial items should, in his view, be redirected to helping combat poverty. Hooker says you are required to give to those in greater need to the point at which the total of the money or time you have given involves a significant personal cost. Against the background of a world in which most affluent people give only a trivial proportion of their income, or none at all, to help the poor, the agreement among the four of us that we all have, at a minimum, moderately demanding obligations to help the poor is more important than the differences between us.

Many people get great pleasure from dressing stylishly, eating well, and listening to music on a good stereo system. I'm all for pleasure—the more the better, other things being equal. There's no denying that there is value in the things that Miller, Cullity, and Hooker think we are entitled to spend our money on. But my argument does imply that it is wrong to spend money on those things when we could instead be using the money to save people's lives and prevent great suffering. The problem is that we are living in the midst of an emergency in which 27,000 children die from avoidable causes every day. That's more than one thousand every hour. And millions of women are living with repairable [obstetric] fistulas, and millions of people are blind who could see again. We can do something about these things.

That crucial fact ought to affect the choices we make. To buy good stereo equipment in order to further my worthwhile goal, or life-enhancing experience, of listening to music is to place more value on these enhancements to my life than on whether others live or die. Can it be ethical to live that way? Doesn't it make a mockery of any claim to believe in the equal value of human life?

> **Obstetric fistula**
> A hole between the vagina and either the rectum or the bladder causing urine or feces to enter the vagina. This is often the result of a baby lodging in the vaginal canal during pregnancy. Women who suffer from this are often socially marginalized because of the odor they emit.

For the same reason, philanthropy for the arts or for cultural activities is, in a world like this one, morally dubious. In 2004, New York's Metropolitan Museum of Art paid a sum said to be in excess of $45 million for a small Madonna and Child painted

Duccio
Duccio di Buoninsegna was an Italian painter active in the thirteenth and fourteenth centuries. He is the founder of the Sienese School of painting.

Cataract operation
A cataract occurs when the lens of the eye loses its transparency, thereby blurring or impairing vision. This is often caused by aging. Cataract surgery involves the removal of the natural lens of the eye, which is then replaced by an artificial lens.

by the medieval Italian master Duccio. In buying this painting, the museum has added to the abundance of masterpieces that those fortunate enough to be able to visit it can see. But if it only costs $50 to perform a cataract operation in a developing country, that means there are 900,000 people who can't see anything at all, let alone a painting, whose sight could have been restored by the amount of money that painting cost. At $450 to repair a fistula, $45 million could have given 100,000 women another chance at a decent life. At $1000 a life, it could have saved 45,000 lives—a football stadium full of people. How can a painting, no matter how beautiful and historically significant, compare with that? If the museum were on fire, would anyone think it right to save the Duccio from the flames, rather than a child? And that's just one child. In a world in which more-pressing needs had already been met, philanthropy for the arts would be a noble act. Sadly, we don't live in such a world. . . .

Study Questions

1. What is the moral principle on which Singer relies in his defence of the idea that we ought to do much more for the global poor? Is it acceptable? Why or why not?

2. How important to Singer's position is the empirical information about the cost of saving a life and the effectiveness of the charities that provide aid?

3. Singer's position implies fairly demanding action on the part of the absolutely wealthy. Is this problematic? Is this worry deflected by noting that other philosophical positions support that we ought to do more?

Notes

1. Richard Miller, "Beneficence, Duty and Distance," *Philosophy and Public Affairs* 32 (2004), pp. 357–83.
2. Garrett Cullity, *The Moral Demands of Affluence* (Oxford, UK: Oxford University Press, 2004). There is much more in Cullity's book than I have discussed here. I have responded to some of the other arguments in my review in *Philosophy and Phenomenological Research* 75:2 (September 2007), pp. 475–83.
3. Brad Hooker, *Ideal Code, Real World: A Rule-Consequentialist Theory of Morality* (Oxford, UK: Clarendon Press, 2000), p. 166.

THREE Domination and Destitution in an Unjust World
Ryoa Chung | *Canadian Journal of Philosophy*, Supplementary Volume 2005; 31: 311-34.

Contemporary problems of poverty and inequality

Globalization
The process by which regional or national economics become more closely linked with each other through legal, political, and technological means. The integration typically involves the absence of barriers to trade and/or foreign ownership and/or worker mobility.

raise philosophical questions and elicit moral intuitions that are intimately linked to the way in which globalization has transformed the international order over the last 30 years. In light of the empirical factors that shape the basic interaction between states, some claim that this descriptive analysis forces us to re-evaluate the normative principles that govern our understanding of international obligations towards the world's least advantaged peoples. In this article, I would like to explore this hypothesis through the case study of the HIV/AIDS crisis in sub-Saharan Africa. . . . I will argue that the moral discomfort of the world's most affluent citizens goes beyond simple compassion to reveal a diffuse, but nonetheless justified, feeling of collective responsibility towards the *extreme vulnerability* of African populations battling this plague. . . . But this contention begs the following question: is it possible to extend principles of justice to a global scale? In order to demonstrate that this may indeed be possible, we need to show that the structural conditions of globalization create *inequities*, by which I mean systematic inequalities that are *unjust*. I will . . . attempt to show that there exists a codependent relationship between the internal and external conditions of economic growth and political emancipation that no international actor can escape. The view I will defend in this paper takes its point of departure from the conceptual paradigm in international ethics developed by T. W. Pogge, especially his powerful thesis of collective causal responsibility for the origins and perpetuation of an unjust global institutional scheme. However, I will attempt to complement Pogge's analysis by showing how globalization transforms the international order into an institutionalized system of social interaction characterized by the features of *domination*, as conceptualized in another area of contemporary political philosophy by P. Pettit. If my descriptive analysis of the world order proves to be correct, it follows that the international community shares a collective responsibility in the origins of unjust inequalities that expose certain populations to what I will call *extreme vulnerability*. . . .

It is important to stress some well-documented facts concerning the current situation brought on by HIV/AIDS in sub-Saharan Africa in order to capture the appalling extent of human suffering. In 2005, two million individuals, adults and children died of AIDS in Africa (which represents nearly 5500 individuals dying every day). According to the most recent UNAIDS report, published in May 2006,[1] 64 per cent of all individuals infected with HIV throughout the world (24.5 million out of 38 million) live in sub-Saharan Africa, a region that accounts for only 10 per cent of the world population. The average life expectancy does not exceed 49 years. . . .

> **UNAIDS**
> The Joint United Nations Programme on HIV/AIDS, involving various parts of the UN and other institutions, the aim of which is to stop the spread of HIV/AIDS and to increase preventative measures and access to treatment and care for the disease.

It is a well-known fact that these countries are grappling with regionalized pockets of absolute poverty (according to the World Bank index of less than $1 per day, per person), and that they are overburdened by substantial foreign debts while being utterly excluded from world trade (sub-Saharan Africa benefited from less than 0.4 per cent of the total foreign investments in 2000). The countries most afflicted by AIDS have no financial means to purchase and provide adequate medical treatment to combat the pandemic. In 2001, public health expenditures represented, on average, less than $10 per inhabitant in most of these countries, whereas the average cost of basic medical treatment for AIDS patients was around $30 per patient, without taking into account the costs related to antiretroviral therapy. . . .

The case of Africa is deeply disturbing since it gives rise to ambivalent moral intuitions. What, exactly, is the nature and extent of the international community's moral obligations, especially for the rich countries of the OECD, in the face of the HIV/AIDS crisis?

I would like to emphasize Shue's important work on *basic subsistence rights*. According to Shue, the satisfaction of subsistence rights, which are defined as essential material needs, determines the conditions that allow individuals to function as

> **OECD**
> Organization for Economic Co-operation and Development; an organization comprising thirty countries, which provides a forum for members (including Canada) to debate and develop common economic and social policy.

genuine autonomous moral agents and truly to exercise their fundamental liberties. . . . For the purpose of my argument, the principal attraction of a theory of subsistence rights consists in its universalizable contribution to a theory of global justice. Specifically, if we temporarily restrict ourselves to subsistence rights—those rights that are defined by criteria of indigence and extreme morbidity which prevent individuals from exercising the minimal autonomy as moral agents—this may provide an uncontroversial moral axiom on the international level. . . .

> **Indigence**
> Extreme poverty or destitution.

Moreover, rights based on subsistence needs provide a more concrete answer

> **Morbidity**
> Illness, poor health.

to the problem of establishing a threshold that determines the scope of the international responsibility of mutual aid. Since an open-ended threshold of international obligations is too vague to effectively guide political action, the subsistence needs criterion offers an initial, identifiable stage that functions negatively: we *know* when an individual or group of individuals suffer from indigence, avoidable mortality, and extreme morbidity because of an index of health that objectively measures hunger, thirst, disease, and avoidable death. It goes without saying that we could and should add other strata of primary goods, fundamental rights and individual liberties to this first stage of basic needs in order to fully realize all the requirements of justice. But insofar as the minimum threshold of subsistence hasn't yet been met, a pragmatic approach of international ethics can limit itself to the normative defence of primary conditions of global justice at this first stage.

The moral discomfort caused by the HIV/AIDS crisis brings us to the heart of this distinction between the spheres of justice and charity, which is even more troublesome in the international sphere in the absence of a common institutional framework analogous to a world government that clearly identifies reciprocal rights and duties enforced by common institutions. Now, the tension may simply be apparent, insofar as our spontaneous moral intuitions seem to tell us that international obligations of mutual aid actually stem from compassionate good will and virtuous charity rather than from considerations of justice. It can easily be presumed that our common assumptions will lead us to hold that, although we sincerely deplore the tragic consequences of inequality, it is an inescapable fact of the human condition and that the domestic political institutions of each society must attempt to resolve it as best they can, according to the resources and institutional means available. In other words, according to the liberal framework which the majority of Western countries subscribe to, not all inequalities demand a moral response. Only inequalities that are considered *unnecessary*, *avoidable*, *unfair* and *therefore unjust* properly make up the *inequities* . . . that form the proper object of ethical and political reflection about justice. It is not obvious at first blush that global inequalities should be treated as inequities that need to be remedied. . . .

Still, another point of view reflects another range of spontaneous moral intuitions that are more obscure and difficult to articulate, but are still, in my opinion, deeply embedded in our collective moral consciousness. One of the most highly involved figures in the fight against AIDS is undoubtedly Dr Paul Farmer,[2] who suggested at *The Inaugural Jonathan Mann Lecture on Health and Human Rights*[3] that the question of our

moral responsibility should be construed in terms of generational responsibility. We rightfully condemn past generations for having caused and upheld abominable forms of slavery and for having supported institutions that encouraged the most denigrating form of discrimination against races and women. In the same way, we condemn those who actively (and passively through their indifference) participated in the genocide of millions of innocent people. Should we not judge ourselves just as severely for tolerating the suffering of millions of our contemporaries afflicted by AIDS—especially since evidence shows that we do have the means to help them? . . .

With respect to the normative justification of the international community's collective responsibility for inequality and poverty (of which health outcomes are an important indicator), it seems to me that we can benefit from Charles Beitz's[4] much-discussed thesis on interdependence in the context of globalization, provided we carefully specify what this claim actually means. In the following I will attempt to show that in the context of globalization it is correct to speak about a scheme of social cooperation based on a structure of interdependence, providing no possibility of exit. This carries over, of course, to the normative defence of basic principles of global justice. . . .

It is a serious error to analyze something as complex and multifaceted as poverty simply in terms of domestic causes. It is not only a factual error, but also a moral one. The moment we attribute the principal causes of poverty to endogenous factors, no obligation of justice can bind the international community. Instead, we will be happy to prescribe obligations of charity that states can interpret freely, applying them to their foreign policy as they see fit. This analysis is all the more regrettable since it follows from a faulty analysis of the facts. . . . The thesis I want to defend here is to the effect that, for each domestic society, a significant number of its choices and ability to manoeuvre depends on its power in the international sphere, i.e., its economic and political power of negotiation. For example, the economic power of each country in the context of neoliberal economic globalization determines the relationship of political power (the ability to persuade, the influence of lobbying, and the

> **Endogenous factors**
> Factors that proceed from within. In this context, it would involve explaining poverty solely by reference to factors that are internal to the country of focus.

IMF
International Monetary Fund; an organization of 188 countries promoting (among other things) international trade, long-term economic growth and the elimination of poverty.

WTO
World Trade Organization; an international organization dealing with the rules governing trade between the world's nations. These rules are meant to facilitate the flow of goods and services around the globe.

Bretton Woods institutions
This refers to the IMF and the World Bank, which were created in Bretton Woods, New Hampshire in 1944. Although they were originally created for the purpose of financing the reconstruction of Europe after World War II, the two institutions now have broader functions.

power to negotiate international conventions to its advantage) between countries in institutions like the IMF or the WTO. Only when we admit this (aside from the historical conditions that have given rise to the Bretton Woods institutions) can we explain why the United States is actually the only country with the right to a veto within the IMF. A country's power of political negotiation depends on its financial and technological capacity to exploit the available internal resources, and to realize conditions for the accumulation of capital and the capacity to access the global economic market. The effects of this codependence of external and internal conditions may appear less important to citizens living in the rich countries of the OECD, but this is simply a question of perception due to the position of power they enjoy in the international arena. . .

Once we acknowledge the codependence of internal and external conditions for fair economic growth and political emancipation in the context of globalization, how does this help us extend our account of international obligations of justice? The answer is that we then have no choice but to acknowledge that economic globalization has created a scheme of social *cooperation* (or a "basic structure" as one would say) on an international scale in the *political* sense of the term (in contrast to the mere empirical fact of interdependence or the less precise notion of a web of more or less contingent social *interactions* that are not conditioned by institutional conventions). We can therefore define the political notion of a scheme of social cooperation according to three criteria: (1) a structural interdependence exists between states; (2) this scheme of social cooperation rests on a logic

of mutual costs and benefits—which doesn't imply, however, that the structural interdependence rests on a fair division of costs and benefits for all parties; and (3) participation in this scheme of cooperation is obligatory. Participation isn't necessarily voluntary (it certainly isn't in many cases), but all submit to a set of common conditions and institutions characterized by a scheme of social cooperation arising from economic globalization. We can then speak, in a more or less general, but nonetheless operational sense, of a system of social cooperation based on a structure of reciprocity, i.e., a set of institutional and legal conventions that predetermine the behaviours of international actors regarding international trade, law, and politics. In this respect, the impossibility of members escaping this set of structural rules without paying the catastrophic price of exclusion testifies to the mandatory character of membership. From this point of view, the economic autarchy of a state has become an obsolete illusion in the context of globalization and may eventually lead to political annihilation. In this respect we can claim, not without reason and indeed with some anxiety, that globalization has produced an *inescapable* system of cooperation that isn't mediated by a world government. . . .

If it is true that we all participate in a system of social cooperation on a global scale, questions concerning the principles of global justice then become increasingly acute. The reason for this is that the system of social cooperation arising from economic globalization is marked by the features of *domination* in Philip Pettit's sense: we are subjected to insidious and arbitrary forms of interference and coercion in the context of unequal relations of power. It is important to recall some of the central elements of Pettit's notion of domination. . . .

According to Pettit, a relation of domination exists when someone has the capacity to interfere in another's sphere of action, and when this intervention is arbitrary, which is to say that it is not governed by collectively agreed upon norms and laws but rather by the interests and will of the dominator. Whether this power is insidious or blatant, it is always a form of *arbitrary* and *coercive* interference. By this we understand that the agent does not in any way take into account the proper interests of the subjugated person but rather subjects them to their influence and authority. In the worst case, the agent that takes advantage of the weakness, needs, or poverty of the other in order to define the parameters of her context of choice. Relations of domination rest fundamentally on the inequality of power of negotiation stemming from the inequality of resources of domination. . . .

The resources in virtue of which one person may have power over another are extraordinarily various: they range over resources of physical strength, technical advantages, financial clout, political authority, social connections, communal standing, informational access, ideological position, cultural legitimization, and the like.[5]

Attempting to provide concrete examples of how relationships of domination in the context of neo-liberal economic globalization in certain international institutions like the IMF or the WTO escape normal democratic regulatory mechanisms lies beyond the scope of this essay. A cursory analysis of the daily news as well as many case studies in the contemporary literature on globalization suggest a strong correlation between economic and political inequality in countries' capacity to negotiate. . . . The power exercised by the IMF is the most obvious example of institutional forms of domination on the global scale. No one can remain indifferent to the fact that the rules of the game of international credit and trade are, in fact, dictated by the IMF, the World Bank, and the American Treasury Council in the name of a neo-liberal ideological consensus. . . . In a globalized system of social cooperation that affords no possibility of exit, countries in the process of development or in crisis can only submit to the conditions of their creditors and cannot exercise their fundamental right to contest . . . the terms of loans or the international trade conventions. They rightly fear the sphere of influence (another resource of domination) of financial and political elites that might harm their precarious conditions of existence.

In a similar way, we can also briefly show that

> **World Bank**
> A global institution that provides financial and other forms of assistance to the world's developing countries. The main aim of this assistance is to combat poverty; the assistance often comes in the form of loans that may be invested in education and economic development, among other things.

> **Neo-liberal ideological consensus**
> The idea that there is a consensus amongst the world's powers that free trade, low taxes, fiscal austerity, and minimal governmental intervention in the economy are the most appropriate way to organize a national economy.

negotiations of WTO treaties are marked by inequality. . . . Pogge's . . . work[6] . . . reminds us that the flagrant protectionism of the rich countries of the OECD, the asymmetric policy of custom tariffs, and the recognized practice of unfair competition in terms of agricultural subsidies are simply some of the better-known examples of the unequal conditions of "free trade," which privilege the most powerful and oblige the most vulnerable to dance to their tune. . . . It is in these circumstances that we grasp the extreme vulnerability that our international system inflicts upon its most powerless members.

Now, faced with the HIV/AIDS pandemic, how should we determine the

> **Free trade**
> The position that the trade of goods and services is most efficient when the legal and financial barriers to it are minimal in nature. This typically involves making borders more porous and eliminating trade subsidies and tariffs. This is more often advocated than acted upon, hence the scare quotes here.

ways in which obligations of international justice should be made good? This question is undoubtedly complex, and I will not be able to answer it fully in the context of this paper. . . . However, it is important to note that we should not define *a priori* duties of global justice solely as obligations of distributive justice. Rather, a deeper analysis leads us to envisage a fair division of moral labour between domestic and international institutions both economically and politically that will lead us to develop institutional reforms at the international level. According to this more

> **Distributive justice**
> A conception of justice dictating a certain distribution of (usually scarce) resources. Developing a theory of distributive justice typically involves outlining what a fair or equitable distribution of resources consists in.

elaborate view of global justice, duties of mutual assistance involving transfers of resources will appear as one of the necessary and primary implications of global justice, prescribing duties to rectify unjust economic inequalities and readjust the unequal ability to secure terms of fair negotiation between parties in international institutions. But again, these extremely complex and important questions point in the direction of a multi-faceted and multidisciplinary task. This challenge that awaits our generation goes far beyond my proposal, which, in this article, is restricted to a purely normative defence of international obligations of global justice in light of the HIV/AIDS pandemic in order to better analyze the conceptual parameters in political philosophy that the contemporary structural conditions of globalization force us to reconsider. . . .

If our analysis of economic neo-liberal globalization is accurate, . . . then it is necessary to admit that the international community shares a causal responsibility for the conditions of extreme vulnerability that condemns its most destitute inhabitants to endure the unthinkable. As such, the call for principles of global justice is entirely justified.

Study Questions

1. Chung argues that industrialized nations are in part responsible for the "extreme vulnerability" of those living with HIV/AIDS in sub-Saharan Africa. Is the evidence she relies on sufficient to justify her claim?

2. In her argument, Chung employs the idea of basic subsistence rights. What does she mean by this idea?

3. Chung relies heavily in her analysis on the idea that economic globalization has "created a scheme of social cooperation." What does this mean? Why is it important?

Notes

1. ONUSIDA, *Rapport sur l'épidémie mondiale de SIDA*, 2006.
2. Paul Farmer, *Pathologies of Power: Health, Human Rights, and the New War on the Poor* (Berkeley: University of California Press, 2003).
3. B. Kouchner, and Paul Farmer. "From Doctors without Borders to Patients without Borders." At The Inaugural Jonathan Mann Lecture on Health and Human Rights, organized by the François-Xavier Bagnoud Center for Health and Human Rights, Harvard School of Public Health, 6 March 2003.
4. Charles Beitz, *Political Theory and International Relations*, (Princeton NJ: Princeton University Press, 1979).
5. Philip Pettit, *Republicanism: A Theory of Freedom and Government*, Oxford: Oxford University Press, 1997, p. 59.
6. Thomas Pogge, *World Poverty and Human Rights: Cosmopolitan Responsibilities and Reforms* (Cambridge: Polity Press, 2002).

Chapter Study Questions

1. Sreenivasan defends a non-ideal theory. Is the theory defended by Singer ideal or non-ideal? Is this relevant to Singer's argument?

2. Chung and Singer argue for fairly weighty obligations to the absolutely poor. Singer appeals to intuitions regarding positive obligations to people in need, while Chung appeals to intuitions respecting the requirement to redistribute resources in order to rectify past injustices. Which strategy is more plausible?

3. All of the authors agree that we have some obligation to the global poor. Is this a legitimate assumption? On what grounds might one dissent from this claim?

Critical Analysis

Consider the following from the excerpt by Peter Singer:

"Philanthropy for the arts or for cultural activities is, in a world like this one, morally dubious. In 2004, New York's Metropolitan Museum of Art paid a sum said to be in excess of $45 million for a small Madonna and Child painted by the medieval Italian master Duccio. In buying this painting, the museum has added to the abundance of masterpieces that those fortunate enough to be able to visit it can see. But if it only costs $50 to perform a cataract operation in a developing country, that means there are 900,000 people who can't see anything at all, let alone a painting, whose sight could have been restored by the amount of money that painting cost. At $450 to repair a fistula, $45 *million could have given 100,000 women another chance at a decent life. At $1000 a life, it could have saved 45,000 lives—a football stadium full of people. How can a painting, no matter how beautiful and historically significant, compare with that? If the museum were on fire, would anyone think it right to save the Duccio from the flames, rather than a child? And that's just one child. In a world in which more-pressing needs had already been met, philanthropy for the arts would be a noble act. Sadly, we don't live in such a world."*

Outline Singer's argument in your own words, paying particular attention to the premises that he relies on to support his main conclusion. Choose one of the premises for evaluation. Try to think of at least one objection to this premise.

Case Study

It is not uncommon for doctors, nurses and other health care workers trained in developing nations, e.g., the Philippines and Ghana, to immigrate to developed nations. This is often a result of the fact that the environment, pay, and working conditions are better. However, it is often also the result of being recruited by or on behalf of wealthy nations. In Canada, Regional Health Authorities, private companies and provincial governments recruit foreign-trained health care professionals, including pharmacists, nurses, and physicians. An increasing number of these health care professionals (especially physicians) have been trained in sub-Saharan Africa, a region which suffers from 25 per cent of the world's disease burden. The loss of such health care workers often makes it difficult or impossible to achieve positive health outcomes. Data produced by the World Health Organization shows that an average of 2.5 skilled health care workers per 1000 people is needed to establish basic health care provision. Canada has about 12 such workers for every 1000 of its citizens. By contrast, the countries in Africa have on average only 1.4 per 1000. If a health care professional moves from sub-Saharan African to Canada, she or he is moving from a location with a serious shortfall of medical professionals to a location that is already more than able to meet its basic health care needs.

1. Is it wrong for Canada to recruit health care professionals from areas of the world that are experiencing a shortage of health care providers? Why?
2. Which factors are most important to deciding this question?
3. Do the theories discussed above have implications for the ethics of recruiting health care providers from the world's poorest regions?

Further Reading

Academics Stand Against Poverty [Internet]. Available from: http://www.yale.edu/macmillan/globaljustice/ASAP.html. Date Accessed: 10 June 2012.

Blake M. International Justice. In: Zalta EN, editor. Stanford encyclopedia of philosophy [Internet]. 2005. Available from: http://plato.stanford.edu/entries/international-justice/. Date Accessed: 10 June 2012

Brock G. Health in developing countries and our global responsibilities. In: Dawson A, editor. *The philosophy of public health.* Aldershot: Ashgate; 2009. p. 73-84.

Incentives for Global Health [Internet]. Yale: The Whitney and Betty MacMillan Center for International and Area Studies at Yale. Available from: http://www.yale.edu/macmillan/igh/. Date Accessed: 10 June 2012.

Pogge T. *World poverty and human rights.* 2nd ed. Cambridge: Polity Press; 2008.

Assisted Suicide and Euthanasia

Do Canadians suffering from a painful and incurable disease have a moral right to ask their physician to help them die if this expresses their autonomous wish? If they hold such a right, should the practice be permitted as social policy, or will it inevitably lead to unacceptable abuses? Many Canadians believe that assisted suicide and voluntary euthanasia ought to be permitted. According to a 2010 Angus Reid Poll, 67 per cent of respondents indicated that they are in favour of legalizing voluntary euthanasia; and an even greater proportion (85 per cent) said that doing so would provide people who are suffering with a chance to ease their pain. Legalization would require changes to the Criminal Code of Canada. While it is not a criminal offense to commit suicide, assisting another in their suicide is punishable by up to 14 years in prison (section 241(b)). Voluntary euthanasia falls under the prohibition of murder in section 229 of the Criminal Code, and is punishable by a mandatory minimum sentence of life with no possibility of parole for 25 years. The obstacles to legalization are practical as well as legal. According to a 1996 survey of Canadian physicians, if assisted suicide or voluntary euthanasia were legalized, the majority of physicians (55 per cent) indicated they would not participate in either practice.

The readings in this chapter consider the moral permissibility of assisted suicide and voluntary euthanasia. In the first reading, the Royal Society of Canada Expert Panel argues for permitting assisted suicide and euthanasia in Canada. According to the Panel, there is a broad social consensus that autonomy—the right to decide for oneself how one's life ought to proceed—is a core value for Canadians. If a person concludes, on the basis of careful deliberation and consistent with a stable set of values, that his life is no longer worth living then he has a moral right to request assisted suicide or voluntary euthanasia. It is important to note that the Panel does not restrict this right to individuals who are terminally ill; it is the right of all people who are suffering. It is well recognized, however, that the autonomous claims of individuals are limited insofar as they put others at risk. Thus, before assisted suicide and voluntary euthanasia are adopted as social policy, the consequences of enacting such a policy must be carefully considered.

The debate about the social consequences of assisted suicide and voluntary euthanasia centre on slippery slope arguments. The Royal Society of Canada Expert Panel considers two broad types of these arguments. Conceptual slippery slope arguments posit that vagueness in key terms, such as competence, will lead to an unacceptable expansion of practice. The Panel rejects this, believing that clear lines can be drawn, for instance, between competent and incompetent requests for assisted suicide and euthanasia. Causal (or empirical) slippery slope arguments posit that once assisted suicide and voluntary euthanasia is permitted, human decision-making driven by psychological, social, or institutional factors will lead to an unacceptable expansion in practice. The members of the Panel believe that the experience in such policies from other countries (including the Netherlands) is reassuring, and that effective regulation can prevent abuses from occurring.

In the second reading, Benjamin Freedman reviews the Supreme Court of Canada's most important decision regarding assisted suicide, *Rodriguez* v. *British Columbia (Attorney General)*. Sue Rodriguez was afflicted with a progressive neuromuscular disease that would leave her unable to commit suicide at the time of her choosing. She sought, therefore, to have section 241(b) of the Criminal Code overturned on the grounds that it failed to provide persons with disability with equal protection and benefit of the law without discrimination. Able persons can commit suicide at the time of their choosing; persons with advanced neuromuscular disease require assistance to commit suicide late in the course of their disease, and this is precisely what section 241(b) prohibits. Freedman points out that, in fact, at the time of application Sue Rodriguez was able to commit suicide. The question at issue was not whether the disabled have the right to kill themselves (they do), but rather whether others may be legitimately involved in the act of suicide. As Freedman puts it, the question is "the right to publicly ratify, in court, a new form of cooperative action bent upon inducing a certain person's death." Freedman's deep reservations about allowing a novel right of "cooperative action" in a person's death stem from causal (or empirical) slippery slope concerns. The proposed requirements that assisted suicide be restricted to terminally ill patients, who are fully informed and of undoubted competence, and whose request for assistance in dying is firm and unwavering are all, he argues, open to dangerous expansion in practice.

In the third reading, Downie and Sherwin provide a feminist analysis of assisted suicide and voluntary euthanasia. Their analysis relies upon the concept of relational autonomy, which understands the person as an essentially social being, whose relationships with others play an integral role in shaping the self and which may foster or inhibit autonomous action. Relational autonomy helps us focus on the effects of a person's position within an oppressive power structure on her competency, voluntariness, and choice to die at home. Downie and Sherwin argue that gender socialization may diminish a woman's competency for autonomous decision-making. As a result, oppression-sensitive standards for assessing competency ought to be developed. They further argue that women may be at greater risk of deciding to end their lives so as not to burden others, and that the voluntariness of these decisions requires careful attention. Finally, home care may simply not be an option for elderly women if demographic patterns of the greater longevity of women continue. Thus, the special needs of elderly women ought to be accounted for in social policy.

ONE **The Royal Society of Canada Expert Panel: End-of-Life Decision Making**

Udo Schuklenk, Johannes J.M. van Delden, Jocelyn Downie, Sheila McLean, Ross Upshur, and Daniel Weinstock | Royal Society of Canada Expert Panel. *End of Life Decision Making*. Ottawa: Royal Society of Canada, 2011.

Introduction

. . . The Panel holds that there is both sufficient consensus with respect to core values in the Canadian policy context and a sufficient grasp of the relevant facts that justifiable conclusions can be drawn about what the legal status of assisted suicide and voluntary euthanasia should be. . . .

Assisted suicide
The act of intentionally killing oneself with the assistance of another person. For instance, when a patient deliberately takes a fatal overdose of prescription drugs provided by her physician for that purpose.

Voluntary euthanasia
The act of one person killing another in accordance with the competently expressed wishes of that person. For example, when a competent patient asks her physician to kill her, and the physician injects her with a lethal dose of drugs.

Core Values

What are the values over which there is broad societal consensus as evinced by Canada's foundational texts and institutions? The Panel holds that the value of individual autonomy . . . should be seen as paramount, though not as exclusive. . . .

> **Evinced**
> Revealed or indicated by; the claim is that the presence of clear values in Canada's foundational texts and institutions is evidence that such values are broadly endorsed by Canadians.

The philosophical and institutional importance of individual autonomy for liberal democracies is clearly reflected in the decisions that have been taken by the *Supreme Court of Canada* since 1982, when a Charter of Rights and Freedoms was entrenched in Canada's Constitution, and in the language that the members of the Court have chosen in order to justify their decisions. What is striking is just how central they have taken individual self-determination to be in decisions that relate to the area of health care. . . . For example, in *Ciarlariello v. Schacter*, the Court affirmed patients' rights to refuse treatment and to have treatment withdrawn even after it has begun. Justice Cory, writing for the Court wrote:

> **Charter of Rights and Freedoms**
> A bill of rights entrenched in the Constitution of Canada by the Constitution Act and the Canada Act of 1982. The Charter of Rights and Freedoms greatly expands the scope of judicial review of provincial and federal statutes and regulations by the courts. Protections relevant to this debate include the right to life, liberty, and security of the person (Section 7), the right not to be subjected to cruel and unusual punishment (Section 12), and the right to equal protection and benefit of the law without discrimination (Section 15).

> **Ciarlariello v. Schacter**
> A 1993 decision of the Supreme Court of Canada that established a patient's right to withdraw consent after a procedure has begun. After a suspected bleed into her brain, Mrs Ciarlariello underwent two angiograms to image the blood vessels in her head. During the second procedure she began to hyperventilate and asked the physician to stop. The procedure was nonetheless completed, and she suffered a severe reaction that left her a quadriplegic.

"Every patient has a right to bodily integrity. This encompasses the right to determine what medical procedures will be accepted and the extent to which they will be accepted. Everyone has the right to decide what is to be done to one's own body. This includes the right to be free from medical treatment to which the individual does not consent. This concept of individual autonomy is fundamental to the common law."[1]

The centrality is, importantly, also affirmed in *Rodriguez* v. *British Columbia (Attorney General)*, the case that reaffirmed the criminal status of physician-assisted death, where Justice Sopinka refers to the importance of "control over one's physical and psychological integrity."[2] Thus, . . . the value of autonomy occupies a paramount place among the values of Canada's constitutional order. . . .

Autonomy is properly conditioned and limited by considerations to do with . . . "public safety, order, health, or morals or the fundamental rights and freedoms of others".[3] Equality is clearly also a core value in our constitutional order. . . .

Informed choice . . . constitutes a central pillar of contemporary health ethics and of Canadian health law. Informed choice is grounded in autonomy; it seeks to apply the abstract value of autonomous decision making to the context of health care. It requires that competent patients must not be subjected to treatment unless they have consented to it.[4] That consent is subject to three conditions: first, it must be uncoerced; second, it must result from the decision making capacity of a cognitively competent individual; and third, it must be informed. A conception of autonomy can thus be read in informed choice as the cornerstone of modern medical ethics and Canadian health law. An autonomous person would, according to this conception, be a substantively cognitively competent and uncoerced individual who arrives at his or her decisions after having been offered relevant information about the decision at hand.

Autonomy and Assisted Death

If autonomy is a central constitutional value, then it quite clearly grounds the right to request assistance in dying according to one's considered and stable views about when one's own life is not worth living any longer. . . .

If we believe that one of the roles of the state is to provide people with the institutional framework within which they can lead autonomous lives, that is, lives that reflect their values, convictions, and conceptions of what makes life worth living, it follows that the state should, to the degree that it is able to protect citizens against obstacles to their being able to live their lives according to their own lights.

The state should be particularly vigilant in protecting citizens with respect to the important choices in their lives. . . . Who to marry, what religion to profess, if any, whether to have children or not; these are choices that contribute powerfully to an individual's being able to view her life as one that corresponds to her "conception of the good life." Deciding how one will die clearly belongs to the choices that ought to be protected by the state, given our commitment to individual autonomy. The manner of our dying reflects our sense of what is important just as much as do the other central decisions in our lives. . . .

The commitment to autonomy, which is a cornerstone of our constitutional order, thus quite naturally yields a *prima facie* right to choose the time and conditions of one's death, and thus, as a corollary, to request aid in dying from medical professionals. . . .

Arguments Against the Legal Right to Assisted Death

It does not follow from the fact that an individual has a moral right to X that she should also have the legal right thereto. . . . The existence of a moral right establishes a presumption in favour of the establishment of a legal right. . . . The Panel will . . . now consider an argument to the effect that though there may very well exist a *prima facie* right to assisted death, this right is defeated by countervailing considerations, such as the rights of third parties. . . . This line of argument warrants our attention because it invokes a value that clearly has the same kind of foundational status that autonomy has in our constitutional moral order—the safety and security of the Canadian population and its most vulnerable members. . . .

> **Moral right**
> A particular kind of constraint on what it is permissible to do to a person. If one has a right to die then it is impermissible for another person to interfere with actions that facilitate this aim. The right to die is a liberty right, which implies the absence of a duty to refrain from killing oneself, in addition to the absence of a duty to kill oneself. This right does not typically imply a duty that others assist, unless they consent to doing so.

> **Legal right**
> An entitlement established by legal principle, court decision, regulation or statute.

The main reason that might block the passage from the morality to the legality of assisted dying has to do with the concern that . . . it would be difficult or impossible to design protective institutional mechanisms to oversee the decriminalized practice. . . . A fear might be that assistance with suicide or voluntary euthanasia will be administered to less than fully competent patients . . . or to people who fail to satisfy the voluntariness condition.[5] . . . In other words, decriminalizing morally permissible cases of assisted suicide and euthanasia might create a slippery slope that could lead to assisted suicide and voluntary euthanasia occurring in morally impermissible circumstances. . . . Thus, slippery slope arguments tacitly concede that certain cases of assisted suicide and euthanasia are morally permissible, but cast doubt on our ability to institutionalize them without producing catastrophic consequences. . . . Opponents of assisted suicide argue, in particular, that the decriminalization of this practice will elicit a slide into involuntary euthanasia.[6] . . .

Slippery slope arguments are, in almost all cases, logically invalid arguments. . . . Literature on the logic of argumentation distinguishes two basic forms of slippery slope argument. Both types are present in the assisted suicide and voluntary euthanasia debate. Some slippery slopes are *conceptual*. They claim the concepts used to set up criteria governing a practice are fuzzy, and that this conceptual vagueness will lead to the practice being abused. Others are *causal*. They claim that if a certain morally acceptable decision or policy is implemented, causal mechanisms will be put in motion that will unavoidably lead to other, morally dubious, decisions. . . .

According to conceptual slippery slope arguments against assisted suicide and

> **Slippery slope argument**
> An argument that permitting a desirable action will lead to undesirable consequences and that, as a result, the desirable action ought not be permitted. In many cases, the claim is that the desirable action makes the undesired consequences more probable but not certain and, thus, such arguments are logically invalid.

> **Logically invalid argument**
> A logically valid argument is one in which the truth of the premises guarantees the truth of the conclusion. A logically invalid argument is one in which this is not the case. Not all logically invalid arguments are bad arguments. For instance, in many scientific arguments, the truth of the premises makes the conclusion more likely (but not certain).

> **Conceptual slippery slope argument**
> A slippery slope argument in which the undesired consequences of the desired action are brought about as a result of ambiguities in a concept key to the desirable action. In this case, ambiguities in the concept of competency undermine the ability to clearly demarcate competent wishes to die from incompetent ones. As a result, permitting voluntary euthanasia will inevitably lead to instances of non-voluntary euthanasia.

euthanasia many of the concepts employed to create guidelines and criteria to limit the practice to morally acceptable cases are vague. A good example is the concept of *competence*. The argument of this Report proposes that the practice should be limited to competent individuals. Philosophical literature on the subject and clinical practice show that . . . the line between competence and incompetence is ambiguous at best.

The conceptual slippery slope argument against assisted suicide and voluntary euthanasia takes the ambiguity of the concept as the premise of an argument that practicing assisted dying on incompetent people is unavoidable. The argument takes the form of . . . a sorites paradox: for every competent person, there will be one just slightly less competent, where the difference between the two hardly seems significant enough to ground the claim that one is competent whereas the other is not. But then, there will be a person just slightly less competent than the second, and then another just slightly less competent than the third, and quickly, medically assisted dying is being practiced on patients of whom it would be very difficult indeed to claim that they are competent. . . .

> **Sorites paradox**
> A paradox that can be constructed from vague predicates such as "tall," "rich" or, in this case, "competent." For example, consider a heap of sand from which grains of sand are removed one at a time: is it still a heap of sand when a single grain of sand remains? If not, when did it cease to be a heap of sand? Also known as the paradox of the heap; sorites derived from the word in Ancient Greek for "heap."

The conceptual slippery slope argument against assisted suicide and voluntary euthanasia points to a real problem. But it is a problem that is ubiquitous across the full range of areas in which public policy and laws are enacted. Seeing it as a reason to rescind from enacting such laws and policies would lead to stasis. Consider a much less dramatic area of policy such as the determination of the age at which individuals can obtain a driver's license. There is no bright conceptual line that separates the competence and reliability of a person of 15 years and 364 days and a person of 16 years. The gain in competence from one day to the next is infinitesimally small.

Since it is not acceptable not to grant people drivers' licenses because of our inability to determine thresholds of competence with precision, the law establishes a line that is to some degree arbitrary.

By fixing the minimal age requirement at 16, society attempts to do as well as possible in ensuring that only competent people get on the road, accepting a certain number of false negatives and false positives as an acceptable cost for allowing people to be able to drive.

The exponent of the slippery slope argument against assisted suicide and voluntary euthanasia will naturally disagree with the analogizing of cases of public policy with cases in which moral principles are in play. Whereas the former are amenable to cost/benefit reasoning, the latter, he or she will claim, are not. Thus, the argument might run, when the placing of an arbitrary line at one point rather than another risks placing the defense of a principle on the wrong side of the line, we should avoid drawing lines altogether, and prescind from the impugned practice . . . no matter what the potential benefit.

> **Prescind**
> Avoid or separate ourselves from.

Thus, for example, if it is settled that stringency test "X" accommodates requests for assisted dying, and that there exists a more stringent test "X+1," the space between "X" and "X+1" can be cashed out in terms of lives lost that ought not to have been lost. Thus the most stringent test there is should be chosen: namely outright, or almost outright, prohibition.

This line of argument can be resisted in a number of ways. First, prohibition will not lead to the elimination of lives lost through assisted dying. It will rather mean that the practice will continue as it does in all jurisdictions where it is prohibited in the absence of *any* principle or institutional safeguard. Second, moral costs must be reckoned that flow both from permission and from prohibition—the moral costs of the latter are needless suffering and thwarting the wills of autonomous individuals.[7] . . . We must account, . . . in other words, . . . for the costs of *not* drawing a line somewhere.

Finally, the vagueness of concepts can only be of limited use to the partisan of slippery slope arguments. For, though a concept like that of competence is ambiguous, it cannot be reasonably inferred that there are not clear, paradigm cases of competence and, correspondingly, that there are not paradigm cases of incompetence. The fallacy of the *sorites paradox* upon which the conceptual slippery slope is grounded claims there will not come a point when the succession of imperceptibles gives rise to cases in which it is known that it is no longer competent individuals being dealt with.

Causal slippery slopes, being based on empirical premises, are not amenable to logical refutation. Unless their empirical premises run counter to the laws of physics, they invoke real possibilities. It is, rather, that human decisions will unavoidably give rise to other human decisions, and that, whereas the first set of decisions were morally acceptable, . . . the second set of decisions . . . are clearly unacceptable. The inevitability of the second set of decisions is seen in this way to impugn the first.

> **Causal slippery slopes**
> Slippery slope arguments in which the undesired consequences of the desired action are brought about as a result of empirical (psychological, social, institutional, etc.) mechanisms. The plausibility of such arguments turn on evidence that the mechanisms do in fact bring about the undesired consequence and that regulation is unlikely to be effective in preventing it. These are also referred to as empirical slippery slope arguments.

These arguments imply that such mechanisms will hold sway, even when the possibilities are laid bare and steps are taken to counteract them. . . . Consider: an agent supports "Decision 1," but has serious moral qualms about "Decision 2," which may flow from "Decision 1." She is aware of the fact that there are empirical (psychological, social, institutional, etc.) mechanisms that may make it more likely that "Decision 2" will come to seem more plausible to some, once "Decision 1" has been taken. This person is aware of the risk of a slippery slope, but intent as she is to resist it, she will put safeguards in place—both psychological and institutional—to make it less likely than it might otherwise have been that policy or "Decision 2" will come to be adopted as a result of policy or "Decision 1" having been adopted.

The supporter of slippery slope arguments . . . will have to claim, not only that a slippery slope might be set in motion by the adoption of "Decision 1," but that it will overpower whatever—legal, institutional, psychological, moral—resistances and safeguards responsible citizens and politicians, aware of the risks, are intent on putting in place in order to avoid the morally problematic decision being made. . . . Indeed, slippery slopes might fail to eventuate not only because . . . the causal mechanisms linking a morally acceptable decision or policy to a morally problematic one may not be as reliable as hypothesized, but also because there will be various obstacles built along the path of the slope that are the result of deliberate human intent. . . .

Much already existing public policy takes precisely the form just described. Measures are taken, and watchdog institutions are put in place to guard against abuse; . . . for example auditors general and ombudsmen. . . . There is no reason to think that this could not also be done in the case of assisted death. . . . In designing the regulatory structure that would govern the practices of voluntary euthanasia and assisted suicide, some of the arguments of opponents of these practices should be attended to, not because they are convincing as refutations of the practices in question, but because they do point to potential risks against which prudent policy-makers will want to take steps to counteract.

Some slippery-slope arguments suggest real risks and . . . deserve attention. . . . First, the argument in this Report limits the justification of assisted dying to competent persons. Safeguards must be put in place . . . to ensure that assisted dying is only provided to competent agents. Second, opponents of the decriminalization of assisted dying often formulate the fear that it would lead to a reduction in resources for . . . palliative care, and for . . . persons with disabilities. . . . This fear is not unfounded. . . . Institutional safeguards must be put in place that would be effective in offsetting the risk in question. . . . Decriminalization . . . could be accompanied by legislation requiring that funding of programs related to palliative care, . . . chronic diseases and disability be maintained at certain levels. . . . Legislation could be accompanied by the creation of a watchdog body . . . with a public education mandate. . . .

The logic of slippery slope arguments, most charitably construed, is that there are certain risks that might accompany a policy, and that those risks are so grave, and/or society's capacity reliably to counteract them so limited, that it would be better not to enact the policy. This logic is premised on a faulty assumption, namely that the status quo is itself without costs or risks, and that the only costs and risks to be factored into our deliberations are the ones that accompany the move away from the status quo. But this is never the case. . . . The practice of assisted death presently occupies a shady area in which it is both prohibited, and the prohibitions against it sometimes unenforced. The result is that assisted dying presently goes on in various medical contexts in Canada, governed not by transparent, reliable norms but by the private convictions of individuals. The present dispensation is fraught with all of the anxiety and needless suffering that attends any policy area governed by arbitrariness and lack of clarity rather than transparent, democratically enacted norms. . . . Evidence . . . strongly suggests that jurisdictions that have liberalized laws concerning assisted death have not succumbed to slippery slopes. . . . Opponents of decriminalization have not adequately taken into account the very real costs and harms that the present situation regarding assisted dying in Canada involves.

The Panel concludes that an important argument, that would . . . block the legal recognition of the *prima*

facie moral right to assisted suicide, fails. . . . The slippery slope argument . . . from the decriminalization of assisted death in voluntary contexts to acceptance of euthanasia in non-voluntary contexts . . . does not constitute a refutation of the argument in favour of a legal right to choose assisted death. Instead, it points us toward safeguards that must accompany decriminalization. . . . With this conclusion, the argument in favour of a legal right to choose assisted death is complete. We have shown that there is a strong autonomy-based argument in favour of the right that is not defeated by other constitutional values to do with safety and security, or the rights of third parties.

Study Questions

1. According to the authors, why is there a broad societal consensus that autonomy is a core value in Canada?

2. How does autonomy support a moral right to assisted suicide and voluntary euthanasia?

3. What is the causal (or empirical) slippery slope argument against assisted suicide and voluntary euthanasia? How do the authors deal with it?

Notes

1. *Ciarlariello* v. *Schachter*, [1993] 2 S.C.R 119 at 135 (emphasis added). See also *Hopp* v. *Lepp* (1980), 112, D.L.R. (3d) 67 (S.C.C.), and *Reibl* v. *Hughes* (1980), 114 D.L.R. 3d 1 (S.C.C.).

2. *Rodriguez v. British Columbia (Attorney General)* [1993] 3 S.C.R. 519 at 588.

3. *R.* v. *Big M Drug Mart Ltd.* [1985] 1 S.C.R. 211 at 397.

4. Faden RR and Beauchamp TL. *A History and Theory of Informed Consent.* New York: Oxford University Press; 1986.

5. It is appropriate to note at this point that the decision not to grant Sue Rodriguez the right to receive medically assisted death was grounded not in the Justices' denial of the value of individual autonomy, but in large measure on slippery slope reasoning on the part of the majority Justices. It is quite likely that the same Supreme Court would have decided the issue differently, given the fact that two of the reasons that the Court had this worry—namely that no other country had

decriminalized it and there was no data to either confirm or disprove the worry—now no longer exist. See Downie J. and Bern S. "Rodriguez Redux". *Health Law Journal.* 2008;16:27-54. On the general appropriateness of the Supreme Court engaging in slippery slope reasoning, given that it does not have the wherewithal with which to handle the relevant evidence, see Freedman B. "The Rodriguez Case: Sticky Questions and Slippery Answers." *McGill L.J.* 39:644.

6. Somerville M. "Euthanasia's Slippery Slope", in *The Mark* at http://www.themarknews.com/articles/1146-euthanasia-s-slippery-slope>. [Accessed 26 July 2011].

7. These points are made in most philosophical treatments of euthanasia and physician-assisted suicide. See, most recently, Warnock M and Macdonald E. *Easeful Death: Is there a case for assisted dying?* (Oxford: Oxford University Press, 2009).

TWO The Rodriguez Case: Sticky Questions and Slippery Answers
Benjamin Freedman | *McGill Law Journal* 1994; 39: 644-56.

Introduction

In its decision in *Rodriguez* v. *Canada* (A.G.)[1] the Supreme Court of Canada came within a whisker of

transforming Canadian legal and medical practice regarding euthanasia and assisted suicide. . . . Lost in

Sue Rodriguez (1950–94)
An advocate of assisted suicide, Rodriguez was diagnosed with amyotrophic lateral sclerosis (also known as Lou Gehrig's disease) in early 1991. She fought to have a legal right to assisted suicide in a series of highly publicized court battles. On 30 September 1993, in a landmark decision, *Rodriguez* v. *British Columbia (Attorney General)*, the Supreme Court of Canada held that there was no legal right to assisted suicide by a vote of 5 to 4. In 1994, she decided to take her own life with the help of an anonymous physician.

the judgments . . . are two essential issues raised by the case. First, what was Sue Rodriguez actually requesting from the Court—as opposed to the issue that the Justices were actually deciding? Second, how should society reason about that actual request? . . . I will discuss both issues. . . .

The Court's Question

The *Rodriguez* case is commonly understood to pose the question of the legality of physician-assisted suicide, or more specifically, the constitutional question of whether the Canadian criminal prohibition on assisting suicide is contrary to the *Charter*.[2] . . . These are the marks of the "slippery slope": the proponent of a change seeks to emphasize the limited nature of the question, while the opponent insists upon analyzing the broader implications of an answer. . . . Justice Sopinka saw the case as posing a broad question, not restricted to the terminally ill. He stated: "The result of the reasons of my colleagues is that all persons who by reason of disability are unable to commit suicide have a right under the *Canadian Charter of Rights and Freedoms* to be free from government interference in procuring the assistance of others to take their life." However, Madam Justice McLachlin insisted, to the contrary, on speaking of one specific disabled person who happens to be facing inevitable death. She writes: "Our task was the much more modest one of determining whether, given the legislative scheme regulating suicide which Parliament has put in place, the denial to Sue Rodriguez of the ability to end her life is arbitrary and hence amounts to a limit on her security of the person which does not comport with the principles of fundamental justice."[3]

As the argument progresses . . . other traditional hallmarks of the slippery slopes argument can be discerned. Justice Sopinka maintained, per contra McLachlin J., that the principles of fundamental justice must take

Per contra
A Latin term meaning on the contrary.

cognizance of a state interest—in effect, that the broad social implications of a decision can help to determine (or undermine) private assertions of right.[4] He cited with approval the conclusion of the Law Reform Commission of Canada, arguing that in the event of a legal reform permitting euthanasia or physician-assisted suicide, "there is no certainty that abuses can be prevented";[5] and, noting Dutch evidence . . . "relaxation of the absolute prohibition takes us down 'the slippery slope.'"[6] Chief Justice Lamer rejected such an argument as a legal matter: "While I share a deep concern over the subtle and overt pressures that may be brought to bear on such persons if assisted suicide is decriminalized, even in limited circumstances, I do not think legislation that deprives a disadvantaged group of the right to equality can be justified solely on such speculative grounds, no matter how well intentioned . . . we simply do not and cannot know the range of implications that allowing some form of assisted suicide will have for persons with physical disabilities. What we do know and cannot ignore is the anguish of those in the position of Ms Rodriguez."[7]

Law Reform Commission of Canada (1971–93, 1997–2006)
An independent body that was created to study and undertake a systematic review of Canadian law. Disbanded in 1993 as a part of federal budget cuts, it was resurrected in 1997 as the Law Commission of Canada.

There is a conceptual or logical, as well as an empirical, version of the slippery slope argument. The Justices spoke of the empirical slippery slope. If assisted suicide is permitted under careful conditions (of free and informed consent and competence, for example), will society experience abuses as a result? . . . The conceptual slippery slope instead asks, "By accepting the Rodriguez claim—or, what the Justices understood to be the Rodriguez claim—to what has society rationally committed itself, under logical canons of consistency?"

And here, there is troubling consistency within the Court. The case before them was brought by an individual who was, and remained, capable of suicide, and whose personal freedom of action was unimpaired by law.[8] Her claim was not, then, self-regarding. Rather, what she desired was that a new form of cooperative action be legalized—one involving a decision and a "final act" on her part, and the construction of some suicide device on the part of doctors and others (technicians, bioengineers, *etc.*).

The factual nature and background of Rodriguez's case, as well as the way in which her request involved not autonomy and private action but rather the legally-sanctioned social construction of death machines, is denied or obscured in all of the judgments. Sopinka J. writes: . . . "The prohibition in s. 241(b) deprives the appellant of autonomy over her person and causes her physical pain and psychological stress. The complaint is that the legislation is over-inclusive because it does not exclude from the reach of the prohibition those in the situation of the appellant who are terminally ill, mentally competent, but cannot commit suicide on their own. . . ."9

The basis of McLachlin J.'s judgment is that the law against assisted suicide denied Rodriguez a right (to commit suicide) that was available to others. She writes: "It is argued that the denial to Sue Rodriguez of the capacity to treat her body in a way available to the physically abled is justified because to permit assisted suicide will open the doors, if not floodgates, to the killing of disabled persons who may not truly consent to death . . . . In short, it does not accord with the principles of fundamental justice that Sue Rodriguez be disallowed what is available to others. . . ."10 At a structural level McLachlin J.'s argument requires that one accept that Rodriguez is incapable of committing suicide, and that her co-optation of the legal and medical systems to the end of managing her death in the manner and at the time that she chooses is a private exercise of her own self-determination. . . .

Structurally, since Lamer C.J. relied upon a claim of equality rights, he too was committed to arguing that the right to commit suicide in private without others interfering is equivalent to the right to arrange one's death with the assistance of medical personnel and with the knowledge and approval of the Canadian judiciary. The Chief Justice, however, recognized that this case did *not* concern one who was at the time incapable of committing suicide. . . .

Sue Rodriguez's Question

Sue Rodriguez suffered from a motor neuron disease, amyotrophic lateral sclerosis (ALS), that progressively destroys the body's capacity for movement. . . . When told the diagnosis of ALS, the typical patient has the physical capacity to exercise the full range of suicidal acts. The range diminishes over time, and increasing assistance is required over time. . . . Ultimately all capacity for motion is irretrievably lost, and with it, all prospect for communication. . . . ALS does not damage the intellect, however. . . . This is the macabre progression Ms Rodriguez faced, providing the backdrop against which her lawsuit seeking the right to assisted suicide must be understood. . . .

Sue Rodriguez had chosen to manage her dying process by killing herself, but she did not approach the Court to seek that right, since suicide had been legalized (or more precisely, decriminalized) decades before. At the time of the initiation of this litigation, and for a long time thereafter, Sue Rodriguez retained the capacity to kill herself. Yet as long as she retained this degree of capacity, she found life worth living and chose not to exercise her suicide option. Her specific desire was to have the assistance of a physician in installing a self-activated device which she could actuate at a time of her own choosing. . . .

The Justices seem to have all agreed with her on this crucial point: it is unjust to allow an able-bodied person to kill himself or herself and to deny a handicapped person assistance to achieve the same end. But the Justices all erred in finding equivalency between a private right to kill oneself, which only calls upon others not to interfere, thus literally asks them to do nothing, and the right Sue Rodriguez sought: the right to publicly ratify, in court, a new form of cooperative action bent upon inducing a certain person's death. . . .

The questions remain: If a person has a right to commit suicide, how broadly should such a right be construed? Should it include both the negative right of non-interference and the positive right to seek assistance (or perhaps even to have assistance provided)? . . . What do we as a society mean by a right to suicide, and what consequences are we prepared to bear on behalf of that right? . . . These questions of the slippery slope, that lie at the heart of any dispute over assisted suicide, cannot be adequately addressed in any court other than one of public opinion. . . .

The Slippery Slope: Considering the Social Impact of Approved Assisted Suicide and Euthanasia

The slippery slope reflects a complex of considerations regarding normative (legal, ethical or behavioural) social changes. . . . What unintended, deleterious,

Ineluctable
Unable to be resisted or avoided; inescapable.

Apodictically
Provably and necessarily true; incontrovertible.

ineluctable effects are they likely to have over time? Arguments from within this complex are cautionary, rather than apodictically certain.[11] . . .

What specific slippery slope cautions might have been raised in the event that the *Rodriguez* case had been decided in her favour? Brock has argued convincingly that no important logical or ethical difference stands between physician-assisted suicide and euthanasia; legalizing one should logically entail legalizing the other.[12] . . . Using complicated technology, involving the collaboration of physicians and technical personnel, Rodriguez could have installed a machine that would have provided her with a lethal injection after a coded eye-blink; or, we could . . . have the physician perform the injection. . . . It matters little whether a command is given to a person or a machine programmed by that person.

McLachlin J. writes: "If the justification for helping someone to end life is established, I cannot accept that it matters whether the act is "passive"—the withdrawal of support necessary to sustain life—or "active"—the provision of a means to permit a person of sound mind to choose to end his or her life with dignity."[13] The Chief Justice went one step further in recognizing the equivalency of the two: "One of McEachern C.J.'s conditions is that the act of terminating the appellant's life be hers and not anyone else's . . . Why should she be prevented the option of choosing suicide should her physical condition degenerate to the point where she is no longer even physically able to press a button or blow into a tube? Surely it is in such circumstances that assistance is required most. . . ."[14] This, then, is the first slippery slope consequence: in spite of the fact that Rodriguez's case was framed and understood as an issue of physician-assisted suicide, had the dissent succeeded, physician-assisted euthanasia would quickly have followed.

There are a number of other slippery slope concerns, potentially consequent upon legalization of physician-assisted suicide. . . . Very recent evidence confirms the fear that heightened social visibility concerning death-dealing volitional acts of the terminally ill leads to increased suicide of the mentally infirm. . . . "Efforts to destigmatize euthanasia or even encourage it for some groups may have the untoward effect of promoting suicide in other groups. . . ."[15] . . .

The definition of "terminal illness" is an elastic matter, given to slippery slopes of its own. For example, last year's Washington State initiative to legalize "physician aid-in-dying" (assisted suicide and euthanasia) was to be restricted to the terminally ill. However, "I-119 would have expanded the state's definition of 'terminal condition' to include patients with as long as six months to live and also those who were not actually about to die, but in irreversible comas or persistent vegetative states."[16]

All of the dissenting judgments expressed concern about the possibility that illegitimate pressure to accede to suicide might be brought to bear. However, they failed to account for the fact that what actually counts as "illegitimate" pressure changes over time. This slippery slope phenomenon is already evident in the Netherlands. John Keown describes a conversation with Dr Herbert Cohen: "One of Holland's leading practitioners of euthanasia told me that he would be put in a very difficult situation if a patient told him that he really felt a nuisance to his relatives because they wanted to enjoy his estate. Asked if he would rule out euthanasia in such a case, he replied: 'I . . . think in the end I wouldn't. . . .'"[17]

Similar arguments can be made with respect to two other conditions stated by the dissenting Justices: that the request for euthanasia or assisted suicide be firm and unwavering, and that it be provided by a fully informed person of undoubted competence. These conditions are not self-interpreting. They are, moreover, in large degree, social constructions, often understood as relative to accepted or expected choices. What the slippery slope reminds us is that social expectations change over time, under pressure of the previous choice. At present, for example, asking to be killed is an odd choice and might trigger searching questions about competence. Over time, however, this rigour might well give way. It is not hard to envision a time when quite the reverse obtains, when an ill person who fails to ask to be killed is judged to be "in denial," and for that reason in need of therapy.

The same holds concerning the unwavering nature of the choice, something that is inevitably judged relative to the social acceptance of the choice in question. Compare one case of ambivalent euthanasia with a recent Supreme Court of Canada decision concerning ambivalent consent to medical treatment. The euthanasia case unfolded as follows: "In February, Kevorkian assisted in the suicide of Hugh Gale, 70, an emphysema patient who may, at the last minute, have changed his mind. According to one version of the report that Kevorkian wrote, about 45 seconds after putting on the carbon-monoxide mask, Gale became flushed, agitated, saying 'Take it off!' The mask was immediately replaced with oxygen, which helped calm him down. 'The patient wanted to continue,' the report states. 'After about 20 minutes, with nasal oxygen continuing, the mask was replaced over his nose and mouth, and he again pulled the clip off the crimped tubing . . . immediately after saying 'Take it off!' once again, he fell into unconsciousness. The mask was then, left in place . . . .Heartbeat was undetectable about 3 minutes after last breath."[18]

This would not, at this time, satisfy the requirement that a request be unwavering; but would it not do so shortly after such requests became a commonly-accepted part of medical practice? Compare this situation with the Supreme Court of Canada decision regarding consent to medical treatment. During an angiogram, the appellant, Mrs Ciarlariello, began to spasm. After calming herself she said, "Enough, no more, stop the test." Her neurologist assessed her and assured her that five more minutes were required. The patient responded, "Please go ahead." The Court's opinion was that this consent was acceptable. . . . At that point, the insistence that consent to euthanasia be firm and unwavering would dissolve, for, as Mrs Ciarlariello's case demonstrates, the law will not insist upon such conditions for consent to medical treatment.[19]. . .

Yet I believe the dissenters were correct in excluding these slippery slope concerns from their constitutional deliberations. As *Charter* jurisprudence is constructed, once an infringement of a right has been demonstrated, the burden of proof is upon the State to demonstrate that the infringement has been legally "saved" under section 1, because the law in question is demonstrably justified in a free and democratic society. . . . Properly understood, slippery slope arguments cannot satisfy this requirement. They are cautionary in nature, providing reasons to pause, to reconsider, to temporize and to carefully weigh, but by their nature, they are not knock-down, conclusory points. A slippery slope consideration is, by definition, speculative, and so it cannot play the role of satisfying the burden of proof required. And yet—and the point must be repeated—it is agreed on all sides that slippery slope concerns are at the centre of any decision regarding change in the laws respecting euthanasia and assisted suicide.

What can be done to escape this jurisprudential dilemma? I believe the solution is simple. . . . The debate must proceed in the public arena, in particular, through the political process. In regard to those views in which no answer is probably right or wrong, in which expertise fails to reliably help, democracies rely upon one procedure: discuss, debate, propagandize—and then, vote. . . . How far along the path to euthanasia—for whom, with what safeguards, under what circumstances—is society prepared to walk? . . . What cost, in the form of abuse, is likely to accompany this path, and is the gain worth the price? These questions are at the heart of the debate, and a democratic nation has only one means of addressing them.

> **Section 1**
>
> The section of the Canadian *Charter of Rights and Freedoms* that confirms that the rights listed in that document are guaranteed, but also subject to reasonable limitations, allowing the government to abridge an individual's *Charter* rights when compelling justification for doing so exists.

Study Questions

1. What, according to Freedman, was Sue Rodriguez's question? Do you agree?

2. What is the distinction between empirical and conceptual versions of slippery slope arguments? Give an instance of each as it pertains to the Rodriguez case.

3. How does Freedman argue that permitting assisted suicide leads to physician assisted euthanasia? Is he right?

Notes

1. [1993] 3 S.C.R. 519, (sub nom. *Rodriguez v. British Columbia (A.G.)*) 107 D.L.R. (4th) 342 [hereinafter Rodriguez cited to S.C.R.]

2. *Canadian Charter of Rights and Freedoms*, Part I of the *Constitution Act*, 1982, being Schedule B to the *Canada Act 1982* (U.K.), 1982, c. 11 [hereinafter Charter].

3. *Supra* note 1 at 628.

4. *Ibid.* at 592–3.

5. *Ibid.* at 601.

6. *Ibid.* at 603.

7. *Ibid.* at 566.

8. This comment does not deal with another fundamental point of consistency amongst the Justices. They all held in common the view that Parliament had established a "right to suicide" when it amended the *Criminal Code* so that attempting suicide was no longer a crime. This is not obviously true. Kamisar (*supra* note 3) has noted that by far the more convincing reading of the American legislative history is that suicide was decriminalized in the strict sense - not "legalized," still less made the basis of further rights. By withdrawing the crime of attempted suicide from the books, the legislators were simply acknowledging that no useful purpose could be gained by continuing to prosecute for this act. None of the Justices in *Rodriguez* attempted any serious discussion of the legislative history surrounding the Canadian reform that resulted in the decriminalization of attempted suicide. I am skeptical that Parliament, in decriminalizing attempted suicide, contemplated the reconstruction of this decision, an acknowledgment of the limits of legal effectiveness, into a fertile source of further rights. I further believe that the burden was upon the Justices to demonstrate to the contrary; however, I will not pursue this issue further here.

9. *Supra* note I at 588–92.

10. *Ibid* at 620–3.

11. [N]ormative behavior—accepting norms, or acting in accordance with expressed or unexpressed norms—has consequences and develops its own momentum. Because there are limits to human predictive capacity and rationality, the congeries of slippery slope arguments serve, not as a conclusive basis for rejecting change, but as a warning flag concerning the possible effects of change. Slippery-slope arguments are not apodictic, conclusively true, but rather more or less well grounded; and are always one among the many arguments that will need to be mounted concerning any given normative choice A (whether A be a policy or an action—the acceptance of a norm or action in accordance with a norm) by an individual, group, or society. Slippery-slope arguments are comprised of or bolstered by numerous observations and generalizations. Socially, we note evidence of and experiments upon conformity and the effect of social pressure upon individual moral judgments; we note the phenomenon of immigrants, coming to a new land with their independent values, assimilating to the host culture. Biologically, we note phenomena such as desensitization: the organism adjusting its own reactions to accommodate its environment. We note further how this may form a positive feedback loop, since the organism's environment is partly self-generated. Psychologically, we note the phenomenon of cognitive dissonance and the normal reaction it evokes: discrepancies between a person's behavior and his or her beliefs are as likely to result in an alteration of belief as in a reform of behavior. Historically, in retrospectively examining regimes of horror and human degradation, we note that there were early, small, incremental steps taken by members and institutions of society that permitted the later holocaust to nakedly proceed (B. Freedman, "The Slippery-Slope Argument Reconstructed: Response to van der Burg" (1992) 3:4 J. *Clinical Ethics* 293 at 296–7).

12. D. Brock, "Voluntary Active Euthanasia" (1992) 22:2 Hastings Center Rep. 10.

13. Justice Sopinka writes that "the active participation by one individual in the death of another is intrinsically morally and legally wrong . . ." (*supra* note 1 at 624).

14. *Ibid.* at 578–9.

15. (1993) 329:20 *New England J. Med. 1510.*

16. R. Carson, "Washington's 1-119" (1992) 22:2 Hastings Center Rep. 7 at 8.

17. "On Regulating Death" (1992) 22:2 Hastings Center Rep. 39 at 41-42.

18. N. Gibbs, "Death Giving" *[Canadian] Time* (31 May 1993) 44 at 48.

19. *Ciarlariello v. Schacter,* [1993] 2 S.C.R. 119, 100 D.L.R. (4th) 609.

THREE **A Feminist Exploration of Issues Around Assisted Death**

Jocelyn Downie and Susan Sherwin | *St. Louis University Public Law Review* 1996; 15: 303-30.

Introduction

. . . Policies on assisted death . . . may have a significant negative and disproportionate impact on women. . . . We support a limited permissive legislative policy, *provided that it is sensitive and responsive to the many ways in which* *oppression can complicate decision-making around assisted death. . . .*

> **Assisted death**
> Death that results from an intentional act or omission of a second person. According to the authors, this includes assisted suicide, euthanasia, *and* withholding or withdrawing life-sustaining treatments.

The Need for a Feminist Analysis

Policies and precedents on assisted death may have oppressive consequences for women . . . and gender patterns are emerging in the area of assisted death that merit investigation. . . . First, almost all of the legal cases involving assisted death in Canada and the United States have involved women. . . . Moreover, the majority of Dr Kevorkian's "clients" have been women.[1] Further, women's wishes concerning the withholding and withdrawal of life-sustaining treatment have been treated differently than men's by American courts.[2]

In *Courts, Gender and The Right to Die*, Steven Miles and Allison August examined all civil state appellate-level "right-to-die" cases involving incompetent, adult patients between 1976 and 1989.[3] They found slightly gender-patterned *results* . . . and seriously gender-patterned *reasoning*. There were twenty-two cases involving newly incompetent persons without written advance directives. In seventy-five per cent of the cases involving men but only fourteen per cent of the cases involving women, the courts constructed the preference for medical care from the memories and insights of family and friends. In twelve per cent of the cases involving men but forty-three per cent involving women, the decision was held to belong to the family/guardian. In twelve per cent of the cases involving men but twenty-one per cent involving women, the decision was held to be a medical matter. In zero percent of the cases involving men but twenty-one per cent involving women, the decision was held to belong to the health care institution.[4] There were three cases involving incompetent persons with written advance directives. The court rejected the living will of one of the women and accepted the living wills of the man and one of the women. However, even in the cases involving the acceptance of the living wills, the courts required that a higher burden of proof be met for the woman than for the man.[5]

Through careful analysis of the reasoning . . . in the above cases Miles and August conclude that:

> "[There are] four major differences in how courts speak of previously competent women's or men's moral preferences. The first difference is the courts' view that a man's opinions are rational and a woman's remarks are unreflective, emotional, or immature. Second, women's moral agency in relation to medical decisions is often not recognized. Third, courts apply evidentiary standards differently to evidence about men's and women's preferences. Fourth, life-support dependent men are seen as subjected to medical assault; women are seen as vulnerable to medical neglect."[6]

They conclude that:

> "Gender profoundly affects judicial analysis of the right-to-die cases. Judicial reasoning about men stresses the role of personal autonomy. Judicial reasoning about women examines the role of caregivers."[7]

. . . Because gender patterns have emerged around assisted death, these patterns need to be explored to determine whether they are caused by gender oppression. If they are, then the practices and underlying assumptions giving rise to the patterns must be challenged.

A Feminist Analysis of the Issues Around Assisted Death

We believe that the principle of respect for autonomy establishes a strong *prima facie* case in favor of a permissive policy with respect to assisted suicide and euthanasia. . . .[8] Therefore, we shift our attention to arguments against a permissive policy. . . . We do not find these arguments persuasive, . . . yet they raise special concerns when considered from a feminist perspective. . . .

Competence

It is often argued that it is very difficult to assess the competence of dying individuals; their capacity to make autonomous decisions can be compromised by grief, fear of dying, illness, or by the treatments they are receiving. . . . It is true that pain, drugs, and disease can impair competence. However, . . . first, . . . competence is not an all-or-nothing concept. . . . One may at any one time be competent to make some decisions and not others. Even if an individual's competence is compromised by her condition, she might be . . . competent to make a decision about the value or disvalue of continued existence to her. . . . Second, the existence of *some* individuals who have been rendered incompetent by pain, drugs, or disease does not justify concluding that *all* individuals with similar pain, drugs, or disease are not competent. . . . Third, it is possible for individuals who are competent to anticipate future incompetence and set forth their wishes in advance directives. . . .

In addition, . . . if one wishes to use the competence argument against assisted suicide and euthanasia, one has to explain why it is relevant in assisted suicide and euthanasia but not in the withholding and withdrawal of life-sustaining treatment and the provision of life-shortening palliative treatment. We do not believe that this can be accomplished. Nevertheless, . . . competency is of particular concern . . . since competency standards are typically constructed around the paradigm of members of the most dominant social groups, and they are often biased against members of oppressed groups.[9] . . .

Competence is often linked to ideals of rationality, but women are more likely than men to be seen as irrational when they are perfectly rational. . . . The very concept of rationality is usually constructed in opposition to the traits that are stereotypically assigned to women (e.g., by requiring rational agents to be objective and emotionally distant from the effects of their actions).[10] It is important to consider the criteria used to evaluate competency to eliminate gender or other forms of bias that allow this standard to be used to discriminate against the oppressed. . . .

Oppression tends to rob its victims of some of the necessary traits for exercising autonomy well, such as self-esteem and self-knowledge. . . . Feminism suggests we . . . pay . . . attention to . . . ways in which oppression can undermine a person's ability to make decisions in accordance with her own interests or values. . . . It seems, then, that there are reasons for believing that gender socialization reduces women's levels of competency for autonomous decision-making. . . .

This, however, is not an argument against the use of competency criteria, nor for believing that those who are oppressed are insufficiently competent to make autonomous choices about assisted suicide or euthanasia. It is, rather, an argument that suggests the importance of developing oppression-sensitive standards of competency. . . .

Voluntariness

The concern here is that individuals may not always be acting voluntarily when they make requests for assisted death. For example, it seems plausible . . . that individuals will see themselves as being a burden on their loved ones or on society, and feel pressured into choosing an earlier death. Others may be vulnerable to financial or other sorts of coercive pressures. . . . Although this is a legitimate concern, there are several responses.

First, the fact that an individual is concerned with the well-being of others is not evidence that she is not acting voluntarily. People may quite voluntarily choose to end their lives rather than bankrupt their families in an effort to prolong a painful existence. Criteria of voluntariness demand that such individuals be acting in accordance with their own values, not that they be acting in accordance with their own self-interest, narrowly defined. . . .

This problem may dissolve given a sensitive regulatory scheme. . . . Further, . . . the voluntariness argument applies as much to individuals consenting to the withholding or withdrawal of life-sustaining treatment or the provision of life-shortening palliative treatment as it does to assisted suicide and euthanasia. It does not block accepting the former so it should not block accepting the latter.

Nevertheless, there are reasons for feminists to be concerned about voluntariness requirements. . . . Women . . . may be at particular risk of being manipulated into accepting early death rather than burdening others. . . . Part of gender socialization for women is towards self-sacrifice and self-abnegation. . . . In general, women are raised to be docile and compliant, to fit into others' life plans rather than to define their own. They are often deprived of the opportunity of controlling their reproductive, sexual, economic and political lives. They may well be lacking in opportunities to make autonomous, i.e., suitably voluntary, choices for themselves, and, hence, not have had the opportunity to develop autonomy skills.

However, . . . putting further restrictions on the lives of those already limited by oppressive social structures will neither reduce their oppression nor improve their autonomy skills. Rather, we need to develop more sensitive measures for evaluating standards of voluntariness and more democratic means of promoting the development of autonomy skills. . . .

Home/Palliative Care

Some suggest that many individuals seek an early death because they want to escape from the expense and alienation of a prolonged dying process in hospital. They argue that most of the requests for assisted suicide and euthanasia would not be made if there were more home and palliative care available. In their view, . . . the number of . . . individuals who cannot be helped by home or palliative care will become so small that the harms of permitting assisted suicide and euthanasia will then outweigh the benefits. . . .

Home care is not always an option. Sometimes an individual's condition requires hospitalization. . . .

Some people have no homes to return to or their homes are dangerous. . . . Not all homes have someone present who can help to provide care. For example, while most elderly men have wives at home who can care for them, many elderly women are widowed and alone. . . . We must not develop a model based on the resources available to those who are greatly advantaged, without paying careful attention to the needs and opportunities available to less privileged members of society.

Finally, this argument seems to ignore the well-entrenched gendered division of labor which places a disproportionate share of the burden of home care on women. There are higher expectations on women than on men to provide such care, and those who do are penalized in the workplace for having home care responsibilities. This is not *per se* a counter-argument to the home care argument, but, rather, a caveat that if home care is increased without acknowledging and providing a remedy for these inequities, for example respite care programs and employment protection, the oppression of women will be increased. . . .

Towards a Feminist Policy on Assisted Death

We propose that guidelines regarding practices of assisted death be built around an ideal of relational autonomy that grounds social policies in a recognition of the difficulties of asserting autonomy in the face of oppression. . . .

A relational interpretation of autonomy . . . rejects the traditional liberal individualist conception which views the self solely as a rational, self-conscious, socially unencumbered agent,[11] in favor of understanding the self as an essentially social being at least partly shaped and modified within a web of interconnected relationships. . . . The various relationships in which a person finds herself all play a role in fostering or inhibiting her capacity for autonomous action. They are the context for activities constitutive of autonomy (e.g., defining, questioning, revising, pursuing one's interests and goals). Both interpersonal and political relationships (i.e., those having to do with personal

> **Relational autonomy**
> A feminist view of autonomy that rejects an atomistic or highly individualistic view of the self. Rather, it understands the person as an essentially social being, whose relationships with others play a role in shaping the self and which may foster or inhibit autonomous action.

interactions and those deriving from existing patterns of power, privilege, dominance, and oppression) influence the sort of self that a person becomes.

The exercise of autonomy involves the use of essential capacities and skills (e.g., self-knowledge, self-direction, and self-esteem) which are products of an agent's social experience and situation.[12] Relational autonomy, then, is a capacity that is developed (and constrained) by social circumstances; it is exercised within relationships and social structures. . . . By recognizing how a person's position within an oppressive power structure can affect her ability to develop the requisite skills for exercising autonomy effectively, we can appreciate that autonomy is a product of personal resources and skills which are themselves, at least partly, a product of structural conditions.

A relational interpretation of autonomy can help clarify how voluntariness standards can be adjusted to account for oppression. Standard . . . assessments of whether a particular decision is autonomous . . . ask whether there are any external forces directly interfering with the choice. A relational approach asks whether there are any external or internal forces directly or indirectly interfering with the choice. . . . By "internal forces interfering with choice" we mean a woman's own desires that are grounded in the perceptions of herself and her options that have been oppressively constructed through socialization so that the woman does not accurately perceive herself or her options. By "forces indirectly interfering with choice," we mean forces that limit the set of options available to the individual. Examples: . . .

"External direct forces" – the power imbalance between physicians and patients is particularly strong between male physicians and female patients. As a result, women may be more likely than men to be pressured into decisions about assisted death by their physicians.[13]

"External indirect forces" – more women than men are socially and economically disadvantaged, so conditions near the end of life are more often worse for women than for men.[14] As a result, women may have limited options with respect to pain control and comfort care. Moreover, more women than men end up on their own with no one to care for them.[15] As a result, women may have limited options all of which are unattractive to them.

"Internal direct forces" – sexism and ageism cause women (especially older women) to have lower self-esteem than men. This might lead them to see their lives as having less value and to request assisted death more readily than men.

"Internal indirect forces" – since there is so much legal regulation of women's reproduction, women are more used to having less importance attached to, and more restrictions placed upon, their bodily integrity than men. As a result, they may believe that expressing resistance to treatment that they do not want is not an option. . . .

Implications of a relational interpretation of autonomy for a permissive policy for assisted death: With regard to competence, when confronted with a request for an assisted death, courts and health care professionals should be careful not to assume that women are not rational.[16] They should take care not to mistakenly think a woman is incompetent because they believe that women are less competent than men or because they fail to understand alternative ways of reasoning (commonly associated with women) and assume incompetence in the face of such reasoning. . . . In cases in which women are not sufficiently rational or competent, courts and health care professionals should try to help them become rational and to improve competence. . . .

With regard to voluntariness, at a macro level, courts, policy-makers, and health care providers should strive to remove external direct forces, increase the options available to women so as to remove external indirect forces, and remove the sources of direct and indirect internal forces. This means, for example: putting in place patient empowerment programs;

fighting against poverty, . . . for universal health care, and . . . for more effective and available palliative and comfort care; determining whether (and, if so, why) members of oppressed groups are disproportionately seeking assisted deaths; and improving respect for women's bodily integrity.

At a micro level, courts and health care professionals should try to remove external direct forces, increase the options available to the woman so as to remove external indirect forces, and assist the woman to reconstruct her perceptions to remove the direct and indirect internal forces compromising her freedom. When members of oppressed groups express a desire for assisted death, they should be helped to review and evaluate their choices and be given non-directive counselling to ensure that their decisions are not grounded in low self-esteem which derives from their oppressed status or exploitation. . . . It should further be ensured that death is indeed their preference and that they are not being coerced into this option because they lack the resources to obtain appropriate health care. If their condition can be relieved by health care and if they would prefer to receive health care, then efforts should be made to ensure access to care.

Once a best effort has been made at all of this, then the woman's wishes should be respected no matter what others may think of the consequences for her and even if her decision seems to be in response to oppressive social conditions. . . . We do not believe that the fight against oppression should be conducted at the expense of individual women; we should fight *for* women but not fight *the* women. . . .

Study Questions

1. Why, according to the authors, is a feminist analysis of assisted suicide and voluntary euthanasia required? Are their reasons convincing?

2. Why is voluntariness a worry in assisted suicide and voluntary euthanasia? What is the authors' response to this concern?

3. What is relational autonomy? How is it reflected in the authors' policy approach to assisted suicide and voluntary euthanasia?

Notes

1. Nancy J. Osgood & Susan A. Eisenhandler, Gender and Assisted and Acquiescent Suicide: A Suicidologist's Perspective, 9 *Issues L. & Med.* 361 (1994), p. 362. At least sixty-three per cent of Dr Kevorkian's "clients" have been women.

2. Steven H. Miles & Allison August, Courts, Gender and "The Right to Die", 18 *Law, Med. & Health Care* 85 (1990); pp. 85–95.

3. Ibid. p. 85 n.3. It might be argued that Miles and August's sample size was too small to justify drawing conclusions.

However, while the conclusions drawn by Miles and August are based on a small number of cases, they are not extrapolations from data on a small subset of a large set of cases. The twenty-five cases discussed in the article are *all* the cases, and so their conclusions about what the courts *have been doing* are not vulnerable to sample size criticisms.

4. Ibid. at 86.
5. Ibid. at 91.
6. Ibid. at 87.
7. Ibid. at 91.
8. We should acknowledge here that autonomy is a concept about which many feminists have expressed serious reservations. We share many of these reservations but do not believe that the solution to the problems with autonomy is to abandon the concept. Rather, we believe that the solution is to reconceptualize autonomy. Much more is said about this feminist reconceptualization of autonomy in section V of this paper.
9. See Miles & August.
10. See generally Genevieve Lloyd, *The Man of Reason: "Male" and "Female" in Western Philosophy.* (Minneapolis: University of Minnesota Press, 1984).
11. See, e.g., Immanuel Kant, *Foundations of the Metaphysics of Morals and What is Enlightenment?* (Lewis White Beck trans., Bobbs-Merrill Company, 1959) (1785); John Locke, *An Essay Concerning Human Understanding* (Peter H. Nidditch ed., Ward, Lock & Co., 1982) (1883); John Rawls, A Theory of Justice (1971).
12. See generally Diana T. Meyers, *Self, Society and Personal Choice.* (New York: Columbia University Press, 1989) for a full discussion of autonomy skills.
13. "Inevitably, there is a built-in power imbalance in medical encounters: (relatively) healthy, well-educated, affluent doctors provide services to patients who are typically ill and frightened, and, often, are also poor, and lacking in education and social authority. This general difference in power between patients and physicians is further exacerbated by the fact that, most commonly, the patient is female and the physician is male. In fact, according to nearly all of the standard dichotomies supporting dominance in our culture-gender, class, race, ability status-odds are that if there is a difference between the affiliations of physician and patient, the physician is likely to fall on the dominant side of that distinction and the patient on the subordinate side." Meyers p. 1.
14. "In 1993, women over 65 had a median annual income of $8,499 — 57 percent of the $14,983 median income of older men." Tamar Lewin, Income Gap For Sexes is Seen Wider in Retirement, *N.Y. Times*, Apr. 26, 1995, at A19.
15. We are not concerned here with the simple biological fact that men die younger than women do and hence the biological component of a complete explanation for the fact that a greater percentage of women than men are single when they are old. Rather, we are concerned with the societal reasons for a greater percentage of women than men being single when they are old. For example, society has different expectations regarding remarriage for men and women: it is more widely accepted that widowers or divorced men "need" to remarry while widows or divorced women do not, and that older widowers or divorced men will marry younger women while older widows or divorced women will not marry younger men.
16. See Miles & August, see also Meyers.

Chapter Study Questions

1. The Royal Society of Canada Expert Panel use competency as an example of a sorites paradox and argues that it can be responded to. Freedman gives at least two other examples of key terms that are in effect open to sorites paradoxes. What are they? Can they be responded to in the same way?

2. Both the Royal Society of Canada Expert Panel and Freedman consider the implications of slippery slope arguments for assisted suicide and euthanasia in Canada. The Royal Society of Canada Expert Panel argues that slippery slope considerations are best thought of as a tool to shape effective regulation. Freedman argues that they highlight the need for further public debate. Who is right?

3. Compare and contrast the use of autonomy in the argumentation of the Royal Society of Canada Expert Panel with relational autonomy in Downie and Sherwin. Can the policy implications of these two views be reconciled?

Critical Analysis

Consider the following excerpt from the Royal Society of Canada Expert Panel:

"The conceptual slippery slope argument against assisted suicide and voluntary euthanasia takes the ambiguity of the concept as the premise of an argument that practicing assisted dying on incompetent people is unavoidable. The argument takes the form of a sorites paradox: for every competent person, there will be one just slightly less competent, where the difference between the two hardly seems significant enough to ground the

claim that one is competent whereas the other is not. But then, there will be a person just slightly less competent than the second, and then another just slightly less competent than the third, and quickly, medically assisted dying is being practiced on patients of whom it would be very difficult indeed to claim that they are competent."

Outline this argument in your own words, paying particular attention to the premises that are relied on to support the main conclusion. Choose one of the premises for evaluation. Try to think of at least one objection to this premise.

Case Study

Assisted suicide or voluntary euthanasia are legally permitted in seven places in the world: Belgium, Luxemburg, the Netherlands, Switzerland, and three states in the United States of America (Montana, Oregon, and Washington State). The longest experience with both practices comes from the Netherlands, where assisted suicide and euthanasia have been permitted since 1973 in restrictive cases. In the Netherlands a physician may provide a patient with the means to take his or her own life or inject the patient with a lethal cocktail of drugs only if the patient is terminally ill, in unbearable pain, and repeatedly expresses the wish to die.

Hilly Bosscher was a 50-year-old woman who was divorced from a man she described as an abusive alcoholic. She approached Dutch psychiatrist Dr Boudewijn Chabot and asked him to assist in her suicide. Ms Bosscher was not dying of cancer; she did not have a terminal illness. Rather, she was chronically depressed after the deaths of her sons. One son had died of cancer, and the other committed suicide. She clearly and repeatedly expressed the wish to die. She said, "I long for the day that I do not have to stand at their grave anymore, but will be allowed to lie there forever between my darlings." She went on to say ask "Why do I have to

keep on living when I am already 50? I am not religious, but everything is so senseless, so empty, so useless. The grief, the despair, it is all so terrible."

Dr Chabot tried to talk her out of the decision, but she remained steadfast. He ultimately provided her with a prescription for sleeping tablets, and she took them and died. When details of the case came to light, Dr Chabot was prosecuted for violating the regulations surrounding permissible assisted suicide and euthanasia. However, on 21 April 1993, a Dutch court ruled that Dr Chabot was justified in helping the 50-year-old woman end her life. The court thereby affirmed the use of assisted suicide for people who are not terminally ill but who are suffering from mental illness.

1. Was Hilly Bosscher's choice autonomous? Would the Royal Society of Canada Expert Panel and Downie and Sherwin agree? Why?

2. Is this case evidence of a slippery slope when assisted suicide is permitted? What kind of slippery slope?

3. What does this case say about what should be done in Canada?

Further Reading

Canadian Broadcasting Corporation. Dying on her own terms [Internet]. Available from: http://www.cbc.ca/archives/categories/politics/rights-freedoms/sue-rodriguez-and-the-right-to-die-debate/dying-on-her-own-terms.html. Date Accessed: 28 May 2012.

Government of Canada. The Rodriguez Case: a review of the Supreme Court of Canada decision on assisted suicide [Internet]. Prepared by Margaret Smith, Law and Government Division (October 1993). Available from: http://dsp-psd.pwgsc.gc.ca/Collection-R/LoPBdP/BP/bp349-e.htm. Date Accessed: 28 May 2012.

Royal Society of Canada. End of life decision making [Internet]. November 2011. Available from: http://www.rsc.ca/documents/RSCEndofLifeReport2011_EN_Formatted_FINAL.pdf. Date Accessed 28 May 2012.

Special Senate Committee on Euthanasia and Assisted Suicide. Of life and death. Final report [Internet]. Ottawa: Special Senate Committee on Euthanasia and Assisted Suicide; 1995. Available from: http://www.parl.gc.ca/Content/SEN/Committee/351/euth/rep/lad-e.htm. Date Accessed: 28 May 2012.

Sumner LW. *Assisted death: a study in ethics and law.* New York: Oxford University Press; 2011.

Defining Death

The ethics of assisted suicide is not the only philosophical problem connected with death and dying; defining death is a moral problem in and of itself. This chapter addresses some very hard philosophical and practical questions. What counts as "death?" When is a person dead? What are the physical and medical characteristics that signify death to the medical community and society at large? The papers in this chapter address some of these questions.

In the course of watching medical dramas on television, you will often see a team of doctors trying to revive someone whose heart has stopped. The team will work away and then the head doctor will say, "Let's call it." She will then announce a time of death. If you are a beginning philosophy student, you might well wonder what they are up to. "Call it?" you might ask. "Surely death is a fact. The patient is either dead or alive. Which is it?" This ambiguity raises questions concerning how death is determined. If the doctor is only applying a set of criteria, does that make her nothing more than an umpire or referee? This should make us feel somewhat uncomfortable as the doctor's judgment alone cannot determine whether a patient has died. Surely there are universal truths about death that are observable and knowable by health care professionals and the public. If this is the case, then are the criteria they are using the correct ones in light of what it means for a person (as opposed to a squirrel or a patch of moss) to be dead?

The first paper introduces the range of views held when it comes to defining death for persons. In "What is Death?: A Crisis of Criteria," Louis Pojman presents four definitions of death:

1. the departure of the soul from the body;
2. the irreversible cessation of cardiovascular pulmonary function;
3. whole brain death; and
4. neocortical (or higher) brain death.

In Pojman's article, we see how death is connected to philosophical questions about the nature of personhood. If people were just like other animals, then the second or third definition of death would seem to be adequate. However, the thought that personhood involves rationality and conscious awareness pushes some philosophers to argue that without higher brain activity, a person cannot be said to be alive, in spite of the fact that his heart continues to beat. Pojman's article makes clear the difficulties posed by philosophical questions about the nature of personhood, on the one hand, and by the increasing use of life-prolonging medical technology, on the other. A further complicating factor is the need for clear criteria for defining death for the purposes of organ donation.

The second article, by Roland Puccetti, is a direct and forceful argument for one of the views presented by Pojman, namely, that death occurs with cessation of functioning in the higher brain or neocortex. Puccetti's line of reasoning may shock and provoke some readers. He begins by gathering our intuitions about a pair of cases, the first involving his dog, Fido, and the second involving a neighbour's infant son, Bobby; both of whom have lost all higher brain function but continue to breathe. Puccetti urges us to accept not just that there is nothing of worth left in a life without higher brain function, but that the person who has lost higher brain function is in fact dead. Thinking about death this way, we see a separation between the death of the person and the death of the human body. Much of Puccetti's article takes up arguments against the whole brain account of death. Rather than getting mired in anatomical details about the human brain, it's important to keep the larger philosophical picture in mind. While you may not agree with Puccetti's particular view, he is surely right that the debate between the advocates of the whole brain account of death and advocates of the higher brain account of death is at root a philosophical debate about personhood.

The third paper argues that the issue is not as simple as choosing between differing accounts of death. According to Linda Emanuel, decisions about death are much more complicated than weighing the arguments for and against the neocortical death definition. Emanuel's paper asks us to re-examine the assumptions that lie behind the questions posed by Pojman and Puccetti. Both of these authors assume that life and death are distinct states and the transition from the former to the latter is a distinct, definable event. Emanuel shows there are problems with this view and proposes a "bounded zone definition," which conceives of death as a process. It is a mistake, she maintains, to think of being dead as a state which suddenly obtains when death arrives. Death, in her view, is the process of losing life, which occurs gradually and in stages. Through a series of examples, Emanuel shows how this way of thinking about death allows us to cope more effectively with the reality of dying.

Typically ethicists have been concerned with what we may do to a person once she is dead (remove and donate her organs, for example), but the bounded zone account focuses our moral obligations on other stages at the end of life, when some residual life still remains. However, even if we conceive of death in this manner we still require criteria for declaring someone dead. Emanuel concludes that a "person's life must be considered ceased for any individual whose cardiorespiratory function has irreversibly ceased, and can be considered ceased for any individual having neurological function no more than in the persistent vegetative state if he or she or his or her proxy clearly indicated the wish that life be considered ceased in such a state."

ONE   What Is Death? The Crisis of Criteria

Louis P. Pojman | In his book *Life and Death*. 2nd ed. Belmont, CA: Wadsworth, 2000: 95-101.

On 24 May 1968, in Richmond, Virginia, a worker named Bruce Tucker fell, sustaining a severe head injury. When the ambulance delivered him to the emergency ward of the Medical College of Virginia Hospital, he was found to be bleeding within his brain. He was put on a ventilator and an operation was performed to relieve the strain on the brain. It was unsuccessful, and Tucker was described by the physician in charge as "mechanically alive . . . [his] prognosis for recovery is nil and death imminent."

At the same time a patient named Joseph Klett was in a ward waiting for a donor heart. When the electroencephalogram (EEG) attached to Tucker showed a flat

> **Electroencephalogram** (EEG)
> A medical test that measures and records the electrical activity of the brain through a net of sensors attached to the scalp. A "flat line" means that there is no electrical activity in the brain, and this finding is consistent with a brain that has ceased to function.

line, the doctors concluded that he was "brain-dead." They operated and transplanted his heart to Klett. Tucker's kidneys were also removed for transplantation.

Although Tucker's wallet contained his brother's business card, including a telephone number and address only fifteen blocks away from the hospital, no attempt was made to contact him. William Tucker, the brother, brought suit against the doctors who performed the operation, but the doctors were exonerated in court, even though Virginia law defined death as total cessation of all bodily functions. William Tucker, disappointed with the verdict, exclaimed, "There's nothing they can say to make me believe they didn't kill [my brother]."[1]

When is someone dead? Until the mid-twentieth century this was seldom a serious question. If someone failed to have a pulse and stopped breathing, this determined that he or she was dead. But in the middle of this century biomedical technology developed ways to keep the body alive almost indefinitely, causing us to reflect anew on the meaning of death. Moreover, this same technology can transplant organs from one patient to another, so that we need a definition of death to guide us when to remove the organs from the person declared dead.

Several physicians, philosophers, and medical ethicists, led by Henry Beecher and Robert M. Veatch, have called for a redefinition of death in terms of brain function, "brain death." Others, like Paul Ramsey and Hans Jonas, have opposed this move.

Four definitions of death appear in the literature: (1) the departure of the soul from the body; (2) the irreversible loss of the flow of vital fluids or the irreversible cessation of cardiovascular pulmonary function; (3) whole brain death; and (4) neocortical brain death.

Loss of Soul

The first major philosopher to hold that death occurred with the departure of the soul was Plato, but the view is found in the Orthodox Jewish and Christian traditions and in [the work of] Rene Descartes (1596–1650), who believed that the soul resided in the pineal gland at the base of the brain and left the body at death. The sign of the departure was the cessation of breathing. Orthodox Jews say

that a person is dead only when the last breath is drawn.[2] Note that the Hebrew word for spirit, *ruach*, is the same word used for breath, and the Greek word *pneuma* has the same double meaning.

This view is beset with problems. First, it is difficult to know what the soul is, let alone whether we are endowed with one or more. Second, neurological science can explain much of human behavior by appeal to brain function, so the notion of a separate spiritual entity seems irrelevant. Third, if a soul is in us and if it only leaves us after we have breathed our last, medical technology can keep the soul in the body for scores of years after the brain has ceased to function and, as far as we can tell, all consciousness has long disappeared. Unless we are really convinced that God has revealed this doctrine to us, we should dismiss it as unsupported by the best evidence available.

The Cardiopulmonary View

When the heart and lungs stop functioning, the person is dead. This has been the traditional medical definition. *Black's Law Dictionary* puts it this way: "The cessation of life: the ceasing to exist; defined by physicians as a total stoppage of the circulation of the blood, and a cessation of the animal and vital functions consequent thereupon, such as respiration, pulsation, etc." In *Thomas v. Anderson*, a California District Court in 1950 quoted Black and added, "Death occurs precisely when life ceases and does not occur until the heart stops beating and respiration ends. Death is not a continuous event and is an event that takes place at a precise time."[3]

This standard definition is problematic in that it goes against the intuitions of many people that irreversibly comatose patients, like Karen Ann Quinlan or Nancy Cruzan, are not alive at all. Bodily functions alone do not constitute human life. We need to be sentient and self-conscious.

The Whole Brain View

As Roland Puccetti puts it, "Where the brain goes, there the person goes."[4] In the same year that Bruce Tucker had his heart and lungs removed,

> **Whole brain view**
> The definition of death according to which a person is dead when all brain functions have ceased, including functions of the higher brain (consciousness, language, and voluntary movement) and those of the lower brain (spontaneous breathing and pupillary reflexes).

Ad Hoc Committee of the Harvard Medical School
A group at Harvard University, convened in the late 1960s and chaired by Henry Beecher, that was tasked with producing a definition of death that could be applied in the face of life sustaining technology, including mechanical ventilators, in modern intensive care units. The criteria for whole brain death published by the committee in 1968 was widely influential.

the Ad Hoc Committee of the Harvard Medical School, under the chairmanship of Dr Henry K. Beecher, met to decide on criteria for declaring a person dead. The study was a response to the growing confusion over the uses of biomedical technology in being able to keep physical life going for an indefinite period of time after consciousness has been irretrievably lost. It also was a response to the desire to obtain organs from "donors" who were permanently comatose but whose organs were undamaged, because of the ability of technology to keep the vital fluids flowing.

The committee came up with four criteria that together would enable the examiner to pronounce a person dead:

1. unreceptivity and unresponsivity (i.e., no awareness of externally applied stimuli);

2. no movement or breathing without the use of artificial mechanisms;

3. no reflexes; the pupil is fixed and dilated and will not respond to bright light; and,

4. a flat electroencephalogram (EEG), which indicates no cerebral activity.

The tests must be repeated at least twenty-four hours later in order to rule out rare false positives.

The Harvard committee's criteria have been widely accepted as a safe set, allowing medical practitioners to detach patients from artificial respirators and to transfer organs to needy recipients. Of thousands of patients tested, no one has regained consciousness who has met the criteria.

But critics have objected that the Harvard criteria are too conservative. By its norms, patients who are permanently comatose or in persistent vegetative states, like Karen Ann Quinlan and Nancy Cruzan, would be considered alive, since their lower brain stems

Lower brain stem
The brain may be divided into higher and lower structures. Lower brain structures include the mid-brain and brain stem. So-called vegetative functions, such as the regulation of heart beat, breathing, and body temperature, are located in the lower brain structures.

continued to function. Indeed, people have been recorded as living as long as thirty-seven years in such an unconscious state. Since they are alive and can be fed intravenously, or via gastric feeding tubes, we have an obligation to continue to maintain them. The worry is that hospitals and nursing homes could turn into mausoleums for the comatose. So a fourth view of death has arisen.

Gastric feeding
Providing a person with nutrition in liquid form via a tube that passes through the mouth or nose and into the stomach or duodenum.

The Neocortical Brain Death

What is vital to human existence? Henry Beecher, head of the Harvard Ad Hoc Committee, says it is consciousness. Robert M. Veatch says it is our capacity for social interaction, involving the power of thought, speech, and consciousness. These higher functions are located in the neocortex of the cerebrum or upper brain; when a sufficient part of this section of the brain is destroyed, the patient is dead. An electroencephalogram (EEG) can determine when the cerebrum has ceased to function.

Neocortical Brain Death
The definition of death according to which a person is dead when higher brain functions have ceased, including consciousness, language, and voluntary movement. Lower brain functions, including heartbeat, spontaneous breathing, sleep-wake cycles, and non-voluntary movements, may persist in such individuals.

Neocortex
A part of the "higher brain" comprising the surface of the two cerebral hemispheres. Higher brain functions located in the neocortex including the capacity for thought, language, and voluntary movement.

Beecher and Veatch see human death as the loss of what is significant for human life. Veatch . . . defines death this way: "Death means a complete change in the status of a living entity characterized by the irreversible loss of those characters that are essentially significant to it." By this reasoning, Karen Ann Quinlan would have been declared dead as soon as she was discovered to be in a persistent vegetative state. . . .

David Mayo and Daniel Winkler oppose the redefinition of death, arguing that a comatose human being whose lower brain stem is still functioning and whose heart is beating is still a living organism. According to them, death is an event, not a process, in which the biological organism ceases to function. If Mayo and Winkler are right, we should give up our notion of the sanctity of biological life and recognize that some lives are not worth living, including life as an organism in a persistent vegetative state. Although the irreversibly comatose being is biologically alive, it is no longer a life possessing any quality. If we see that personhood involves being self-conscious, we may say in these cases that although the body is alive the *person* is dead. Not only should the body be detached from expensive lifesaving machines, but its organs should be removed for use on the living. Organs are a precious medical resource that can be used to enable people to live longer and better lives.

Study Questions

1. Why has the definition of death become contentious?

2. What is the cardiopulmonary view of death and why, according to Pojman, is it problematic? Do you agree?

3. What is the whole brain view of death and why, according to Pojman, is it problematic? Do you agree?

Notes

1. Cited in Robert M. Veatch, *Death, Dying, and the Biological Revolution* (New Haven, Conn.: Yale University Press, 1976), pp. 21–4.

2. Immanuel Jakobovits, *Jewish Medical Ethics* (Philadelphia: Block, 1959), p. 277.

3. Quoted in Tom Beauchamp and Seymour Pedin, eds., *Ethical Issues in Death and Dying* (Englewood Cliffs, N.T.: Prentice Hall, 1978), p. 14.

4. Roland Puccetti, "Brain Transplantation and Personal Identity," *Analysis* 29 (1969), p. 65.

TWO   Does Anyone Survive Neocortical Death?

Roland Puccetti | In: Zaner, RM (ed.). *Death: Beyond Whole-Brain Criteria*. Dordrecht, The Netherlands: Kluwer Academic Publishers, 1988: 75–90.

One day on a very cold morning, I started the engine of my car without opening the garage door, then retreated to the kitchen to let it warm up. At that moment there was a long distance phone call from my publisher, and I spent a half hour haggling over the terms of a contract. Upon returning to the garage I found there, alongside the car, my dog Fido. Of course I immediately opened the automatic door and carried him outside into the fresh air. When I saw he wasn't breathing I pressed rhythmically on his chest cavity, and sure enough his heart and lungs started to respond. But still he did not wake up, so I took him to the vet's on the way to the university. The vet said Fido appeared to be comatose as a result of carbon monoxide poisoning, and advised that I prepare myself for the worst. He said it seemed the dog would not recover consciousness because the top of the brain was destroyed, although the brain stem must be intact, since Fido could breathe unaided. What should I do?

Now suppose I told you that I did the following. I took Fido home, made a special bed for him, shaved his body and fitted him with diapers, learned to feed him intravenously and nasogastrically, and arranged to have him turned in his bed often so he would not develop pressure sores. Evenings I would watch TV alongside Fido, stroking his warm body and listening to his breathing, though never again did he go for a walk with me, fetch the newspaper, bark, or do anything dogs normally do.[1] Would you think I am a rational person? Or worse, suppose I asked the vet to put Fido down for me and he replied that he couldn't do that to a comatose canine capable of spontaneous breathing, *because the law forbade it*. Would you think this a rational society?

If your answers to those questions are, as I think they would be, resoundingly negative, then presumably the main reason for your negative response is simply that my ministrations would do *no good* for Fido, who has permanently lost consciousness even

Nonapneic
A person (or other animal) who has lost the capacity for consciousness but who retains the capacity to breathe without the need for mechanical ventilation.

Apocryphal
Untrue. The Apocrypha are biblical writings appended to the Old Testament in historical editions of the Bible but which do not form the accepted cannon of the Scripture.

if he is nonapneic; for the same reason, *no harm* can be done to him by stopping his breathing. In other words, a permanently unconscious dog is, for all practical purposes, a dead dog anyway.

Now change the above apocryphal story in just one detail. Instead of it being Fido on the garage floor, it is my neighbor's infant son, little Bobby. I rush him to a children's hospital, but with the same result. Now could what was agreed to be irrational behavior in Fido's case become rational in Bobby's case? That a human life is much more valuable and worth preserving at all costs is completely irrelevant, since we agreed before that the main consideration was simply that one can do neither good nor harm to an irreversibly comatose being, and that should hold true independently of his species identity.

Yet, and this is what I find amazing, a great number of otherwise very able people in the legal and health professions think just the opposite. But before we examine their arguments, let us get one point absolutely straight. No matter what your calling, any position you adopt on this issue is going to be a *philosophical* stand. For the question we are addressing here is quintessentially philosophical: namely, *what constitutes* (in this world anyway, to avoid begging religious questions) *personal death?* . . . The question, of course, is whether you are doing philosophy well or badly. I begin with an example of what I consider bad philosophizing on this subject. . . .

Walton on [Neocortical] vs. [Whole Brain] Death

Douglas N. Walton asks why proponents of the . . . neocortical criterion of brain death are not even more selective.

> "The reply (that it is the cerebrum which mediates cognitive activity in the brain) is still not entirely satisfactory. However, it seems equally plausible to say that mental activity of the higher cognitive sort takes place essentially in the cerebral cortex, the thin membranous substance that forms a mantle

over the cerebrum. Why include the lobes of the cerebrum under the cortex if lower parts of the midbrain or the cerebellum and brain stem are excluded? . . . [The cerebral death advocate] might argue that it is safer to include the whole cerebrum, because there is a possibility of indeterminacy or error. But then, if tutiorism (chancing error to be on the safe side) is brought in, why not be even safer and take into account the whole-brain? . . ."*

Cerebellum
The cerebellum is located in the back of the brain and it coordinates muscle movement. The cerebellum is one of the lower brain structures.

To which one can counter: if it is better to err on the side of safety, why not wait until complete somatic death (including, e.g., cartilage cells in the knee) occurs, thereby foregoing organ transplantation? . . .

The case for excluding other subcortical structures mentioned by Walton in passing has nothing at all to do with tutiorism anyway. The midbrain is of course just the top of the brain stem, where . . . [midbrain structures] trigger orientating reflexes related to sources of visual and auditory stimuli: such reflexive responses do not require conscious mediation, as we all know from finding ourselves turned towards an abrupt movement in the peripheral visual field, or in the direction of a sudden sound, before such stimuli register in consciousness. If a brain structure does its job unconsciously, then there is no reason to think its integrity in a comatose patient is evidence of residual conscious functions. Similarly with the cerebellum, which preorchestrates complex bodily movements, and under . . . electrode stimulation does not yield clear sensations. The cerebellum probably also stores learned subroutines of behavior, like swimming or typing: precisely the kinds of things you do better when not concentrating on them. Why then is it necessary for the cerebellum to be dead in order to have a dead person on your hands?

Yet Walton seems to think that everything above the level of C1 directly contributes to a conscious mental life. His attitude seems to be that if something moves, it must or at least might have a life of its own, with its own kind of feeling. . . . As we all know, when the doctor flashes his penlight on the eye, we do not feel the pupil contract, then expand again

Level of C1
The first cervical vertebrae upon which the skull rests. "Above the level of C1" here refers to "everything from the neck up."

when he turns the light off. If not, then why in the world does Walton suppose that a deeply comatose patient feels anything in the same testing situation? The whole point of evolving reflexes like this, especially in large brained animals that do little peripheral but lots of central information processing, is to shunt quick-response mechanisms away from the cerebrum so that the animal can make appropriate initial responses to stimuli *before* registering them consciously. If one could keep an excised human eye alive *in vitro* and provoke the pupillary reflex . . . would Walton argue that the isolated *eye* might feel something as its pupil contracts?[2] . . .

Walton makes the claim that, to be on the safe side, "we should presume that the whole-brain is required to produce mental activity." Normally, of course, that is true, but from this it would hardly follow that, when the ultimate neuronal destination of neural input is no longer there, or is dead, sensations still occur. We can liken this proposal to having an express elevator that whisks passengers from the ground floor to executive offices on the top floor. If a nuclear strike blows off the top floor, it would be unreasonable to suppose that you could nevertheless conduct your business at still-standing intermediate floors. What Walton is doing is confusing the normally necessary contribution of subcortical mechanisms to sensation with the sufficient condition of neocortical functions . . .

Probably the sensation we worry most about in irreversibly comatose patients is pain. Now Walton may know that electrode stimulation intended to relieve intractable "central" or "thalamic" pain (where the pain is not localized at all), indicates that there are discrete "pain centres" in the thalami (Melzack 1973; Sem-Jacobsen 1968), and these are certainly subcortical structures that could survive neocortical death. Would this fact not tend to show that such patients might nevertheless experience pain, in line with Walton's tutioristic cautions?

Such a suggestion would be, I think, doubly wrong. It is wrong, first, because it incorporates an excessively homuncular

> **Thalamic**
> Pertaining to the thalamus; the thalamus is a midbrain structure where sensory impulses are relayed from the body to the neocortex.

> **Homuncular**
> Pertaining to a homunculus, or a small human being or form. Representations of the brain's motor cortex may be drawn with a homunculus, that is, a human form superimposed on the surface of the brain. Here the author is referring to a view according to which there is a one-to-one correspondence between a part of the brain and a unique function.

view of the relation between brain structures and conscious experience. The "little men in the thalami getting pain messages" picture is absurd: it is we who get the pains, not those structures. And it is wrong, secondly, because if the firing of thalamic pain centres by itself gave rise to pain experience, then it surely follows that if we could excise this tissue, keep it alive in vitro, stimulate it electrically to threshold for discharge and record the neurons' discharging, we would have to say that there is pain going on *in the vat*! Anyone who would believe this is beyond reason . . .

People As Brain Stems

This clinical picture . . . [of] neocortical death without brain stem death . . . [is known as persistent vegetative state (PVS). Anatomically, it is characterized by] destruction of the . . . cortical mantle of grey matter covering the surface of the cerebrum. . . . As it happens, neurons composing the [neocortex] are the most vulnerable to oxygen deprivation during transient cardiac arrest or . . . asphyxiation. Whereas in . . . whole-brain death, therefore including the brain stem that monitors respiration (which in turn provokes cardiac activity), the patient can be sustained on a ventilator for only up to a week in adults and two weeks in children before cardiac standstill, the [PVS] patient breathes spontaneously and demonstrates [lower brain] reflexes (also brain stem mediated), so that if fed nasogastrically or intravenously and kept free from infection, he or she can sustain somatic life for years or even decades after losing the top of the brain.

I said "somatic life," for without a [neocortex] the basis for a conscious and hence a personal life in this world is gone forever. But then what are we doing supplying intensive care to [PVS] patients? . . . Permanent unconsciousness is permanent unconsciousness whether the condition is associated with a body that lives by virtue of being able to breathe spontaneously or not. To deny this is to elevate spontaneous breathing to a principle of human life, something I find incredible. Yet this is actually the emerging consensus of the medico-legal community in North America. . . .

To sum up: either human life is rooted in brain stem function or it is rooted in the capacity for personal experience. If the former, then all vertebrate species are on an equal footing and what counts in medical ethics is just long-term organic functioning independently of our capacity to intervene. If the latter, then there is no ethically relevant difference in the status of [whole brain] and [neocortically] dead people: they have both lost the neocortical basis of an ongoing personal life. The only surprising fact to come out of [PVS] is, or should be, that corpses are really of two kinds: the vast majority that cannot breathe unaided, and a small minority that nevertheless can do this. Apneic or nonapneic, a corpse is still a corpse.

The Diagnostic Problem

In a still more recent writing Walton (1981) returns to defense of the whole-brain criterion of death. He begins by restating his earlier skepticism about our ability to avoid negative error in diagnosis of [PVS]. He says:

> *"However, physicians have not yet developed or tested proven, certainly safe criteria for [PVS] . . . more highly localized in dysfunction than whole-brain death. For the present, tutioristic reasoning dictates cleaving to criteria for whole-brain death."*

I do not know what Walton understands by "certainly safe" criteria for diagnosis of [PVS]; since the practice of medicine is an empirical science, there is always room for error. However, an accumulation of diagnostic results . . . [may seem] strongly conclusive. If one can safely exclude the possibility of hypothermia or intoxication with a [central nervous system] depressant, which drastically lowers oxygen requirements of the neocortex, a repeated finding of diminished cerebral blood flow, to less than 20 per cent of normal, is itself powerful evidence of [neocortical] destruction. In fact Lassen and colleagues (1978) reported firm correlations between increases in blood flow to specific regions of the cortex of patients in the waking, conscious state when problem solving, and also a significant overall increase in blood flow to the cerebrum as a whole of about 10 per cent during such activity. It therefore seems exceedingly unlikely that any kind of conscious experience is going on in a brain with use for less than a fifth of normal blood flow.[3] . . .

Ethical Considerations

Many who have followed me so far would nevertheless balk at the problem of disposing of human remains capable of breathing spontaneously. They would say that active intervention to stop the breathing prior to preparation for burial is not only presently illegal (laws can be changed, and already have, to facilitate organ harvesting), but morally murder; and it is often argued that passive (by the non-continuance of treatment) as opposed to active euthanasia is the more humane course.

Both these replies miss the point. You can stab a corpse, but you cannot *kill* it, for it is already dead whether breathing or not. If neocortical death is agreed to constitute personal death, then a firmly diagnosed [PVS] patient is in no better or worse situation than the [whole brain]-dead patient sustained on a respirator, whom we all agree is dead though still breathing artificially. Similarly, "euthanasia" means "mercy killing," but one cannot be merciful to a cadaver, for cadavers are beyond pain and indeed all further experience of this world. Indeed, if it were *my* nonapneic remains causing the problem, I want to insist in advance that the breathing be stopped, for by treating my body as if *I* were still alive, hospital personnel would be stripping me of human dignity: it is enough to have others change your diapers in the first years of life.[4]

Someone might suggest that the difference between defenders of the whole-brain criterion and defenders of the neocortical standard is that they envisage different logical subjects: the former taking that to be a still living, spontaneously breathing human *body*, the latter a *mind* now gone from this world. But if this were just a verbal dispute, it ought not to matter much to the disposal problem in a more enlightened age. But in fact it does matter. Those taking the first view would have to say to enquiring relatives and friends, "He's still alive but permanently unconscious, so we're going to let him die of dehydration, starvation, or infection, whichever comes first." Whereas those taking the second view, which is my own, would logically respond in words like these: "She's dead but her body is still breathing, so we're going to stop the breathing and prepare her body for burial."

Needless to say, the latter formulation seems to me less cruel.

Study Questions

1. Explain the analogy Puccetti draws at the opening of the article between Fido and Bobby. Do you find it convincing? Why?

2. Why, according to Puccetti, are reflexes such as the pupillary reflex, not evidence that a neocortically dead person might feel something?

3. Puccetti argues that if one accepts a neocortical definition of death, then it makes little sense to object to "killing" a PVS patient. Explain his reasoning. Do you agree?

Notes

1. He might, however, occasionally wag his tail. Apparently this is spinal cord mediated, as dogs coming out of anaesthesia often wag their tails. I owe this suggestion to John Fentress.

2. Of course no such contradiction would occur, since the pupillary reflex is brain stem mediated; the point is strictly hypothetical.

3. D.H. Ingvar has recently reported that cerebral blood flow in apallic patients has been measured using Xenon 133 gas inhalation and 254 scintillators that monitor oxygen and glucose uptake in as many square centimetres of superficial cerebral cortex on each side of the head. The video display is uniform: dark blue or purple on the entire screen, indicating little or no uptake of blood, because "these patients have no neocortex to supply with blood" (Ingvar, in a Symposium organized by the Faculty of Medicine, University of Montreal, entitled "Two Hemispheres: One Brain," on 18 May 1984).

4. The point was originally supplied by a former student of mine who has nursed apallic syndrome patients (name withheld).

References

Basser, LS, 1962, "Hemiplegia of Early Onset and the Faculty of Speech with Special Reference to the Effects of Hemispherectomy," *Brain* 85, 427–60.

Brindley, GA and Lewin, WS, 1968, "The Sensations Produced by Electrical Stimulation of the Visual Cortex," *Journal of Physiology* 196, 479–93.

Cooper, IS et al. 1974, "The Effect of Chronic Stimulation of Cerebellar Cortex on Epilepsy in Man," in IS Cooper, M Riklan, and RS Snider (eds.), *The Cerebellum, Epilepsy, and Behavior,* Plenum Press, New York and London, pp. 119–71.

Feindel, W, 1982, personal communication.

Geschwind, N, et al., 1968, "Isolation of the Speech Area," *Neuropsychologia* 6, 327–40.

Hassler, R et al., 1969, "Behavioural and EEG Arousal Induced by Stimulation of Unspecific Projection Systems in a Patient with Post-traumatic Apallic Syndrome," *Electroencephalography and Clinical Neurophysiology* 27, 306–10.

Holmes, G, 1945, "The Organization of the Visual Cortex in Man," *Proceedings of the Royal Society* (Biology) 132, 348–61.

Ingvar, DH et al., 1978, "Survival After Severe Cerebral Anoxia, with Destruction of the Cerebral Cortex: The Apallic Syndrome," *Annals of the New York Academy of Sciences* 315, 184–214.

Jerison, HJ, 1973, *Evolution of the Brain and Intelligence,* Academic Press, New York and London.

Lassen, NA et al. 1978, "Brain Function and Blood Flow," *Scientific American* 239, 62–71.

LeBlanc, M, 1983, personal communication.

Lewin, R, 1980, "Is Your Brain Really Necessary?" *Science* 210, 1232–4.

McWhirter, ND, 1984, *Guinness Book of World Records,* Bantam, New York.

Melzack, R, 1973, *The Puzzle of Pain,* Penguin, London.

President's Commission for the Study of Ethical Problems in Medicine and Biomedical and Behavioral Research: 1981, *Defining Death: Medical, Legal, and Ethical Issues in the Determination of Death,* US Government Printing Office, Washington DC.

Puccetti, R, 1981, "The Case of Mental Duality: Evidence from Split–brain Data and Other Considerations," *The Behavioral and Brain Sciences* 4, 92–123.

Sem-Jacobsen, C, 1968, *Depth-Electrographic Stimulation of the Human Brain and Behavior,* Thomas, Springfield, Illinois.

Walton, DN, 1980, *Brain Death, Ethical Considerations,* Purdue University Press, West Lafayette, Indiana.

Walton, DN, 1981, "Epistemology of Brain Death Determination," *Metamedicine* 2, 259–74.

THREE Re-examining Death: The Asymptotic Model and a Bounded Zone Definition

Linda L. Emanuel | *Hastings Center Report* 1995; 25(4): 27-35.

This paper combines reflection, argument, and exploration to re-examine death. First, it reflects on the reigning concept of death, and finding it inadequate, argues for an alternative. The concerns that drive this critique are recurrent and persistent, being found in almost every confrontation with death. Yet they are difficult to tease out because they challenge the traditional model of death deeply entrenched in Western thought and language, and require the suspension of fundamental assumptions. The alternative model involves a transformation of concept that has extensive ramifications. Second, this paper drafts a framework for beginning to address real world problems in a fashion consistent with the new model. This framework is offered as a first exploration in what will inevitably be a more extensive inquiry. To begin the inquiry, it's useful to consider descriptions and models of dying.

The Traditional Model of Life and Death: What's Wrong?

The reigning view has assumed that life and death are non-overlapping, dichotomous states.[1]

This view acknowledges that dying may take time, but presumes that a threshold event is nevertheless definable; a person is thought to be either alive or dead, not both. More recent proposals have viewed death as a process, and have pointed out the need to focus on definable states in that process.[2] While these recent proposals are important, they leave two fundamental problems with the traditional model unaddressed.

One fundamental problem is that there is no *state* of death.[3] No one can *be* in a state of death. Once life is lost the individual *is not* and therefore cannot *be* in any state. To say "she is dead" is meaningless since "she is" is not compatible with "dead." "State of death" is similarly as meaningless as "condition of conditionlessness." All are oxymorons. "Death" is not like "night," a time in a particular condition. It is not like a room one enters when life is lost. When life is gone there is no being to be in any state or space. Belief in an afterlife is belief in life after life, not death after life. There is a state of life, but there is no state of death.

Dying is the process of losing life. What is meant by *death* or *dead* turns out to be no more than loss of life. Life may be described and dying may be described. The states when most relevant life is gone may also be described. But, again, dying does not culminate in a state; it culminates in a nonstate. The traditional model of life and death as poles of a binary opposition is therefore in need of modification. The new model must have only one state; there is only life and its cessation. The challenge shifts from understanding death to understanding life and its loss. Attempts to define death must therefore be recast as attempts to define loss of life.

Another fundamental problem is that dying or loss of life is not always a definable event. It has never been controversial that dying can be protracted. But now it is clear that there is not death but only dying. Is there an event that can identify final and complete loss of life? The answer appears to be no. To examine why, consider an ordinary example. . . .

Tracking Declining Vital Signs

Janet was dying of liver failure. Her liver failure led to a rapid decline in her kidney function. Despite appropriate therapies she was losing consciousness gradually and increasingly. Two days ago she recognized her husband and pressed his hand in response to his words. Yesterday she looked at him but without obvious response. Since this morning she no longer opened her eyes and responded only to deep pain. Tests indicated that she was getting enough oxygen, but her blood pressure was dropping. Between the toxic substances resulting from liver and kidney failure and her low blood pressure her higher brain cells were probably beginning to lose their function. Her heartbeat was regular, as was her breathing until a few hours ago. Gradually her breathing began to be deep and sighing with longer and longer intervals. Next her heart rhythm became irregular and then

Dichotomous
Divided into two distinct parts or categories, as in (traditionally) alive or dead.

Oxymoron
A figure of speech that combines contradictory terms, as in an "open secret."

extremely slow. Then her blood pressure became undetectable by a regular blood pressure cuff. Her breathing slowed to twice a minute or so, suggesting that her brain stem was also losing ground. She was still warm. Her pupils became wide and did not respond to tight. Her heart was still going at about twenty beats a minute, but with ever increasing intervals. Then her breathing seemed to stop—she would breathe once and stop again. Her heart monitor began to show an almost flat line, with every so often an electrical complex. Then, seemingly from the middle of nowhere, a deep sigh. Her heart complexes carried on, just one every so often, until none was seen for so long that all stopped looking. The death certificate had to be made out by the doctor. The doctor put down the time she had happened to notice as she left the room; any time during that whole process was close enough, she reasoned. . . .

Consider in Janet's case how biological life tapers off. The difficulty experienced by Janet's care providers in pinpointing her time of death corresponds to the fact that biological life declines as a continuing process. The process of dying occurs at different levels of organization, from the organism to the organ, cellular, and subcellular levels, and each set of systems can decline on a somewhat independent trajectory. . . . Biological loss of life was happening progressively in all these systems. It could have been faster or slower, and each stage blended into the next. Biological loss of life did not happen at any single, definite instant. . . .

That personhood dies slowly is an observable reality too. What constitutes personhood is controversial, but proposed critical capabilities have included continuing self-consciousness, possessing rationality and the ability to have desires and make plans, modifying instincts with second-order desires, pursuing critical interests, or having the capacity to feel love or otherwise meaningfully relate to other people.[4] . . . The dying may lose each capacity in a gradual fashion. Thus, however it is defined, human beings can go through states with more complete and less complete personhood. From a religious perspective the issue is the soul rather than personhood, but the observation is equivalent. The capacities that comprise the soul—ability to pray, to relate to another, or to experience—can be lost in sequential stages too. Not only the body, but also the person can undergo a process rather than an event of life cessation.

Discontent among many with existing definitions of death also reflects the need for a reconceptualization. . . . That the traditional model of life and death conflicts with experience and moral perception can also be illustrated by the history of definitions of death, whether as event or state, and the challenges that have been raised against each. The cardiorespiratory definition, which declared death when neither respirations nor cardiac function were detectable, was in widespread use until the advent of cardiopulmonary resuscitation.[5] Since resuscitation allows some people who had met criteria of death to return to life, this definition needed adjustment Even though the phrase "irreversible loss" helped, the definition has been discarded in favour of or supplemented with a whole brain definition in many sections of society. The whole brain death definition asserts that death can be declared when the entire brain has lost function.[6] However, when further technical progress brought to society's attention the persistent vegetative state, in which higher but not lower brain functions have ceased, yet a third definition appeared to be necessary, and many commentators have supported a so-called neocortical definition.[7] But this definition seems only to emphasize that life can be lost in an uncoordinated fashion. Popular characterizations of the persistent vegetative state reflect the same conceptual impasse. One grade school educated patient described Karen Quinlan to the author as "living-dead."[8] Others have coined the term "biomort" or used phrases such as "death in life" to describe this and analogous states.[9]

Second-order desire
A desire that has as its object another desire. To have a first-order desire is to want a state of affairs to occur; a second-order desire is to want to want something. The distinction is captured by the example of an alcoholic who wants a drink (first-order desire) but wishes that he didn't want a drink (second-order desire). Second-order desires, it is often thought, reflect more reasoned and more sober attitudes.

Biomort
Someone in a persistent vegetative state. The term refers to a human being who has "biological life" but who has permanently lost the capacity for personhood.

The Asymptotic Model of Life Cessation

Acceptance of "death" as no more than loss of life, and of dying as a process, requires accepting that there is no describable event or state that is death itself. Can the describable process of dying yield a coherent understanding of life cessation to replace the traditional concept of death? In the following section the asymptotic model of life cessation is delineated.

Algebraic Depictions

To bring the description of dying into a conceptual model it may be useful, if only as a heuristic device, to explore an algebraic analogue. Life seems to slip away almost as the end of a curve approaches its baseline axis. Indeed, an asymptotic curve may come close to describing a key aspect of reality. Dying is depicted graphically as an asymptote-like process in Figure 10.1. In this two-dimensional graphical depiction, life is represented by a continuous multifactorial variable that combines the full range of life's aspects. Accurate quantification of life is not the main idea; rather it is to illustrate how life and the losing of it can be understood as a continuous rather than dichotomous phenomenon.

This algebraic model is simplistic, but the basic idea can be elaborated to further depict the complexities of life. At least four types of algebraic sophistication could be used. First, three dimensions could be introduced. Life could be depicted as the product of two variables with biological life on one axis and personhood on the other (Figure 10.2). Second, more than three dimensions could be used. Multiple dimensions would allow, for instance,

> **Multifactorial variable**
> A complex quantity that may assume different values; a multifactorial variable encompasses several different measures, in this case measures of life. Thus, the variable "life" in Figure 10.1 might include measures of heartbeat, breathing, consciousness, and the ability to reason.

the biological entity to be further distinguished into its various organic, cellular, and molecular systems. Or different aspects of personhood could be separately represented, such as continuing self-awareness, ability to love, etc. Then different criteria for personhood could vary somewhat independently, helping to represent the fact that different aspects of personhood can exist in different degrees at different times. Third, multivariate depictions in each dimension would allow modeling of another level of necessary moral complexity, namely differences among value systems. For every set of dimensions, multiple variables could be used to assign different value weightings, each according to the individuals and societies. For instance, one group or person may value highly an aspect of personhood such as love while another may value cognitive capacity more, and within the axis of either one, different aspects of the capacity may be valued differently. Fourth, the level of determinacy of such depictions may also vary.

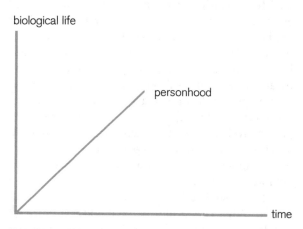

FIGURE 10.2

Some of life's properties, for instance physiological capacities, are precisely determinable, but many are more elusive and interactive capacities, such as creativity or friendship. These more indeterminate phenomena may be better depicted as areas or fuzzy bands or a series of patches. Again, the intent is not to offer a strict mathematical definition of life, but rather to illustrate the kinds of relationships among salient aspects that the traditional dichotomous model cannot capture.

Biological Recycling and Identity

Often, fragments of biological life are reused, either in natural processes of recycling or by transplantation.

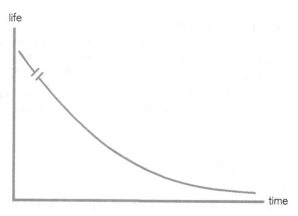

FIGURE 10.1

The fragments become part of one or many other organisms. In this circumstance, the totality of biological life does not reach zero, but takes off again into the life curve of other organisms.

This well-known fact of biological recycling implies that ultimate life cessation of an organism's component parts does not necessarily occur. Rather, fragments can be appropriated, piece by piece, over differing periods of time, and by different organisms. They do not die but their integration and identity changes. This could be depicted as shown in Figure 10.3. Perhaps only the remains of Egyptian mummies and Jeremy Bentham (whose preserved and clothed body sits in a display case at University College in London) hover near zero, barred by their preservation from recycling components into new life. . . .

> **Jeremy Bentham**
> (1748–1832) An English philosopher and social reformer, Bentham is one of the architects of utilitarianism, according to which, "it is the greatest happiness of the greatest number that is the measure of right and wrong." His ideas for social reform, including a proposal for the modern prison called the "Panopticon," were rooted in a universal utilitarian code of law. Bentham's preserved head was on public display at University College London for many years, but, as it was the object of repeated student pranks, it has been replaced with a wax replica.

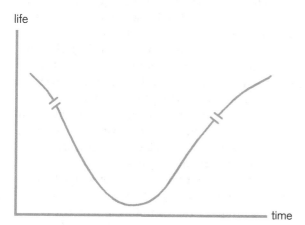

FIGURE 10.3

Life and Person

The asymptotic view of life cessation implies a distinct theory of person. Bodily parts versus the organism's whole are distinguishable only as interdependent aspects, as are biological life versus personhood, and all other life capacities. The living person is the product of all the interacting systems of the body. Life is understood as the totality of biological and cognitive and spiritual life. The mind and "essence" (or in religious terms, soul) of the person are supraeffluences of the whole interacting system, almost as orchestral music is from the sounds of each instrument. Many properties—of the neurological, hormonal, immune, and other systems—make up the abilities that have been referred to under the title of personhood.[10] No single site or system is the "seat of the soul" or the sine qua non of personhood. A person's being is understood to be time-bound and dependent on material things, but still not totally and precisely locatable in space or time. Partly a thing and partly an occurrence, a product of both matter and active capacity, a being passes in phases. . . .

> **Supraeffluence**
> A substance that flows out of something. In this case, the author is referring to life flowing out of the complex interactions of the body's biological machinery.

> **Sine qua non**
> Essential or critical; it translates literally from the Latin as "without which not."

Residual Life

The asymptotic view of life cessation and the view of person bound up with it leads to the understanding that life exists in residual forms. Whether extreme dementia, the persistent vegetative state, or fragments of tissue are cited as examples, the fact is that these are forms of human life that are less than the individual in question once was. The palpable reality of residual life does not fit under a dichotomous view of life and death. But under the asymptotic model residual life, greater or smaller, is conceptually unproblematic. States of diminished being such as those of Janet . . . are no longer conceptually dissonant; they are states of residual life.[11] Instead of wondering if a brain-dead person's organs live on in the transplant recipient as the donor or the donee's life, the organs are accurately described as the donor's residual life reintegrated into the donee's fuller life. . . .

The asymptotic model is not without its critics, however. Some might counter the asymptotic model by pointing out that loss of life at least *can* be instantaneous. Individuals who die by guillotine or explosion must surely have a definable moment of loss of life. But even these individuals must have a process of dying, albeit extremely contracted. If the guillotine victim's heart were monitored, no doubt it would continue for a few beats after the head was off. Tissues of the brain are well known to continue viability for some minutes after oxygen and consciousness are lost. Many who die by explosion do so slowly, as documented by at least one trauma physician.[12] Even for the victim who dies at the epicentre of a huge explosion, the person's tissues or molecules, in some form, can potentially be retrieved. Thus, no matter how contracted the time scale or how thorough the disintegration, loss of life is still accurately seen as a process or series of states.

But, the critic of the asymptotic model might continue: all events could be, when examined so closely, described as a process. What, after all, is an instant?[13] Philosophers have considered whether events have any ontological status at all, since events mark changes that can all be understood in terms of transitions among states.[14] These positions may be accepted on their merits; they are not problematic for the asymptotic model. The question is only whether our understanding of life cessation may be sufficiently different, when seen as a process, that we may alter its definition and wish to behave differently toward the end of life. . . .

Residual Life and a Bounded Zone of Life Cessation

The fact that a clear moment of life's demise cannot be found in no way diminishes the importance of defining its cessation. Boundaries and definitions are of profound importance and indeed are a quintessential part of most perceptual, cognitive, social, and moral processes. Accepting now that the descriptively more accurate model of loss of life is an asymptotic one, the question becomes how to attain useful constructed boundaries that acknowledge and are consistent with the asymptotic model.

One approach would be to draw a line somewhere in or near the asymptote's greatest gradient, thus obtaining one clear-cut definition of life's end. This approach, however, involves imposing the dichotomous model on the asymptotic model and leaves untapped all the potential benefits of modelling life cessation more accurately.

An approach more consistent with the asymptotic model would be to define a *zone* of life cessation. The zone would be bounded, but it would allow for the observed reality of the continuum of life cessation. Then the continuum of life cessation can be defined in a way that acknowledges its perceived continuous

nature while still providing the boundaries that are essential to defining moral conduct. This approach may resolve much of the tension caused by the need for delineations in the face of actual continua.

The key feature of the asymptotic model is that it admits the reality of residual states of life. Rather than categorizing all states as dead or alive it allows unhindered examination of the residual states *as* residual states. This opens up for inquiry what the appropriate behaviour is toward particular states, unhindered by the distracting implications of either an ultimately false category (death) or a false dichotomization (life versus death).

The bounded zone approach does not *per se* provide answers either to where the boundaries should be drawn or to questions of how to behave toward individuals within the zone. Rather, it is necessary to identify the nature of the residual life under consideration and examine the moral value of that residual life. Understanding the moral value of the residual life involves or leads to an understanding of what is appropriate behaviour—personal, medical, and otherwise—toward individuals in the specified state. Similar approaches have already been used.[15]

In notable contrast with traditional reasoning, the bounded zone approach does not assume the *conceptual* state (death) for which appropriate behaviour is known, and then identify physiological states and criteria for it. The approach instead identifies an *observable* state, complete with physiological features that may readily translate into criteria, and then asks what is the correct approach to it. Alternatively, the approach permits starting with specific *behaviours*— such as burial, activation of inheritance plans, or provision of artificial nutrition and hydration—and then asking what are the physiological states toward which the behaviours are morally correct.

Exploration of the moral value of residual states of life can usefully start by acknowledging that human life has unique moral standing whether it is at its fullest or profoundly diminished. Though few would argue that an amputated limb has great moral value, equally few would dispose of it in the same casual manner that people dispose of leftover chicken at dinner. Even an amputated human limb has some unique moral standing for people. So, as the residual state of a human being is defined and its moral standing inquired into, it can be kept in mind that there is no possibility of saying that it has no moral standing. . . .

Defining the Zone of Life Cessation

Each of the three contending definitions of death under the dichotomous model (cardiorespiratory, whole brain, and neocortical) corresponds to a point on the curve of declining life, as shown in Figure 10.1. Importantly, each definition falls on a point such that there is obvious residual life of one degree or another. What has been created by this series of three definitions is a zone. This zone can provide, for illustration, a zone within which life can be declared to have ceased. Other areas of the life cessation curve could be picked out, but the importance of contending definitions of death makes this area a salient one.

The lower limit of declarable life cessation is irreversible cessation of pulmonary and cardiac function. States of residual life more minimal than this would likely not be useful for defining when life has ceased. For instance, the forms of remaining life in rigor mortis or stages of putrefaction carry moral meaning only as artefacts. The persistent vegetative state defines a point at the upper limit. Since a coherent moral argument has been put forward for understanding this state as "dead" in the traditional model it is included in the zone for this illustration. It is necessary, in a

> **Rigor mortis**
> The process of the stiffening of muscles of the body after death, beginning within hours of death and lasting several days.

bounded zone definition, to safeguard the people who do not subscribe to the upper limits. In this model, for instance, it would be essential that the persistent vegetative state be included as life cessation only for those individuals who provide, or whose proxies provide, a clear statement about their wishes to that effect.

A definition of the zone of life cessation might state:

> *"A person's life must be considered ceased for any individual whose cardiorespiratory function has irreversibly ceased, and can be considered ceased for any individual having neurological function no more than in the persistent vegetative state if he or she or his or her proxy clearly indicated the wish that life be considered ceased in such a state."*

By this definition, life cessation could be declared any time within the bounded zone. Life cessation would have to be declared as soon as cardiorespiratory function is known to have ceased irreversibly, and before states that occur after cardiopulmonary death. Life cessation could be declared for the persistent vegetative state but not for any state more intact than this. It would be permissible to declare life ceased for any state of neurological function less intact than the persistent vegetative state. This would include brain death, and states near brain death yet without prospect for persistent vegetative existence. . . .

Study Questions

1. What, according to Emanuel, are the problems with the traditional definitions of death?

2. Describe in your own words the asymptotic view of life cessation.

3. How does Emanuel define the cessation of life? Is this just a definition of death?

Notes

1. President's Commission for the Study of Ethical Problems in Medicine and Biomedical and Behavioral Research, *Defining Death* (Washington, D.C.: US Government Printing Office, 1981), esp. pp. 61–70; Ad Hoc Committee of the Harvard Medical School, "A Definition of Irreversible Coma," *JAMA* 205 (1968): 337; M. B. Green and Daniel Wikler, "Brain Death and Personal Identity," *Philosophy & Public Affairs* 9 (1980): 105–33.

2. Fred Feldman, "On Dying as a Process," *Philosophy and Phenomenological Research* 50, no. 4 (1989): 375–90; Anir

Halevy and Baruch Brody, "Brain Death: Reconciling Definitions, Criteria, Tests," *Annals of Internal Medicine* 119 (1993): 519–25; R Sean Morison, "Death: Process or Event?" *Science* 173 (1971): 694–98; Kathleen Stein, "Last Rights," *Omni* 9, no. 12 (1987): 60–117.

3. Linda L. Emanuel, "What Is Wrong with 'Dead'?" In *Proceedings IInd International Symposium on Brain Death*, ed. C. Machado (Amsterdam: Elsevier, in press).

4. Harry Frankfurt, "Freedom of the Will and the Concept of a Person," *The Importance of What We Care About* (Cambridge:

Cambridge University Press, 1988); Ronald Dworkin, *Life's Dominion* (New York: Alfred Knopf, 1993).

5. President's Commission, *Defining Death*.

6. John M. Fisher, *The Metaphysics of Death* (Stanford, Calif.: Stanford University Press, 1993); Ad Hoc Committee, "A Definition of Irreversible Coma"; Alexander M. Capron and Leon R. Kass, "A Statutory Definition of the Standards for Determining Human Death: An Appraisal and a Proposal," University of Pennsylvania Law Review 121 (1972): 87–118.

7. Fisher, *The Metaphysics of Death*; Robert M. Veatch, "The Whole-Brain-Oriented Concept of Death: An Outmoded Philosophical Formulation," *Journal of Thanatology* 3 (1975): 1–30; David R. Smith, "Legal Recognition of Neocortical Death," *Cornell Law Review* 71 (1987): 850–88.

8. In re Quinlan, 70 NJ 10 (1976).

9. Mark Dowie, "The Biomort Factor," *American Health* 9, no. 10 (1990): 18–19; Mark Dowie, "Death in Life," *The Economist* 323 (1992): 29.

10. S. Reichlin, "Neuroendocrine-Immune Interactions," *NEJM* 329 (1993): 1246–52.

11. Anir Halevy and Baruch Brody, "Brain Death: Reconciling Definitions, Criteria, Tests," *Annals of Internal Medicine* 119 (1993): 519–25; Dworkin, *Life's Dominion*; Sherwin B. Nuland, *How We Die* (New York: Alfred Knopf, 1994); *Cruzan v. Director*, Missouri Department of Health, 110 Sct 2841 (1990); Elisabeth Rosenthal, "A Will to Die," *Discover* 13, no. 12 (1992): 45–7.

12. John A. Parrish, *12, 20 & 5: A Doctor's Year in Vietnam* (New York: E.P. Dutton & Co., 1972).

13. Leon R Kass, "Death as an Event: A Commentary on Robert Morison," *Science* 173 (1971): 698–702.

14. Judith J. Thomson, *Acts and Other Events* (Ithaca, N.Y: Cornell University Press, 1977); Laurence B. Lombard, *Events: A Metaphysical Study* (Boston: Routledge and Kegan Paul, 1986); Mia Gosselin, *Nominalism and Contemporary Nominalism: Ontological and Epistemological Implications of the Work of WVO Quine and N. Goodman* (Boston: Kluwer Academic Publishers, 1990).

15. Christopher Meyers, "Intended Goals and Appropriate Treatment: An Alternative to the Ordinary/Extraordinary Distinction," *Journal of Medical Ethics* 10, no. 3 (1984): 128–30; Malcolm H. Parker, "Moral Intuition, Good Deaths and Ordinary Medical Practitioners," *Journal of Medical Ethics* 16, no. 1 (1990): 28–34.

Chapter Study Questions

1. Defining death is a way of stating who counts morally. Who counts morally for Pojman, Puccetti, and Emanuel? Which view do you find the most convincing and why?

2. Define whole brain death and neocortical brain death. What arguments support each view? Which is more convincing?

3. What is Emanuel's critique of the whole brain and neocortical definitions of death? Discuss how her asymptotic model might lead to a broader view of moral obligation at the end of life.

Critical Analysis

Consider the following quotation from Walton in the Puccetti article:

"The reply (that it is the cerebrum which mediates cognitive activity in the brain) is still not entirely satisfactory. However, it seems equally plausible to say that mental activity of the higher cognitive sort takes place essentially in the cerebral cortex, the thin membranous substance that forms a mantle over the cerebrum. Why include the lobes of the cerebrum under the cortex if lower parts of the midbrain or the cerebellum and brain stem are excluded? ... [The cerebral death advocate] might argue that it is safer to include the whole cerebrum, because there is a possibility of indeterminacy or error. But then, if tutiorism (chancing error to be on the safe side) is brought in, why not be even safer and take into account the whole-brain."

Outline Walton's argument in your own words, paying particular attention to the premises that he relies on to support his main conclusion. Choose one of the premises for evaluation. Try to think of at least one objection to this premise.

Case Study

Terri Schiavo, the centre of a media and political storm over the moral status of patients in a persistent vegetative state, died on 31 March 2005, days after a feeding tube was ordered removed by a Florida court. Terri was born in a Philadelphia suburb on 3 December 1963. After high school, she attended Bucks County Community College where, in 1982, she met Michael Schiavo. Terri and Michael married in 1984, and moved to Florida in 1986 where she worked for an insurance company. Although her parents were conservative Roman Catholics, it seems that Terri did not share their religious views.

Her life took a tragic turn in the early morning on 25 February 1990, when she suddenly collapsed, possibly due to a low level of potassium in her bloodstream. When paramedics arrived, she was not breathing and had no pulse. Paramedics were able to restore her heartbeat and she was intubated and placed on a mechanical ventilator in hospital. Although she never regained consciousness, other functions did return. Terri regained the ability to breathe on her own, and no longer needed the ventilator. She had normal sleep-wake cycles, and would open her eyes when awake. She moved all of her limbs, although not purposefully. She would make noises; at times tears would run down her face; at other times she would smile. Imaging of her brain revealed extensive damage to her cerebral cortex, a finding consistent with the clinical diagnosis of persistent vegetative state.

Her husband Michael was her court appointed guardian. For three years, she underwent various attempts at rehabilitation and experimental treatments to no avail. Eventually, Michael accepted the fact that Terri would never recover. In 1998, he requested that her feeding tube be removed so that she could be allowed to die, a move vigorously opposed by Terri's parents. A total of 30 legal decisions over the next seven years all supported Michael's decision on behalf of his wife.

1. When did Terri Schiavo die according to cardio-pulmonary, whole brain, and neocortical definitions of death?

2. How would Emanuel's definition of the zone of life cessation apply in this case? Do you think it a useful criterion? Why?

3. Puccetti says that "You can stab a corpse, but you cannot *kill* it, for it is already dead whether breathing or not." Would it have been better to inject Terri Schiavo with a drug to stop her heart immediately rather than withdrawing her feeding tube? Why?

Further Reading

Kagan S. Philosophy of death. Yale University Open Courses [Internet]. Available from: http://academicearth.org/lectures/death-intro. Date accessed: 6 June 2012.

Luper S. Death. In: Zalta EN, editor. Stanford Encyclopedia of Philosophy [Internet]. 2008. Available from: http://plato.stanford.edu/archives/sum2009/entries/death/. Date accessed: 6 June 2012.

President's Council on Bioethics. Controversies in the determination of death [Internet]. 2008. Available from: http://www.thenewatlantis.com/docLib/20091130_determination_of_death.pdf. Date accessed: 6 June 2012.

Rubinstein A. What and when is death? The New Atlantis [Internet]. 2009 24:29–45. Available from: http://www.thenewatlantis.com/publications/what-and-when-is-death. Date accessed: 6 June 2012.

Harvesting Organs from the Dead

In this chapter, we turn our attention to the question of when organs for transplantation may be removed from the dead. The conditions under which organs may legitimately be harvested from the dead turn on our understanding of what role autonomy ought to play in these decisions and our response to the question, "can the dead be harmed?" Canada's first kidney transplant was performed in Montreal in 1958. Since then thousands of people with end-stage organ disease have received organ transplants resulting in improved function and longer lives. The list of organs and tissues transplanted routinely includes bone, bowel, cornea, heart, kidney, liver, lung, pancreas, and skin. The demand for organs for transplantation in Canada is much greater than the supply. In 2009, 2155 organ transplants were performed in Canada, while 3796 patients remained on a waiting list for organ transplant. Unfortunately, 249 patients died that year while waiting for an organ transplant.

A variety of strategies have been proposed to improve access to organs for transplantation in Canada. Currently, Canada has an "opt-in policy" with regard to the retrieval of organs from the recently deceased. This means that either people must provide their informed consent to organ removal after death while still alive, or informed consent must be obtained from next-of-kin. A national database for transplant donors may enhance the number of donors and facilitate the prompt identification of an organ donor at the time of death (organs must be transplanted within a few hours of death). Others have argued for an "opt-out policy" that would eliminate the requirement for informed consent but would allow individuals to register their desire to not have their organs removed after death. Proposals for the creation of a "market" for organs in which donors would be paid by a government agency to donate an organ have generated considerable controversy.

In the first article, Aaron Spital and James Stacey Taylor argue for the routine removal of organs after death without the informed consent of the donor or next-of-kin. They point out that the ethical principle of respect for autonomy is prima facie, that is, it can be over-ridden by a sufficiently weighty competing moral demand. Improving the supply of organs would prevent needless suffering and save lives and, accordingly, represents an important social good. Just as the state legitimately uses its coercive powers for a military draft for self-protection, so too an "organ draft" would protect the health of citizens in need of an organ transplant. The authors dismiss the suggestion that their proposal would violate individual autonomy and harm those who would not have wished their organs removed after death. They argue that "after a person dies, the person whom he or she was ceases to exist and so cannot be harmed." After death, the demands of autonomy are either irrelevant or so mitigated as to be clearly outweighed by the pressing claims of those who might benefit from the organs of the deceased.

In the second article, Walter Glannon takes issue with Spital and Taylor's proposal for the routine harvesting of organs. He argues that serious consideration of the surviving interests of the dead supports the necessity of informed consent for organ harvesting. Respect for autonomy implies the right to live one's life according to one's own life plan. For some, bodily integrity—living, dying, and being buried with one's body intact—is a central part of that life plan. Harvesting organs without informed consent is problematic precisely because it would take organs from individuals who, if they had been asked when alive, would have refused. It is not the interests of the dead person per se that are harmed in this case; rather, it is the interests of that person when alive—their surviving interests—that are harmed. It is in this latter sense that routine organ harvesting creates posthumous harm and is therefore not morally sustainable. Glannon goes on to argue that people in fact generally ought to donate their organs after death because of the many benefits they receive in their lifetime as members of a community. While a broader recognition of this fact may improve organ donation rates, he concludes that the informed consent of organ donors is still required.

In the third article, Charles A. Erin and John Harris believe that the magnitude of the shortage of organs for transplantation is such that all options must be considered. They argue for what they call a "strictly regulated and highly ethical market in live donor organs and tissues." According to their proposal, a government agency such as Health Canada would offer financial incentives to healthy people to donate an organ for transplantation while they are alive. They recognize that the payment for someone's eye, kidney, lung, or a part of their liver would have to be "high enough to attract people into the marketplace." Such payments would not only increase the supply of organs, they would also enhance equity. They claim that the current system is unfair in that the surgeon, nurses, and transplant coordinator are all paid for their essential role in organ transplantation while the donor is not. The creation of a market in organs for transplantation does raise the threat of exploitation. The authors address these concerns by arguing against the direct sale of organs between donor and recipient, and restricting participants to citizens of a state. Thus, as they put it, there would be no "buying in Turkey or India to sell in Harley Street." Whether these protections go far enough to rule out exploitation is open to question.

ONE   Routine Recovery of Cadaveric Organs for Transplantation: Consistent, Fair, and Life-Saving

Aaron Spital and James Stacey Taylor | *Clinical Journal of the American Society of Nephrology* **2007; 2: 300**

Transplant candidates and the people who care for them know only too well that there is a severe shortage of acceptable organs. As a result, in the United States alone, approximately 19 people on the transplant waiting list die every day.[1] Compounding this tragedy is the fact that many potentially life-saving cadaveric organs are not procured.[2] Clearly, our organ procurement system fails to meet our needs. Recognition of this failure has led to several radical proposals designed to increase the number of organs that are recovered for transplantation, including legalization of organ sales[3] and offering priority status to people who agree to posthumous organ recovery.[4] But before reaching for a new approach, we need to ask first, "What is wrong with our current cadaveric organ procurement system?"

The Need for Consent: Widely Accepted but Sometimes Deadly

We believe that the major problem with our present cadaveric organ procurement system is its absolute requirement for consent. As such, the system's success

> **Cadaveric organs**
> Human tissue—such as heart, lung, kidney, liver, cornea, skin, and bone—that can be removed from someone after death for the purpose of transplantation into a living person.

depends on altruism and voluntarism. Unfortunately, this approach has proved to be inefficient. Despite tremendous efforts to increase public commitment to posthumous organ donation, exemplified most recently by the US Department of Health and Human Services-sponsored Organ Donation Breakthrough Collaborative,[5] many families who are asked for permission to recover organs from a recently deceased relative still say no.[6] The result is a tragic syllogism: nonconsent leads to nonprocurement of potentially life-saving organs, and nonprocurement limits the number of people who could have been saved through transplantation; therefore, nonconsent results in loss of life.

> **Organ Donation Breakthrough Collaborative**
> An organization created in 2003 by the Secretary of the US Department of Health and Human Services, involving leaders in transplantation, health care, and communities, whose goal is to increase organ donation rates in US hospitals to 75 per cent.

In an attempt to overcome this consent barrier while retaining personal control over the disposition of one's body after death, several countries have enacted "opting out" policies, sometimes referred to (erroneously, we believe) as presumed consent.[7] Under these plans, cadaveric organs can be procured for transplantation unless the decedent—or her family after her death—had expressed an objection to organ recovery. Although there is evidence that this approach increases recovery rates, perhaps by changing the default from nondonation to donation[8,9] the recent Institute of Medicine (IOM) report on organ donation concluded that a presumed consent policy should not be adopted in the United States at this time.[10] One of the most important concerns noted by the IOM committee is the results of a 2005 survey in which 30 per cent of the respondents said that they would opt out under a presumed consent law. The IOM report also pointed out that in the United States there seems to be a lack of public support for this approach, that the organ donation rate in the United States currently exceeds that of many countries with presumed consent policies, and that in most of these countries the family of the decedent is still consulted.[11] It should

> **Opting out**
> An approach to organ procurement in which organs are removed routinely for transplantation unless the organ donor or next-of-kin has registered an objection in advance; the informed consent of the organ donor or next-of-kin is not required in this approach.

also be noted that even opting out countries do not have enough organs to meet their needs, and for people who remain unaware of the plan, presumed consent becomes routine recovery in disguise.

Given that some people do not want to donate, it is clear that whether we follow an opting in or an opting out approach, life-saving organs are and will continue to be lost because of refusals. In other words, the requirement for consent, whether explicit or presumed, is responsible for some deaths. But isn't this the price that we must pay to show respect for people after they die? We believe that the answer is no.

> **Opting in**
> An approach to organ procurement that requires the informed consent of the organ donor (before death) or their next-of-kin before organs are removed for transplantation.

The view that consent is an absolute requirement for cadaveric organ recovery has long been accepted as self-evident, and few experts in the field have seen the need to justify it. We agree that the pre-mortem wishes of the deceased regarding the post-mortem disposition of his or her property should generally be respected. However, we believe that the obligation to honor these (or the family's) wishes is prima facie, not absolute, and that it ceases to exist when the cost is unnecessary loss of human life, which is often precisely what happens when permission for organ recovery is denied. Therefore, given the current severe organ shortage and its implications for patients who are on the waiting list, we propose that the requirement for consent for cadaveric organ recovery be eliminated and that whenever a person dies with transplantable organs, these be recovered routinely.[12] Consent for such recovery should be neither required nor sought. In our opinion, the practical and ethical arguments for this proposal are compelling.

Routine Removal: Consistency with Other Socially Desirable but Intrusive Programs

One of the major reasons for insisting on consent is to show respect for autonomy, a major principle of biomedical ethics. However, Beauchamp and Childress[15] pointed out that as important as this principle is, it "has only prima facie standing and can be overridden by competing moral considerations." One such consideration occurs when society is so invested in attaining a certain goal that is designed to promote the public good that it mandates its citizens to behave in a manner that increases the probability of achieving that goal, even though many of them would prefer not to act in this way. Silver[16] pointed out the legitimacy of this approach in his discussion of an "organ draft": "The sense behind the coercive power of democratic governments is to move society forward by public decree where individuals will not, by private volition, act in their own best interests." Examples of such situations include a military draft during wartime, taxation, mandatory vaccination of children who attend public school, jury duty, and, perhaps most relevant to routine removal of cadaveric organs, mandatory autopsy when foul play is suspected. Although some people may not like the fact that they have no choice about these programs, the vast majority of us accept their existence as necessary to promote the common good. Routine removal of cadaveric organs would be consistent with this established approach, and it would save many lives at no more (and we believe much less) cost than these other mandated programs. Furthermore, had we been born into a world where cadaveric organ removal for transplantation were routine, it is likely that few if any people would question the policy, just as few of us question mandatory autopsy today. And while most of us will never need a transplant, nonrecipients would also benefit from the plan in the same way that people who never file a claim benefit from the security of having insurance. It should also be noted here that, as discussed below, a person's autonomy is lost after death.

Recovering Cadaveric Organs without Consent: Life-Saving and Fair

Few would argue against the view that routine removal of usable cadaveric organs would save many lives. Under such a program, recovery of transplantable organs should approach 100 per cent. It is unlikely that any program designed to increase consent rates could even come close. Although the expected high efficiency of routine recovery is its major raison d'être, it also has several other advantages. Routine

> **Raison d'être**
> The principal reason or purpose for a thing or person's existence; literally the "reason to exist" in French.

recovery would be much simpler and cheaper to implement than proposals designed to stimulate consent because there would be no need for donor registries, no need to train requestors, no need for stringent governmental regulation, no need to consider paying for organs, and no need for permanent public education campaigns. The plan would eliminate the added stress that is experienced by some families and staff who are forced to confront the often emotionally wrenching question of consent for recovery. Delays in the removal of transplantable organs, which sometimes occur while awaiting the family's decision and which can jeopardize organ quality, would also be eliminated.

A final advantage of routine posthumous organ recovery is that it is more equitable than are systems that require consent. All people would be potential contributors, and all would be potential beneficiaries. No longer could one say, "Thank you," when offered an organ but say, "No," when asked to give one; such "free riders" would be eliminated. And concern about exploitation of the poor, as sometimes arises during discussions of organ sales, is not an issue here.

> **Free rider**
> Someone who consumes a resource without paying for it, such as a person who refuses to pay taxes but who nonetheless uses state services paid for with the taxes of others. In this context, a free rider is someone who will, if the need arises, accept an organ from someone else, but who will not agree to posthumously provide organs to others in need.

Concerns about Routine Removal of Cadaveric Organs for Transplantation

Opponents of this proposal allege that eliminating the requirement for consent would violate individual autonomy and could cause harm.[17-19] But as Jonsen[20] pointed out, "consent is ethically important because it manifests and protects the moral autonomy of persons . . . [and] it is a barrier to exploitation and harm. These purposes are no longer relevant to the cadaver which has no autonomy and cannot be harmed." Moreover, a policy of routine organ recovery would not violate the autonomy of the living, even if they would object to the posthumous removal of their transplantable organs. Because the existence of the plan would be broadcast widely, autonomy would not be compromised by deceit, and people would be just as free as they were before the implementation of this policy. It therefore would not affect their autonomy at all.

Some authors disagree and have argued that the dead or at least their "surviving interests" can be harmed.[21,22] The prime example given of a surviving interest is a wish for bodily integrity after death, an interest that routine posthumous organ recovery would thwart and, it is claimed, thereby harm the decedent.

We strongly believe that the concept of posthumous harm is a fallacy.[23,24] Although some people may wish it were not so, as Emson[25] pointed out, dead bodies decay very quickly and cannot remain intact. More importantly, after a person dies, the person whom he or she was ceases to exist and so cannot be harmed. But even if we are mistaken in our skeptical view of the concept of posthumous harm, this would not change our belief that routine removal of usable cadaveric organs is the way to go. As Harris[26] pointed out, "rights or interests would have to be extremely powerful to warrant upholding such rights or interests at the cost of the lives of others . . . the interests involved after death [be there any] are simply nowhere near strong enough [to maintain the consent requirement for cadaveric organ recovery while potential recipients continue to die]."

The possibility of offending and thus harming surviving family members is more concerning, but even this possibility is not sufficient to reject routine removal of cadaveric organs. Professor Harris again: "If we can save or prolong the lives of living people and can only do so at the expense of the sensibilities of others, it seems clear to me that we should. For the alternative involves the equivalent of sacrificing people's lives so that others will simply *feel* better or not feel so bad, and this seems nothing short of outrageous".[27] And consider that during wartime the occasional necessity of a military draft is widely accepted even though the death of a young son or daughter would be much more painful for families than would be the drafting of organs from a relative who is already dead. Finally, it should be noted that organ recovery does not interfere with the ability to have an open-casket funeral.

Another objection to routine recovery of cadaveric organs is that it would violate religious or other moral convictions of "conscientious objectors." This is an important issue. One approach is to conclude that routine removal is so much in society's interest that no one should have a choice regardless of his or her beliefs. Another possibility is to allow conscientious objectors to opt out;[28] but given that this approach could dilute the value of our proposal, we favor not allowing exemptions, as is true for forensic autopsies. . . .

> **Conscientious objector**
> A person who refuses to participate in a socially-mandated program on grounds that it is offensive to his religious or other deeply held beliefs. Legitimate conscientious objectors to a military draft may be assigned to service in hospitals or other similar roles in lieu of military service.

A final objection is that routine recovery would generate outrage among the public. This is possible. However, we believe that it is likely that given education and time, most of the public would soon recognize the tremendous benefit and fairness of the plan and therefore come to accept it just as they now accept other mandated behaviors designed to promote the public good. Preliminary data suggesting that 30 per cent of the US public would already accept routine removal of cadaveric organs, without education regarding the value of this approach, provide support for this view.[29] . . .

Study Questions

1. What, according to Spital and Taylor, is the problem with the organ procurement system in the United States and Canada? How do they propose to fix it?

2. How is an "organ draft" like a military draft or other legitimate instances of the state's use of coercive power? Is the analogy apt? Why?

3. How do Spital and Taylor deal with the issue of "conscientious objectors" to their proposal? Is the response adequate? Why?

Notes

1. US Department of Health and Human Services. Donate Life. Available at: http://www.organdonor.gov. Accessed 27 September 2006

2. Sheehy E, Conrad SL, Brigham LE, Luskin R, Weber P, Eakin M, Schkade L, Hunsicker L: Estimating the number of potential organ donors in the United States. *N Engl J Med* 349: 667–74, 2003

3. Friedman EA, Friedman AL: Payment for kidney donors: Pros and cons. *Kidney Int* 69: 960–2, 2006

4. Landry DW: Voluntary reciprocal altruism: A novel strategy to encourage deceased organ donation. *Kidney Int* 69: 957–9, 2006

5. US Department of Health and Human Services. Organ Donation Breakthrough Collaborative. Available at: http://www.organdonationnow.org. Accessed 27 September 2006

6. Sheehy et al. Estimating the number of potential organ donors. *N Engl J Med,* 2003

7. Veatch RM, Pitt JB: The myth of presumed consent: Ethical problems in new organ procurement strategies. *Transplant Proc* 27: 1888–92, 1995

8. Johnson EJ, Goldstein D: Do defaults save lives? *Science* 302: 1338–9, 2003

9. Childress JF, Liverman CT, eds. *Organ Donation: Opportunities for Action. A Report from the Institute of Medicine*, Washington, DC, National Academies Press, May 2006, pp 205–28

10. Ibid.

11. Ibid.

12. Emson HE: It is immoral to require consent for cadaver organ donation. *J Med Ethics* 29: 125–7, 2003

13. Harris J: Organ procurement: Dead interests, living needs. *J Med Ethics* 29: 130–4, 2003

14. Spital A, Erin CA: Conscription of cadaveric organs for transplantation: Let's at least talk about it. *Am J Kidney Dis* 39: 611–5, 2002

15. Beauchamp TL, Childress JF: Respect for autonomy. In: *Principles of Biomedical Ethics*, 4th Ed., New York, Oxford University Press, 1994, p 126

16. Silver T: The case for a post-mortem organ draft and a proposed model organ draft act. *Boston University Law Review* 68: 681–728, 1988

17. Giordano S: Is the body a republic? *J Med Ethics* 31: 470–5, 2005

18. Glannon W: Do the sick have a right to cadaveric organs? *J Med Ethics* 29: 153–6, 2003

19. Hamer CL, Rivlin MM: A stronger policy of organ retrieval from cadaveric donors: Some ethical considerations. *J Med Ethics* 29: 196–200, 2003

20. Jonsen AR: Transplantation of fetal tissue: An ethicist's viewpoint. *Clin Res* 36: 215–9, 1988

21. Glannon. Do the sick have a right to cadaveric organs?

22. Hammer, Rivlin. A stronger policy of organ retrieval from cadaveric donors.

23. Callahan JC: On harming the dead. *Ethics* 97: 341–52, 1987

24. Taylor JS: The myth of posthumous harm. *Am Philos Q* 42: 311–22, 2005

25. Emson. It is immoral to require consent for cadaver organ donation.

26. Harris. Organ procurement: Dead interests, living needs.

27. Harris J: Human resources. In: *Wonderwoman and Superman: The Ethics of Human Biotechnology*, Oxford, Oxford University Press, 1992, pp 100–3

28. Kreis H: The question of organ procurement: Beyond charity. *Nephrol Dial Transplant* 20: 1303–6, 2005

29. Spital A: Conscription of cadaveric organs for transplantation: A stimulating idea whose time has not yet come. *Camb Q Healthcare Ethics* 14: 107–12, 2005

TWO Do the Sick Have a Right to Cadaveric Organs?

Walter Glannon | *Journal of Medical Ethics* 2003; 29: 153

. . . In the United States, 69,399 people were waiting for an organ in 2000. A total of 8059 organs were recovered. Living donors contributed 3268 organs, while 4791 were cadaveric organs. In that same year, 5794 Americans died waiting for an organ transplant.[1] Given the global disparity between the supply of and demand for human organs for transplantation, and given that living and cadaveric organ donation have done little to alleviate this shortage, some might argue that those who are sick due to organ failure should have a right to cadaveric organs. This right would entail the coercive transfer of organs by the state from those who have been declared dead, even if they did not consent to the harvesting of their organs while they were alive. . . .

But humans can have interests that survive their deaths. Failing to respect interests that humans expressed while they were alive and which survive their deaths can harm them posthumously. . . . Thus the expression of an interest in how our bodies are treated after we die commands respect and places deontological constraints on what others can or cannot do to our bodies.

> **Deontological constraint**
> A moral restriction on what it is permissible for individuals or governments to do in the service of socially desirable goals, e.g., increasing the availability of organs. In this case the restriction is represented by individual autonomy.

Because of these constraints, while non-consensual harvesting of organs from the dead is medically desirable, it is not morally justifiable. . . . The

> **Negative right**
> A moral claim to be free from unwanted interference; in this case, the freedom to not have one's organs removed after death without one's consent.

> **Positive right**
> A moral claim on another person or institution for something; in this case, a claim on the organs of someone who has recently died.

negative right not to be harmed by the defeat of one's interest in dying with one's body intact overrides the putative positive right of the sick to one's organs after death. . . . Against the rights-based nonconsensual model, I will argue that a communitarian-based model that respects individual autonomy is a morally defensible alternative to the problem of organ scarcity. On this model, the obligation to have one's organs harvested after death is not generated by claims of the sick, but instead by the sharing of interests, needs, and values with others in a social or religious community. This will not solve the problem of organ scarcity, but it can promote increased organ donation in a morally justifiable way.

Surviving Interests and Posthumous Harm

The idea that the sick have a right to cadaveric organs is grounded partly in the belief that these organs are no longer of any use to the dead. Viable and therefore useful body parts can be treated as state property. This was the rationale behind what Jesse Dukeminier and David Sanders called "routine salvaging."[2] They reasoned that no harm could be done by salvaging organs from human cadavers, so it was justifiable for society to routinely take viable body parts without the formal permission of the dying or their families. . . . The utilitarian argument behind this policy would appear to outweigh any deontological concerns about the rights or interests of the dead. For the dead would no longer have any interests that could be defeated or rights that could be violated.

Many philosophers hold that having interests presupposes the capacity for consciousness and other forms of mental life. Personhood consists in this capacity, which requires the structural and functional integrity of the higher brain, the cerebral cortex.[3] A person dies when this integrity is irreversibly lost. . . .

This does not mean, however, that there are no deontological constraints on taking organs from the deceased. Before dying, an individual may have expressed a conviction in the importance of bodily integrity and a corresponding wish that his body remain intact once he is declared dead. Harvesting his organs could defeat his surviving interest and thus harm him. Joel Feinberg and other philosophers have argued that humans can be harmed by the defeat of their interests after they have died.[4] Feinberg maintains that the subject of the surviving interest defeated posthumously is the living individual before death whose interest it was. The harming relation is not causal but logical. That is, if one's interest in bodily integrity and not having one's organs harvested after death fails to be respected by others, then this makes it true that one's interest fails to be respected while one is alive. This is a harm that can befall one posthumously because it is timelessly true of one. The idea of posthumous harm generates obligations for others to respect the surviving interests of the dead, and these obligations entail constraints on what we can do to their bodies after they die. Because individuals can be harmed by failing to respect their interests and values in this way, deontological considerations of what can be done to the body can outweigh utilitarian considerations of the good that harvesting organs from the body would do for the sick needing organ transplants. . . .

> **Surviving interest**
> A good—such as freedom or bodily integrity—that was valued by a person while they were alive.

> **Posthumous harm**
> Injury that is inflicted on people after they are dead. Some assert that the dead cannot be harmed because they no longer have interests. Here it is argued that after death a person's surviving interests may be violated and that therefore a person may be posthumously harmed.

The principle underlying this view is not a property right over one's body, but rather individual autonomy, the right to live out one's life according to a plan of one's own making. A surviving interest in bodily integrity after death can be an integral part of one's life plan, and it can generate an obligation for others not to interfere with the realization of that life plan. Some might argue that, once they have been declared dead, humans no longer can have any interests regarding what is or is not done to their bodies. To insist that they can is to ignore the fact that, although we are constituted by our bodies, we are not identical to them.[5] Nevertheless, even if humans and their bodies are distinct ontological types, humans stand

> **Ontological types**
> Categories of people or things; in this case, one might speak of a person and that person's body as if they were distinct—though intimately connected—entities.

in a special relation to their bodies. The body is essential to the development of a self in a life-plan. Because the body is so closely associated with who we are, we can have an interest in what is done to it even after we cease to exist. If it is treated in a way that does not accord with my wishes or interests, then in an important respect this can be bad for me and I can be harmed. The special relation between humans and their bodies can make it wrong for others to ignore the expressed wish that one's organs not be harvested at death, despite their viability for transplantation.

Negative rights have more moral force than positive rights. The right not to be interfered with puts a stronger moral obligation on others than does the right to be aided by them.[6] This is not due to the risk of harm to oneself in aiding others, but instead to the moral importance of individual autonomy. We may be morally permitted or obligated to aid others in need, depending on such factors as their degree of need and the risk of harm to ourselves in aiding them. But there is a greater degree of moral obligation not to interfere with one's autonomy. Given the special relation between humans and their bodies, the moral importance of individual autonomy in having a life-plan, and that what happens to one's body after death is part of such a plan, the negative right to bodily integrity after death outweighs any presumed positive right of the sick to receive organs from those who did not consent to cadaver donation. This deontological constraint can be sustained despite the utilitarian good that would result from the transfer of organs from the dead to those who are dying from organ failure. The main objection to the utilitarian argument for nonconsensual harvesting is that it ignores or overrides one's basic negative right to decide what others can or cannot do to one's body.

The motivation for a constraint on routine salvaging of cadaveric organs is that it would mistakenly presume tacit consent from a significant number of individuals who would not have given consent if they had been asked. . . . The concern here is with taking organs from the dead when they had made no decision about donation while they were alive. This is distinct from not allowing individuals to make such a decision. A right of the sick to cadaveric organs would mean that individuals would have no choice about what is done to their bodies. It would be more morally objectionable than presumed consent because it would entirely ignore individual autonomy and the negative right to bodily non-interference.

Individuals should have the unconditional choice of opting out of routine salvaging of their future cadaveric organs. We should follow the policy of routine salvaging with opting out. Crucially, this policy requires explicit consent to cadaver organ procurement, not merely presumed consent. In the absence of explicit consent, a wish not to donate and a decision to opt out of salvaging should be presumed. . . .

All of the points in this section undermine any possible justification for the practice of taking organs from the dead without their previous consent. A right is a claim by some entailing an obligation for others to fulfil that claim. A right of the sick to cadaveric organs would entail a strict obligation for people to give up their organs when they die. But if autonomy means that there is no strict obligation to give up one's organs, then there cannot be a corresponding right of the sick to these organs. When people express the wish that their bodies remain intact after death, this wish should be respected. Given the moral importance of individual autonomy in general and bodily integrity in particular, it would be morally unjustifiable to override such a wish, despite any benefit that might go to those needing organ transplants. . . .

Communitarian-based Donation

I propose a model of organ donation as a form of giving back something to the community from which one has benefited over the course of one's life. The idea of donation as giving back (as distinct from simply giving) implies an obligation and accordingly should not be confused with the idea of donation as a gift or an altruistic act.[7] By definition, these actions are not obligatory but supererogatory, beyond the call of duty or obligation. The sense of obligation to donate cadaveric organs is not generated from a right or claim by others, but instead from the idea that one shares common interests, needs, and values with other individuals in a community. . . .

> **Altruistic act**
> A behaviour that potentially benefits one person at a net loss to another person. Such behaviour is often considered morally optional.

Because an individual who has had a reasonably long and healthy life is likely to have had her medical needs met at some or many times over the course of her life, the benefit she has received generates an expectation to act so that the medical needs of others can be met over the course of their lives.[8] This expectation creates an obligation to act in this way, provided that doing so does not come at a significant risk or cost to oneself. Just as one can have a surviving interest in bodily integrity after death, one can have a surviving obligation to benefit others after death, specifically in the form of cadaveric organ donation. The obligation is not rights-based but community-based; it is grounded in the concept of mutual benefit, of what we receive from and what we owe to each other as members of a community. Still, the obligation is not strict or absolute but prima facie. Some weight can be given to individual autonomy and the option of not donating if cadaveric donation entails too much cost to the individual by violating her interest in bodily integrity. Intuitively, the interest in surviving for those in need of an organ transplant should have more weight than the interest of the deceased in bodily integrity. Yet autonomy allows some weight to be given to the decision to die with one's body and organs intact.

In so far as interests, needs, and values are shared commonly rather than held separately, there is an obligation for those in the community to promote the common good. In this regard, community-based organ donation may be compatible with a moderate utilitarian argument for donation. . . . Emphasizing promotion of social good while at the same time respecting the choice to opt out can be an incentive to donate by generating trust in the medical profession and organ-sharing networks. This is significant, given that public mistrust in these institutions is a major reason for people's refusal to donate. Nonconsensual harvesting would likely increase this mistrust because it would ignore individual autonomy. But respecting an individual's right to choose whether to donate would likely increase public trust in the relevant institutions. Decisions about donation would be made by individuals, not for them by the sick, the medical profession, or the state. This, combined with an emphasis on one's obligation to promote the good by aiding others in need, could encourage more donation. . . .

As I have noted, consensual opt-in harvesting thus far has done little to alleviate the shortage of organs for transplantation. Still, a consensual communitarian model is morally preferable to a rights-based non-consensual model allowing the coercive transfer of body parts from the dead to the

living. . . . Donation could be promoted by broad education encouraging people to consent to donate on drivers' licenses, specialized donor cards, or in a medical file following discussion with a primary care physician. Moreover, it could be promoted by not allowing families to override an individual's expressed wish to donate. Overriding such a wish is equivalent to ignoring the conditions stipulated by an individual in a living will. This occurs frequently; yet it is a violation of autonomy and respect for the deceased.

Some might point to religious communities as a counterexample of what I have been proposing. . . . Although some religions prescribe an obligation to die with one's body parts intact, this obligation may be overridden when an organ can save a human life. In these cases, it is permissible for one to donate an organ and thereby pass on life to another. Most religions permit the use of cadaveric organs for transplantation, provided that it is consented to in accord with religious beliefs and values.[9]

Conclusion

Those who are sick from organ failure do not have a right to cadaveric organs. Such a right would entail the coercive transfer of organs from the dead to the sick and a strict obligation for the living to give up their organs after death. Strictly obligating one to give up one's organs, or salvaging them without consent, would violate individual autonomy and the special relation between humans and their bodies. For these reasons, non-consensual harvesting of cadaveric organs is morally unjustifiable. So there is no strict obligation to give up one's organs and therefore no right of the sick to them. . . .

A communitarian-based model emphasizing donation as a form of giving back something to a community from which one has benefited over the course of one's life is morally preferable to a rights-based model of coercively transferring organs from the deceased without their previous consent. . . . Although this policy is not the most medically desirable way to address the problem of organ scarcity, it offers a morally justifiable alternative to the policy of non-consensual harvesting.

Study Questions

1. According to Glannon, how does a program of routine recovery of organs without consent violate respect for autonomy?

2. What does Glannon mean when he says that "[n]egative rights have more moral force than positive rights?" How does this fit into his argument?

3. According to Glannon, do people have a moral obligation to donate their organs to others? Why?

Notes

1. UK Transplant, www.uktransplant.org, Eurotransplant, www.eurotransplant.nl, United Network for Organ Sharing, http://www.unos.org.
2. Dukeminier J, Sanders D. Organ transplantation: a proposal for routine salvaging of cadaver organs. *New England Journal of Medicine* 1968;279:413.
3. Parfit D. *Reasons and persons*. Oxford: Clarendon Press, 1984. Noonan H. *Personal identity*. London: Routledge, 1991.
4. Feinberg J. *Harm to others*. New York: Oxford University Press, 1984: 79–95. Also, Nagel T. Death. In: *Mortal questions*. Cambridge: Cambridge University Press, 1979: 1–10.
5. Baker LR. *Persons and bodies: a constitution view*. New York: Cambridge University Press, 2000.
6. Thomson JJ. *The realm of rights*. Cambridge, MA: Harvard University Press, 1990. Kamm, FM. *Morality, mortality: death and whom to save from it: volume II: rights, duties, and status*. Oxford: Oxford University Press, 1996.
7. Veatch RM. *Transplantation ethics*. Washington, DC: Georgetown University Press, 2000: 171. My position differs from Veatch's on this point. As Veatch notes, the distinction between "giving" and "taking" in organ procurement was introduced by Ramsey P. *The patient as person*. New Haven: Yale University Press, 1970.
8. Emanuel E. *The ends of human life: medical ethics in a liberal polity*. Cambridge, MA: Harvard University Press, 1991, offers a defence of communitarianism in health care.
9. Veatch RM. *Transplantation ethics*. Washington, DC: Georgetown University Press, 2000: ch 1.

THREE An Ethical Market in Human Organs

Charles A. Erin and John Harris | *Journal of Medical Ethics* 2003; 29: 137

While people's lives continue to be put at risk by the dearth of organs available for transplantation, we must give urgent consideration to any option that may make up the shortfall. A market in organs from living donors is one such option. The market should be ethically supportable, and have built into it, for example, safeguards against wrongful exploitation. This can be accomplished by establishing a single purchaser system within a confined marketplace.

Statistics can be dehumanizing. The following numbers, however, have more impact than most: as of 24 November 2002 in the United Kingdom, 667 people have donated organs, 2055 people have received transplants, and *5615 people are still awaiting transplants*.[1] It is difficult to estimate how many people die prematurely for want of donor organs. "In the world as a whole there are an estimated 700,000 patients on dialysis . . . . In India alone 100,000 new patients present with kidney failure each year"[2] (few if any of whom are on dialysis and only 3000 of whom will receive transplants). Almost "three million Americans suffer from congestive heart failure . . . deaths related to this condition are estimated at 250,000 each year . . . 27,000 patients die annually from liver disease . . . In Western Europe as a whole 40,000 patients await a kidney but only . . .

> **Exploitation**
> To benefit unfairly from the work or labour of another person. For instance, the poor may be exploited by an employer who offers low wages and poor workplace conditions knowing that they have few other options for work.

10,000 kidneys"[3] become available. Nobody knows how many people fail to make it onto the waiting lists and so disappear from the statistics. It is clear that loss of life, due in large measure to shortage of donor organs, is a major crisis, and a major scandal.

At its annual meeting in 1999, the British Medical Association voted overwhelmingly in favour of the UK moving to a system of presumed consent for organ donation,[4] a proposed change in policy that the UK government immediately rejected.[5] What else might we do to increase the supply of donor organs? At its annual meeting in 2002, the American Medical Association voted to encourage studies to determine whether financial incentives could increase the supply of organs from cadavers.[6] In 1998, the International Forum for Transplant Ethics concluded that trade in organs should be regulated rather than banned.[7] In 1994, we made a proposal in which we outlined possibly the only circum-

> **International Forum for Transplant Ethics**
> An international consortium of ethicists and lawyers who advocate for expanding access to organs for transplantation. They have argued for routine organ procurement from the dead and a market for organs from living donors.

stances in which a market in donor organs could be achieved ethically, in a way that minimizes the dangers normally envisaged for such a scheme.[8] Now may be an appropriate time to revisit the idea of a market in donor organs.[9] Our focus then, as now, is organs obtained from the living since creating a market in cadaver organs is uneconomic and is more likely to reduce supply than increase it and the chief reason for considering sale of organs is to improve availability.

To meet legitimate ethical and regulatory concerns, any commercial scheme must have built into it safeguards against wrongful exploitation and show concern for the vulnerable, as well as taking into account considerations of justice and equity.

There is a lot of hypocrisy about the ethics of buying and selling organs and indeed other body products and services—for example, surrogacy and gametes. What it usually means is that everyone is paid but the donor. The surgeons and medical team are paid, the transplant coordinator does not go unremunerated, and the recipient receives an important benefit in kind. Only the unfortunate and heroic donor is supposed to put up with the insult of no reward, to add to the injury of the operation.

We would therefore propose a strictly regulated and highly ethical market in live donor organs and tissue. We should note that the risks of live donation are relatively low: "The approximate risks to the donor . . . are a short term morbidity of 20 per cent and mortality, of 0.03 per cent . . . The long term risks of developing renal failure are less well documented but appear to be no greater than for the normal population."[10] And recent evidence suggests that living donor organ transplantation has an excellent prognosis, better than cadaver organ transplantation.[11] Intuitively, the advantage also seems clear: the donor is very fit and healthy, while cadaver donors may well have been unfit and unhealthy, although this will not be true of many accident victims.

The bare bones of an ethical market would look like this: the market would be confined to a self-governing geopolitical area such as a nation state or indeed the European Union. Only citizens resident within the union or state could sell into the system and they and their families would be equally eligible to receive organs. Thus organ vendors would know they were contributing to a system which would benefit them and their families and friends since their chances of receiving an organ in case of need would be increased by the existence of the market. (If this were not the case the main justification for the market would be defeated.) There would be only one purchaser, an agency like the National Health Service (NHS), which would buy all organs and distribute according to some fair conception of medical priority. There would be no direct sales or purchases, no exploitation of low income countries and their populations (no buying in Turkey or India to sell in Harley Street). The organs would be tested for HIV, etc., their provenance known, and there would be strict controls and penalties to prevent abuse.

Prices would have to be high enough to attract people into the market-place but dialysis, and

> **Harley Street**
> A street in London, England that houses the offices of a large number of private specialist physicians and surgeons.

other alternative care, does not come cheap. Sellers of organs would know they had saved a life and would be reasonably compensated for their risk, time, and altruism, which would be undiminished by sale. We do not after all regard medicine as any the less a caring profession because doctors are paid. So long as thousands continue to die for want of donor organs we must urgently consider and implement ways of increasing the supply. A market of the sort outlined above is surely one method worthy of active and urgent consideration.

Study Questions

1. According to Erin and Harris, what is an ethical market in human organs? Why do we need one?

2. The authors argue that it is hypocritical to pay surgeons, nurses, and transplant coordinators but not organ donors. Do you agree? Why?

3. How is their proposal structured to avoid exploitation? Do they succeed? Why?

Notes

1. UK Transplant. http://www.uktransplant.org.uk/

2. Cooper DKC, Lanza RP. *Xeno—the promise of transplanting animal organs into humans.* New York: Oxford University Press, 2000: 7–17.

3. Ibid.

4. Beecham L. BMA wants presumed consent for organ donors. *BMJ* 1999;319:141.

5. Anon. Organ donor reform rejected. BBC News Online. 16 July 1999. http://news.bbc.co.uk/1/hi/health/396430.stm

6. Josefson D. AMA considers whether to pay for donation of organs. *BMJ* 2002;324:1541.

7. Radcliffe-Richards J, Daar AS, Guttman RD, et al. The case for allowing kidney sales. *Lancet* 1998;351:1950–2.

8. Erin CA, Harris J. A monopsonistic market—or how to buy and sell human organs, tissues and cells ethically. In: Robinson I, ed. *Life and death under high technology medicine.* Manchester: Manchester University Press in association with the Fulbright Commission, London, 1994:134–53. See also Harris J, Erin CA. An ethically defensible market in organs. *BMJ* 2002;325:114–15.

9. Tuffs A. Debate fuels controversy over paid-for live organ donation. *BMJ* 2002;325:66; Hopkins Tanne J. International group reiterates stance against human organ trafficking. *BMJ* 2002;325:514.

10. Allen RDM, Lynch SV, Strong RW. The living organ donor. In: Chapman JR, Deierhoi M, Wight C, eds. *Organ and tissue donation for transplantation.* London: Arnold, 1997: 165 (original references omitted). See also—for example, Bay WH, Herbert LA. The living donor in kidney transplantation. *Ann Intern Med* 1987;106:719–27; Spital A. Life insurance for kidney donors—an update. *Transplantation* 1988;45:819–20. In this last study it was reported that in a sample of American life insurance companies, all would insure a transplant donor who was otherwise healthy and only 6 per cent of companies would load the premium. We are indebted to Søren Holm for pointing us to these latter two sources.

11. Hariharan S, Johnson CP, Bresnahan BA, et al. Improved graft survival after renal transplantation in the United States, 1988 to 1996. *N Engl J Med* 2000:342:605–12. See also Gjertson DW, Cecka, MJ. Living unrelated kidney transplantation. *Kidney International* 2000; 58:491–9; Terasaki PI, Cecka JM, Gjertson DW, et al. High survival rates of kidney transplants from spousal and living unrelated donors. *N Engl J Med* 1995;333:333–6. We are indebted to Aaron Spital for pointing us to these sources.

Chapter Study Questions

1. Each article contains a different proposal to enhance the supply of organs for transplantation. What are the three proposals? What arguments support each proposal? Which do you believe is superior and why?

2. Spital and Taylor, and Glannon disagree about the moral force of surviving interests and the prospect of posthumous harm when organs are harvested from the dead without informed consent. How do they support their differing positions? Who has the more plausible position?

3. Erin and Harris reject payments for organs from the dead as "uneconomic and . . . more likely to reduce supply than increase it." How might one justify a market for cadaveric organs? What advantages and disadvantages might it have compared with the market proposed by Erin and Harris?

Critical Analysis

Consider the following selection from Spital and Taylor's article:

"The view that consent is an absolute requirement for cadaveric organ recovery has long been accepted as self-evident, and few experts in the field have seen the need to justify it. We agree that the premortem wishes of the deceased regarding the postmortem disposition of his or her property should generally be respected. However, we believe that the obligation to honor these (or the family's) wishes is prima facie, not absolute, and that it ceases to exist when the cost is unnecessary loss of human life, which is often precisely what happens when permission for organ recovery is denied. Therefore, given the current severe organ shortage and its implications for patients who are on the waiting list, we propose that the requirement for consent for cadaveric organ recovery be eliminated and that whenever a person dies with transplantable organs, these be recovered routinely. Consent for such recovery should be neither required nor sought."

Outline Spital and Taylor's argument in your own words, paying particular attention to the premises that they rely on to support their main conclusion. Choose one of the premises for evaluation. Try to think of at least one objection to this premise.

Case Study

The last year and a half has been a difficult time for Todd Frank and his brother Jim. Todd, only 32 years old at the time, was diagnosed with chronic kidney failure 18 months ago, and he has not been doing well. Nine months ago, Todd's kidney function declined to the point at which dialysis was required. Jim has cut back on his hours at a job at the assembly plant in order to accompany his brother to dialysis sessions three times a week. The four-hour sessions also take time away from Jim's wife, who also works, and their young daughter. While dialysis prevents the build-up of toxins in Todd's blood, he has been suffering from anemia and fatigue resulting from the treatments. He can no longer work, and wonders how he will pay the bills. A kidney transplant offers Todd the best chance at a better quality of life. Todd's nephrologist has placed him on the kidney transplant waiting list, but he is told it may be two years or more before a match for him is found. Jim is willing to donate one of his two healthy kidneys to his brother, but tests conducted a month ago revealed that his tissue type is not a close enough match for the transplant to have a good chance of success.

The nephrologist suggests that Todd and Jim enter into Canada's Living Donor Paired Exchange Registry.

The registry, launched in January 2009, facilitates living kidney donations by matching incompatible patient-donor pairs with other compatible donors and patients. Thus, if another incompatible patient-donor pair is in the registry, such that Jim is a match for the patient, and Todd is a match for the donor, both transplants can go ahead simultaneously. It is, put simply, an organ swap between otherwise incompatible patient-donor pairs. More complex exchanges are also possible within the registry. In 2009, the first multiple province "domino" kidney transplant was performed in Toronto, Edmonton, and Vancouver, involving three incompatible patient-donor pairs, an unpaired donor, and a high-priority patient on the transplant list. As of May 2011, 217 incompatible patient-donor pairs have been registered, and 75 transplants have been completed.

1. How does living organ donation avoid some of the challenges, both practical and ethical, involved with harvesting organs from the dead?

2. Compare the Living Donor Paired Exchange Registry with Erin and Harris' ethical market in human organs. Which is ethically preferable?

3. Should Todd and Jim enter the registry? Why?

Further Reading

BC Transplant [Internet]. Available from: http://www.transplant.bc.ca/index.asp. Date accessed: 6 June 2012.

Canadian Blood Services. Living Donor Paired Exchange (LDPE) registry [Internet]. Available from: http://www.ccdt.ca/english/ldpe/index.htm. Date accessed: 9 January 2012.

Canadian Medical Association. Organ and tissue donation and transplantation (update 2000) [Internet]. Available from: http://www.organsandtissues. ca/s/english-public/living-kidney-donation. Date accessed: 6 June 2012.

Childress JF, Liverman CT, eds. Organ donation: opportunities for action. A report from the Institute of Medicine [Internet]. Washington, D.C.: National Academies Press; 2006. Available from: http://www.iom.edu/Reports/2006/Organ-Donation-Opportunities-for-Action.aspx. Date accessed: 6 June 2012.

Norris S. Organ donation and transplantation in Canada. Parliamentary information and research service [Internet]. 25 June 2009. Available from: http://www2. parl.gc.ca/Content/LOP/ResearchPublications/ prb0824-e.htm. Date accessed: 6 June 2012.

Bioethics in a Pluralistic Society

The current chapter is the last of the core chapters of this textbook. To this point we have explored such topics as the ethics of abortion and assisted suicide, the ethics of using human embryos and adults in medical research, justice in health care, and the concepts of death and informed consent. These chapters explicitly function to exhibit the complexity of the most important bioethical issues that can and do present themselves in the typical human lifespan. They illustrate two further facts. First, that there is a thriving discussion about the most pressing bioethical issues in the period between life and death. Second, that there are deep and unsettled disagreements about these very same bioethical issues. This may not be a difficulty in the classroom where diversity of opinion is usually an asset. Indeed, it is a rather happy circumstance when it comes to discussing these very questions. It is, however, a problem when you are attempting to formulate public policy regulating the very issues about which there appears to be deep and lasting disagreement. The problem is that there appears to be no moral framework that is agreed to by all for the purpose of conducting bioethical reasoning. Policies and legislation regulating bioethical issues have a profound effect on our lives and on our well-being. They affect health care professionals who must decide what to do in the ethical dilemmas they face, patients and loved ones who are significantly affected by such decisions, and society at large. Therefore, they need to be compellingly justified to all. Without agreement on a method of ethical reasoning, however, this seems difficult to achieve.

One common mechanism for attempting to produce agreeable policy on bioethical matters in Canada is to put together a Royal Commission. This is the mechanism that Canada used in part to develop its policies on new reproductive technologies and on health care insurance. These bodies are to collect and analyze information from a wide variety of individuals belonging to a cross-section of society. On the basis of this information, they are to try to develop policy recommendations that will be acceptable to those who will be affected. To determine whether this mechanism or other options like it is a good way to proceed, we have to examine the range of views about the relationship between moral principles and public policy. The articles in this chapter address the issue of how to formulate public policy in societies in which people have deep bioethical and moral disagreements.

In his article, R. M. Hare discusses the relationship between moral principles and the justification of public policy. Hare canvasses three possible positions about this relationship: the view that morality has no place in the justification of public policy and that legislators ought to promote only the self-interest of those they govern; the view that there is a natural moral law that legislators ought to embody in the legislation they enact; and the position that legislators ought to consider the outcomes of their legislative options and then select the option that produces the best outcome. Hare opts for the last, which he calls consequentialism, arguing that the first two options encourage irresponsibility in governing, since they neglect at least some of the consequences relevant to the justification of legislation or public policy. Additionally, Hare appears to suggest that the consequentialist position more closely mirrors the fashion in which legislators do seek to justify their legislative decisions.

In his paper, Donald Ainslie argues for a Rawlsian or liberal view of the justification of public policies regulating bioethical issues. In Ainslie's view, the justification of such policies ought not to appeal to any particular moral doctrine, such as Hare's consequentialism, rival ethical theories or religious-based moral frameworks. Rather, it is important to recognize what the American political philosopher John Rawls calls the "fact of reasonable pluralism," i.e., that without committing any logical or factual errors, people reasoning under conditions of freedom arrive at distinct and conflicting views about how best to live and about what morality requires. To justify public policies by appeal to a controversial moral view would involve forcing those who disagree to live by policies that are not justified to them on grounds that they accept. Instead, Ainslie argues that bioethicists should seek to justify policies by reference to what those holding "reasonable" moral views can agree to. Ainslie goes on to argue that in addition to adopting this orientation toward public policy, bioethicists should assist in articulating ideas about what he calls the "bioethics of everyday life." This facilitates the aim of producing agreeable policies, and the aim of understanding the range of attitudes and values at work when people deal with disease and death, among other issues.

In the final reading of this chapter, Will Kymlicka discusses the role that moral philosophers should play in public policy decisions, especially those dealing with new reproductive technologies. Kymlicka focuses on government commissions, considering and rejecting two prominent views about the proper role of moral philosophers in this public policy context. The first, more ambitious view is that moral philosophers should convince government commissions to adopt and apply a specific, comprehensive moral framework, e.g., utilitarianism or Kantianism. Kymlicka rejects this on grounds that it is inconsistent with the aim of a commission, which is to arrive at policy prescriptions that are "acceptable to a variety of ethical perspectives." The second, more modest view is that the role of the moral philosopher in public policy is to facilitate the production of clear, consistent and cogent arguments. Kymlicka rejects this view on the grounds that a good argument may ignore important and compelling moral considerations. He advocates a position according to which commissions ought to take the moral point of view rather than moral philosophy seriously. This involves generating (1) a list of stakeholders or individuals who are affected by a policy's prescriptions; and (2) a list of principles or goals that the policy should advance or protect. He thinks that commissions that follow this method are much less likely to make moral mistakes or issue morally unsatisfactory policy prescriptions. There is little need for moral philosophy in this case, and, Kymlicka argues, moral philosophy may interfere with arriving at morally defensible public policy.

> **Utilitarianism**
> The moral doctrine according to which an agent's act is right insofar as it produces at least as much net well-being for the aggregate as any other action the agent could have performed in the same situation.

> **Kantianism**
> The anti-utilitarian moral doctrine inspired by the writings of the Prussian moral philosopher Immanuel Kant (1724–1804) according to which an action is permissible if it is capable of being willed as a universal moral imperative for all rational beings. Such a law is said to respect all rational beings as ends in themselves.

ONE   Public Policy in a Pluralist Society

R. M. Hare | In: Singer, P, Kuhse, H, Buckle, S, Dawson, K, Kasimba, P (eds.). *Embryo Experimentation.* New York: Cambridge University Press, 1990: 183-94.

What is the proper relation between the moral principles that should govern public policy, including legislation, and moral principles which may be held—often passionately — by individuals, including individual legislators? The adherents of such "personal" principles often object that proposed laws would allow people, or even compel them, to transgress the principles. Obvious examples are homosexuality and abortion law reform. People who think homosexuality an abominable sin object to the repeal of laws that make it a crime; and those who think that abortion is as wrong as murder of grown people object that a law permitting abortion in certain cases might make it permissible for other people to—as they would say—murder unborn children, or even, if they are nurses and want to keep their jobs, compel them to do so themselves. . . .

We live in a pluralist society, which means that the moral principles held sacred among different sections of society are divergent and often conflicting; and we live in a democratic society, in which, therefore policy and legislation have to be decided on by procedures involving voting by all of us or by our representatives; so the question becomes: what attention should we pay, whether we are legislators in parliaments or simply voters in a constituency, to the personal moral opinions of other people, or even to our own? . . .

But we cannot address this question until we have answered a prior one, namely: what consideration ought in general to be given to moral principles of any kind when framing legislation and policy? There are three positions on this which I wish to distinguish. The first two seem to me unacceptable, for reasons which I shall give. I will call the first the "keep morality out of polities" position. It holds that the function of policy and of legislation is to preserve the interests, which may be purely selfish interests, of the governed; if moral considerations seem to conflict with this function, they should be ignored. Politicians have a moral duty to subordinate, in their political actions, all *other* moral duties to that of preserving the interests of the governed. This position leaves them with just one moral duty. . . .

The difficulty with this position is that no reason is given by its advocates why that should be the politician's supreme and only duty. When a moral question is in dispute, as this one certainly is, we need some method, other than appeals to the convictions of those who maintain the position, of deciding whether to believe them or not. I shall, therefore, postpone discussion of this position until we are in possession of such a method, which will be after we have examined the third position.

The second position goes to the opposite extreme from the first. It holds that morality does apply to political actions and to legislation (very much so). The way it applies is this: there are perfect laws (laid up in heaven, as it were), to which all human laws ought morally to be made to conform. There are various versions of this position, which I shall call generically the, "natural law" position, although that expression also has other different uses. One version says that there is a moral law and that the function of ordinary positive laws is to copy this and add appropriate penalties and sanctions. Thus murder is wrong according to the moral law, and the function of positive law and the duty of the legislators is to make it illegal and impose a penalty. . . .

> **Natural law position**
> The view according to which there are objectively true moral requirements, which are part of nature and especially human nature. A central tenet of this view is that unjust laws are not really laws, since they are contrary to (objectively true) morality, and it would be wrong to use state force to make people act immorally, or to prevent them from acting morally.

The trouble with this position is very similar to that with the first and extreme opposite position. No way has been given of telling what is in the natural law, nor of telling what sins ought to be made crimes, and which crimes are also sins. That is why, when appeal is made to the natural law, or to a moral law to which positive laws morally ought to be made to conform, people disagree so radically about what in particular this requires legislators to do. To quote the great Danish jurist Alf Ross, "like a harlot, the natural law is at the disposal of everyone."[1] Here again we shall have to postpone discussion until we have a safe method of handling such questions as "How do we decide rationally, and not merely by appeal to prejudices dignified by the name of 'deep moral convictions,' what legislators morally ought to do?"

There is another, more serious, thing wrong with the second or natural law position. It assumes without argument that the only moral reason for passing laws is that they conform to the natural law. But there can be many reasons other than this why laws ought to be passed. If, for example, it is being debated whether the speed limit on freeways ought to be raised or lowered, the argument is not about whether it is in accordance with the moral or natural law that people should drive no faster than a certain speed. There may, certainly, be moral reasons, irrespective of any law, why people ought not to drive faster than, or slower than, a certain speed on certain parts of the freeways at certain times and under certain traffic and weather conditions. But that is not what legislators talk about. They talk about what the *consequences* of having a certain law would be. For example, they ask what effect a lower limit would have on the overall consumption or conservation of fuel; what the effect would be in total on the accident figures; whether a higher limit would make it necessary to adopt a higher and, therefore, more costly specification for the design of freeways; whether a lower limit would lead to widespread disregard of and perhaps contempt for the law; and so on. What they are asking, as responsible legislators, is not whether 100 or 110 kph conforms to the natural law, but what they would be doing, i.e. bringing about, if they passed a certain law.

And this requirement to consider what one is doing does not apply only to the decisions of legislators. What I have said responsible legislators do is what all responsible agents have to do if they are to act morally. To act is to do something, and the morality of the act depends on what one is doing. And what one is doing is bringing about certain changes in the events that would otherwise have taken place—altering the history of the universe in a certain respect. For example, if in pulling the trigger I would be causing someone's death, that is a different act from what it would be if I pointed my gun at the ground; and the difference is morally relevant. The difference in the morality of the acts is due to a difference in what I would be causing to happen if I tightened my finger on the trigger. This does not imply that I am responsible for *all* the consequences of my bodily movements. There are well-canvassed exceptions (accident, mistake, unavoidable ignorance, etc.), and there are many consequences of my bodily movements that I cannot know of and should not try, such as the displacement of particular molecules of air. Only some, not all, of the consequences are morally relevant.[2] But when allowance has been made for all this, what I am judged on morally is what I bring about.

It is sometimes held that we are only condemned for doing something when we *intend* to do it. This is right, properly understood. If we are judging the moral character of an agent, only what he does intentionally is relevant. But it is wrong to think that we can circumscribe intentions too narrowly for this purpose. There is a distinction, important for some purposes, between direct and oblique intentions. To intend some consequence directly one has to desire it. To intend it obliquely one has only to foresee it. But in the present context it is important

that oblique intentions as well as direct intentions are relevant to the morality of actions. We have the duty to avoid bringing about consequences that we ought not to bring about, even if we do not desire those consequences in themselves, provided only that we know that they will be consequences. I am to blame if I knowingly bring about someone's death in the course of some plan of mine, even if I do not desire his death in itself—that is, even if I intend the death only obliquely and not directly. As we shall see, this is very relevant to the decisions of legislators (many of whose intentions are oblique), in that they have a duty to consider consequences of their legislation that they can foresee, and not merely those that they desire.

The legislators are to be judged morally on what they are doing (i.e. bringing about) by passing their laws. They will be condemned morally, in the speed limit example, if they make the limit so high that the accident rate goes up significantly, or so low that it is universally disregarded and unenforceable and, as a result, the law is brought into disrespect. And this brings me to my third possible position on the question of how morality applies to law-making. I will call it the "consequentialist" position. It says that legislators, if they want to make their acts as legislators conform to morality (that is, to pass the laws they morally ought to pass and not those they ought not), they should look at what they would be doing if they passed them or threw them out. And this means what changes in society or in its environment they would be bringing about.

What legislators are doing, or trying to do, is to bring about a certain state of society rather than some other, so far as the law can effect this—that is, a state of society in which certain sorts of things happen. The legislators are not going themselves to be doing any of these things directly, though, as I have been maintaining, they will be bringing it about intentionally that the things happen, and the bringing about is an act of theirs. . . .

Consequentialism as a theory in moral philosophy, which I have been advocating, has received a lot of hostile criticism in recent years. This is because people have not understood what the consequentialist position is. I do not see how anybody could deny the position I have just outlined, because to deny it is to deny that what we are judged morally for (what we are responsible for) is our actions, i.e. what we bring about. What makes people look askance at what they call consequentialism is the thought that it might lead people to seek good consequences at the cost of doing what is morally wrong—as it is said, to do evil that good may come. But this is a misunderstanding. It would indeed be possible to bring about certain desirable consequences, at the cost of bringing about certain other consequences which we ought not to bring about. But if the whole of the consequences of our actions (what in sum we do) were what we ought to do, then we must have acted rightly, all things considered. . . .

It is now time to look again at the first two positions I distinguished. What is wrong with both of them is that they ignore what the third position rightly takes into account, namely the consequences of legislation and policy, that is, what the legislators and policy-makers are *doing* by their actions. In short, both these positions encourage irresponsibility in governments. The first position, indeed, does impose on governments a moral duty of responsibility so far as the interests of their subjects go. But what about the effects of their actions on the rest of the world? Ought the British government not to have thought about the interests of Australians when it arranged its notorious atomic tests at Maralinga? Ought it not now to think about acid rain in Norway when regulating power station emissions? . . . If we are speaking of moral duties, surely governments have duties to people in other countries. . . .

What I have called the natural law position is even more open to the charge of irresponsibility. It says that there are model laws laid up in heaven, and that the legislators have a duty to write these into the positive law of the land no matter what the consequences may be for those who have to live under them. This might not be so bad if we had any way of knowing what was in the model code. But we have not; all we have is a diversity of moral convictions, differing wildly from one another, without any reasons being given by those who hold them why we should agree with them. That is one of the facts of life in a pluralist society. So what happens in practice is that people set up pressure groups (churches are ready-made pressure groups, and there are others on both sides of most disputes), and produce rhetoric and propaganda in attempts to bounce the legislators into adopting their point of view. It cannot be denied that in the course of this exercise useful arguments may be produced on both sides. But when the legislators come to their own task, which is to decide what they morally ought to do, we could wish that they had more to go on than a lot of conflicting propaganda. There ought to be a way in which they can think about such matters rationally, and decide for themselves what they really ought to do. . . .

Reasoning about moral questions should start by asking what we would be doing if we followed a certain proposal. And what we would be doing is bringing about certain consequences. So what we have to ask first is: what consequences would we be bringing about if we followed it? That is what any responsible government, and any responsible committee advising a government, has to ask first.

It is not, of course, the last thing that they have to ask. They have then to go on to ask which of these consequences are ones that they morally ought to be trying to bring about and which not. But at least they will have made a good start if they have tried to find out what the consequences would be.

Study Questions

1. Why does Hare reject the natural law position? Is his criticism of the view compelling?

2. Hare considers three different views about the relationship between moral principles and the framing of public policies. What are they? Is he right to think that these are the only possible options?

3. At the end of his paper, Hare maintains that legislators need to determine which consequences "are ones that they morally ought to be trying to bring about and which not." What sort of consequences might be the most appropriate to appeal to in justifying public policies?

Notes

1. Ross, A., *On Law and Justice* (*Om ret og retfaerdighed*), trans. M. Dutton (London, Stevens, 1958).

2. Hare, R.M., *Moral Thinking* (Oxford University Press, Oxford, 1981), pp. 62 ff and references.

TWO Bioethics and the Problem of Pluralism

Donald C. Ainslie | *Social Philosophy and Policy* 2002; 19: 1-28.

Introduction

The state that we inhabit plays a significant role in shaping our lives. For not only do its institutions constrain the kinds of lives we can lead, but it also claims the right to punish us if our choices take us beyond what it deems to be appropriate limits. Political philosophers have traditionally tried to justify the state's power by appealing to their preferred theories of justice, as articulated in complex and wide-ranging moral theories—utilitarianism, Kantianism, and the like. One of John Rawls' greatest contributions to political philosophy has been his recognition that this is the wrong way for this field to approach its task. He points to what he calls "the fact of reasonable pluralism," which is the incontestable fact that in a free society people striving to lead their lives ethically will subscribe to conflicting moral and religious doctrines, many of which will be "reasonable" in the special sense of leaving their adherents willing to cooperate with those with whom they have moral disagreements.[1] And this means that political philosophers can no longer rely on any particular "comprehensive" doctrine in their attempts to justify the state. For doing so would be unfair to those who subscribe to a conflicting reasonable doctrine; it would mean that the coercive power of the state would not be justified *to them* in terms *they* can accept, even while they were forced to abide by its terms. Instead, Rawls suggests that the fundamentals of the state, that is, its "basic structure,"[2] should be governed by a "political conception of justice"—a set of norms for the basic structure of society—formulated not by appealing to any particular comprehensive doctrine, but by asking what those with reasonable and yet conflicting doctrines would agree to as the terms for their interaction.[3] Political philosophy is thus a "free-standing" endeavor with its own burdens of justification; it is not merely the application to the state of an independently justified moral theory.[4]

Bioethicists, like political philosophers, are in the business of providing norms for institutions that have enormous power over us. For our lives are at least in part shaped by the condition of our bodies, and health care professionals are empowered to intervene in our bodies with medications or surgery in order to help us in our attempts to overcome the constraints that disease and disability put on us. Bioethicists have sometimes tried to set the terms for the appropriate use of this biomedical power by appealing to their preferred moral theories—utilitarianism, Kantianism, and the like. I will argue in what follows that this is the wrong way for them to approach their task, for Rawls' insight about political philosophy also applies to bioethics: insofar as bioethicists attempt to formulate policy—either public health policy or norms for the health professions—they too must come to terms with the fact of reasonable pluralism. And this means that bioethicists cannot simply appeal to their preferred comprehensive moral doctrine to justify their policy suggestions; instead, they must show that their suggestions are justified to those with reasonable and yet conflicting doctrines. . . .

A Liberal Partition

My suggestion is that bioethics should be seen as free-standing in relation to comprehensive moral doctrines, just as Rawls thinks that political philosophy is. In each case, the norms that are to apply to all members of society—whether as citizens or as participants in the delivery of health care—are justified not by appeal to any particular comprehensive doctrine, but in terms that those with conflicting yet reasonable doctrines can accept. . . . When considering how best we should live, what we should value,

---

> **The fact of reasonable pluralism**
> The fact that without making any factual or logical errors, individuals who live in free societies will arrive at distinct and conflicting views about how best to live and about the demands of morality.

> **Comprehensive doctrine**
> A system of values and beliefs about the fundamental requirements of morality and about how best to lead one's life, e.g., Catholicism and utilitarianism.

> **Basic structure of society**
> This notion as it is used by John Rawls refers to the features of society to which principles of justice primarily apply; it comprises such things as our rights and freedoms, the family, and the economy.

whom we should admire, and so on, we must rely on comprehensive moral doctrines with their aspirations toward a general theory of the good. But when attempting to formulate policy that will put limits on what any of us can do with our lives, theorists—in political philosophy and policy-oriented bioethics—must show to those whose lives are to be constrained that they have reason to accept it despite their disagreements over comprehensive doctrines.

The appropriateness of the Rawlsian distinction for formulating policies on the allocation of scarce resources or the distribution of health care—questions directly linked to justice in health care—is especially clear. These questions are best treated in terms of the proper organization of the basic structure of society. But, interestingly, Rawls himself has never addressed these issues largely because, as he admits, the complexities arising from human embodiment drop from view in his theory.[5] He emphasizes that the political conception of justice he endorses is to act as an ideal, something that we should use as a goal as we go about the messy business of reforming our particular society. We are to construct a conception of justice that best serves our sense of ourselves as sources of value *throughout complete, healthy lives*—as agents with fairly clear comprehensive moral doctrines, coherent life-plans formulated in light of these doctrines, and the rational capacities needed for living together with other such agents—all the while recognizing the many ways in which we fall short of this description.[6]. . .

One central question for bioethics arises when we move from the ideal to the nonideal case: what is the duty of the state to its citizens when they are in need of health care? Given my desire in this essay to stay neutral on the content that a political conception of justice should have, I cannot hope to answer this question here.[7] But it is important to note that the move to non-ideal theory that any such answer would require does not mean that we could once more resort to idiosyncratic features of particular comprehensive moral doctrines. For, if an answer is to be justified to all members of society, we should continue to use what Rawls calls "public reason," that is, reason based in the recognition that we are to cooperate on reasonable terms with those who differ from us in their substantive moral commitments. I do not mean to suggest that seeing an issue like the right to health care from a Rawlsian perspective guarantees that

there is an easy resolution. It is by no means clear what position on health care can be justified to people who have reasonable disagreements about the nature of justice, the duty of charity, the moral status of the body, and so on. What Rawls helps us to see is that the task of bioethicists is not to resolve these disagreements, but to see what policy can be justified to people despite their disagreements.[8]. . .

What are we to do with those whose moral commitments lead them to reject the political conception of justice (whatever its content turns out to be) that is to ground all social policies in a liberal society? Rawls' solution to this problem involves a distinction between what he calls *reasonable* and *unreasonable* comprehensive doctrines.[9] A comprehensive doctrine is reasonable if it includes an acceptance of the fact of pluralism and a concomitant willingness to live within the terms set down by the political conception of justice. Thus, a reasonable comprehensive doctrine does not claim to contain a moral truth to which the rest of society should be forced to adhere, whether those people accept the tenets of that doctrine or not. An unreasonable comprehensive doctrine leads its subscribers to reject the idea of cooperation with those whose comprehensive doctrines differ from theirs. It is people who are intolerant in this sense—in their unwillingness to live peacefully, on terms acceptable to all, among those with whom they have moral disagreements—whom Rawls thinks that a liberal society cannot tolerate. Accordingly, he argues that the state can legitimately take steps to prevent those with unreasonable comprehensive doctrines from interfering with the lives of others.[10]

Rawls' distinction allows for a response to the justice-rejecting Nietzschean [who] . . . might even think that *any* conception of justice is an unjustified constraint on one's power that only reflects the interests of the weak. Why, then, should he accept the organ-distribution network established by the state rather than pursuing a needed transplant by any means that he has at his disposal? . . . Rawls allows us to say not that we are compelling him to accept our particular moral commitments, but that since justice is what allows us to live together *despite* our different moral commitments, we can compel him to follow its terms simply in order for society to be possible.

While it is fairly easy to see the applicability of the Rawlsian approach to those bioethical issues having to do with justice, it is less easy to apply it to bioethical questions concerning the physician-patient relation-ship and other aspects of professional ethics, because they do not concern the basic structure of society. . . .

The problem . . . is that medicine . . . concerns our bodies.[11]. . . Even though different comprehensive moral doctrines will ascribe different values to our bodies—indeed, different doctrines will understand the metaphysics of our relation to our bodies differ-ently . . . —they nonetheless must be recognized as having a special place in our lives. They are, after all, the unique[12] vehicles for our lives, the artificial and organic replaceability of some parts notwithstanding. What we can do in the world thus depends on our physical condition; pain and suffering can undermine even our capacity to think clearly. This means that we cannot remain neutral about our bodies in the way we might about a car. A harm to my body is a harm *to me*, even if my moral commitments require me to rise above the limits that my body puts on me.[13]

But given the significance of our bodies to us, who should be allowed to intervene in them? Given that our different comprehensive doctrines lead us to make sense of this significance in diverse ways, health professionals cannot simply appeal to their own particular doctrines in deciding to operate on someone, to give her drugs, or the like, even if they do it with the best intentions. For if the intervention fails to accord with the person's comprehensive doctrine, she has been given no reason to accept the interven-tion; she can legitimately view it as an assault. . . . The doctrine of informed consent offers a solution to this problem, however, by allowing each of us to use our own comprehensive doctrines to decide what happens to our bodies, if that is at all possible. It thus sets up conditions for bodily access that we can all accept, despite our different moral commitments. . . . On my view, no claim is being made about the ultim-ate moral importance of autonomy since that issue is best left to people to deal with in their own compre-hensive doctrines. Instead, we say to those who do not value autonomy that their informed consent is still necessary in medical care, not because they should hold this value, but because the terms for our living together in a society despite our different moral commitments require that each person make her own decisions about her body (even if her decision is to defer to the relevant man in her life). For this is the only way to allow each of us to subscribe to our own moral doctrines and yet still live together.

My analysis of the status of the body in a liberal approach also offers us a way to understand two other principles—beneficence and non-maleficence. Once we recognize that we must allow our own compre-hensive values to remain paramount in issues arising from our embodiment, we must also consider how to enable us best to have them play this role. For when we are sick or otherwise in need of health care, we are especially vulnerable and open to exploitation. In particular, we are unable to negotiate contracts on a case-by-case basis with those who offer medical services.[14] Instead, bioethicists rightly urge that the medical profession itself must be structured in keep-ing with an understanding of the significance of bod-ily interventions. In reflecting on what this structure should look like, they ask: how can medical care be arranged so as best to guarantee that patients consent freely to the actions done to their bodies? And, given the desperation that often comes with illness, how can patients be protected from possible exploitation at the hands of medical-service providers? The prin-ciples that health professionals should act in their patients' best interests (beneficence) and in such a way that does not harm them (non-maleficence)—where what a patient's interests are and what counts as a harm are left to him to decide for himself, if pos-sible—are the answers to these questions. Patients are thus able to take at face value the information offered to them about the details of their care; they will be in a better position to decide which health choices most reflect their own values—that is, to make an informed choice. . . .

On my view, the defense of beneficence and non-maleficence is not based on a moral claim that we should all respect—such a claim belongs only in comprehensive doctrines. Instead, it is based on the pragmatic need to structure health-care institutions to promote patients' capacity to consent freely to care. . . .

The Bioethics of Everyday Life

We have seen that the liberal partition for bioethics that I have been advocating would require structur-ing health care institutions so that people can live in terms of their own reasonable comprehensive doc-trines when it comes to disease and health. Notice, however, that the liberal partition has another con-sequence for bioethics. Since it demands that we be able to make decisions about health and disease for ourselves, our comprehensive doctrines must be able to offer us guidance on these matters. But, just as contemporary bioethics got its start when policymakers found themselves somewhat at a loss when first confronted with the revolution in medical technology, so also many of us are ill-prepared to come to terms with the decisions we must face in the current medical world. Our comprehensive doctrines often fail to equip us adequately for what liberal bioethical policies impose on us.

The liberal partition, then, not only requires that bioethicists formulate norms for biomedical policy using the fact of reasonable pluralism as their starting point, it also requires that they engage in what I call the *bioethics of everyday life*—a consideration of what values we ought to hold on issues relating to our status as embodied beings who suffer from illness and death, who can alter our bodies cosmetically, who can infect one another with various diseases, who can find out about some aspects of our biological futures through genetic testing, and so on.[15] The aim here is not to formulate policies that everyone must be compelled to accept, but to explore the moral options open to us when we try to make sense of our biological natures. This involves elaborating and extending our comprehensive doctrines, all the while recognizing that reasonable people might reach different verdicts in this domain.

The two tasks—policy-oriented bioethics and the bioethics of everyday life—are complementary; they are not just two different perspectives from which the same issues can be addressed. For example, consider the policy question: when is it acceptable for health professionals to withhold or withdraw life-sustaining treatments from patients? There is an equivalent question from patients' perspectives: can patients require that their physicians remove them from (or keep them attached to) life-sustaining treatments? Neither of these asks a question in the bioethics of everyday life.

For they still fundamentally concern a question of policy, one that must be answered in light of the fact that reasonable people differ in their moral convictions about the end of life and the physician-patient relationship. The complementary question from the bioethics of everyday life to these two policy-oriented questions asks: what is the morally preferable way to die—ongoing medical treatment, which is likely to lead to a lingering decline but leaves open the possibility of recovery, or an almost certain death by having the treatment in question removed? Answering this question will require thinking through the disvalue of death, and the moral significance of acquiescence to it as opposed to struggle against it. Such an answer will likely involve a consideration of some of the deepest moral issues, such as the source of meaning in life and the importance of our directing the shape of our lives. . . .

My analysis helps to show the importance of this kind of work. For without ongoing exploration in the bioethics of everyday life, policy-oriented bioethics ends up being somewhat incoherent, at least in its liberal guise. For why set up policies that promote the ability of people to make decisions for themselves if they are not equipped to do so? At the moment, most comprehensive doctrines, especially nonreligious ones, have little to say about the moral significance of our struggles with disease, our reproductive choices, and the like, even though bioethical policy often requires that we address these very issues. Imagine a comparable situation in political philosophy: a liberal state combined with a lack of attention to how we should live. Philosophers here would be urging the state to recognize the importance of people's living by their own values, but would also at the same time be refusing to treat those values as being important enough to merit study and reflection. Bioethicists, like moral philosophers, must work on both sides of the partition I am advocating. . . .

Study Questions

1. Why does Ainslie describe his position as liberal?
2. What is the difference between policy-oriented bioethics and the bioethics of everyday life?
3. Which values (if any) does an individual have to be committed to in order to be convinced of the Rawlsian methodology to which Ainslie appeals?

Notes

1. John Rawls, *Political Liberalism* (New York: Columbia University Press, 1993), xvi–xviii. Note, then, that Rawls distinguishes between the fact of pluralism and the fact of *reasonable* pluralism (xvii). The former points only to the fact that people disagree about morality, sometimes quite radically. The latter points to those cases where these disagreements are reasonable, in a special sense noted here (see Section V below).

2. Ibid., 257–88.

3. Ibid., 11–15.

4. Ibid., 10.

5. Ibid., 184.

6. Ibid., 281–5. See also Rawls, *A Theory of Justice*, 8–9, 245–6.

7. Norman Daniels uses a Rawlsian strategy to confront the problem of whether justice could require a state to offer its citizens health care when they reasonably differ on the moral importance of bodily health. His solution is to draw an analogy with Rawls' principle of fair equality of opportunity. Just as the state must guarantee that offices and positions are open to all who have the relevant skills and talents, it should also aim to preserve people's access to the range of life-plans that would be open to them were they to be healthy throughout their lives; see Norman Daniels, *Just Health Care* (Cambridge: Cambridge University Press, 1985), 19–58. Even though Daniels' argument draws only on the version of Rawls' theory in *A Theory of Justice*—before Rawls acknowledged the significance of the fact of reasonable pluralism and the need for a political conception of justice—Rawls supports Daniels' approach at *Political Liberalism*, 184.

8. As Rawls points out when discussing the problem of abortion, "[r]easonable political conceptions of justice do not always lead to the same conclusion," in which case deciding by a vote might be the best means to settle issues of public policy (John Rawls, "The Idea of Public Reason Revisited," *University of Chicago Law Review* 64, no. 3 [1997]: 798).

9. Rawls, *Political Liberalism*, 58–66.

10. Rawls points out, however, that the mere fact that people hold an unreasonable doctrine does not legitimate the state's limiting their freedom. For they might also hold that they are required to follow the law even when it supports what they see to be immoral kinds of behavior. It is only when people who are pursuing their unreasonable moral doctrine actively interfere with others that the state should step in to protect the victims of their activities; see Rawls, *A Theory of Justice*, 216–21.

11. See Gerald Dworkin, *The Theory and Practice of Autonomy*, (Cambridge: Cambridge University Press, 1988) 113–14, for a similar account of the special place of the body.

12. Some comprehensive doctrines do allow for the possibility of reincarnation. Nonetheless, even on these views, one's body for a given lifetime is irreplaceable.

13. Political philosophy acknowledges the special status of the body in its treatment of punishment, which ultimately involves a bodily intervention of some sort, such as medication, amputation, the physical restriction of movement, or the infliction of pain; even the payment of a fine must be enforceable by bodily measures, and a bodily measure must be supplied as an alternative for those lacking monetary resources. Now, if citizens were allowed to decide for themselves on which occasions such bodily interventions were warranted, the one receiving the punishment could reasonably complain that he or she was being treated unfairly. Thus, the state should instead set up a monopoly on bodily interventions—a legal and penal system—that is fair to all, one that those in the original position would recognize as needed, given the evident necessity of an enforcement mechanism for the preservation of society. Accordingly, the *political conception of the person*, which Rawls uses to characterize citizens within a political conception of justice (Rawls, *Political Liberalism*, 29–35), must include as a complement a *political conception of the body*. Each person is entitled to integrate the status of embodiment into her comprehensive doctrine in any reasonable fashion, but the state preserves a right to bodily access (when mandated by a suitably constituted system of justice) in order to enforce the norms that make society possible.

    Note that the issue of punishment takes us beyond ideal theory, where there is an assumption of full compliance (Rawls, *A Theory of Justice*, 145, but see also ibid., 240–1). Thus, the body plays a role in extending ideal theory in two respects: in accounting for responses to injustice and in accounting for natural limitations such as disease and disability.

14. The institutional complexity of modern medicine makes this point readily apparent. A hospital, for example, cannot tailor its procedures to meet the exact requirements of each individual who enters it; instead, the institution aims to promote beneficent and non-maleficent care, leaving patients the right to make the final choices about their care within those constraints.

15. The German rationalists, from Baron Christian von Wolff onward, constitute one tradition of moral thought that has recognized the need for a bioethics of everyday life, that is, for a consideration of the moral questions posed by our biological natures. See, for example, Kant's discussion of "man's duty to himself as an animal being," where he rejects such things as castration (to improve one's singing career), selling one's hair, gluttony, and nonreproductive sexual activities, in Immanuel Kant, *The Metaphysics of Morals*, trans. Mary Gregor (Cambridge: Cambridge University Press, 1991), 218–24.

    Engelhardt sometimes sounds as if he means by his "bioethics of moral friends"—bioethics for those who share comprehensive doctrines—what I call the bioethics of everyday life; see Engelhardt, *The Foundations of Bioethics*, (New York: Oxford University Press, 1986, 1996) 14, 74–5 (2nd ed). But sometimes he restricts all kinds of bioethics to the policy-oriented questions, as when he says that "moral visions give rise to content-full bioethics and offer substantive guidance about how one should properly act as patient, physician, nurse, or citizen framing health care policy. This volume does not address these moralities and the bioethics they support. It does not explore the particular content-full morality that ought to shape the bioethics and guide the health care policy through which moral friends can collaborate" (ibid., 102).

THREE Moral Philosophy and Public Policy:
The Case of New Reproductive Technologies

Will Kymlicka | In: Sumner, LW, Boyle J (eds.). *Philosophical Perspectives on Bioethics.*
Toronto: University of Toronto Press, 1996: 244-70.

Introduction

In this paper I will express some reservations about the usefulness of moral philosophy for the analysis of public policy issues. I want to emphasize right away, however, that I am not questioning the importance of morality. On the contrary, I take it as a given that morality is important, that moral considerations should be given their due weight in public policy deliberations, and indeed should have primacy. Policy-makers should do the right thing, morally speaking. Moreover, I believe that constant vigilance is required to ensure that moral considerations are not drowned out by the forces of self-interest, prejudice, or inertia, and that the moral viewpoint is not submerged underneath a more narrowly scientific, economic, or political viewpoint. My question is whether taking *morality* seriously requires taking *moral philosophy* seriously.

This paper focuses on one particular public policy context—namely, government commissions into new reproductive technologies (NRTs),[1] such as Britain's Warnock Committee,[2] Australia's Waller and Michael Committees,[3] Canada's Baird Commission,[4] and many others.[5] These commissions share a number of features: (1) the members of the commission, who usually number from five to sixteen, come from various backgrounds, such as law, social work, medicine, and the church, and they represent a wide range of interests and perspectives; (2) they are asked to consider the social, legal, economic, and ethical implications of NRTs for the purpose of developing appropriate public policy recommendations; and (3) in the process of developing recommendations, the commissions generally conduct some form of public consultations and often seek out expert advice on various medical, legal, and ethical issues.

Moral philosophers are sometimes asked to participate in these commissions, either as commissioners, staff, or expert advisers. How can moral philosophers contribute to the analysis of public policy recommendations on NRTs? A survey of the literature suggests that there are two main views on this question, one of which is ambitious, the other more

modest. The ambitious view says that moral philosophers should attempt to persuade commissioners to adopt the right comprehensive moral theory (e.g., adopt a deontological theory, rather than utilitarianism) and then apply this theory to particular policy questions. The more modest view shies away from promoting a particular moral theory, given that the relative merits of different moral theories are a subject of dispute even among moral philosophers. Instead, it says that moral philosophers should

> **Deontological theory**
> A moral view according to which factors other than good consequences or outcomes matter to the moral status of actions. A typical version of this view states that one ought to tell the truth even though this may have worse consequences than lying or that one ought to refrain from harming people even though this produces worse outcomes than harming them.

attempt to ensure that the commission's arguments are clear and consistent. On this view, philosophers should focus on identifying conceptual confusions or logical inconsistencies within the commission's arguments, without seeking to influence its choice of the underlying theory. . . .

The Ambitious View: Selecting a Comprehensive Moral Theory

Proponents of the ambitious view believe that government commissions should adopt a comprehensive moral theory and apply it to the various ethical issues raised by NRTs. . . . The idea of seeking a single moral theory is actually quite inappropriate. . . . Citizens generally have different views on these issues, and commissioners are chosen to represent different viewpoints.[6] Hence they are expected to come up with recommendations that, so far as possible, are acceptable to a variety of ethical perspectives. Government commissions are instruments within the system of representative democracy. Like elected representatives in parliament, commissions are intended to be representative of the general community, although, unlike elected representatives, they are intended to be insulated somewhat from the day-to-day pressures of interest groups and power politics. This is intended to allow more room for flexibility, for reasonable (as opposed to purely political) compromise, and for long-term (rather than short-term) policy initiatives. This increased room for persuasion and flexibility, however, cannot, and is not intended to, displace the need for recommendations that are acceptable to a wide range of view points. The adoption of a particular ethical theory, therefore, not only is unrealistic, it defeats the purpose of the commission.

The Modest View: Philosophers as Technicians

Some philosophers recognize the impossibility of arriving at a consensus on an ethical theory. They focus their attention on the more modest goal of ensuring that a commission's arguments are clear and consistent. . . .

If the first view of the role of philosophers is too ambitious, this one is far too modest. These authors make it sound like the role of philosophers is to be technicians, ensuring that the internal plumbing of the report is sound. The problem is that arguments can be clear and consistent and yet be morally bankrupt. An argument can be clear and consistent and yet give no weight to any moral considerations or submerge them beneath economic or prudential considerations. I'm sure that proponents of the modest view believe that morality is important, and that NRTs should be examined from a moral perspective, as well from a scientific, economic, or political perspective. But neither the modest nor the ambitious view actually does much to explain what it means to look at issues from a moral perspective.[7] . . .

From a moral point of view, all people matter in and of themselves. It matters how well their lives go, and if our decisions affect their wellbeing, then we must take that fact into account. Adopting the moral point of view, therefore, requires that we sympathetically attend to people's interests and circumstances, try to understand how things look from their point of view, and give due weight to their wellbeing. Adopting the moral point of view requires that we "put ourselves in other people's shoes" and ensure that our actions are acceptable from their point of view as well as our own. . . .

If this account of the moral point of view is right, then we can see what is wrong with both the ambitious and the modest views of the role of philosophers. Both assume that taking morality seriously requires taking moral philosophy seriously—whether it be a philosophical theory (on the ambitious view), or a philosophical skill (on the modest view). But this assumption is misplaced. Taking morality seriously, in the first instance, requires taking *people* seriously—showing concern for people's lives and interests.[8]

A Third Approach

How do we take people seriously? First, by identifying which people are affected by NRTs. Second, by ensuring that NRTs are used in such a way as to promote, or at any rate not to harm, their legitimate interests. This suggestion is only an outline, of course. But I think it helps point out what, in the first instance, is needed to write a morally responsible report. We need a list of affected parties (or "stakeholders"), and a list of their legitimate interests.

We can call the first list our "stakeholder list." The stakeholder list tells us to consider how each recommendation affects the various stakeholders: that is, women; people with disabilities; visible minorities; children; gays and lesbians; as well as doctors and patients. How do we identify these stakeholders? To a large extent, they identify themselves through the public consultations process, either directly or indirectly (e.g., through advocates for children or the disabled). We can identify the stakeholders by listening to the public, and seeing who expresses a concern about the impact of NRTs.

We can call the second list our "guiding principles."[9] The guiding principles identify the legitimate interests and goals that must be considered when the impact of NRTs on the various stakeholders is considered. These interests and goals include:

1. autonomy (including informed consent);
2. accountability;
3. respect for human life;
4. equality (both in the general sense of promoting equal respect for all members of the community by combating prejudice and discrimination, and the more specific sense of equal access to health care);
5. the appropriate use of resources (ensuring that funding decisions are made in the light of health care priorities);
6. the non-commercialization of reproduction; and
7. protection of the vulnerable (including children).

. . . I think that each identifies a legitimate and distinct goal of public policy, and since we are aiming for a useful checklist of interests and goals, they are worth being listed separately.

Where do these principles come from? Evidence from the public consultations held by Canada's Royal Commission suggests that there is in fact a general consensus on these goals, at least in Canada.[10] The principles were endorsed by all sectors of society who appeared before the commission, and I believe the same would be true of most other western democracies.

Of course, the fact that there is a consensus on these principles does not show that they are morally defensible. They could merely reflect arbitrary cultural prejudices. However, there are two reasons for moral confidence in this consensus. First, the fact that these principles were endorsed by such a broad range of groups—professional and lay, men and women, religious and secular, visible minorities, the disabled, doctors and patients—as well as by many international inquiries—suggests that they capture important moral values. The fact that they are endorsed by the marginalized and disadvantaged, as well as the vocal and powerful, suggests that they are not merely the biases of a particular group or tradition.[11]

Second, the principles are consistent with the moral point of view. For example, once we put ourselves in other people's shoes, it is only natural that we will affirm the importance of respecting their points of view (the autonomy principle) and of protecting those who are unable to look after themselves (protecting the vulnerable principle). All of the principles are consistent with, and indeed help spell out, the belief that each person matters in and of herself.[12] . . .

People do not need to subscribe to a particular moral theory in order to evaluate what counts as a good reason. The fact that a policy will promote the child's interests is clearly a good reason for endorsing that policy. The public and policy-makers accept this as a good reason, even though they may not have adopted or even understand specific moral theories. Anyone who doubts whether promoting the child's interests counts as a moral good is lacking in the most basic ethical sensibilities. He or she has failed to understand what it means to look at things from the moral point of view. . . .

So we have a list of stakeholders and a list of guiding principles, neither of which requires adopting a comprehensive moral theory. These lists provide the essential basis for a morally responsible government

report, because they ensure that the commission will take people's lives and interests seriously. Using these two checklists, a government commission can consider people's interests with empathy. It can consider the fate of the weak and marginalized, as well as the legitimate interests of the more vocal or powerful. A responsible commission will do what it can to put itself in the shoes of all those who are affected by NRTs, to take those effects into account in its recommendations, and to seek creative policies that accommodate them wherever possible. . . .

I believe that a commission that does these things properly cannot go too far wrong, morally speaking, even if it is entirely lacking in philosophical sophistication. Conversely, commissions that do not use these checklists are likely to produce morally flawed reports, no matter how philosophically sophisticated they are. . . .

Using this checklist, of course, won't solve all the ethical problems raised by NRTs. Some potential conflicts between principles cannot be eliminated, no matter how creative we are, and then we are faced with a difficult decision regarding the relative weighing of competing principles. In these circumstances the commissioners will have to balance the competing principles as best they can, giving due weight to each. This is similar to the process of balancing values that judges are often confronted with. In both contexts, we have a rough sense of when the process is being carried out impartially and when someone is unduly biased towards particular interests.

Of course, this talk of "balancing" values, or of giving principles their "due weight," is not very helpful from a philosophical standpoint. Without a comprehensive moral theory, the justification for giving priority to some principles over others in a particular context may seem sketchy and unsatisfying. Some philosophers pick up on this fact and insist that because we may face certain kinds of conflicts between principles at the end of the day, and because only a comprehensive moral theory can give a fully satisfactory explanation of why some principles take precedence over others, we therefore should adopt a comprehensive moral theory at the beginning of the day.

There are reasons for resisting this advice. First, most disagreements over NRTs are not about how to weigh conflicting principles. Rather, the disagreements are about facts. Generally speaking, most of the public's concerns over NRTs are of the "slippery slope" variety. That is, some people believe that NRTs will (over time) reduce the status of women in society, lead to intolerance of those who are disabled, undermine family stability, lead to eugenics, etc. On this view, the use of NRTs will inevitably lead to the abuse of NRTs. Other people think that NRTs won't have these negative effects, and that society is capable of regulating any possible abuses. This view reflects a deep disagreement in society, but it is not a disagreement over values.[13] Everyone agrees that eugenics is wrong, that prejudice against women or the disabled is wrong, that family instability is undesirable, etc. They simply disagree about whether NRTs will have any of these implications, and this disagreement, in turn, often reflects differences in power—that is, some of those who are most concerned about the implications of NRTs are those who feel that they have no say over the future development.

We can go a long way towards resolving these conflicts by finding more reliable or more conclusive evidence and by establishing regulatory schemes that give all groups in society the feeling that they have some input over the future development of NRTs. Adopting a comprehensive moral theory is neither necessary nor relevant to resolving these conflicts, since the conflicts are not about competing fundamental principles. . . .

For all these reasons, I believe that a government commission into NRTs can go a long way in its moral deliberations on the basis of relatively uncontroversial guiding principles. This may not be true of government commissions into other bioethical issues, where conflicts between principles are both more common and more pressing. However, it may be unrealistic to suppose that government commissions would be of much help in these cases, which is why no one (to my knowledge) has proposed a royal commission on abortion in Canada. If the only issue on the table is that of conflicting principles, then we know in advance that any commission that is representative of Canadians will not come to a consensus but rather will divide along familiar lines. A commission on reproductive health care only is useful if there are other kinds of issues, other ways of responding to public concerns that do not entail having to resolve divisive issues of moral philosophy. I think this is precisely the case with public concerns about NRTs.

Appealing to guiding principles may be inadequate as an approach to bioethics in other contexts,[14] but it is, I believe, uniquely appropriate for public policy deliberations on issues such as NRTs. To expect a more sophisticated moral theory in this context is unnecessary and unrealistic. . . .

It may be that we can't expect philosophical acumen from commission reports, no matter how morally committed the commissioners are. Morally serious deliberations in these contexts may often lead to philosophically superficial reports. Conversely, philosophically sophisticated reports may be full of moral hypocrisy and insensitivity. This possibility suggests that a greater understanding of moral philosophy would not necessarily improve government reports on NRTs from a moral point of view. On the contrary, I believe that attempts to immerse policy-makers in academic philosophy may be partly responsible for the lack of moral seriousness and sensitivity found in many government reports. . . .

I worry that taking philosophy seriously may undermine people's confidence in their everyday moral sensibilities. The problem . . . is that . . . moral theories are very controversial, and the debates between them can be quite confusing. People's confusion at the philosophical level may then erode their confidence at the level of everyday principles. . . . Given that moral commitment is always threatened by the forces of self-interest, prejudice, and inertia, anything that discourages people from giving morality its due weight should be resisted, including moral philosophy. . . .

Study Questions

1. Kymlicka considers three different roles for the moral philosopher in the context of advising or serving on government commissions. What are they? Is he right to think that these are the only roles?

2. Kymlicka appeals to a number of moral attitudes that in his view remain beyond doubt. Does this limit the appeal of his view? Explain your answer.

3. Kymlicka claims that the study of moral philosophy may undermine "people's confidence in their everyday moral sensibilities" and that this may mean that those serving on government commissions should be discouraged from immersing themselves in moral philosophy. Is this a persuasive view?

Notes

1. The term "new reproductive technologies" often encompasses three different kinds of procedures or technologies: (1) procedures intended to assist individuals or couples to conceive a child (e.g., artificial insemination, *in vitro* fertilization, and surrogate childbearing); (2) procedures intended to assess or promote the health of the embryo or fetus after conception (e.g. prenatal diagnosis, sex selection, embryo therapy or fetal surgery, and judicial intervention in pregnancy); and (3) the use of human gametes, embryos, or fetuses in research (e.g. embryo experimentation, or the use of fetal tissue transplants in the treatment of Parkinson's Disease). Some government commissions into NRTs were asked to address all of these procedures; others focused primarily on (1) or (2). I shall be using the term "NRTs" to refer to all three of these procedures.

2. Department of Health and Social Security, *Report of the Committee of Inquiry into Human Fertilization and Embryology,* London, 1984.

3. Western Australia Government, *Report of the Committee to Enquire into the Social, Legal, and Ethical Issues Relating to In Vitro Fertilization and Its Supervision,* Perth, 1986 (the Michael Committee); Victorian Government, Committee to Consider the Social, Ethical and Legal Issues Arising from *In Vitro* Fertilization, *Report on Donor Gametes in IVF,* Melbourne 1983, and *Report on the Disposition of Embryos Produced by In Vitro Fertilization,* Melbourne 1984 (the Waller Committee).

4. Royal Commission on New Reproductive Technologies, *Proceed with Care: Final Report of the Royal Commission on New Reproductive Technologies,* 2 volumes, Ottawa, 1993 (the Baird Commission).

5. LeRoy Walters identified eighty-five committee statements on NRTs from twenty-five countries in the period from 1979 to 1987, of which he reviewed fifteen in depth; "Ethics and New Reproductive Technologies: An International Review of Committee Statements," *Hastings Center Report,* Special Supplement, June 1987, pp. 3–9. The number has at least doubled since then. In researching this paper, I have focused on government commission reports from Australia, Canada, Great Britain, and the United States, of which there are over forty.

6. Of course, very few people, other than moral philosophers, identify themselves as "contractualists" or "utilitarians." Most people carry around a mixture of utilitarian, contractarian, and other ideas, combined in often unreflective ways. There are important differences in ethical perspective between different groups in society, however, and a government commission must take account of this fact.

7. In another discussion, Singer does attempt to give an account of the moral point of view that should inform government commissions on NRTs. He says, "we all agree on enough basic ethical principles to make it unnecessary to prejudice the argument with . . . controversial assumptions." According to Singer, we all can agree on the importance of meeting needs and avoiding suffering: "To see their validity, all we have to do is to think about the significance our own needs and desires have for us and then apply the Golden Rule so that we allow to others as much significance for their needs and desires as we would have them allow to ours. The outcomes of this kind of 'universalizing' of

our own needs and desires is a concern for the welfare of everyone;" Singer and Deane Wells, *Making Babies: The New Science and Ethics of Conception* (New York: Charles Scribner's Sons, 1985), p. 181. This is closer to the approach I defend in the next section. Wikler may have a similar idea in mind when he talks about the value of "reasoning from shared premises," rather than from a comprehensive moral theory (see n14). Neither Wikler nor Singer, however, gives this idea of a moral point of view the sort of centrality, or priority, that I think is required. For a related discussion, see Forsman and Wellin, *The Treatment of Ethics in a Swedish Government Commission on Gene Technology,* Centre for Research Ethics, Göteburg, 1995–Studies in Research Ethics #6, pp. 34–5.

8. More accurately, morality requires taking sentient life seriously, human or animal. For a discussion of the status of non-human animals within moral theory, see Will Kymlicka and Paola Cavalieri, "Expanding the Social Contract," *Etica & Animali* Vol. 8, 1996, pp. 5–33.

9. The term "principles" is perhaps misleading, since the seven "principles" state legitimate interests or goals, not decision-making rules. For a helpful discussion of this issue, see Bernard Gert and K Clouser, "A Critique of Principlism," *Journal of Medicine and Philosophy,* Vol. 15, 1990, p. 222.

10. For a summary of the views presented in these public hearings, see *What We Heard: Issues and Questions Raised during the Public Hearings,* Royal Commission on New Reproductive Technologies, Ottawa, September 1991. Of the 296 individuals and groups who appeared at the public hearings, seventy-five endorsed a list of specific guiding principles. The seven principles listed in the text constitute clear points of consensus among these witnesses, representing a wide range of groups in society. For a detailed analysis of the moral arguments made during the public hearings, with particular attention to the principles endorsed by the various sectors of society, see my "Approaches to the Ethical Issues Raised by the Royal Commission's Mandate," in *New Reproductive Technologies: Ethical Aspects,* Vol. 1 of the Research Studies of the Royal Commission on New Reproductive Technologies Ottawa, 1993.

11. It is important, therefore, to distinguish this sort of genuine consensus from the idea of "community standards" appealed to in many government reports, which is often nothing more than the arbitrary and unprincipled biases of the majority. For example, many reports recommend that single women and lesbians be denied access to artificial conception procedures. In some cases this recommendation is defended by the claim that children are harmed by being raised in such families. This argument appeals to a widely shared principle concerning the need to protect children from harm, and if the claim of harm could be supported, then it would be a principled (though not necessarily conclusive) argument for restricting access to married couples. There is in fact little or no basis for this claim of harm, however, so other reports simply say that allowing access to single women or lesbians violates "community standards." In this case the community's standards are neither shared nor principled but simply reflect the majority's prejudice against a minority. Kasimba and Singer discuss and criticize this sort of appeal to "community values" in "Australian Commissions

and Committees on Issues in Bioethics," *Journal of Medicine and Philosophy,* Vol. 14, 1989, pp. 414, 417.

12. What if there is a consensus on principles that violate the moral point of view (e.g. a consensus on racial or sexual discrimination)? In this case a moral philosopher should try to encourage government commissions to question that consensus. Since government commissions are political bodies, however, it would make more sense for someone who sees the consensus as morally illegitimate to work outside the political system entirely. Participating in government commissions presupposes, to some extent, that the political system is legitimate.

13. For discussions of the deep disagreement between technological optimists and pessimists, see Max Charlesworth, *Life, Death, Genes and Ethics* (Crows Next, NSW: Australian Broadcasting Corporation Books, 1989), pp. 24–33; Wilbren van der Burg, "The Slippery Slope Argument," *Ethics,* Vol. 102/1, 1991, pp. 64–5; and the British Columbia Royal Commission on Family and Children's Law, *Artificial Insemination,* 1975, p. 7. It would be misleading to suggest that this disagreement is entirely factual. People often search for "facts" that will support a position that they've adopted on other grounds. For example, people who reject donor insemination (AID) because it is unnatural may, for the purposes of a public debate, seek out factual evidence that AID leads down a slippery slope to family instability, partly because the latter argument is more likely to be effective in public debate than the former. Hence moral disagreements can be displaced onto factual ones. Even if slippery slope arguments are sometimes a cover for other concerns, however, it is still true and important that the public debate over NRTs is largely empirical. People appeal to slippery slope arguments not only for strategic reasons, but also because they acknowledge that public policy in a pluralistic society cannot be based on matters of personal belief. Public policy must be based on non-sectarian reasons and arguments that can be understood by all. The prevalence of slippery slope arguments in public debate partly reflects the fact that they pass this test, since they

depend on shared values. David Lamb, *Down the Slippery Slope: Arguing in Applied Ethics* (London: Croom Helm, 1988), p. 5. While resolving the slippery slope disputes might not eliminate all moral disagreement over NRTs, it would remove much of that disagreement from the public policy arena to the sphere of personal belief. It is important to note that the slippery slope argument can cut both ways—that is, technological optimists worry that constraints on embryo research or surrogacy may lead down a slippery slope to wholesale restrictions on forms of medicine and scientific research that are perceived by some members of society as "unnatural."

14. For discussions of the limits of 'principlism' in bioethics, see Gert and Clouser, "Critique of Principlism"; Wikler, "What Has Bioethics to Offer Health Policy?" *Milbank Quarterly,* Vol. 69/2, 1991, pp. 238–40; and Paul Menzel, "Public Philosophy: Distinction without Authority," *Journal of Medicine and Philosophy,* Vol. 15, 1990, p. 415. It is worth noting, however, that most of these critics focus on a particular form of principlism, deriving from the work of Beauchamp and Childress, which uses only very vague and indeterminate principles (e.g., "benevolence"). In so far as the principles endorsed in this paper are more determinate (e.g., "non-commercialization"), they may be more useful as guides to deliberation and so avoid some of these authors' criticisms. Still, I agree that principlism cannot serve as a complete theory of bioethics. Identifying a checklist of principles leaves unanswered some of the most philosophically interesting questions about bioethics (e.g., how to resolve cases where individual practitioners or institutions face tragic choices between competing principles regarding the treatment of patients). However, the most interesting cases from a philosophical perspective are not always the most interesting or important from a public policy perspective. While principles are not adequate for all bioethical contexts, they are particularly useful in the context of government commissions on NRTs, whose recommendations are aimed at the general structure of public policy, not the specifics of individual cases.

Chapter Study Questions

1. Hare argues that justifying public policies involves examining the outcomes of the policy options open to the relevant government. He does not take up a position on the nature of the consequences that matter to his deliberations. Kymlicka outlines a series of aims or goals that a policy on NRTs should protect and a list of stakeholders. In what ways are the methods adopted by Hare and Kymlicka compatible? In what ways are they incompatible? Might Hare rely on Kymlicka's view to fill out his own position?

2. Kymlicka says that his approach may not be suitable for all policy contexts. Ainslie appears to make no such claim about his own Rawlsian methodology. What reason might Ainslie provide for thinking that his view applies more widely than Kymlicka's?

3. What sort of mistake might Hare be said to be making according to the Rawlsian view outlined and defended by Ainslie?

Critical Analysis

Consider the following from R. M. Hare:

> "Consequentialism as a theory in moral philosophy, which I have been advocating, has received a lot of hostile criticism in recent years. This is because people have not understood what the consequentialist position is. I do not see how anybody could deny the position I have just outlined, because to deny it is to deny that what we are judged morally for (what we are responsible for) is our actions, i.e. what we bring about. What makes people look askance at what they call consequentialism is the thought that it might lead people to seek good consequences at the cost of doing what is morally wrong—as it is said, to do evil that good may come. But this is a misunderstanding. It would indeed be possible to bring about certain desirable consequences, at the cost of bringing about certain other consequences which we ought not to bring about. But if the whole of the consequences of our actions (what in sum we do) were what we ought to do, then we must have acted rightly, all things considered."

Outline Hare's argument in your own words, paying particular attention to the premises that he relies on to support his main conclusion. Choose one of the premises for evaluation. Try to think of at least one objection to this premise.

Case Study

Until 1988, Section 251 (now the invalid Section 287) of the Criminal Code of Canada made it illegal to obtain or provide an abortion unless it was performed in an accredited hospital by a doctor and approved by a therapeutic abortion committee composed of three doctors. The majority of this committee had to agree that the abortion was a necessary means to protect either the health or the life of the pregnant woman. In the landmark legal case *R.* v. *Morgentaler*, the Supreme Court of Canada struck down the law on grounds that it violated certain sections of Canada's *Charter of Rights and Freedoms*. In particular, the court found that the law violated Section 7 of the *Charter*. This section states that each Canadian has the right to life, liberty and security of the person, and the right not to be deprived of these rights except in accordance with the principles of fundamental justice. By being forced to submit to an often arbitrary and time-consuming process that took control over her body out of her hands, Section 251 of the Criminal Code violated a woman's right to bodily security, and there was no principle of fundamental justice that might morally compel us to override that right. Since this court ruling, abortion has been decriminalized in Canada. Canada therefore has no law specifically regulating abortion. It is possible to obtain an abortion in Canada. Abortions are often paid for by publicly funded health insurance. In a typical year in Canada about 100,000 abortions are performed, most of which occur in the first 13 weeks of pregnancy. However, for many women it is difficult to obtain an abortion in their province of residence (e.g., Prince Edward Island), and both gestational limits and the time it takes to get the procedure vary widely from place to place. In some provinces (e.g., New Brunswick) only abortions performed in hospitals rather than private clinics are publicly funded. Therefore, although in theory the current legal situation may seem to be a boon for the rights of women, in practice it is less clear that women have reproductive freedom. This legal and social situation is a consequence of the divisive nature of the debate over the morality of abortion.

1. R. M. Hare argues that the most appropriate framework for assessing the morality of a public policy is consequentialism. This involves determining the costs and benefits of a public policy and then determining whether the benefits outweigh the costs. What are the costs and the benefits of the current legal situation regarding abortion in Canada?

2. Will Kymlicka argues that to form policy on bioethical issues, we need to generate a list of stakeholders or affected parties and a list of legitimate interests that must be considered when developing a policy. In the case of a policy on abortion, who are the main stakeholders and which interests seem most compelling?

3. Donald Ainslie argues that the liberal view is able to justify four principles for regulating health care and the professional obligations of health care professionals. The four principles are autonomy, justice, benevolence, and non-maleficence. Do these principles help us arrive at a policy for the regulation of abortion? What policy on abortion does the liberal view entail?

Further Reading

Donchin A. Feminist bioethics. In: Zalta EN, ed. Stanford Encyclopedia of Philosophy [Internet]. 2008. Available from: http://plato.stanford.edu/entries/feminist-bioethics/. Date Accessed: 7 June 2012.

Fox RC, Swazey J. *Observing bioethics*. Oxford: University Press, 2008.

Marchildon G. Royal Commissions and the policy cycle in Canada: the case of health care [Internet]. Regina: Saskatchewan Institute of Public Policy, 2001. Available from: http://www.uregina.ca/sipp/documents/pdf/ssgm.pdf. Date Accessed: 7 June 2012.

Skelton A. Henry Sidgwick's practical ethics: a defense. Utilitas [Internet]. 2006 18:199-217. Available from: http://philpapers.org/rec/SKEHSP. Date Accessed: 7 June 2012.

What is Disease?

In this chapter, we explore the question: "What is disease?" At first glance, this might seem like a simple question. There are numerous afflictions, such as multiple sclerosis, coronary artery disease, or breast cancer, that no one could reasonably doubt count as diseases. Upon reflection, though, in a surprising number of instances it may be unclear whether a condition ought to count as a disease. Should states that are nearly universal, such as dental caries, count as diseases? What of conditions that are merely risk factors for the development of disease, such as mild hypertension, a risk factor for cardiovascular disease? Or what of bodily features that exist on a continuum, like height? When precisely—if ever—does being too short or too tall become a disease?

A disease may be defined as a condition that impairs the normal functioning of the human body. We commonly think of disease as a disvalued state—one that we would rather avoid, if possible—because it may be associated with pain or discomfort. We also think of diseases as real. Indeed, when someone is thought to be falsely displaying the symptoms of a disease, it may be commented that it is "all in his head." But whether a particular condition is characterized as a disease can vary considerably from time to time, and from place to place. Being overweight was considered a sign of wealth and prosperity in late 19th and early 20th century North America; today, anyone with a body mass index greater than 30 is diagnosed as "obese." The diagnosis of asthma, hay fever, and nasal allergies varies considerably from one country to the next, with high rates in the United States and the United Kingdom, and low rates in continental Europe. The variability of disease classification raises the question whether these conditions are real or if they are socially constructed, that is, a function of sociocultural factors.

What difference does it make whether a condition counts as a disease? Consider a 10-year-old boy who is frequently restless and agitated and who has difficulty paying attention in the classroom. What is the difference between labelling him as "fidgety" on the one hand, or as "suffering from attention deficit hyperactivity disorder (ADHD)" on the other? One important difference relates to blame and moral responsibility. It may be appropriate to discipline a boy who is merely fidgety, but a boy whose behaviour is the result of a disease deserves sympathy rather than punishment. Another difference is found in the scope of appropriate solutions. Viewed as a matter of ill fit between the requirements of the classroom and the behaviour of many boys, we might seek to increase his physical activity and diminish time spent sitting at a desk during the school day. But viewed as a disease, we might conclude that prescribing Ritalin is the appropriate solution to the boy's behaviour. Thus, the repercussions of whether we conceptualize a condition as a disease go well beyond merely attaching one label or another.

In the first article, Christopher Boorse seeks to provide an account of disease, according to which diseases are both real and objective. Boorse argues against normativism, the view that disease and value—a sociocultural feature—are inextricably intertwined. It can't be the case, he argues, that "to call a condition unhealthy is at least in part to condemn it," because there exist diseases that are of indeterminate value (such as infertility) and others that are positively valued (such as the flat feet of an unwilling military conscript). In the place of normativism, he provides an objective view of disease according to which the science of disease (or "medical theory," as he calls it) is continuous with biology, physics, or astronomy. Disease is simply a deviation from the normal functioning of a part of the human body, and to conclude that a condition is a disease does not imply that it is "bad." Questions of ethics and value (or broader sociocultural features) are not relevant to medical theory, but they do apply to medical practice and what he calls "illness." An illness, according to Boorse, is a disease that is both undesirable and implies that the person with it is deserving of special treatment and has diminished moral accountability. Thus, even though what counts as an illness may vary from one time or place to another, what counts as a disease remains an unvarying fact.

In the second article, Ian Hacking takes issue with the strict objective account of disease as articulated by Boorse. Disease categories, he argues, are complicated in interesting and important ways, and interact with sociocultural factors. Hacking is surely not an anti-realist when it comes to disease, but, rather, he seeks "to create a space in which both ideas [realism and social construction] can be developed without too much immediate confrontation." He takes issue with the view of diseases as simply natural or (what he calls) indifferent kinds, that is, as classifications in which the classification schema does not interact with the thing classified. This view misses the interplay between the classification of a disease and its manifestations—an understanding of disease as an interactive kind. Even if schizophrenia is ultimately reduced to a single or small set of biological types, the methods used to treat it and the broad social understanding of what it means to be schizophrenic interact with and change both the expression of the disease and even who counts as being afflicted with it. Thus, Hacking provides us with a view of diseases like schizophrenia according to which they are real, but in which they vary by time and place. Indeed, for Hacking, the dynamics of the interactions between classification and expression is precisely "where the action is."

In the third article, Joan Callahan examines whether menopause ought to be considered a disease, and, if so, whether it requires treatment with exogenous estrogen. Menopause is a challenging case precisely because it is a *normal* part of the female lifespan. Assuming a typical lifespan, all women will go through a period of change in which their ovaries stop producing eggs, and in which symptoms from fluctuating hormone levels may be prominent. It seems odd, of course, to suggest that a part of the lives of all women should be considered a disease. As Callahan explains, though, both the availability of exogenous estrogen to replace flagging estrogen levels and prevailing medical attitudes towards women drove the medicalization of menopause. She correctly observes that motivations for treatment have changed and that a "rhetoric of retaining femininity has evolved into a rhetoric of maintaining health." Estrogen replacement came to be seen as a preventive health treatment, one that would diminish the chances of developing heart disease, stroke, and osteoporosis. Callahan is skeptical of these purported health benefits—and rightly so. Since the publication of her article, the use of estrogen has been proven to *increase* the risk of heart attack and stroke in women, and its use has dramatically diminished. While for most women the symptoms of menopause are mild, for a minority the symptoms are severe. Those who are severely afflicted are now left with a difficult choice between the ability to eliminate those symptoms in the short-term with estrogen versus the drug's potentially serious long-term consequences.

ONE   **On the Distinction Between Disease and Illness**

Christopher Boorse | *Philosophy and Public Affairs* 1975; 5.1: 49-68.

> **Evaluative notion**
> A concept that implies a judgment about the value or worth of a thing or activity. Here it is referring to a view of health according to which the goodness of health and the badness of disease are built into the concepts.

> **Value-free**
> Not involving judgments about the value or worth of a thing; not evaluative.

> **Disease**
> A deviation from the normal functioning of a part of the human body. For the author, "disease" is a concept that belongs to the domain of medical theory and is value-free.

> **Illness**
> A subset of disease; a disease that is both undesirable and implies that the person with it is deserving of special treatment and has diminished moral accountability (e.g., may take a missed examination without penalty). For the author, "illness" belongs to the domain of medical practice and is, therefore, an evaluative notion.

. . . With few exceptions, clinicians and philosophers are agreed that health is an essentially evaluative notion. According to this consensus view, a value-free science of health is impossible. This thesis I believe to be entirely mistaken. I shall argue in this essay that it rests on a confusion between the theoretical and the practical senses of "health," or in other words, between disease and illness.

Two presuppositions of my whole discussion should be noted at the outset. The first is substantive: . . . I shall assume that the idea of health ought to be analyzed by reference to physiological medicine alone.[1] . . . The other presupposition of my discussion is terminological. For convenience in distinguishing theoretical from practical uses of "health," I shall adhere to the technical usage of "disease" found in textbooks of medical theory. In such textbooks "disease" is simply synonymous with "unhealthy condition." Readers who wish to preserve the much narrower ordinary usage of "disease" should therefore substitute "theoretically unhealthy condition" throughout.

Normativism about Health

It is safe to begin any discussion of health by saying that health is normality, since the terms are interchangeable in clinical contexts. But this remark provides no analysis of health until one specifies the norms involved. The most obvious proposal, that they are pure statistical means, is widely recognized to be erroneous. On the one hand, many deviations from the average—e.g. unusual strength or vital capacity or eye color—are not unhealthy. On the other hand, practically everyone has some disease or other, and there are also particular diseases such as tooth decay and minor lung irritation that are nearly universal. Since statistical normality is therefore neither necessary nor sufficient for clinical normality, most writers take the following view about the norms of health: that they must be determined, in whole or in part, by acts of evaluation. More precisely, the orthodox view is that all judgments of health include value judgments as part of their meaning. To call a condition unhealthy is at least in part to condemn it; hence it is impossible to define health in non-evaluative terms. I shall refer to this orthodox view as normativism.

> **Statistical mean**
> The average; the sum of the values for each member of a sample space divided by the number of members.

> **Normativism**
> The view of health according to which health is an essentially evaluative notion; saying what counts as "health" or "disease" unavoidably involves a judgment as to whether a particular state is valued or disvalued.

Normativism has many varieties, which are often not clearly distinguished from one another by the clinicians who espouse them. . . . For the most part my arguments against normativism will apply to all versions indiscriminately. It will, however, be useful to make a minimal division of normativist positions into strong and weak. Strong normativism will be the view that health judgments are pure evaluations without descriptive meaning; weak normativism allows such judgments a descriptive as well as a normative component.[2] . . .

> **Descriptive meaning**
> A statement about the state of the world that is value-free, e.g., "there is a coffee cup on the desk in front of me."

Even weak normativism runs into counter-examples within physiological medicine. It is obvious that a disease may be on balance desirable, as with the flat feet of a draftee or the mild infection produced by inoculation. It might be suggested in response that diseases must at any rate be prima facie undesirable. The trouble with this suggestion is that it is obscure. Consider the case of a disease that has infertility as its sole important effect. In what sense is infertility prima facie undesirable? Considered in abstraction from the actual effects of reproduction on human beings, it is hard to see how infertility is either desirable or undesirable. Possibly those who see it as prima facie undesirable assume that most people want to be able to have more children. But the corollary of this position will be that writers of medical texts must do an empirical survey of human preferences to be sure that a condition is a disease. No such considerations seem to enter into human physiological research. . . .

I suggest that normativism's current prevalence is largely the result of two quite tractable causes. One is the lack of a plausible descriptive analysis; the other is a confusion between theoretical and practical uses of the health vocabulary. The required descriptive analysis I shall try to sketch in the next section. As for the second cause, one should always remember that a dual commitment to theory and practice is one of the features that distinguish a clinical discipline.

Unlike chemists or astronomers, physicians and psychotherapists are professionally engaged in practical judgments about how certain people ought to be treated. It would not be surprising if the terms in which such practical judgments are formulated have normative content. . . .

But behind this conceptual framework of medical practice stands an autonomous framework of medical theory, a body of doctrine that describes the functioning of a healthy body, classifies various deviations from such functioning as diseases, predicts their behavior under various forms of treatment, etc. This theoretical corpus looks in every way continuous with theory in biology and the other natural sciences, and I believe it to be value-free.

The difference between the two frameworks emerges most clearly in the distinction between disease and illness. It is disease, the theoretical concept, that applies indifferently to organisms of all species. That is because, as we shall see, it is to be analyzed in biological rather than ethical terms. The point is that illnesses are merely a subclass of diseases, namely, those diseases that have certain normative features reflected in the institutions of medical practice. An illness must be, first, a reasonably *serious* disease with incapacitating effects that make it undesirable. . . . Secondly, to call a disease an illness is to view its owner as deserving special treatment and diminished moral accountability. . . . There are, then, two senses of "health." In one sense it is a theoretical notion, the opposite of "disease." In another sense it is a practical or mixed ethical notion, the opposite of "illness."[3] Let us now examine the relation between these two concepts more closely. . . .

Disease and Illness

What is the theoretical notion of a disease? An admirable explanation of clinical normality was given thirty years ago by C. Daly King: "The normal . . . is objectively, and properly, to be defined as that which functions in accordance with its design."[4] The root idea of this account is that the normal is the natural. The state of an organism is theoretically healthy, i.e. free of disease, insofar as its mode of functioning conforms to the natural design of that kind of organism. . . .

The crucial element in the idea of a biological design is the notion of a natural function. . . . A function in the biologist's sense is nothing but a standard causal contribution to a goal actually pursued by the organism.[5] Organisms are vast assemblages of systems and subsystems which, in most members of a species, work together harmoniously in such a way as to achieve a hierarchy of goals. Cells are goal-directed toward

> **Function**
> A causal contribution to one of the goals pursued by an organism by one of its systems or subsystems. For instance, the function of the eye is to provide the organism with accurate visual representations of the world. This, in turn, is important for navigating efficiently from one place to another and recognizing dangers in the environment.

metabolism, elimination, and mitosis; the heart is goal-directed toward supplying the rest of the body with blood; and the whole organism is goal-directed both to particular activities like eating and moving around and to higher-level goals such as survival and reproduction. . . . The single unifying property of all recognized diseases of plants and animals appears to be this: that they interfere with one or more functions typically performed within members of the species.

The account of health thus suggested is in one sense thoroughly Platonic. The health of an organism consists in the performance by each part of its natural function. And as Plato also saw, one of the most interesting features of the analysis is that it applies without alteration to mental health as long as there are standard mental functions. In another way, however, the classical heritage is misleading, for it seems clear that biological function statements are descriptive rather than normative claims.[6] Physiologists obtain their functional doctrines without at any stage having to answer such questions as, "what is the function of a man?" Or to explicate "a good man" on the analogy of "a good knife." Functions are not attributed in this context to the whole organism at all, but only to its parts, and the functions of a part are its causal contributions to empirically given goals. What goals a type of organism in fact pursues, and by what functions it pursues them, can be decided without considering the value of pursuing them. Consequently health in the theoretical sense is an equally value-free concept. The notion required for an analysis of health is not that of a good man or a good shark, but that of a good specimen of a human being or shark.

All of this amounts to saying that the epistemology King suggested for health judgments is, at bottom, a statistical one. The question therefore arises how the functional account avoids our earlier objections to statistical normality. King did explain how to dissolve one version of the paradox of saying that everyone is unhealthy. Clearly all the members of a species can have some disease or other as long as they do not have the same disease. . . . But this answer does not touch universal diseases such as tooth decay. Although King nowhere considers this objection, the natural-design idea nevertheless suggests an answer that I suspect is correct. If what makes a condition a disease is its deviation from the natural functional

> **Platonic**
> Referring to the philosophy of Plato (434–348 BCE), a Greek philosopher famous for his theory of Forms, according to which non-material abstract ideas, and not the material world known to us through the senses, have the highest form of reality.

organization of the species, then in calling tooth decay a disease we are saying that it is not simply in the nature of the species—and we say this because we think of it as mainly due to environmental causes. In general, deficiencies in the functional efficiency of the body are diseases when they are unnatural, and they may be unnatural either by being atypical or by being attributable mainly to the action of a hostile environment. If this explanation is accepted,[7] then the functional account simultaneously avoids the pitfalls of statistical normality and also frees the idea of theoretical health of all normative content.

Theoretical health now turns out to be strictly analogous to the mechanical condition of an artifact. Despite appearances, "perfect mechanical condition" in, say, a 1965 Volkswagen is a descriptive notion. Such an artifact is in perfect mechanical condition when it conforms in all respects to the designer's detailed specifications. Normative interests play a crucial role, of course, in the initial choice of the design. But what the Volkswagen design actually is is an empirical matter by the time production begins. Thenceforward a car may be in perfect condition regardless of whether the design is good or bad. If one replaces its stock carburetor with a high-performance part, one may well produce a better car, but one does not produce a Volkswagen in better mechanical condition. . . . Perfect working order is a matter not of the worth of the product but of the conformity of the process to a fixed design. In the case of organisms, of course, the ideal of health must be determined by empirical analysis of the species rather than by the intentions of a designer. But otherwise the parallel seems exact. A person who by mutation acquires a sixth sense, or the ability to regenerate severed limbs, is not thereby healthier than we are. Sixth senses and limb regeneration are not part of the human design, which at any given time, for better or worse, just is what it is.

We have been arguing that health is descriptively definable within medical theory, as intelligence is in psychological theory or validity in logical theory. Nevertheless medical theory is the basis of medical practice, and medical practice unquestioningly presupposes the value of health. We must therefore ask how the functional view explains this presumption that health is desirable.

In the case of physiological health, there are at least two general reasons why the functional normality that defines it is usually worth having. In the first place, most people do want to pursue the goals with respect to which physiological functions are isolated. Not only do we want to survive and reproduce, but we also want to engage in those particular activities, such as eating and sex, by which these goals are typically achieved. In the second place—and this is surely the main reason the value of physical health seems indisputable—physiological functions tend to contribute to all manner of activities neutrally. Whether it is desirable for one's heart to pump, one's stomach to digest, or one's kidneys to eliminate, hardly depends at all on what one wants to do. It follows that essentially all serious physiological diseases will satisfy the first requirement of an illness, namely, undesirability for its bearer.

This explanation of the fit between medical theory and medical practice has the virtue of reminding us that health, though an important value, is conceptually a very limited one. Health is not unconditionally worth promoting, nor is what is worth promoting necessarily health. Although mental-health writers are especially prone to ignore these points, even the constitution of the World Health Organization seems to embody a similar confusion: "Health is a state of complete physical, mental, and social well-being, and not merely the absence of disease or infirmity."[8] Unless one is to abandon the physiological paradigm altogether, this definition is far too wide. Health is functional normality, and as such is desirable exactly insofar as it promotes goals one can justify on independent grounds. But there is presumably no intrinsic value in having the functional organization typical of a species if the same goals can be better achieved by other means. A sixth sense, for example, would increase our goal of efficiency without increasing our health; so might the amputation of our legs at the knee and their replacement by a nuclear-powered air-cushion vehicle. Conversely, as we have seen, there is no a priori reason why ordinary diseases cannot contribute to well-being under appropriate circumstances.

In such cases, however, we will be reluctant to describe the person involved as ill, and that is because the term "ill" *does* have a negative evaluation built into it. Here again a comparison between health and other properties will be helpful. Disease and illness are related somewhat as are low intelligence and stupidity. Sometimes the presumption that intelligence is desirable will fail, as in a discussion of qualifications for a menial job such as washing dishes or assembling auto parts. In such a context a person of low intelligence is unlikely to be described as stupid. . . . And sometimes the presumption that diseases are undesirable will fail, as with alcoholic intoxication or mild rubella intentionally contracted. Here the term "illness" is unlikely to appear despite the presence of disease. One concept of each pair is descriptive; the other adds to the first evaluative content, and so may be withheld where the first applies.

If we supplement this condition of undesirability with two further normative conditions, I believe we have the beginning of a plausible analysis of "illness." A disease is an *illness* only if it is serious enough to be incapacitating, and therefore is: (1) undesirable for its bearer; (2) a title to special treatment; and (3) a valid excuse for normally criticizable behaviour. The motivation for condition (2) needs no explanation. As for (3), the connection between illness and diminished responsibility has often been argued,[9] and I shall mention here only one suggestive point. Our notion of illness belongs to the ordinary conceptual scheme of persons and their actions, and it was developed to apply to physiological diseases. Consequently the relation between persons and their illnesses is conceived on the model of their relation to their bodies. It has often been observed that physiological processes, e.g. digestion or peristalsis, do not usually count as actions of ours at all. By the same token, we are not usually held responsible for the results of such processes when they go wrong, though we may be blamed for failing to take steps to prevent malfunction at some earlier time. . . .

World Health Organization
Established in 1948 and based in Geneva, Switzerland, it is the entity within the United Nations that coordinates international public health. The WHO understands health broadly as including physical, mental, and social well-being.

Rubella
German measles; a viral illness characterized by fever, rash, headache, and swollen glands. The illness is usually self-limited in children and adults, but can be particularly dangerous in pregnant women. If a woman is infected before the 20th week of pregnancy, the virus can pass into the fetus, possibly leading to serious defects of the heart, brain, eyes, or ears.

Peristalsis
The rhythmic waves of the smooth muscle of the digestive tract that propel ingested food forward.

Study Questions

1. What is normativism? Why, according to Boorse, is it is flawed notion?

2. What is the difference between a disease and an illness? Give an example of each.

3. Explain what Boorse means when he says: "The notion required for an analysis of health is not that of a good man or a good shark, but that of a good specimen of a human being or shark."

Notes

1. Thomas S. Szasz, *The Myth of Mental Illness* (New York, 1961); Antony Flew, *Crime or Disease?* (New York, 1973), pp. 40, 42.

2. R. M. Hare, in *Freedom and Reason* (New York, 1963), chap. 2, argues that no terms have prescriptive meaning alone. If this view is accepted, the difference between strong and weak normativism concerns the question of whether "healthy" is "primarily" or "secondarily" evaluative.

3. Thomas Nagel has suggested that the adjective "ill" may have its own special opposite "well." Our thinking about health might be greatly clarified if "wellness" had some currency.

4. C. Daly King, "The Meaning of Normal," *Yale Journal of Biology and Medicine* 17 (1945): 493–494. Most definitions of health in medical dictionaries include some reference to functions. Almost exactly King's formulation also appears in Fredrick C. Redlich and Daniel X. Freedman, *The Theory and Practice of Psychiatry* (New York, 1966), p. 113.

5. "Wright on Functions," to appear in *The Philosophical Review.*

6. The view that function statements are normative generates the third argument for normativism. It is presented most fully by Margolis in "Illness and Medical Values," *The Philosophy Forum* 8 (1959): 55–76, section II. It is also suggested by Ronald B. de Sousa, "The Politics of Mental Illness," *Inquiry* 15 (1972): 187–201, p. 194, and possibly by Flew as well in *Crime or Disease?* pp. 39–40. I think philosophers of science have made too much progress in giving biological function statements a descriptive analysis for this argument to be very convincing.

7. For further discussion of environmental injuries and other details of the functional account of health sketched in this section, see my forthcoming essay "Health as a Theoretical Concept."

8. Quoted by Flew, *Crime or Disease?* p. 46.

9. A good discussion of this point and of the undesirability condition (1) is provided by Flew in the extremely illuminating second chapter of *Crime or Disease?* Flew takes these conditions as part of the meaning of "disease" rather than "illness"; but since he seems to be working from the ordinary usage of "disease," there may be no real disagreement here.

TWO Madness: Biological or Constructed?

Ian Hacking. *The Social Construction of What?* **Cambridge, MA: Harvard University Press, 1999: 100-124.**

> **Schizophrenia**
> A serious mental illness characterized by flat emotional responses, detachment from reality, and hallucinations.

. . . It is easy to be skeptical about many of the entries in contemporary diagnostic manuals. . . . I will examine illnesses such as schizophrenia and conditions such as mental retardation. . . . These have been with the human race in most places and times. There are no mental retardation epidemics in Argentina, even if the various words used to describe the condition, such as "feeble minded," were used only at a specific time and place and very strongly reflect social attitudes and institutional practices. The name schizophrenia was invented only in 1908. So what? These are real illnesses

> **Real**
> Something that exists in the world and that is separable from the ideas that people at a particular time and place may have about it.

or conditions. And yet, and yet, there is a minority that will say that these disorders—and not just our ideas about them—are social constructs. Very often arguments are expressly put as: *X* is real—No, *X* is constructed.

It is not only the constructed that confuses us here, but also the real. Hilary Putnam (1994) hit the nail on the head, when

> **Social construct**
> Something that exists as a product of human social interaction; it is not separable from the ideas that people at a particular time and place may have about it.

he wrote about a "common philosophical error of supposing that 'reality' must refer to a single super thing, instead of looking at the ways in which we endlessly renegotiate—and are *forced* to renegotiate—our notion of reality as our language and our life develops." One of the reasons that we become confused in debates about whether an illness is real or not is that we fail to attend carefully enough to the grammar of the word itself (Austin 1962; Hacking 1983; 1995). But in the special context of mental illness we have, for the past two centuries, been constantly renegotiating our notion of reality.

"Social construct" and "real" do seem terribly at odds with each other. Part of the tension between the real and the constructed results from interaction between the two, between, say, child abuse, which is real enough, and the idea of child abuse, which is constructed. But that is not all. We can also confuse more complex types of interactions, which make some people think of antique dualisms between mind and body. These come out most clearly when we turn to the very habitus of mind and body, psychopathology. Most present-day research scientists take schizophrenia to be at bottom a biochemical or neurological or genetic disorder (perhaps all three). A minority of critics think that in important ways the disease has been socially constructed. I do not want to take sides, but to create a space in which both ideas can be developed without too much immediate confrontation—and without much social construction talk either. . . .

Children

Childhood has been called a social construct. Some people mean that the idea of childhood (and all that implies) has been constructed. Others mean that a certain state of a person, or even a period in the life of a human being, an actual span of time, has been constructed. Some thinkers may even mean that children, as they exist today, are constructed. States, conditions, stages of development, and children themselves are worldly objects, not ideas. Thus it may be contended that children now—take two small individuals named Sam and Charlie-boy—are different from children at some other time, because the idea of childhood—the matrix of childhood—is different now. . . . Conversely, the idea of childhood may have changed from what it was long ago, if children now are different from children then.

To use a less grand example than the whole of childhood, there has been a historical succession of ideas: fidgety, hyperactive, attention deficit, and attention deficit hyperactivity

Attention deficit hyperactivity disorder (ADHD)
A syndrome of inattentiveness, overactivity, or impulsiveness (or some combination thereof) out of the range of normal childhood behaviour. The diagnosis of ADHD has increased dramatically in recently years and it is now thought to affect up to 5 per cent of school-aged children.

disorder (ADHD).[1] . . . Perhaps children diagnosed with ADHD are different from the children once called fidgety—in part because of the theories held about them, and the remedies that have been put in place around their bad habits. Conversely, it may be that the resulting changes in the children have contributed to the evolution of ideas about problem children. That is an example of interaction.

I want to focus not on the children but on the classification, those *kinds* of children, fidgety, hyperactive, attention-deficient. They are interactive kinds. I do not mean that hyperactive children, the individuals, are interactive. . . . Interactive is a new concept that applies not to people but to classifications, to kinds, to the kinds that can influence what is classified. And because kinds can interact with what is classified, the classification itself may be modified or replaced.

Interactive kinds
Classifications in which the classification schema may interact with the thing classified and vice versa. With respect to human disease, an interactive kind is a disease classification in which people classified as having a disease change in response to being classified.

I do not necessarily mean that hyperactive children, as individuals, on their own, become aware of how they are classified, and thus react to the classification. . . . The classification *hyperactive* did not interact with the children simply because the individual children heard the word and changed accordingly. It interacted with those who were so described in institutions and practices that were predicated upon classifying children as hyperactive. . . .

We are especially concerned with classifications that, when known by people or by those around them, and put to work in institutions, change the ways in which individuals experience themselves—and may even lead people to evolve their feelings and behaviour in part because they are so classified. Such kinds (of people and their behaviour) are interactive kinds. This ugly phrase has the merit of recalling actors, agency and action. The "inter" may suggest the way in which the classification and the individual classified may interact, the way in which the actors may become self-aware as being of a kind, if only because of being treated or institutionalized as of that kind, and so experiencing themselves in that way. . . .

Too much philosophy has been built into the epithet "natural kind." All I want is a contrast to interactive kinds. Indifferent

Indifferent kind
Classifications in which the classification schema does not interact with the thing classified.

will do. The classification "quark" is indifferent in the sense that calling a quark a quark makes no difference to the quark. Indifferent does not imply passive. The classification *plutonium* is indifferent, but plutonium is singularly nonpassive. It kills. . . . But plutonium does not interact with the idea of plutonium, in virtue of being aware that it is called plutonium, or experiencing existence in plutonium institutions like reactors, bombs, and storage tanks. So I call it indifferent. . . . The classification *microbe* is indifferent, not interactive, although we are certainly not indifferent to microbes, and they do interact with us. But not because they know what they are doing.

When philosophers talk about natural kinds, they take the indifference—in my technical sense—of natural kinds for granted. That is to be expected. . . . The things classified by the natural-kind terms favoured in philosophical writing are not aware of how they are classified, and do not interact with their classifications. The canonical examples have been: water, sulphur, horse, tiger, lemon, multiple sclerosis, heat and the colour yellow. . . . None is aware that it is so classified. . . .

> **Multiple sclerosis**
> An autoimmune disease affecting the brain and spinal cord that may cause loss of balance, fatigue, double vision, and paralysis. It is most commonly diagnosed in adults between 15 and 40 years of age, and it is three times more common in women than in men. Canada has one of the highest rates of MS in the world.

Psychopathologies

A far more interesting issue is, what happens if something is both an interactive kind and an indifferent kind? Psychopathology furnishes obvious candidates. I do not want to insist on any one psychopathology, but will mention a range of cases. Each of them is to some extent a dreadful mystery, a veritable pit of human ignorance: mental retardation, childhood autism, schizophrenia. It is true that childhood autism was diagnosed only in 1943, and that schizophrenia was named only in 1908, but there is a widespread conviction that these disorders are here to stay, and were with us long before they were named.

There are competing theses about these three examples. One type of thesis tends, speaking very loosely, to the constructionist camp. The other type tends, once again speaking loosely, to the biological camp. In the constructionist camp, these disorders are interactive kinds of illness. In the biological camp, they are thought of as indifferent kinds. Here is a very sharp

instance of the fundamental tension between the "real" and the "constructed." I am attempting to address the felt tension with a less tired set of opposites. We need to make room, especially in the case of our most serious psychopathologies, for both the constructionist and the biologist. . . . I shall begin by stating the constructionist attitude to three severe mental disorders.

Biolooping

First, a warning. We have contrasted indifferent and interactive kinds: conscious human beings may interact with interactive kinds of which they are aware. There is a substantially different phenomenon. It too may properly be called interaction, and I want at first to keep it quite separate from the looping effects that I have been discussing.[2]

Everyone knows that our physical states affect our sense of well-being. Many of us believe that our mental states may have some effect on our physical condition. . . . Yoga is the technique that spans mind and body most conclusively, and serves as the model for notions of biofeedback. This phenomenon, which is well established but not understood, is distinct from the looping effect of interactive kinds. For lack of better nametags I shall call the mind/body effect biolooping, by analogy with biofeedback. The other is *classificatory looping*. I need the distinction because of course, in particular cases, both types of looping may be at work, and indeed mutually reinforce each other. . . .

Closer to mental illness, serotonin levels are now correlated with depressive states. An experimental study—not just statistical analysis—is possible. Take a class of patients diagnosed with depression, who improve under purely behavioural treatment. There is no chemical intervention whatever, only a type of psychobehavioural therapy. Results indicate that the serotonin levels of

> **Biolooping**
> The interaction between our physical and mental states, for instance, the ability of deep breathing exercises to calm the mind.

> **Biofeedback**
> Using instruments (such as a heart rate monitor) to provide information on a bodily function with the goal of being able to manipulate the system at will (for instance, slowing the heart rate).

> **Serotonin**
> A neurotransmitter found in the digestive tract, platelets, and the brain. It is involved in the regulation of intestinal movements, blood clotting, and mood. Selective serotonin reuptake inhibitors, a commonly used class of antidepressant drugs, are thought to work by increasing the availability of serotonin in the brain.

those who improve under such treatment are close to the levels in nondepressive patients, whereas before treatment serotonin was depleted. Once again, for convenience, I shall call this biolooping.

There is every reason to suppose that biolooping and classificatory looping could both be at work in some psychopathologies—and, who knows, in much of ordinary life as well. But first let me focus on classificatory looping. I briefly sketch both the constructionist and the biological attitudes to three terrible mental problems. I start with constructionist visions of each, and then pass to biological ones.

The Feeble Mind

On the construction side we have, for example, *Inventing the Feeble Mind*, a book that shows how the seemingly inevitable classification, "retarded child," overlaps with and has evolved from a host of earlier labels: ill-balanced, idiots, imbeciles, morons, feebleminded, mental deficients, moral imbeciles, subnormals, retardates. Each of these classifications has had its moment of glory. . . . At the time that each classification was in use, it seemed somewhat inevitable, a perfectly natural way to classify children with various sorts of deficit. Yet when we see the parade of ungainly labels, we quickly realize that these classifications are highly contingent. . . .

Schizophrenia

Or take schizophrenia. Here we have for example *Schizophrenia: A Scientific Delusion* by Mary Boyle who, in her preface, avows that she is a social constructionist. Her subject is seemingly less amenable to such treatment than that of mental retardation. . . . As Boyle herself says, she concentrates not on schizophrenics but on those who diagnose schizophrenia. She recounts the history of this kind of patient. She notes stark mutations in the concept of schizophrenia. She claims that clinicians are often benignly unaware of them. She argues that the introduction, definition, and characterization of this theoretical notion fails to satisfy criteria of adequacy set out by C. G. Hempel, that most careful of logical empiricists. . . . Her conclusion, stated baldly, is that schizophrenia is a construct. Attempts to

> **Criteria of adequacy**
> Conditions that must be fulfilled in order for a scientific explanation to be considered satisfactory. The criteria of adequacy include: the explanation must be in the form of an argument; it must contain at least one general law; it must be true; and, it must be maximally specific.

identify its etiology by neurochemistry are doomed. Schizophrenia is not a kind of disease. The motley of impaired individuals that at different times, and in different ways, have been handily lumped together as schizophrenics are not of a kind. Schizophrenia, in short, is a scientific delusion. . . .

We need not embrace anti-psychiatry to realize that the classification as schizophrenic, and current attitudes to and treatments of schizophrenics, are matters of which the patients, for all their periodic deficits of logic and sense of reality, are intensely aware. More of them are more aware now than they used to be. This is because of the continually developing arsenal of psychotropic drugs that is already able to bring some semblance of ordinary life to more than half of those patients diagnosed with severe schizophrenia. The medications make it easier for someone who is afflicted by such a mental illness to think of it as something "other," a thing, almost an agent that acts upon one. . . . Classification as schizophrenic affects the sensibilities of those classified in many ways. . . . The schizophrenic, as a kind of person, is a moving target, and the classification is an interactive kind.

Childhood Autism

My third example, childhood autism, bridges my first two. The name "autism" was invented by Bleuler to describe a characteristic family of symptoms in the group of schizophrenias. Adult patients lost the usual sense of social relationships, they became withdrawn, gave inappropriate responses, a phenomenon deeply disturbing to family and friends. Then the word "autism" was applied to some children previously regarded as feeble-minded, or even deaf-and-dumb. This was the result of Leo Kanner's many years of study of a quite small number of children. He published it in 1943. At that time the prevailing view, influenced by the (brief) dominance of psychoanalysis in American psychiatry, was that the autistic child had a "refrigerator mother," one who could not express emotion to the child. . . .

Cognitive science now rules some roosts. Since autistic children have many linguistic and other deficits, theories of cognition may be invoked. A recent fashion has been to argue that the autistic child lacks a "theory of mind." A single ingenious experiment originally suggested by philosophers has spawned an

> **Theory of mind**
> The ability to attribute mental states, including beliefs, desires, and knowledge, to oneself and others. It is thought to be critical to the capacity to understand and interact successfully with other people.

experimental industry.³ That is often the case in psychology, where new experimental ideas are as rare and as hard to invent as deep mathematical proofs or truly new magic tricks. But as with retardation and schizophrenia, there continues to be a substantial iconoclastic literature urging that autism is not something people just have, and that autism is no single disorder. . . .

By interaction I do not mean only the self-conscious reaction of a single individual to how she is classified. I mean the consequences of being so classified for the whole class of individuals and other people with whom they are intimately connected. The autistic family, as we might call it—a family with an autistic child—was severely influenced, and some would say damaged, by the doctrine of the refrigerator mother. The subsequent changes in the family contributed to a rethinking of what childhood autism is—not because one found out more about it, but because the behaviour itself changed. Most of the behaviours described by Kanner seem not to exist anymore.

Indifferent versus Interactive

There is, then, not only a strong pull towards a constructionist attitude to many mental disorders, but also a great interest in what the classifications do to the individuals classified. One of the defects of social-construction talk is that it suggests a one-way street: society (or some fragment of it) constructs the disorder (and that is a bad thing, because the disorder does not really exist as described, or would not really exist unless so described). By introducing the idea of an interactive kind, I want to make plain that we have a two-way street, or rather a labyrinth of interlocking alleys.

There is obviously another side to this story. There is a deep-seated conviction that retarded children, schizophrenics, and autistic people suffer from one or more fundamental neurological or biochemical problems which will, in the future, be identified. It is not claimed that every person now diagnosed will have the same problem. . . .

We need not argue that nearly all children diagnosed with autism today have exactly one and the same biological disorder. We need only hold possible that there are a few (possibly just one) basic fundamental biological disorders that produce the symptoms currently classified as autistic. Imagine, however,

that there is just one such pathology, call it *P*, and that in reasonable time, we discover what *P* is. A great discovery is reported: "Autism is *P*." Optimists will say that we won't have to wait long. . . . By hypothesis the pathology *P* will be an indifferent kind. The neuro-geno-biochemical state *P* is not aware of what we find out. It is not affected simply by the fact that we have found out about it, although of course our new knowledge may, with luck, enable us to intervene and either prevent or ameliorate the pathology. . . .

A Dilemma

Suppose that childhood autism is at bottom a biological pathology *P*, namely . . . what I call an indifferent kind. What then happens to the claim that childhood autism is an interactive kind? That is, a kind in which the humans classified may indeed change through looping effects, because of the ways in which the people classified react to being so classified? How can it be an interactive kind and also an indifferent kind? This is one way in which to address an issue that troubles many cautious people, the idea that something can apparently be both socially constructed and yet real. . . .

Semantic Resolution

At this juncture, philosophers may like to think of childhood autism and the postulated pathology *P* in terms of the theories of reference advocated by Hilary Putnam (1975) and Saul Kripke. The term "autism" is what they would call a natural-kind term, analogous to the multiple sclerosis that

> **Theories of reference**
> An account of how terms acquire specific referents; in this case, an account of how the term "autism" identifies children with autism.

Putnam long used as an example (even before working out his theory on the meaning of "meaning").⁴ If there is in fact exactly one definite biological pathology *P* underlying a broad class of autistic children, then the reference of the name "childhood autism" is *P*. Under this hypothesis, the name "childhood autism" is, in Kripke's terms, a rigid designator of a natural kind, namely the pathology *P*. In my terms, the pathology *P* is an indifferent kind, and "childhood autism" is the name of that kind. . . .

Our difficulty then seems merely verbal. Yes, if there is precisely one neuropathology *P* underlying what we now call autism, then, in Kripke-Putnam semantics, the kind-term "childhood autism" rigidly designates that pathology. Shall we say that when Kanner coined the name "childhood autism," it referred to pathology *P*? Some would give him what Putnam calls the "benefit of the dubbed"—yes, he referred to *P*, even though he (like ourselves) had not the remotest idea what childhood autism really is, namely *P*. . . .

Now for the bottom line. Someone writes a paper titled "The Social Construction of Childhood Autism." The author could perfectly well maintain (1) there is probably a definite unknown neuropathology *P* that is the cause of prototypical and most other examples of what we now call childhood autism; and (2) the idea of childhood autism is a social construct that interacts not only with therapists and psychiatrists in their treatments, but also interacts with autistic children themselves, who find the current mode of being autistic a way for themselves to be.

In this case we have several values for the *X* in the social construction of *X* = childhood autism. . . . For us, the interest would be not in the semantics but the dynamics. How would the discovery of *P* affect how autistic children and their families conceive of themselves; how would it affect their behaviour? What would be the looping effect on the stereotype of autistic children? Which children, formerly classified as autistic, would now be excluded, and what would that do to them? . . .

For the Study of Dynamics, Not Semantics

In the end, the "real vs. construction" tension turns out to be a relatively minor technical matter. How to devise a plausible semantics for a problematic class of kind terms? Terms for interactive kinds apply to human beings and their behaviour. They interact with the people classified by them. They are kind-terms that exhibit a looping effect, that is, that have to be revised because the people classified in a certain way change in response to being classified. On the other hand, some of these interactive kinds may pick out genuine causal properties, biological kinds, which, like all indifferent kinds, are unaffected, as kinds, by what we know about them. The semantics of Kripke and Putnam can be used to give a formal gloss to this phenomenon.

Far more decisive than semantics is the dynamics of interactive kinds. The vast bulk of constructionist writing has examined the dynamics of this or that classification and the human beings that are classified by it. . . . We have a dynamics working at the level of classification and at the level of biolooping. Semantics intrigues the logician, but the dynamics of classification is where the action is. If we begin to move among cyborgs, or to become cyborgs, biolooping will become a common fact of everyday life. Classificatory looping will continue alongside it until, perhaps, the two become one in a world that no one can foresee.

Study Questions

1. Explain Hacking's distinction between interactive and indifferent kinds and give an example of each.

2. What is biolooping? How does it differ from interactive kinds?

3. If a disease is socially constructed does that imply that it is not real? Why?

Notes

1. A research paper by David Pantalony introduced me to ADHD and its precursors, but he might not agree with my take on this series of diagnoses from fidgety to ADHD.
2. I owe this discussion to a question posed in Paris by Pierre-Henri Castel, and clarified for me by Daniel Andler.
3. Jack and Jill are shown a box with plastic dinosaurs in it. Jack is sent out of the room. The dinosaurs are replaced by candies. Jack is asked to come back into the room, but before he enters Jill is asked, what will Jack think is in the box? If Jill says dinosaurs, she has a theory of mind, but if she says candies, she does not.
4. The example occurs in a number of papers of Putnam's, starting no later than his 1961 talk to the American Association for the Advancement of Science, printed in Butler (1965).

References

Austin, John Langshaw. 1962. *Sense and Sensibilia*. Oxford: Clarendon Press.

Boyle, Mary. 1990. *Schizophrenia: A Scientific Delusion?* London: Routledge.

Hacking, Ian. 1983. *Representing and Intervening*. Cambridge: Cambridge University Press.

———. 1995. *Rewriting the Soul: Multiple Personality and the Sciences of Memory*. Princeton: Princeton University Press.

Kripke, Saul. 1980. *Naming and Necessity*. Cambridge, Mass.: Harvard University Press.

Putnam, Hilary. 1975. The meaning of 'meaning.' In Putnam, *Mind, Language and Reality*. Vol. 2 of *Philosophical Papers*. Cambridge, Mass.: Harvard University Press.

———. 1994. Sense, nonsense and the senses: An inquiry into the powers of the human mind. *The Journal of Philosphy* 91: 445–517.

Trent, James W. 1994. *Inventing the Feeble Mind: A History of Mental Retardation in the United States*. Berkeley. University of California Press.

THREE Menopause: Taking the Cures or Curing the Takes?

Joan C. Callahan | In: Margaret Urban Walker (ed.). *Mother Time: Women, Aging and Ethics.* **New York: Rowman & Littlefield, 2000: 151-74.**

> "Menopause is curable . . . The body changes typical of middle age can be reversed, and sexual functions can be restored, along with a fully feminine appearance . . . Menopause is completely preventable. No woman need suffer menopause or any of its symptoms if she receives preventive treatment before the onset of menopause . . . In effect, the new medical possibilities double a woman's emotional lifespan. Forty no longer looms large as a dividing line. No longer is her life in danger of being broken in half by 'the change.' Now at last, her life can be a harmonious continuity not threatened by the sudden disruption of her womanhood, but marked by the growth and enrichment of that womanhood."[1]

Menopause
The cessation of menstruation (periods), or the time in a woman's life in which this occurs. Menopause is commonly associated with symptoms such as hot flashes and headaches, and in some women these symptoms are severe.

So wrote gynecologist Robert A. Wilson in 1966, as he championed estrogen replacement therapy for all women approaching, undergoing, or after menopause. Wilson's manifesto expresses two takes or conceptual constructions—the first of womanhood itself as disrupted by menopause; the second of menopause as a disease in need of medical intervention. . . . It will be obvious in what follows that I have serious reservations about the administration of hormones; but let me make clear from the beginning that my overall concern in this chapter is with appropriate administration of hormones and with women's genuinely informed consent to hormonal intervention.

Cultural Constructions

In order to get a good start on an exploration of the cultural and physiological dimensions of menopause, we need an overview of the conceptual landscape. Several terms are used to talk about menopause, including *perimenopause*, *climacteric*, *premenopause*, and *postmenopause*, as well as *menopause* itself. The use of these terms is not entirely fixed. . . .

Voda[2] defines *menopause* in the standard way, as the permanent cessation of menstruation resulting from loss of ovarian follicular activity, and she defines *perimenopause* phenomenologically, as the

Estrogen (or hormone) replacement therapy
The provision of estrogen, a hormone, in a pill or injection form, to supplement low levels of estrogen associated with menopause. Hormone replacement therapy is effective in reducing the symptoms of menopause. It was widely promoted until its association with increased risks of breast cancer, heart disease, and stroke was discovered.

Ovarian follicular activity
The production of eggs by the female gonads. During a woman's reproductive years, one of the ovaries releases a mature egg each month. All the eggs a woman will produce in her lifetime are present in the ovaries before birth, and some may lie dormant for up to 50 years.

Phenomenological
The description of facts or experiences as opposed to causes that may remain hidden. In this case, hot flashes are the phenomenon experienced by women, whereas the cessation of follicular activity (the cause) is not experienced.

transition that begins with a woman's first hot flash and ends when a woman's hot flashes disappear.[3] As most women with the full experience of menopause know, this period is indefinite in duration, often beginning several years prior to menopause itself and continuing for several years after menopause. It is true that some women do not experience hot flashes. What is helpful about Voda's understanding of perimenopause, however, is its recognition that what we generally call "menopause" is not a discreet event at all, but rather a period of time of indefinite duration (although commonly three to six years) over which a woman moves into a new physiological life phase, which includes the cessation of ovulation and the lowering of hormone levels. What is commonly known as "menopause", then, is really perimenopause. . . . Here, I want to look at how women's aging, perimenopause, and menopause are currently presented in Western culture.

As Jacquelyn Zita points out, aging in general and menopause in particular are culturally represented as heretical changes in the female body.[4] As intolerance of the appearance of the aging woman's body increases, women are under more and more pressure to halt, or even reverse, these changes. . . . As another example, consider a number of contemporary representations of older women in film. Aging actresses, such as Shirley MacLaine, Anne Bancroft, and Vanessa Redgrave, have recently appeared in films representing older women as cranks, witches, characters, or fools of one sort or another.[5] . . .

In line with such degrading cultural representations of older women, states and processes that are perfectly normal for women, such as menstruation, pregnancy, and menopause, are constantly medicalized. There is now an abundant literature on the history and cultural representation of menstruation and the very destructive construction of PMS (premenstrual syndrome)

> **Medicalize**
> To treat something as a medical problem without the justification to do so.

as a malady that places women with regularity under the sway of "raging hormones." . . . And, as the baby boomers move into their fifties, menopause increasingly is billed as a malady requiring medical intervention. . . . Thus, it comes as no surprise that the pharmaceutical industry has become deeply invested in the medicalization of menopause and the marketing of drugs to treat it. . . .

Physicians, of course, deny that pharmaceutical company marketing influences their prescribing practices. . . . But, as I have suggested elsewhere, the pharmaceutical industry is not a bumpkin, and at least one series of studies has found that physicians seem pretty obviously to be influenced by pharmaceutical companies that sponsor continuing education sessions for doctors.[6]

As the baby boomers continue to age, contemporary advertising is changing. The elderly are increasingly represented as vibrant, and more and more products are targeted at the aging population. At the same time, pressure on women to address the marks of aging on our bodies increases—pressure to dye our hair, to have our faces lifted, to do all that we can to preclude menopause. Is it so different from 1966, when Robert Wilson began urging us to be "feminine forever"? It seems not, except that the rhetoric of retaining femininity has evolved into a rhetoric of maintaining health. We need, then, to ask just what women's health at midlife genuinely requires, in particular, whether it generally requires taking hormones. In order to approach an answer to this, we need first to understand what menopause actually involves.

The Basic Endocrinology and Physiology of Menopause

Menopause involves hormonal changes. As intercellular messengers, hormones are part of the body's regulatory system. When certain demands are made of the body, appropriate hormones are secreted into the system, where they find and bind with receptors on cells, which (ultimately) allows tissue to address the body's needs.[7] For women, transitions into and out of the reproductive years are marked by substantial fluctuations of the sex hormones. During puberty, a woman's reproductive hormonal system is gearing up; during perimenopause, her reproductive hormonal system is gearing down. Both are perfectly normal developmental stages, and both generally take from three to six years for completion.

> **Intercellular messengers**
> Transmitters of signals between distant cells in the body. The endocrine system secretes hormones into the blood stream to have effects on distant tissues. For instance, the maturation of eggs in the ovary is triggered by a hormone released in the anterior pituitary gland in the brain.

Menopause is the cessation of menstruation resulting from the cessation of ovulation. . . . It involves the shedding/reabsorption of the outermost layer of the uterine lining. That lining is built up and sustained by estrogen and progesterone. As a woman approaches menopause, her quantities of these hormones fluctuate; . . . a woman can experience effects of *both* high and low estrogen levels. *Low* estrogen levels (associated with hot flashes) can cause a woman's system to suddenly wake up and suddenly overproduce estrogen. This can cause phenomena associated with *high* estrogen levels, such as headaches and breast tenderness. These fluctuations in hormone levels explain why perimenopause can be a time of rapid and sometimes apparently inconsistent changes for a woman.

Negative features of these changes can be moderated by diet, exercise, and other lifestyle choices. But . . . women are constantly encouraged to seek medical intervention for menopause; and when women seek this intervention, we are commonly encouraged by physicians to take so-called hormone replacement therapy as we enter into perimenopause to ease our symptoms and/or prolong our health. Although the dominant rhetoric has changed from Wilson's emphasis on staying feminine forever to the rhetoric of living smart, Wilson's recommendation that women take what is now known as hormone replacement therapy is more strongly and uniformly recommended by physicians than ever before. It is time to ask whether women should accept this recommendation.

The Hormone Replacement Therapy Debate

One clear articulation of the current dominant take on menopause is provided by Theresa Crenshaw: "Menopause is not a natural condition; it is an endocrine disorder and should be treated medically with the same seriousness we treat other endocrine disorders, such as diabetes or thyroid disease."[8] Given that all women will experience menopause if they live long enough, it is certainly difficult to understand how menopause is not a natural condition. . . .

We have already seen that there are significant endocrine changes associated with menopause, and

> **Endocrine disorder**
> Disease affecting the regulation of bodily functions by hormones. Examples of endocrine disorders include diabetes (lack of or resistance to insulin), gigantism (an excess of growth hormone), and Addison's disease (lack of cortisol).

that physicians now recognize women's felt experience of those changes as real is, without question, a good thing. What is so problematic, however, is that this recognition has taken place within a construction of menopause as a hormone deficiency disease. The movement is a breathtaking one, from "It's all in your heads" to "You are all ill and in need of medical intervention." But surely there is an in-between. . . .

The Reported Benefits of Exogenous Hormone Intervention

Before going further, I need to make explicit that it is important to resist the current language of hormone replacement therapy, since this language gives too much to the construction of menopause as a deficiency and a disease. Because there is no reason to simply assume that a woman *should* have the same hormone levels during and after her reproductive years, instead of talking about hormone replacement therapy, I'll adopt the language of exogenous hormone intervention (EHI) and administration of exogenous estrogen (EE). . . .

As we have seen, perimenopause is a time when a woman's system is undergoing substantial change. These changes are not limited to our reproductive organs—*many* cells in our bodies are affected by the hormonal fluctuations taking place in perimenopause, and women commonly have a variety of experiences that are consequent to these changes. It is important to realize, however, that these experiences vary *significantly* across women. Some women experience a few hot flashes, which barely bother them, and little else.[9] Other women have much more distressing experiences—hot flashes that continually wake them from sound sleep, serious skin and vaginal dryness, urinary incontinence and urinary tract infections, headaches, and severe mood swings are among the most frequent of these. . . . There is, then, no question that for some women, the perimenopause is a difficult transition.

There is also no question that EHI, particularly EHI containing estrogen, is effective in relieving these felt effects of hormonal changes at menopause. For most women, these experiential phenomena will stop in a relatively short period of time. However, a number of women accept EHI to help with their most distressing experiences; and for many of these women, short-term use of EHI is an appropriate and substantial help to their comfort during perimenopause.

Long-term use of EHI, however, is a more worrisome matter, and in recent years women have been urged more and more strongly to adopt EHI for the long term (use for ten years or more). Heart disease is the major killer of postmenopausal women. Osteoporosis can lead to fractures, substantially decreased quality of life, and even death for some postmenopausal women. It is now continually claimed in the media and in physicians' offices that women should take exogenous hormones to lower their risk of both heart disease and osteoporosis. What was argued on the basis of femininity in the 1960s is argued on the grounds of longevity in the 1990s. But what do we *really* know about these alleged benefits of long-term EHI? . . .

> **Osteoporosis**
> A disease in which bone mass is lost over time, leading to increased bone fragility and risk of fractures. One in four women in Canada over the age of 50 has osteoporosis, and 25,000 hip fractures a year (in men and women) are attributed to the disease.

As it turns out, researchers are beginning to suggest that the conclusion that estrogen alone lowers cardiovascular risk is much too simple. For example, we now know that women who take exogenous hormones tend to be of higher socioeconomic status than those who don't, they tend to be better educated, they are thinner, they are likely to have had a hysterectomy, and they are more likely in general to have their health closely monitored—in short, we now know that women on EHI tend to start out with a better cardiovascular risk profile than those who are not on EHI.[10] Since this is the case, and since no controlled studies have been done to determine in a precise way what EE contributes to reducing cardiovascular risk, we do not know what, if anything, EE actually does contribute here. This is further complicated by the fact that the cardiovascular survival benefits of EE is thought to diminish with longer duration of use. All of this is not to say, of course, that there are no cardiovascular benefits of EE. But it is to say that if there are any benefits attributable to EE alone, they remain unclear; and it is to say that a woman's risk of developing heart disease increases as she ages, whether she takes exogenous estrogen or not. . . .

The other major claim most frequently made for EHI is that it helps to prevent osteoporosis. Osteoporosis is currently defined as "a disease characterized by low bone mass and microarchitectural deterioration of bone tissue, which lead to increased bone fragility and a consequent increase in fracture risk."[11] But, as Susan Love points out, one of the problems with this definition is that presently there is no way to test the microarchitecture of bones; so diagnoses of osteoporosis are made simply on the basis of bone density tests, and this is pressing the common understanding of osteoporosis as equivalent to low bone density, which, as we shall see in a moment, is simply inaccurate. . . .

This is not to fail to take osteoporosis and the risk of osteoporosis seriously. The quality of life of women affected by severe osteoporosis is profoundly compromised. But it is to call for attention to how the language gets used here. And *most* importantly, it cannot be emphasized strongly enough that despite all the contemporary warnings and worries about osteoporosis, 75 per cent of women will never develop it.[12] . . .

EE, then, does seem to contribute substantially to slowing down bone loss. However, the mechanisms by which it does this remain unclear and, as in the case of cardiovascular risk, the benefits of taking estrogen often can be gleaned in other ways that do not include the known and unknown systemic risks of exogenous hormones. Given these risks, a woman should not be encouraged to accept EHI, particularly over the long term, unless it is very, very clear that she is an appropriate candidate for this intervention. . . .

The Known Major Risks of Exogenous Hormone Intervention

The most serious risks of EHI are breast and endometrial cancers. Since it is now estimated that one in eight American women will develop breast cancer, even a small increase in risk is an enormous concern. What activists in the women's health movement have long worried about is increasingly well documented—EHI is strongly linked to increased risk of endometrial and breast cancers. . . . And researchers are beginning to suggest that even shorter-term use of EHI might increase a woman's risk of breast cancer.[13] What is more, new studies suggest that high bone mineral density might be an important risk factor for postmenopausal breast cancer. . . .

Given that lowering one's risks of cardiovascular disease and osteoporosis so often can be accomplished by diet and exercise, and leaving on consideration of endometrial cancer, why should women increase our known risk of breast cancer by taking exogenous hormones unless this is the last feasible option? . . .

Study Questions

1. According to Callahan, what does it mean for something to be culturally constructed? In what ways has menopause been culturally constructed?

2. Explain Callahan's disagreement with the statement "Menopause is not a natural condition; it is [a] . . . disorder." Is she right? Why?

3. Long-term use of hormone replacement therapy is now known to *increase* risk of heart attack and stroke. In what ways might earlier studies that (falsely) suggested a *lowering* of risk of heart attack have been biased?

Notes

1. Robert A Wilson, *Feminine Forever* (New York: Evans, 1966; reprinted New York: Pocket Books, 1971). Quote from the Pocket Books edition, 17 and 20. Wilson does allow that fertility cannot be restored by medical intervention (17).

2. See Ann M Voda, *Menopause, Me and You: The Sound of Women Pausing* (Binghamton, NY: Haworth Press, 1977). For some slightly different definitions, see the World Health Organization, *Scientific Group on Research on Menopause in the 1990s* (Geneva: World Health Organization, 1966).

3. Menopause itself is never actually directly experienced or demonstrated—it is inferred one year after a woman's last menstrual bleed. Jacquelyn N Zita, "Heresy in the Female Body: The Rhetorics of Menopause," in *Menopause: A Midlife Passage,* ed. Joan C Callahan (Bloomington: Indiana University Press, 1993): 59–78.

5. See, for example, Shirley MacLaine in *Madame Sousatzka, Steel Magnolias, Guarding Tess*; Anne Bancroft in *Critical Care, Great Expectations, GI Jane*; Vanessa Redgrave in *Howard's End* and *Two Mothers for Zachary.* Redgrave's Mrs. Dalloway (though true to Virginia Woolf's character) is also a profoundly foolish woman. For an expanded discussion of older women in film, see Jean Kozlowski, "Women, Film and the Midlife Women's Choice: Sink or Sousatzka?" in *Menopause*, ed. Callahan, 3–22.

6. See Callahan, "Professions, Institutions, and Moral Risk;" and "Pushing Drugs to Doctors," *Consumer Reports* (February 1992): 91–2.

7. See, for example, Ann Voda, "A Journey to the Center of the Cell," in *Menopause,* ed. Callahan, 160–93.

8. Marie McCullough, "Hope or Hype?" *Philadelphia Inquirer* (13 May 1996), cited in Love with Lindsey, *Dr Susan Love's Hormone Book,* (New York: Random House, 1977) 18.

9. See, for example, Mary Lou Logothetis, "Disease or Development: Women's Perceptions of Menopause and the Need for Hormone Replacement Therapy," in *Menopause,* ed. Callahan, 123–35. Logothetis reports that fully 75 per cent of the women she interviewed indicated either no distress or minimal menopausal distress, and only 7 per cent of the women she interviewed indicated severe menopausal distress.

10. KA Matthews, LH Kuller, RR Wing, EN Meilahn, and P Plantinga, "Prior Use of Estrogen Replacement Therapy, Are Users Healthier Than Nonusers?" *American Journal of Epidemiology* 143/10 (15 May 1996): 971–8; C Schaierer, HO Adami, R Hoover, I Persson, "Cause-Specific Morality in Women Receiving Hormone Replacement Therapy," *Epidemiology* 8 (1997): 59–65.

11. Conference Report, Consensus Development Conference: "Prophylaxis and Treatment of Osteoporosis," *American Journal of Medicine* 90 (1991): 107–10, cited in Love with Lindsey, *Dr Susan Love's Hormone Book,* 79.

12. See, for example, "Menopausal Hormone Replacement Therapy," *Cancer Facts,* National Cancer Institute, National Institutes of Health; http://rex.nci.nih.gov/INFOR_CANCER/Cancer_facts/Section3/FS3_10.html (accessed 10 May 1998).

13. F Grodstein and WC Willett, Correspondence: "Postmenopausal Hormone Therapy and Mortality," *New England Journal of Medicine* 337 (1997): 1389–91.

Chapter Study Questions

1. Describe and critically evaluate Boorse and Hacking's claims that diseases are (at least in some sense) real. Which do you prefer and why?

2. Does Hacking's concept of interactive kind fully or partly map onto Boorse's concept of illness? Why?

3. According to Callahan, is menopause a disease? Would Boorse and Hacking agree? Why?

Critical Analysis

Consider the following from the article by Christopher Boorse:

"Health is not unconditionally worth promoting, nor is what is worth promoting necessarily health. Although mental-health writers are especially prone to ignore these points, even the constitution of the World Health Organization seems to embody a similar confusion: 'Health is a state of complete physical, mental, and social well-being, and not merely the absence of disease or infirmity.' Unless one is to abandon the physiological paradigm altogether, this definition is far too wide.

Health is functional normality, and as such is desirable exactly insofar as it promotes goals one can justify on independent grounds. But there is presumably no intrinsic value in having the functional organization typical of a species if the same goals can be better achieved by other means."

Outline Boorse's argument in your own words, paying particular attention to the premises that he relies on to support his main conclusion. Choose one of the premises for evaluation. Try to think of at least one objection to this premise.

Case Study

Mr Jones and Ms Roscoe were recently contacted by the fifth grade teacher of their son Matt expressing concern about his declining performance in school. Matt Jones-Roscoe is 10-year-old, and has a younger brother Sam who is 6-year-old and in first grade. In his first four years of school Matt was a good student, excelling in mathematics and reading at or above his grade level. In the past year, though, his school performance has declined in all subjects; a B+ average in fourth grade has become a C- average in the fifth grade. His teacher reports that Matt is restless, and doesn't pay attention in the classroom. He seems to have trouble focusing on tasks requiring sustained attention such as reading or problem solving. The teacher believes that Matt, like a number of other boys in the school, may have attention deficit hyperactivity disorder (ADHD).

Before seeing their family doctor, the Roscoe-Jones do some reading on the internet about ADHD. They learn that ADHD is syndrome of attention problems and hyperactivity that affects boys four times more commonly than girls. Symptoms usually start at an early age (before the age of seven years) and in about half of cases, continue into adulthood. The primary treatment is a daily dose of a stimulant drug such as Ritalin; the drug has a paradoxical calming effect in children with ADHD. While the diagnosis was very uncommon forty years ago, it is now the most common psychiatric diagnosis in children, affecting 1 in 10 boys Matt's age. Ms Roscoe wonders whether Matt's symptoms are really so recent, and points to restlessness as far back as the first full day of school. Mr Jones is less sure, and is puzzled by the seeming epidemic of ADHD.

1. Do Matt's symptoms meet Boorse's definition of disease or illness?

2. How might attention deficit hyperactivity disorder be what Hacking calls an interactive kind? Does this mean it isn't a real disease?

3. Do you think Matt has a disease? Does it need to be treated? Why?

Further Reading

Angell M. The epidemic of mental illness: why [Internet]? The New York Review of Books; 23 June 2011, pp. 20-2. Available from: http://www.nybooks.com/articles/archives/2011/jun/23/epidemic-mental-illness-why/. Date accessed: 7 June 2012.

Elliott C. A new way to be mad [Internet]. The Atlantic; December 2000. Available from: http://www.theatlantic.com/magazine/archive/2000/12/a-new-way-to-be-mad/4671/. Date accessed: 7 June 2012.

Elliot C. *Better than well: American medicine meets the American dream*. New York: WW Norton and Company; 2003.

Lexchin J. Bigger and better: How Pfizer redefined erectile dysfunction. PLoS Med [Internet] 2006;3.4:e132. Available from: http://www.plosmedicine.org/article/info:doi/10.1371/journal.pmed.0030132. Date accessed: 7 June 2012.

Szasz TS. What counts as disease? Can Med Assoc J [Internet] 1986;135.8:859-60. Available from: http://www.ncbi.nlm.nih.gov/pmc/articles/PMC1491489/pdf/cmaj00128-0029.pdf. Date accessed: 7 June 2012.

14

Public Health

In this chapter, we explore the extent to which the State may act paternalistically to promote the health of its citizens. To what extent, if any, can the autonomous choices of individual citizens be overridden for the ends of public health? The State has a well recognized responsibility to promote the health of communities and populations. In Canada, responsibility for public health is shared between federal and provincial agencies. The Public Health Agency of Canada is responsible for national health promotion and ensuring preparedness for public health emergencies, including disease outbreaks. Provincial public health agencies are responsible for environmental and occupational health, overseeing local health units, inspecting restaurants for food safety, and managing laboratories that test water supplies for safety and infectious diseases diagnosis. Public health officials collect data on injury and disease, investigate disease outbreaks, engage in public health education, and, in certain circumstances, have the power to quarantine individuals and compel their treatment.

The challenges faced by officials are at their most dramatic during public health emergencies. In 2003, Toronto was the scene of a major disease outbreak involving one of the largest uses of quarantine in recent times. The outbreak of severe acute respiratory syndrome (SARS) originated in rural China and, due to the ease of international air travel, reached Toronto in a matter of days. SARS was a new and severe form of viral pneumonia that spread through close contact with infected individuals in households, medical clinics, and hospitals. During the outbreak, there were 438 cases of SARS in Toronto and 43 deaths. Health care facilities were rapidly overwhelmed by patients requiring evaluation and urgent care, as well as by the cumbersome measures to prevent infection of health care workers and other patients. Health care workers were among those infected and quarantined during the outbreak; a minority of health workers refused to work during the outbreak, and a few were fired as a result. As hospitals struggled to deal with the influx of acutely ill patients, treatment for patients with cancer, heart disease, and other chronic ailments was substantially delayed. Individuals who had been exposed to the virus were ordered to stay at home, to prevent spread of the disease, and they faced loss of freedom, privacy, and income as a result. Finally, the World Health Organization issued a controversial international travel advisory advising against travel to Toronto, costing the city and the province of Ontario millions of dollars in lost income from tourism.

The experience with SARS highlights the difficult ethical challenges in public health. What ethical principles ought to guide public health practice? When (and how) are public health decisions that override individual autonomy justified? In the first reading, Childress and colleagues eschew a general theory and argue instead for a set of "general moral considerations" that capture well the "moral content of public health ethics." Moral considerations to produce benefits, avoid harms, and to maximize the balance of benefits over harms are often invoked to justify public health interventions. Other moral considerations, including those to respect autonomous choice, protect privacy, keep promises, build and maintain trust, may—at times at least—constrain public health interventions. Generally, conflicts between moral considerations are resolved through specifying the moral requirements at stake and weighing the moral costs of particular alternatives. Public health interventions that propose to override countervailing moral considerations must be carefully justified. They must demonstrate that the public health intervention is likely to work, that its benefits outweigh its moral costs, that the public health ends could not otherwise be achieved, that there is no other less intrusive way of achieving these ends, and finally, that reasons for so acting will be made public. Only when these conditions are fulfilled may we conclude that paternalistic action by the State for public health is justified.

In the second reading, Wilson takes issue with Childress and colleagues' theory-free approach to public health ethics. Wilson details challenges faced by theoretical or "top-down" approaches to public health ethics, but argues ultimately that a wholly "bottom-up" or theory-free approach cannot succeed. The efficacy of translating philosophical theorizing into defensible public health policy is challenged by the difficulty of dealing with complex systems, such as health insurance. The complexity of health systems may make it difficult to predict the effects of policy changes. Thus, effective public health policy requires a detailed knowledge of the "inner wiring of the complex systems we are trying to reform." Despite this, Wilson argues that some degree of theoretical apparatus is essential to public health ethics. First, an ethics of public health rests on a definition of the goals of health promotion. The possible goals of public health are several—promoting longevity in a population, reducing health inequalities, or enhancing health-related autonomy—and which we choose will have considerable impact on the resulting ethics of public health. Second, public health is but one good among many that society may legitimately pursue. If we are to be able to deal with cases involving conflicting goods (e.g., public health versus economic growth), we will require an account of the relative weight we should give to health and other social goods.

In the third reading, Thompson and colleagues take a different approach to public health ethics and lay out an approach to planning for an influenza pandemic that emphasizes the deliberative process over substantive moral principles. Their approach is based on Daniels and Sabins' "accountability for reasonableness" and sets out five criteria for a fair process leading to a public health policy. First, decision makers ought to view themselves as morally responsible for the outcome of the process. Second, the decision-making process ought to take account of the views of all those affected by the issue. Third, the process followed should be open to public scrutiny. Fourth, decisions should be based on reasons that stakeholders can agree are relevant. Fifth, the decision should be open to appeal, periodic review, and, if needed, revision. Ten key ethical values are also set out, including duty to provide care, equity, individual liberty, privacy, proportionality, protection of the public from harm, reciprocity, solidarity, stewardship, and trust. These values may be viewed as defining a set of reasons to which deliberators may appeal in the decision-making process.

ONE   Public Health Ethics: Mapping the Terrain

James F. Childress, Ruth R. Faden, Ruth D. Gaare, Lawrence O. Gostin, Jeffrey Kahn, Richard J. Bonnie, Nancy E. Kass, Anna C. Mastroianni, Jonathan D. Moreno, and Phillip Nieburg | *Journal of Law, Medicine & Ethics* 2002; 30(2): 170-8.

. . . Public health is primarily concerned with the health of the entire population, rather than the health of individuals. Its features include an emphasis on the promotion of health and the prevention of disease and disability; the collection and use of epidemiological data, population surveillance, and other forms of empirical quantitative assessment; a recognition of the multidimensional nature of the determinants of health; and, a focus on the complex interactions of many factors— biological, behavioural, social, and environmental—in developing effective interventions. . . .

> **Determinants of health**
> Factors that combine together to affect the health of individuals and communities. These factors include biological factors (e.g., genetic predisposition), environmental factors (e.g., pollution), and social factors (e.g., socioeconomic status).

From this starting point, we can suggest that public health systems consist of all the people and actions, including laws, policies, practices, and activities, that have the primary purpose of protecting and improving the health of the public.[1] While we need not assume that public health systems are tightly structured or centrally directed, we recognize that they include a wide range of governmental, private and non-profit organizations, as well as professionals from many disciplines, all of which (alone and together) have a stake in and an effect on a community's health. Government has a unique role in public health because of its responsibility, grounded in its police powers, to protect the public's health and welfare, because it alone can undertake certain interventions, such as regulation, taxation, and the expenditure of public funds, and

> **Police powers**
> The capacity of the State to regulate behaviour and enforce order within its borders.

because many, perhaps most, public health programs are public goods that cannot be optimally provided if left to individuals or small groups.

The Institute of Medicine's landmark 1988 definition of public health provides additional insight:

> **Institute of Medicine**
> The health arm of the US National Academies of Sciences that works to produce authoritative and unbiased advice on matters of health to the government and members of the public.

"Public health is what we, as a society, do collectively to assure the conditions in which people can be healthy."[2] The words "what we, as a society, do collectively" suggest the need for cooperative behaviour and relationships built on overlapping values and trust. The words "to assure the conditions in which people can be healthy" suggest a far-reaching agenda for public health that focuses attention not only on the medical needs of individuals, but on fundamental social

conditions that affect population levels of morbidity and mortality. From an ethical standpoint, public health activities are generally understood to be teleological (end-oriented) and consequentialist—the health of the public is the primary end that is sought and the primary outcome for measuring success.[3] . . .

General Moral Considerations

Conceptions of morality usually recognize a formal requirement of universalizability in addition to a substantive requirement of attention to human welfare. Whatever language is used, this formal feature requires that we treat similar cases in a similar way. . . . Much of the moral argument will hinge on which similarities and differences between cases are morally relevant, and that argument will often, though not always, appeal to general moral considerations.[4] We can establish the relevance of a set of these considerations in part by looking at the kinds of moral appeals that public health agents make in deliberating about and justifying their actions as well as at debates about moral issues in public health. The relevant general moral considerations include:

- producing benefits;
- avoiding, preventing, and removing harms;
- producing the maximal balance of benefits over harms and other costs (often called utility);
- distributing benefits and burdens fairly (distributive justice) and ensuring public participation;
- including the participation of affected parties (procedural justice);
- respecting autonomous choices and actions, including liberty of action;
- protecting privacy and confidentiality;
- keeping promises and commitments;
- disclosing information as well as speaking honestly and truthfully (often grouped under transparency); and
- building and maintaining trust.

Several of these general moral considerations— especially benefiting others, preventing and removing harms, and utility—provide a *prima facie* warrant for many activities in pursuit of the goal of public health. It is sufficient for our purposes to note that public health activities have their grounding in general moral considerations, and that public health identifies one major broad benefit that societies and governments ought to pursue. The relation of public health to the whole set of general moral considerations is complex. Some general moral considerations support this pursuit; institutionalizing several others may be a condition for or means to public health; and yet, in particular cases, some of the same general moral considerations may limit or constrain what may be done in pursuit of public health. Hence, conflicts may occur among these general moral considerations.

The content of these various general moral considerations can be divided and arranged in several ways—for instance, some theories may locate one or more of these concepts under others. But, whatever theory one embraces, the whole set of general moral considerations roughly captures the moral content of public health ethics. It then becomes necessary to address several practical questions. First, how can we make these general moral considerations more specific and concrete in order to guide action? Second, how can we resolve conflicts among them? Some of the conflicts will concern how much weight and significance to assign to the ends and effects of protecting and promoting public health relative to the other considerations that limit and constrain ways to pursue such outcomes. While each general moral consideration may limit and constrain public health activities in some circumstances, for our purposes, justice or fairness, respect for autonomy and liberty, and privacy and confidentiality are particularly noteworthy in this regard. . . .

Specifying and Weighting General Moral Considerations

The various general moral considerations are not absolute. Each may conflict with another and each may have to yield in some circumstances. At most, then, these general moral considerations identify features of actions, practices, and policies that make them *prima facie* or presumptively right or wrong, i.e., right or wrong, all other things being equal. But since any particular action, practice, or policy for the public's health may also have features that infringe one or more of these general moral considerations, it will be necessary to determine which of them has priority. Some argue for a lexical or serial ordering, in which one

> **Lexical or serial ordering**
> A priority ordering of principles according to which higher priority principles trump lower priority principles in the event of conflict.

general moral consideration, while not generally absolute, has priority over another. For instance, one theory might hold that protecting or promoting public health always has priority over privacy, while another might hold that individual liberty always has priority over protecting or promoting public health. Neither of these priority rules is plausible, and any priority rule that is plausible will probably involve tight or narrow specifications of the relevant general moral considerations to reduce conflicts. From our standpoint, it is better to recognize the need to balance general moral considerations in particular circumstances when conflicts arise. We cannot determine their weights in advance, only in particular contexts that may affect their weights—for instance, promises may not have the same moral weights in different contexts. . . .

Resolving Conflicts Among General Moral Considerations

In this paper, . . . we focus on one particular permutation of conflicts among general moral considerations that has received the most attention in commentary and in law. This is the conflict between the general moral considerations that are generally taken to instantiate the goal of public health—producing benefits, preventing harms, and maximizing utility—and those that express other moral commitments. For conflicts that assume this structure, we propose five "justificatory conditions": effectiveness, proportionality, necessity, least infringement, and public justification. These conditions are intended to help determine whether promoting public health warrants overriding such values as individual liberty or justice in particular cases.

Effectiveness: It is essential to show that infringing one or more general moral considerations will probably protect public health. For instance, a policy that infringes one or more general moral considerations in the name of public health but has little chance of realizing its goal is ethically unjustified.

Proportionality: It is essential to show that the probable public health benefits outweigh the infringed general moral considerations—this condition is sometimes called proportionality. For instance, the policy may breach autonomy or privacy and have undesirable consequences. All of the positive features and benefits must be balanced against the negative features and effects.

Necessity: Not all effective and proportionate policies are necessary to realize the public health goal that is sought. The fact that a policy will infringe a general moral consideration provides a strong moral reason to seek an alternative strategy that is less morally troubling. This is the logic of a *prima facie* or presumptive general moral consideration. For instance, all other things being equal, a policy that provides incentives for persons with tuberculosis to complete their treatment until cured will have priority over a policy that forcibly detains such persons in order to ensure the completion of treatment. Proponents of the forcible strategy have the burden of moral proof. This means that the proponents must have a good faith belief, for which they can give supportable reasons, that a coercive approach is necessary. In many contexts, this condition does not require that proponents provide empirical evidence by actually trying the alternative measures and demonstrating their failure.[5]

Least infringement: Even when a proposed policy satisfies the first three justificatory conditions—that is, it is effective, proportionate, and essential in realizing the goal of public health—public health agents should seek to minimize the infringement of general moral considerations. For instance, when a policy infringes autonomy, public health agents should seek the least restrictive alternative; when it infringes privacy, they should seek the least intrusive alternative; and when it infringes confidentiality, they should disclose only the amount and kind of information needed, and only to those necessary, to realize the goal.[6] The justificatory condition of least infringement could plausibly be interpreted as a corollary of necessity—for instance, a proposed coercive measure must be necessary in degree as well as in kind.

Public justification: When public health agents believe that one of their actions, practices, or policies infringes one or more general moral considerations, they also have a responsibility, in our judgment, to explain and justify that infringement, whenever possible, to the relevant parties, including those affected by the infringement. In the context of what we call the "political public," public health agents should offer public justification for policies in terms that fit the overall social contract in a liberal,

> **Political public**
> "[W]hat we collectively do through government and public agency"; a broad reference to the citizens of a democratic state and its political institutions.

pluralistic democracy. This transparency stems in part from the requirement to treat citizens as equals and with respect by offering moral reasons, which in principle they could find acceptable, for policies that infringe general moral considerations. Transparency is also essential to creating and maintaining public trust; and it is crucial to establishing accountability. . . .

Public Health Interventions versus Paternalistic Interventions

An important empirical, conceptual, and normative issue in public health ethics is the relationship between protecting and promoting the health of individuals, and protecting and promoting public health. Although public health is directed to the health of populations, the indices of population health, of course, include an aggregation of the health of individuals. But suppose the primary reason for some restrictions on the liberties of individuals is to prevent harm to those whose actions are substantially voluntary and do not affect others adversely. The ethical question then is, when can paternalistic interventions (defined as interventions designed to protect or benefit individuals themselves against their express wishes) be ethically justified if they infringe general moral considerations such as respect for autonomy, including liberty of action? . . .

Whether an agent's other-regarding conduct is voluntary or non-voluntary, the society may justifiably intervene in various ways, including the use of coercion, to reduce or prevent the imposition of serious risk on others. Societal intervention in non-voluntary self-regarding conduct is considered weak (or soft)

> **Other-regarding conduct**
> The actions of a person that have an impact on others, for instance, an individual's choice to drive a car with serious mechanical flaws not only puts the driver at risk, it also imperils the safety of others on the road.

paternalism, if it is paternalistic at all, and it is easily justified. By contrast, societal interference in voluntary self-regarding conduct would be strong (or hard) paternalism. Coercive intervention in the name of strong paternalism would be insulting and disrespectful to individuals because it would override their voluntary actions for their own benefit, even though their actions do not harm others. Such interventions are thus very difficult to justify in a liberal, pluralistic democracy. . . .

To a great extent, the question is where we draw the boundaries of the self and its actions; that is, whether various influences on agents so determine their actions that they are not voluntary, and whether the adverse effects of those actions extend beyond the agents themselves. Such boundary drawing involves empirical, conceptual, and normative questions that demand attention in public health ethics. On the one hand, it is not sufficient to show that social-cultural factors influence an individual's actions; it is necessary to show that those influences render that individual's actions substantially non-voluntary and warrant societal interventions to protect him or her. Controversies about the strong influence of food marketing on diet and weight (and, as a result, on the risk of disease and death) illustrate the debates about this condition.

On the other hand, it is not sufficient to show that an individual's actions have some adverse effects on others; it is necessary to show that those adverse effects on others are significant enough to warrant overriding the individual's liberty. Controversies about whether the state should require motorcyclists to wear helmets illustrate the debates about this condition. These controversies also show how the inclusion of the financial costs to society and the emotional costs to, say, observers and rescue squads can appear to make virtually any intervention non-paternalistic. But even if these adverse financial and emotional effects on others are morally relevant as a matter of social utility, it would still be necessary to show that they are significant enough to justify the intervention.

Either kind of attempt to reduce the sphere of autonomous, self-regarding actions, in order to warrant interventions in the name of public health, or, more broadly, social utility, can sometimes be justified, but either attempt must be subjected to careful scrutiny. Sometimes both may represent rationalization and bad faith as public health agents seek to evade the stringent demands of the general moral consideration of respect for autonomy. Requiring consistency across an array of cases may provide a safeguard against rationalization and bad faith, particularly when motives for intervention may be mixed.

Much of this debate reflects different views about whether and when strong paternalistic interventions can be ethically justified. In view of the justificatory conditions identified earlier, relevant factors will include the nature of the intervention, the degree to which it infringes an individual's fundamental values, the magnitude of the risk to the individual apart from the intervention (either in terms of harm or lost benefit), and so forth. For example, even though the authors of this paper would disagree about some cases, we agree that strong paternalistic interventions that do not threaten individuals' core values and that will probably protect them against serious risks are more easily justifiable than strong paternalistic interventions that threaten individuals' core values and that will reduce only minor risks. Of course, evaluating actual and proposed policies that infringe general moral considerations becomes very complicated when both paternalistic and public health reasons exist for, and are intertwined in, those policies. . . .

Study Questions

1. According to the authors, what are the general moral considerations relevant to public health? How might they be grouped in different ways by individuals with different moral commitments?

2. How are public health actions that infringe upon other general moral considerations justified? Is this a sufficiently stringent set of criteria?

3. In discussing the issue of when paternalism may be ethically permissible in public health, the authors suggest that the example of mandatory helmet laws for motorcyclists could be used to illustrate the complexity of this issue. Explain.

Notes

1. Our definition builds on the definition of health systems offered by the World Health Organization: health systems include "all the activities whose primary purpose is to promote, restore, or maintain health." See *World Health Report 2000 Health Systems: Improving Performance* (Geneva: World Health Organization, 2000): at 5.

2. Committee for the Study of the Future of Public Health, Division of Health Care Services, Institute of Medicine, *The Future of Public Health* (Washington, DC: National Academy Press, 1988): at 1.

3. We recognize that there are different views about the ultimate moral justification for the social institution of public health. For example, some communitarians appear to support public health as an instrumental goal to achieve community. Others may take the view that the state has a duty to ensure the public's health as a matter of social justice. Although these different interpretations and others are very important for some purposes, they do not seriously affect the conception of public health ethics that we are developing, as long as public health agents identify and inform others of their various goals.

4. Recognizing universalizability by attending to past precedents and possible future precedents does not preclude a variety of experiments, for instance, to determine the best ways to protect the public's health. Thus, it is not inappropriate for different states, in our federalist system, to try different approaches, as long as each of them is morally acceptable.

5. This justificatory condition is probably the most controversial. Some of the authors of this paper believe that the language of "necessity" is too strong. Whatever language is used, the point is to avoid a purely utilitarian strategy that accepts only the first two conditions of effectiveness and proportionality and to ensure that the non-utilitarian general moral considerations set some prima facie limits and constraints and establish moral priorities, ceteris paribus.

6. For another version of these justificatory conditions, see TL Beauchamp and JF Childress, *Principles of Biomedical Ethics,* 5th ed. (New York: Oxford University Press, 2001): at 19–21. We observe that some of these justificatory conditions are quite similar to the justificatory conditions that must be met in US constitutional law when there is strict scrutiny because, for instance, a fundamental liberty is at stake. In such cases, the government must demonstrate that it has a "compelling interest," that its methods are strictly necessary to achieve its objectives, and that it has adopted the "least restrictive alternative." See LO Gostin, *Public Health Law: Power, Duty, Restraint* (Berkeley: University of California Press; New York: The Milbank Memorial Fund, 2000): 80–1.

TWO   Towards a Normative Framework for Public Health Ethics and Policy

James Wilson | *Public Health Ethics*; 2009 2(2): 184-94.

. . . I argue that there are three important complications that we need to take into account when thinking about our normative framework for public health. The first difficulty is one that particularly affects attempts to go from philosophical ethical theorizing into practicable and defensible policy. I call this the problem of complex systems, namely that the distribution of health both affects and is affected by the distribution of other goods. These interactions are not just complicated, they are complex: they outwit (and can be expected to continue to outwit) our best attempts to understand the minutiae of the relevant causal interactions (Edwards 2004). This creates a problem for top-down approaches to public health policy making, in as much as it will always for the foreseeable future be very difficult (if not impossible) to set and then implement policy in a way that reliably leads to things turning out as we envisage that they will, and attempts to do so will tend to be subject to unintended adverse consequences.

The second and third problems will particularly affect bottom-up attempts to construct public health policy without drawing on deep and systematic normative reflection. The second problem is the problem of the limits and goals of public health. It seems intuitively obvious that the main purpose of public health policy should be to improve and protect the health of the population. However, it is far less obvious what we should take health to be in this context, and different answers will make important differences in how we view the goals of public health. Moreover, it is unclear whether the goals of public health activity ought to be simply to maximize population health, or should also include health equity and personal choice.

The third problem is the problem of the relative importance of health. I argue that health looks to be at best one ultimate good amongst several that societies should be pursuing; and it is not always the case that a policy that will further the goals of public health will also be in concert with other ultimate goals we will have as a society. In other words, we face a tough indexing problem of how to trade off between goals that are apparently at least partially incommensurable. Given the causal entanglement of health and other goods and the broader problem of complex systems, it does not make sense to try to set public health goals without reference to a larger framework in which we

> **Complex system**
> A network composed of many interconnected parts, in which the effects of change are difficult or even impossible to predict.

relate the value of health to the value of other goals that a society wishes to pursue. . . .

Normative Theorizing and the Problem of Complex Systems

The problem of complex systems is one that is endemic to any endeavour to reform institutions, though it is one that is particularly problematic for public health interventions. In short, any attempt to change the way that an institution operates will tend to have effects on other aspects of the way this institution operates; and it will also tend to have spreading and somewhat unpredictable effects on the way that other institutions operate. To put the problem in a slightly different way, large institutions, such as a nationalized healthcare system, are not merely complicated, but also complex systems: it is not just that they are comprised of many parts, but also that they are comprised of parts whose interactions make a large difference to how the system as a whole operates. Moreover, these interactions between the parts do not tend to be additive: rather we also see complex positive and negative feedback loops. A set of new ideas, such as those that we now call evidence-based medicine, may start in a small group, then spread to a hospital and then colonize much of medical education. Other ideas and theories, perhaps no less intrinsically helpful, encounter initial turbulence, and are snuffed out.

> **Evidence-based medicine**
> A widely influential approach to medical practice that seeks to apply the best available scientific evidence to treatment decisions made by health care practitioners.

Chapman (2004) argues plausibly that we will tend to see three large problems if we treat a complex system such as the UK's National Health Service as being amenable to a top-down engineering model of reform. First, we will tend to find that many of our reforms have unintended consequences: we will apply a reform that is intended to have one effect, but we will find that, whether it achieves its intended target or not, it also has unintended side effects.[1] The second problem follows on from the first: top-down attempts to reform complex systems will tend to alienate professionals who work inside

> **National Health Service**
> The publicly funded national health care systems in England, Scotland, and Wales. Although they are administered independently, residents of one region may be treated in another without cost.

these institutions, because, given the impossibility of constructing a plan that will require sensible things in all cases, it will require the professionals to sometimes or perhaps regularly work according to goals or targets that they believe to be wrong or mistaken. For instance, a doctor may be required to spend less time with a patient than she thinks necessary, because she has been instructed to see a certain number of patients per hour. Third, we can expect such reforms to fail to improve standards over time: the failures to achieve intended aims, and the need to counteract the unintended consequences of previous reforms, will lead to a perceived need for further reform, "following in the trail of events like an inexperienced boxer who covers the body part that has just been hit only to get hit somewhere else." This continual reform will of course only tend to heighten the sense of alienation felt by professionals, and will tend to add to this alienation a sense of confusion and reform fatigue.[2]. . .

Public Health and the Problem of Complex Systems

The problem of complex systems is vital to address in public health ethics, for two reasons. First, because public health interventions are classically oriented at a population level rather than an individual level, the core of public health interventions is creating and reforming institutional structures in such a way as to improve population health.

Second, we now have solid evidence that a vast array of different factors about the makeup of the basic institutions of society pervasively affect population health.[3] We cannot improve population health without engaging deeply with the structures of these other institutions and the different ways they impact on health. Just to give one small example (and of course, part of my point is that there will be lots of other interactions, which we either do not know about yet, or which will interact unpredictably with one another), our transport and urban policy will have a great impact on health. If we encourage car use, then more people will end up obese than if we encourage cycling and walking. Hence things like the ways we design our towns (whether we place shopping centres out of the centre of town, so that it is very inconvenient to shop unless you have a car), can make a big difference to population health. On the other hand, the way we regulate the distribution of health pervasively affects the distribution of other goods. When people do not have a certain modicum of health, they are unable to work, and are thus deprived of access to other important goods (e.g. work, play, pain-free existence).

An additional problem that normative thinking about public health will need to come to terms with is that the typical structure of government departments creates another layer of difficulty in constructing an effective public health policy. Even if we were in a position to understand all (or enough of) the relevant causal pathways, health ministries are not typically in a position to ensure that the required changes are implemented across sectors such as transport, employment and education, which are usually the responsibility of different government departments. Where we need different bits of government working together in order to ensure a particular result for health, then the typical structure of government departments, which tend to be in competition with one another for resources and prestige make this difficult to achieve, and it is very likely that another department's policy may end up undermining what we would like to achieve from a public health perspective.

The problem of complex systems thus presents a serious challenge to any form of abstract theorizing about public health that is not grounded in an understanding of factors that impede or accelerate our attempts at reform. In short, unless we can factor in a sufficient understanding of the inner wiring of the complex systems we are trying to reform, our attempts as philosophers to suggest how institutions should be reformed will either be dismissed as unworkable by those who are responsible for delivering services on the ground — or perhaps worse ! — they may be implemented, and cause the unintended consequences and alienation of professionals which we saw are the likely results of top-down attempts to reform complex institutions. . . . The solution to this problem depends crucially on the level of abstraction at which we are working: insofar as we are interested in largely conceptual issues, then the problem need not affect us; but if we are interested in actually improving people's lives then it is of vital importance that we take it into account. . . .

The Goals of Public Health

As Munthe (2008) argues, the traditional goal of public health was merely to improve population health,

measured for example by average life expectancy. The problem with this is that merely looking at averages hides potentially normatively problematic variations within the distribution of health. Since the Black Report in 1980, we have become increasingly aware of the extent to which there are inequalities in health, and the fact that these inequalities fall on people who are already disadvantaged for other reasons.[4] Because of this, many public health practitioners have found it plausible to introduce a second goal as a key one for public health, namely a reduction in health inequalities. More recently, a third potential goal for public health has appeared on the horizon: namely, health-related autonomy. The point here is simple: health is only one among many goods, and it is legitimate for citizens in a liberal society to choose to value other goods above their health if they so desire. (For instance, someone might well prefer drinking a bottle of wine per day with its attendant health disadvantages, to a more abstemious intake.) Because of this factor of personal choice, it becomes apparent that perhaps the goal of public health activity should be not simply to promote health *per se*, but also to provide the conditions under which people can freely choose to be healthy if they so desire.[5]

Both equality and the freedom for each citizen to pursue his own conception of the good are compellingly important goals from the perspective of what we think justice is, and hence what we think governments as a whole should be aiming at. The key question for public health is whether we should consider equality in health, and personal freedom to be internal and constitutive constraints on the goals of public health, or whether the values of equality and autonomy should be thought of as external constraints on public health activity. . . . As we cross over to the third problem—the importance of health relative to other goods that a society should be aiming at—we shall notice that there is a theoretical benefit to thinking of them as internal constraints, insofar as we will ultimately need to provide an integrated account of justice that takes into account how health's value is related to the value of other goods. Having

> **Black Report**
> The influential report published in 1980 of an expert committee chaired by Sir Douglas Black investigating health inequalities in the United Kingdom. The report concluded the health inequalities were largely a function of economic inequalities and that the gap between the health of the rich and the poor in the UK was widening.

an account of the goals of public health that already incorporates the core values of our overall theory of justice as constituent parts will make this work of integration less difficult (Munthe 2008).

The Relative Importance of Health

It is vital for normative work on public health to focus on the relative importance of health—that is the importance that health has relative to other goods that a society should be aiming to promote or protect—for two reasons. First, resources that are devoted to the goals of public health cannot be devoted to the pursuit of other goals, and it is important that as a society we should be placing our resources in a position to best meet whatever our goals should be.

Second, we remarked earlier on the way in which health is causally entangled with other goods. Hence policies that we would like to pursue in order to promote other goods (such as liberty) will tend to have effects (both positive and negative) on health, and policies that we enact to promote the goals of public health will often have effects (both positive and negative) on the distribution of other non-health goods. Where we have reason to believe that the complex causal relationships are likely to rebound in a way that is favourable (where, for example, improving women's education and literacy has many other benefits including increased health equality), then this may not be an important practical problem. However, there are cases where goals we might wish to attain in health will conflict with other goals. In such cases we face a choice between these two rival goods, and hence it will be important to work out how important health is relative to the other goods in play.

Questions about the relative weights societies should give to different goods—which goods should be seen as important for their own sake, and which goods of only derivative importance from a policy perspective—are questions about justice. Hence finding a suitable normative framework for thinking about public health ethics and policy requires us, in the end to work out which account of justice we should prefer, and the importance that health should have in this account of justice.[6] . . .

Study Questions

1. What is the "problem of complexity"? Why must it be taken into account when making public health decisions?

2. What are the goals of public health?

3. Why is it important to recognize that citizens value other goods at least as much as health in public health decisions?

Notes

1. The most well-known of such unintended side effects in reform of institutions is probably the effect of setting multiple and specific targets, which will tend to create incentives to meet and to prioritize the targets, and thus sideline other goals which are also important.

2. See for example, Sennett (2008: 50): "Any organizational reform takes time to 'bed in'; people have to learn how to put the changes into practice—whom now to call, which forms to use, what procedures to follow. If a patient is having a heart attack, you do not want to reach for your 'Manual of Best-Practice Performances' to discover the latest rules

about what you are supposed to do. The process of bedding in takes longer the bigger and more complex the organization in which one works."

3. Out of a massive literature, see for example, Wilkinson and Marmot (2003); CSDH (2008).

4. Department of Health and Social Security (1980). See also Marmot (2004) and Wilkinson (1996).

5. Of course, where public health policy has as its focus children and non-competent adults, or choices in adults that tend to be less autonomous such as those concerning food and alcohol, such a "choice-centred" view of public health is markedly less

attractive. In the case of children, few will doubt that public health policy should aim simply at health rather than at the freedom to be healthy.

6. I have written about this problem at greater length in (Wilson, 2009a, b). The next few paragraphs draw on the analysis given there.

References

Bok, S. (2004). Rethinking the WHO Definition of Health. In Harvard Center for Population and Development Studies: Working Paper Series, 14.

Boorse, C. (1975). On the Distinction between Disease and Illness. *Philosophy and Public Affairs, 5*, 49–68.

Boorse, C. (1997). A Rebuttal on Health. In Humber, J.M. and Almeder, R. F. (eds), *What is Disease?* Totowa, NJ: Humana Press, pp. 3–143.

Brennan, G. and Pettit, P. (2005). The Feasibility Issue. In Jackson, F. and Smith, M. (eds), *Oxford Handbook of Contemporary Philosophy*. Oxford: Oxford University Press, pp. 258–82.

Callahan, D. (1973). The WHO Definition of "Health." *Hastings Center Studies, 1*, 77–87.

Caplan, A. (1983). Can Applied Ethics Be Effective in Health Care and Should It Strive to Be? *Ethics, 93*, 311–19.

Chapman, J. (2004). *System Failure: Why Governments Must Learn to Think Differently*, 2nd ed. London: Demos, Available from http://www.demos.co.uk/publications/systemfailure2.

Cooper, R. (2002). Disease. *Studies in History and Philosophy of Biological and Biomedical Sciences, 33*, 263–82.

CSDH (2008). *Closing the Gap in a Generation: Health Equity through Action on the Social Determinants of Health. Final Report of the Commission on Social Determinants of Health.* Geneva: World Health Organization.

Demosthenes (4th Century BCE), *First Philippic*. My translation (which I slightly modified) came from http://www.san.beck.org/EC22-Alexander.html.

Department of Health and Social Security. (1980). *Inequalities in Health: Report of a Research Working Group*. London: DHSS.

Dworkin, R. (2000). *Sovereign Virtue: The Theory and Practice of Equality*. Cambridge, MA: Harvard University Press.

Edwards, N. (2004). Foreword. In Chapman, J. (ed.), *System Failure: Why Governments Must Learn to Think Differently*, 2nd ed. London: Demos, Available from http://www.demos.co.uk/publications/systemfailure2.

Habermas, J. (1992). *Moral Consciousness and Communicative Action*, trans. Lenhardt, C. and Nicholsen, S. London: Polity Press.

Hausman, D. M. (2007). What's Wrong with Health Inequalities? *Journal of Political Philosophy, 15*, 46–66.

Lenman, J. (2000). Consequentialism and Cluelessness. *Philosophy and Public Affairs, 29*, 342–70.

Lewis, P. (2007). The Empirical Slippery Slope from Voluntary to Non-voluntary Euthanasia? *Journal of Law, Medicine, and Ethics, 35*, 197–210.

Marmot, M. (2004). *Status Syndrome: How Your Social Standing Directly Affects Your Health and Life Expectancy*. London: Bloomsbury.

Mill, J. S. (1861). On Liberty.

Munthe, C. (2008). The Goals of Public Health: An Integrated Multidimensional Model. *Public Health Ethics, 1*, 39–52.

Murphy, D. (2008). Concepts of Disease and Health. In Zalta, Edward N. (ed.), *The Stanford Encyclopedia of Philosophy* (Winter 2008 Edition). URL=<http://plato.stanford.edu/archives/win2008/entries/health-disease/>.

Reznek, L. (1987). *The Nature of Disease*. New York: Routledge.

Sen, A. (2006). What Do We Want from a Theory of Justice? *Journal of Philosophy, 103*, 215–38.

Sennett, R. (2008). *The Craftsman*. London: Allen Lane.

Verweij, M. and Dawson, A. (2007). The Meaning of "Public" in Public Health. In Verweij, M. and Dawson, A. (eds), *Ethics, Prevention and Public Health*. Oxford: Oxford University Press.

Wilkinson, R. (1996). *Unhealthy Societies: The Afflictions of Inequality*. London: Routledge.

Wilkinson, R. and Marmot, M. (2003). *Social Determinants of Health: The Solid Facts*. Denmark: World Health Organisation. Available from http://www.euro.who.int/document/e81384.pdf.

Wilkinson, R. and Pickett, K. (2006). Income Inequality and Population Health: A Review and Explanation of the Evidence. *Social Science and Medicine, 62*, 1768–84.

Wilson, J. (2009a). Not So Special After All? Daniels and the Social Determinants of Health. *Journal of Medical Ethics, 35*, 3–6.

Wilson, J. (2009b). Health Inequities. In Dawson, A. (ed.), *Public Health Ethics: Key Concepts in Policy and Practice*. Cambridge: Cambridge University Press.

Wolff, J. and de-Shalit, A. (2007). *Disadvantage*. Oxford: Oxford University Press.

THREE   Pandemic Influenza Preparedness: An Ethical Framework to Guide Decision-making

Alison K. Thompson, Karen Faith, Jennifer L. Gibson, and Ross E.G. Upshur | *BMC Medical Ethics* 2006; E12.

. . . The framework here proposed is an example of practical ethics that attempts to provide decision-makers with an introduction to and articulation of generally accepted ethical principles or values. The significance of this ethical framework is (1) in the unique collaborative approach taken to its development that involved ethicists with different areas of expertise and a variety of health care stakeholders, and (2) that it fills an important need in pandemic planning for an ethical framework to guide decision-making that has been unmet in most pandemic planning processes worldwide. . . .

> **Pandemic**
> An outbreak in which a disease is spreading through populations across a large geographical area, for instance, several countries or the entire world.

Development of the Ethical Framework

Formation of a Working Group

In Ontario the need for guidance on the ethical issues pertaining to an influenza pandemic has been widely acknowledged. As word of our work on an ethical framework for Sunnybrook and Women's College Health Science Centre (S&W) became known, we were invited to join other hospitals' pandemic planning efforts. There was also broader sectoral interest in ethics, and we were invited to join the Ontario Ministry of Health and Long Term Care's (MOHLTC) efforts to design a pandemic plan.

> **Influenza**
> Influenza is a respiratory illness caused by the influenza virus. The virus commonly circulates in the community in winter months causing fever, cough, and chest pain. Serious complications are most common among the very young, those with pre-existing respiratory problems, and the elderly. Periodically, a new strain may emerge that is unaffected by any immunity people have to older strains, and widespread and serious infections may result. The influenza pandemic of 1918–19 infected about one-third of the world's population and killed at least 50,000,000 people in a six-month period.

Our working group was formed in response to the pandemic planning initiative that took place at S&W in early 2005. The hospital's Clinical Ethics Centre was invited to provide ethics support in this planning initiative. It soon became apparent that the scope of the issues went beyond the purview of clinical ethics to include organizational and public health ethics. Expertise in organizational and public health ethics was quickly procured through the University of Toronto Joint Centre for Bioethics, which is a partnership between the University and sixteen affiliated health care organizations that includes S&W among its partners. S&W was subsequently de-amalgamated into Sunnybrook Health Sciences Centre and Women's College Hospital, thus the ethical framework is currently being implemented at Sunnybrook HSC.

As the framework took shape, we were invited to join the MOHLTC planning efforts. We began to work with the Vaccine and Antiviral working group at the MOHLTC, and we adapted our work to meet the related but distinct challenges facing government. . . .

Review of Clinical Ethics and Public Health Ethics Literature

Expertise in clinical ethics was important to the development of this framework because of the knowledge, skills and experience clinical ethicists need to address dilemmas or challenges found in the daily clinical arena. An obvious challenge was how to integrate expertise in public health ethics into a framework designed to guide decision-making in clinical health care settings. A related challenge was to thoughtfully integrate generally accepted principles and values from clinical ethics with those in public health ethics. In order to meet this challenge, the authors turned not only to the respective ethics literature, but also to the SARS experiences of Toronto hospitals and health care providers. A

> **SARS**
> Severe acute respiratory syndrome. SARS is a severe form of pneumonia caused by the coronavirus that has a death rate of about 10 per cent. A large outbreak in 2003 began in Hong Kong and quickly spread globally, infecting 8000 people and killing 750. Toronto, Canada experienced a large number of cases during the outbreak and hospitals were rapidly overwhelmed by infected health care workers and large numbers of patients who required mechanical ventilation.

review of the SARS literature, and that of public health ethics more generally, guided the integration of the public health and the clinical ethics perspectives.[1–9] The Toronto experience with SARS demonstrated that organizations faced unique ethical challenges when dealing with a public health crisis, and much of the ethics literature identified a need for greater forethought in how organizations can foster ethical decision-making in times of crisis.[10–12] . . .

Lessons from Emergency Ethics

Not surprisingly, the literature on clinical ethics has little to say about disaster preparedness and how to make decisions about such things as triage under extraordinary circumstances. The ethics literature on bioterrorism and battle-field triage informed our thinking and called our attention to important issues such as the duty to care, reciprocity, equity and good stewardship.[13–18] The importance of having ethically robust criteria and policies developed in advance of a pandemic influenza outbreak is underscored in this literature, for "critical decisions like these should not be made on an individual case-by-case basis" and "physicians should never be placed in a position of individually deciding to deny treatment to patients without the guidance of policy or protocol."[19] Robust disaster preparedness requires practising preventive ethics.

Stakeholder Vetting

The ethical framework was vetted through S&W's Pandemic Planning Committee, the Joint Centre for Bioethics' Clinical Ethics Group (comprised of the affiliated health care organizations' clinical ethicists), the MOHLTC Vaccine and Antiviral Working Group, and the MOHLTC pandemic planning committee. Through this process, we refined the framework and we are grateful to these groups for their valuable insights.

The Ethical Framework

The ethical framework is intended to inform decision-making, not replace it. It is intended to encourage reflection on important values, discussion and review of ethical concerns arising from a public health crisis. It is intended also as a means to improve accountability for decision-making and may require revision as feedback and circumstances require.

The framework is divided into two distinct parts, and begins with the premise that planning decisions

for a pandemic influenza outbreak ought to be: (1) guided by ethical decision-making processes, and (2) informed by ethical values. Ethical processes can help to improve accountability and it is hoped that, to the extent that it is possible for ethical processes to produce ethical outcomes, the substantive ethical quality of decisions will be enhanced. Recognizing, however, that ethical processes do not guarantee ethical outcomes, we have identified ten key ethical values to guide decision-making that address the substantive ethical dimensions of decision-making in this context.

Ethical Processes

In planning for and throughout a pandemic influenza crisis, difficult decisions will be made that are fraught with ethical challenges. Our framework around ethical processes is based upon the "accountability for reasonableness" model developed by Daniels and Sabin[20] and adapted by Gibson, Martin, and Singer.[21] This model provides a useful means of identifying the key elements of ethical decision-making processes. An extensive literature has developed around Daniels' and Sabin's accountability for reasonableness framework. The Daniels and Sabin framework has broad applicability across institutional settings and priority setting situations.[22–29] Because the Daniels and Sabin framework applies deliberative theories of democratic justice to the specific problem of health care priority setting, and because it is unique in this regard, we felt it promoted the kind of deliberative approach to pandemic planning that this ethical framework is intended to support. Here we outline the characteristics of an ethical decision-making process. Stakeholders will be more able to accept difficult decisions during a pandemic influenza crisis if the decision-making process has, and is perceived to have, ethical legitimacy.

> **Deliberative theories of democractic justice**
> Approaches to democracy in which public deliberation is the source of legitimate law making. In such approaches, considerable attention is paid to the conditions that must obtain in order for public deliberation to be valid. The Daniels and Sabin framework is one instance of a set of criteria that define a fair decision-making process.

Accountability: There should be mechanisms in place to ensure that ethical decision-making is sustained throughout the crisis.

Inclusiveness: Decisions should be made explicitly with stakeholder views in mind and there should be opportunities for stakeholders to be engaged in the decision-making process. For example, decision-making related to staff deployment should include the input of affected staff.

Openness and Transparency: Decisions should be publicly defensible. This means that the process by which decisions were made must be open to scrutiny and the basis upon which decisions are made should be publicly accessible to affected stakeholders. For example, there should be a communication plan developed in advance to ensure that information can be effectively disseminated to affected stakeholders and that stakeholders know where to go for needed information.

Reasonableness: Decisions should be based on reasons (i.e., evidence, principles, values) that stakeholders can agree are relevant to meeting health needs in a pandemic influenza crisis and they should be made by people who are credible and accountable. For example, decision-makers should provide a rationale for prioritizing particular groups for antiviral medication and for limiting access to elective surgeries and other services.

> **Antiviral medication**
> Drugs that are used to treat viral infections. A number of drugs are known to be effective in the treatment of influenza, including oseltamivir (Tamiflu) and zanamivir (Relenza). The effectiveness of these drugs for future strains of pandemic influenza is difficult to predict.

Responsiveness: There should be opportunities to revisit and revise decisions as new information emerges throughout the crisis as well as mechanisms to address disputes and complaints. For example, if elective surgeries are cancelled or postponed, there should be a formal mechanism for stakeholders to voice any concerns they may have with the decision.

Ethical Values

The second part of the framework identifies ten key ethical values that should inform the pandemic influenza planning process and decision-making during an outbreak: duty to provide care, equity, individual liberty, privacy, proportionality, protection of the public from harm, reciprocity, solidarity, stewardship, and trust. These values are intended to provide guidance, and it is important to consider that more than one value may be relevant to a situation. Indeed, the hallmark of a challenging ethical decision is that one or more value(s) are in tension and that there is no clear answer about which one to privilege in making the decision. When values are in tension with one another, the importance of having ethical decision-making processes is reinforced. . . .

The values identified in our ethical framework were based initially on previous research findings on ethics and SARS at the University of Toronto Joint Centre for Bioethics (JCB). . . . These values were then further articulated by our working group and adapted for the pandemic influenza planning context. Through a discursive process of stakeholder consultation with public health specialists, ministry officials, S&W's pandemic influenza committee, and the Clinical Ethics Group at the JCB, we augmented the values to include two new values (stewardship and trust[30, 31]) and refined the definitions of each value in light of the anticipated demands of a pandemic influenza crisis compared to a hospital-based epidemic such as SARS. The substantive values identified and articulated in the framework are not intended to be an exhaustive set, and they may underdetermine how best to achieve the *overall* goals of pandemic planning, which generally include the minimization of morbidity, mortality, and societal disruption. . . .

Lessons for Implementing an Ethical Framework

We have identified three necessary, if not exhaustive elements to the successful integration of ethics into hospital pandemic planning processes. These elements are: (1) sponsorship of the ethical framework by senior hospital administration; (2) vetting of the framework by key stakeholders and; (3) decision review processes.

Sponsorship by Senior Administrators

Whether or not an ethical framework is used to inform decision-making in a health care institution depends to a large extent on people in senior positions of an organization seeing its relevance to the decision-making process. In part, this is dependent on how robust the framework is, but it also requires the willingness to frame (at least some) pandemic planning issues as normative in nature.

Some may argue that the values in the framework are too stringent or impractical to implement under crisis conditions, especially those found in the Ethical Processes part of the framework. . . . Certainly, crisis conditions may place constraints on the extent to which each principle can be acted upon. However, efforts should be made to put them into action to the fullest extent possible under the circumstances and in our experience this is only possible with the support of senior administrators. . . .

Vetting of the Ethical Framework by Key Stakeholders

In order to obtain support for, or "buy in" to an ethical framework, it is important that key stakeholders in an institution vet the framework. This requires careful consideration of who the key stakeholders are in an institution. Not only should this include those with responsibility for decision-making, but also those who will be affected by decisions taken. For the vetting process is not just intended to create "buy in" but also to decrease the likelihood that interests and issues that are (morally) relevant to pandemic planning will be neglected or overlooked, thereby enhancing the moral legitimacy of the values in the framework. In addition, a process of stakeholder vetting increases the likelihood that the values instantiated in the framework resonate with the stakeholder community.

It has been our experience that the values in the framework did resonate with the pandemic planners with whom we have shared this ethical framework. The primarily pragmatic justification for the selection of the values in the framework means that the framework is provisional so it ought to be subject to revision in light of compelling argument, empirical evidence, and further stakeholder feedback. It is important to note, however, that the iterative and inclusive process through which the values in the framework were deliberated amongst the various stakeholder groups lends them a form of discursive ethical legitimacy and helps to justify their inclusion in the ethical framework. We intend that the framework invite further dialogue about its legitimacy and its adequacy. . . .

Ideally, the vetting process would include people who can represent the interests of patients, families and volunteers who are part of the hospital's constituency. Although patient relations, human resources and occupational health representatives from S&W provided guidance and feedback in the development of the framework, direct input from patients and family representatives was not obtained. One limitation of our framework is that is has yet to be vetted by these important stakeholders.

The importance of solidarity to the management of a public health crisis would also suggest that the public and other health care organizations be considered stakeholders in hospital pandemic planning. While it may not be pragmatic for hospitals to undertake broad public consultation and vetting processes for their pandemic plans in general, and their ethical frameworks in particular, solidarity and equity suggest that these broader stakeholder interests are relevant to pandemic planning. Consequently, opportunities for broader ethical dialogue about pandemic planning need to be encouraged.

Decision Review Processes

In order to ensure that the support of key stakeholders is maintained through an outbreak, there need to be effective communication mechanisms in place. An important aspect of responsive decision-making processes is ensuring that there are formal opportunities to revisit and revise decisions as new information emerges. . . . We believe decision review mechanisms are an essential part of ethical decision-making in a public health crisis, and are one way to put the values in the ethical framework into action.

Formal mechanisms for reviewing decisions are needed in order to capture feedback from stakeholders on key decisions, and to resolve disputes and challenges. These processes are important for ensuring that decisions are the best possible under the circumstances given changing information and for engaging stakeholders constructively around the difficult decisions that must be made. Given the unpredictable nature of public health emergencies and the difficulty this poses for those in charge of planning and decision-making, it is reasonable to assume that decisions will be revised throughout the pandemic influenza crisis. Disputes or challenges may arise from the restrictions or requirements imposed on staff, patients, and families during a pandemic influenza outbreak. Thus, decision review processes are essential. Again, while some may argue that this is too stringent a measure for a time of crisis, we argue that reviews of decisions will be taking place regardless (most likely in an *ad hoc* manner), and that to formalize this process is to increase its fairness and moral legitimacy. Indeed, there may be existing mechanisms which can handle these kinds of reviews. . . .

Study Questions

1. What principles do the authors argue are likely to enhance the legitimacy of a decision-making process that gives rise to public health policy?

2. What ethical values do the authors identify? How do these values relate to the ethical process they propose?

3. Does the process outlined guarantee a good or justified conclusion? Why?

Notes

1. Beauchamp T, Steinbock B: *New Ethics for the Public's Health*. New York, Oxford University Press; 1999.

2. Zoloth L, Zoloth S: Don't be chicken: bioethics and avian flu. *The American Journal of Bioethics* 2006, 6:5–8.

3. Kotalik J: *Addressing issues and questions relating to pandemic influenza planning: final report and recommendations*. Health Canada; 2003.

4. Berstein M, Hawryluck L: Challenging beliefs and ethical concepts: the collateral damage of SARS. *Critical Care* 2003, 7:269–71.

5. Singer P, Benatar S, Berstein M, Daar A, Dickens B, MacRae S, Upshur R, Wright L, Zlotnick Shaul R: Ethics and SARS: lessons from Toronto. *BMJ* 2003, 327:1342–4.

6. Bell J, Hyland S, DePelligrin T, Upshur R, Berstein M, Martin D: SARS and hospital priority setting: a qualitative case study and evaluation. *BMC Health Services Research* 2004, 4.

7. Upshur R: Principles for the justification of public health intervention. *Can J Public Health* 2002, 93:101–3.

8. Gostin LO: Public health, ethics, and human rights: a tribute to the late Johnathan Mann. *J Law Med Ethics* 2001, 29:121–30.

9. O'Neill O: Public Health or Clinical Ethics: Thinking beyond Borders. *Ethics & International Affairs* 2002, 16.

10. Berstein and Hawryluck. Challenging beliefs and ethical concepts.

11. Singer et al. Ethics and SARS.

12. Bell et al. SARS and hospital priority setting.

13. Wynia MK, Gostin LO: Ethical challenges in preparing for bioterrorism: barriers within the health care system. *Am J Public Health* 2004, 97(7):1096–102.

14. Iserson K, Pesik N: Ethical resources distribution after biological, chemical or radiological terrorism. *Cambridge Quarterly of Healthcare Ethics* 2003, 12:455–65.

15. Pesik N, Keim M, Iserson K: Terrorism and the ethics of emergency medical care. *Annals of Emergency Medicine* 2001, 37:642–6.

16. Veatch R: Disaster preparedness and triage: justice and the common good. *Mt Sinai J Med* 2005, 72(4):236–41.

17. Kipnis K: Overwhelming casualties: medical ethics in a time of terror. *Accountability in Research* 2003, 10:57–68.

18. Marer S, Sutjita M, Rajagopalan S: Bioterrorism, bioethics and the emergency physician. *Topics in Emergency Medicine* 2004, 26:44–8.

19. Pesik et al. Terrorism and the ethics of emergency medical care.

20. Daniels N: Accountability for reasonableness. *BMJ* 2000, 321:1300–1.

21. Gibson J, Martin D, Singer P: Priority setting in hospitals: fairness, inclusiveness and the problem of institutional power differences. *Social Science and Medicine* 2005, 61:2355–62.

22. Ham C: Tragic choices in health care: lessons from the Child B case. *British Medical Journal* 1999, 319:1258–61.

23. Norheim OF: *Procedures for priority setting and mechanisms of appeal in the Norwegian health care system*; Amsterdam; 2000.

24. Daniels N, Sabin J: *Setting limits fairly: can we learn to share scarce resources?* Oxford, Oxford University Press; 2002.

25. Martin DK, Giacomini M, Singer P: Fairness, accountability for reasonableness and the views of priority setting decision-makers. *Health Policy* 2002, 61:279–90.

26. Martin DK, Shulman K, Santiago-Sorrell P, Singer P: Priority setting and hospital strategic planning: a qualitative case study. *Journal of Health Services Research and Policy* 2003, 8:59–68.

27. Gibson J, Martin DK, Singer P: Setting priorities in health care organisations: criteria, processes, and parameters of success. *BMC Health Services Research* 2004, 4.

28. Gibson J, Martin DK, Singer P: Priority setting in hospitals: fairness, inclusiveness, and the problem of institutional power differences. *Social Science and Medicine* 2005, 61:2355–62.

29. Mitton C, Donaldson C: Health care priority setting: principles, practice and challenges. *Cost Eff Resour Alloc* 2004, 2(1):3.

30. Saltman RB, Feroussier-Davis O: The concept of stewardship in health policy. *Bulletin of the World Health Organization* 2000, 78.

31. Goold SD: Trust and the ethics of health care institutions. *Hastings Center Report* 2001, 31:26–33.

Chapter Study Questions

1. Wilson argues that public health may have differing goals. Which set of goals do you think is the most compelling and why? How do these goals (particularly the inclusion of health-related autonomy) impact upon the public health ethics framework articulated by Childress and colleagues?

2. Does an ethics of public health presuppose an account of the relative weights that societies should give to different goods? How does Wilson argue for this? How might the authors of one of the other two readings respond?

3. Compare and contrast the public health ethics frameworks proposed by Childress and colleagues, and Thompson and colleagues. Which is superior? Why?

Critical Analysis

Consider the following selection from the Wilson article:

"More recently, a third potential goal for public health has appeared on the horizon: namely, health-related autonomy. The point here is simple: health is only one among many goods, and it is legitimate for citizens in a liberal society to choose to value other goods above their health if they so desire. (For instance, someone might well prefer drinking a bottle of wine per day with its attendant health disadvantages, to a more abstemious intake.) Because of this factor of personal choice, it becomes apparent that perhaps the goal of public health activity should be not simply to promote health per se, but also to provide the conditions under which people can freely choose to be healthy if they so desire."

Outline Wilson's argument in your own words, paying particular attention to the premises that he relies on to support his main conclusion. Choose one of the premises for evaluation. Try to think of at least one objection to this premise.

Case Study

Chris van Buren is a 29-year-old man who returned to Toronto from a trip to South Africa eight months ago. Shortly after returning, he developed a cough, fever, and weight loss. After extensive medical tests, he was diagnosed with multi-drug resistant (MDR) tuberculosis (TB). After a period of treatment in hospital, he was released to continue treatment at home for at least another six months. His treatment consists of a burdensome regimen of four different antibiotics. He has been instructed not to leave the house until tests confirm that his sputum is clear of all traces of TB.

From the start of his treatment, there have been issues with Chris' compliance with treatment. In hospital he repeatedly left his hospital room without permission to smoke cigarettes outside. At one point, hospital staff ordered a security guard posted outside of his hospital room. After release, he has been observed twice in a local shopping mall. Because Chris lives alone, public health has arranged for daily delivery of food and medication. In his defense, Chris noted that he needed to buy some clothes and that he was careful to wear a mask to avoid infecting others. The public health officer is considering ordering that Chris be detained in a locked hospital ward until his treatment is completed.

MDR TB refers to tuberculosis that is resistant to at least two drugs in the standard treatment regimen. As a result, it is treated with second line drugs that are more expensive and are associated with more side effects. Additionally, it may require treatment for longer periods of time to ensure that the TB is eliminated. Public health officials are anxious to prevent the spread of drug resistant TB in the community because of the difficulty in treating it and the worry that fully resistant strains of TB may emerge.

1. What is the ethical dilemma in this case? What moral considerations are in conflict?

2. Does forced detention in this case fulfill the conditions for paternalistic public health action laid out by Childress and colleagues?

3. Propose a different solution to the case, and argue why it ought to be preferred to forced detention.

Further Reading

Canadian program of research in ethics in a pandemic [Internet]. Available from: http://www.canprep.ca/. Date accessed: 7 June 2012.

Kass NE. An ethics framework for public health. *Am J Public Health* 2001;91(11):1776-82.

Mann JM. Medicine and public health, ethics and human rights. Hastings Cent Rep 1997;27(3):6-13.

Ontario Public Health Association [Internet]. Available from: http://www.opha.on.ca/resources/. Date accessed: 7 June 2012.

Public Health Agency of Canada [Internet]. Available from: http://www.phac-aspc.gc.ca/index-eng.php. Date accessed: 7 June 2012.

Research on Non-human Animals

In this chapter, we examine ethical issues in research conducted on non-human animals (hereafter animals). The use of animals in medical and other forms of scientific research has proven to be beneficial to the health and well-being of both human beings and animals. Research that established the efficacy of penicillin relied on the use of mice. Dogs were an integral part of the studies that developed insulin for diabetes. Polio vaccines were discovered with experimentation employing monkeys, among other animals. Developing the ability to perform blood transfusions and certain forms of heart surgery required the use of dogs and pigs. Experiments on rats and mice were an essential component of the development of the BCG vaccine for use in preventing tuberculosis. Drugs for the treatment of a wide variety of diseases, including AIDS, cancer, and depression, rely on the use of animals. The safety of many household products, from shampoo to oven cleaner to cosmetics, depends on studies conducted on animals, and in some countries these studies are required by law. In addition, our understanding of the basic anatomy and physiology of animals and humans involves experimentation on animals. In many of these experiments, the animals are killed or harmed in some way.

Of course, not all research conducted on animals is of substantial benefit to human beings. In the late 1960s and early 1970s, scientists at the American Museum of Natural History received funding to conduct research on the sexual behaviour of cats. This involved, among other things, mutilating cats and then studying the implications of this for their sexual conduct. Researchers found that male cats with brain lesions preferred to mount a female rabbit rather than a female cat when placed in a room where both were present. Also in the 1970s, Amnesty International sponsored research that involved burning and electrically shocking pigs in an effort to determine whether an individual could be tortured without leaving marks. More recently, research in agriculture has focused on producing animals that are leaner and more amenable to the generation of agricultural profits, often at the expense of the health and well-being of both humans and animals.

In Canada, there is no federal law that deals specifically with the use of animals in scientific research, though several provinces, including Ontario, Manitoba, Prince Edward Island, and Saskatchewan, have such legislation. Instead, at the national level the use of animals in research is regulated by the Canadian Council on Animal Care (CCAC). The mandate of this body is to articulate and uphold the standards for the use and care of animals used in product testing, instruction, and experimentation. This body is funded mainly by the Natural Sciences and Engineering Research Council of Canada and the Canadian Institutes of Health Research. In order for a researcher to obtain funding from these bodies he or she must conform to its guidelines. However, compliance with the CCAC guidelines is voluntary, and therefore a private scientific research institution that does not wish to receive federal or cognate funding is not legally required to abide by its strictures. In cases in which a research institution chooses to forgo federal funding, the provisions in the Criminal Code of Canada respecting cruelty to animals and the relevant provincial code (if any) govern the research in question.

The CCAC reports that in 2009 the participants in its programme used in excess of three million animals. The majority of these animals were mice, rats, and fish. But dogs, cats, horses, sheep, cows, and non-human primates were also used. Not all of this research is painful or distressing to the animals. However, close to one million animals were used in research and studies that subject them to moderate to severe distress or discomfort, and approximately 140,000 of these animals were involved in studies that produced severe pain at or above their pain threshold (that is, the lowest intensity of stimulation at which pain is felt). Thousands of animals were subject to pain and discomfort simply for the purpose of educating and training students in universities. Hundreds of thousands of animals were subject to the same sort of pain and discomfort simply in order to learn more about their biology, physiology, and biochemistry.

What is the morality of our use of animals in these and other forms of scientific research? Are the costs that scientific and other research imposes on animals justified by the benefits it produces? As in the case of our use of human embryos in medical research (Chapter 1) and of abortion (Chapter 2) an answer to these questions relies in part on an account of moral standing, an account of the characteristic or characteristics an individual must possess in order to have direct relevance to our moral reasoning. The articles in this chapter outline and defend rival conceptions of moral standing in addition to a full interpretation of their implications for research and other such endeavours.

In his article, Carl Cohen argues that animals do not have rights and that their pain and suffering count for less than the similar pain and suffering of humans. He contends that only creatures that are morally autonomous have rights not to be harmed for the benefit of others. Animals are not morally autonomous, since they cannot recognize and act in light of moral standards. Unlike human beings they cannot distinguish between the authority and intensity of desire. Therefore, they do not have rights, and, as a result, using animals in scientific research does not violate their rights. It does not follow from this that we are permitted to do what we want to animals. We have an obligation to treat them humanely. However, the pain and suffering that research causes animals does not count for the similar pain and suffering of humans. This follows from speciesism, the discounting of the pain and suffering of an animal simply by virtue of the fact that it is not a member of the species Home sapiens. Cohen contends that speciesism is justified, since animals do not belong to the moral community. Indeed, he maintains that the benefit that accrues to human beings from research on animals is a conclusive reason to perform it. Anything less would result in the failure to discharge our duty to support and heal one another.

Against Cohen, Tom Regan argues that animals do have rights. His argument involves the assumption that children, the senile, and the seriously mentally impaired have rights, especially the right to bodily integrity. The best explanation of this fact is that they are creatures with certain non-cognitive capacities such as the capacity to experience pleasure and pain. If this is the basis for rights, Regan continues, many animals have rights, for many animals have the capacity to experience pleasure and pain. If they have the right to bodily integrity, this entails that their use in medical and scientific research is impermissible, whatever the benefits of this research may be. Research using animals to benefit humans should cease.

In his article, Wayne Sumner assumes that animals have moral standing. He does not argue for this position, which he regards as beyond doubt. Instead, he addresses a certain disagreement amongst those who accept (as Regan does) that animals have moral standing because they are sentient and therefore have interests. A full interpretation of the moral status of animals involves not only an account of the basis of moral standing, but in addition an account of how they are considered in making decisions about what to do. Consequentialists argue that what we ought to do is maximize the well-being of all sentient creatures. Non-consequentialists reject this view: our obligations involve respecting the rights of humans and other sentient creatures, which constrain what we are permitted to do to maximize aggregate well-being. Respecting such rights may well entail that it is wrong to maximize aggregate well-being. Regan, for example, argues that consequentialism permits the use of animals in research when this produces the best outcome relative to the other options we have for producing well-being. He argues that there is an absolute right against being used in research. Sumner argues that the gap between consequentialists and rights theorists such as Regan is not as great as it may seem. Both views can be modified so that they are closer to each other in terms of their practical implications. Sumner argues that the most appropriate rights theory does not subscribe to absolute rights; instead, a better view holds that rights admit of exceptions when abiding by them would permit or produce substantial harm to the aggregate. The most plausible version of consequentialism involves appeal to rights against being used in research unless the cost of abiding by the right is clearly substantial, since such a provision is the most plausible strategy for the production of maximum well-being in the long run. Sumner suggests that the two sides in this debate better employ their resources by defending themselves against critics of their position that animals have moral standing than by skirmishing with each other. Once the two sides adopt the modified positions they will likely find that they agree that most research involving animals is unjustified.

ONE The Case for the Use of Animals in Biomedical Research
Carl Cohen | *New England Journal of Medicine* 1986; 315: 865-70.

Using animals as research subjects in medical investigations is widely condemned on two grounds: first, because it wrongly violates the *rights* of animals,[1] and second, because it wrongly imposes on sentient creatures much avoidable *suffering*.[2] Neither of these arguments is sound. The first relies on a mistaken understanding of rights; the second relies on a mistaken calculation of consequences. Both deserve definitive dismissal.

Why Animals Have No Rights

A right, properly understood, is a claim, or potential claim, that one party may exercise against another. The target against whom such a claim may be registered can be a single person, a group, a community, or (perhaps) all humankind. The content of rights claims also varies greatly: repayment of loans, non-discrimination by employers, non-interference by the state, and so on. To comprehend any genuine right fully, therefore, we must know *who* holds the right,

against whom it is held, and *to what* it is a right. . . .

This much is clear about rights in general: they are in every case claims, or potential claims, within a community of moral agents. Rights arise, and can be intelligibly defended, only among beings who actually do, or can, make moral claims against one another. Whatever else rights may be, therefore, they are necessarily human; their possessors are persons, human beings.

The attributes of human beings from which this moral capability arises have been described variously by philosophers, both ancient and modern. . . . Most influential has been Immanuel Kant's emphasis on the universal human possession of a uniquely moral will and the autonomy its use entails.[3] Humans confront choices that are purely moral; humans—but certainly not dogs or mice—lay down moral laws, for others and for themselves. Human beings are self-legislative, morally *autonomous*.

Animals (that is, nonhuman animals, in the ordinary sense of that word) lack this capacity for free moral judgment. They are not beings of a kind capable of exercising or responding to moral claims. Animals, therefore, have no rights, and they can have none. This is the core of the argument about the alleged rights of animals. The holders of rights must have the capacity to comprehend rules of duty, governing all including themselves. In applying such rules, the holders of rights must recognize possible conflicts between what is in their own interest and what is just. Only in a community of beings capable of self-restricting moral judgments can the concept of a right be correctly invoked.

Humans have such moral capacities. They are in this sense self-legislative, are members of communities governed by moral rules, and do possess rights. Animals do not have such moral capacities. They are not morally self-legislative, cannot possibly be members of a truly moral community, and therefore cannot possess rights. In conducting research on animal subjects, therefore, we do not violate their rights, because they have none to violate. . . .

It does not follow from this, however, that we are morally free to do anything we please to animals. . . . In our dealings with animals, as in our dealings with other human beings, we have obligations that do not arise from claims against us based on rights. Rights entail obligations, but many of the things one ought to do are in no way tied to another's entitlement. Rights and obligations are not reciprocals of one another, and it is a serious mistake to suppose that they are.

Illustrations are helpful. Obligations may arise from internal commitments made: physicians have obligations to their patients not grounded merely in their patients' rights. Teachers have such obligations to their students, shepherds to their dogs, and cowboys to their horses. Obligations may arise from differences of status: adults owe special care when playing with young children, and children owe special care when playing with young pets. Obligations may arise from special relationships: . . . my dog has no right to daily exercise and veterinary care, but I do have the obligation to provide these things for her. Obligations may arise from particular acts or circumstances: one may be obliged to put an animal out of its misery in view of its condition—although neither the human benefactor nor the dying animal may have had a claim of right.

Plainly, the grounds of our obligations to humans and to animals are manifold and cannot be formulated simply. Some hold that there is a general obligation to do no gratuitous harm to sentient creatures (the principle of non-maleficence); some hold that there is a general obligation to do good to sentient creatures when that is reasonably within one's power (the principle of beneficence). In our dealings with animals, few will deny that we are at least obliged to act humanely—that is, to treat them with the decency and concern that we owe, as sensitive human beings, to other sentient creatures. To treat animals humanely, however, is not to treat them as humans or as the holders of rights.

A common objection, which deserves a response, may be paraphrased as follows:

If having rights requires being able to make moral claims, to grasp and apply moral laws, then many humans—the brain-damaged, the comatose, the senile—who plainly lack those capacities must be without rights. But that is absurd. This proves [the critic concludes] that rights do not depend on the presence of moral capacities.[4]

This objection fails; it mistakenly treats an essential feature of humanity as though it were a screen for sorting humans. The capacity for moral judgment that distinguishes humans from animals is not a test to be administered to human beings one by one. Persons who are unable, because of some disability, to perform the full moral functions natural to human beings are certainly not for that reason ejected from the moral community. The issue is one of kind. Humans are of such a kind that they may be the subject of experiments only with their voluntary consent. The choices they make freely must be respected. Animals are of such a kind that it is impossible for them, in principle, to give or withhold voluntary consent or to make a moral choice. What humans retain when disabled, animals have never had. . . .

In Defense of Speciesism

Abandoning reliance on animal rights, some critics resort instead to animal sentience—their feelings of pain and distress. We ought to desist from the imposition of pain insofar as we can. Since all or nearly all experimentation on animals does impose pain and could be readily forgone, say these critics, it should be stopped. The ends sought may be worthy, but those ends do not justify imposing agonies on humans, and by animals the agonies are felt no less. The laboratory use of animals (these critics conclude) must therefore be ended—or at least very sharply curtailed.

Argument of this variety is essentially utilitarian, often expressly so;[5] it is based on the calculation of the net product, in pains and pleasures, resulting from experiments on animals. Jeremy Bentham, comparing horses and dogs with other sentient creatures, is thus commonly quoted: "The question is not, Can they reason? nor Can they talk? but, Can they suffer?"[6]

Animals certainly can suffer and surely ought not to be made to suffer needlessly. But in inferring, from these uncontroversial premises, that biomedical research causing animal distress is largely (or wholly) wrong, the critic commits two serious errors.

The first error is the assumption, often explicitly defended, that all sentient animals have equal moral standing. Between a dog and a human being, according to this view, there is no moral difference; hence the pains suffered by dogs must be weighed no differently from the pains suffered by humans. To deny such equality, according to this critic, is to give unjust preference to one species over another; it is "speciesism." The most influential statement of this moral equality of species was made by Peter Singer:

> **Speciesism**
> The view that the interests of animals count for less than the very same interests of humans simply by virtue of the fact that they do not belong to the same species as humans do. The interests of Homo sapiens count for more than the interests of other species.

The racist violates the principle of equality by giving greater weight to the interests of members of his own race when there is a clash between their interests and the interests of those of another race. The sexist violates the principle of equality by favouring the interests of his own sex. Similarly the speciesist allows the interests of his own species to override the greater interests of members of other species. The pattern is identical in each case.[7]

This argument is worse than unsound; it is atrocious. It draws an offensive moral conclusion from a deliberately devised verbal parallelism that is utterly specious. Racism has no rational ground whatever. Differing degrees of respect or concern for humans for no other reason than that they are members of different races is an injustice totally without foundation in the nature of the races themselves. Racists, even if acting on the basis of mistaken factual beliefs, do grave moral wrong precisely because there is no

morally relevant distinction among the races. The supposition of such differences has led to outright horror. The same is true of the sexes, neither sex being entitled by right to greater respect or concern than the other. No dispute here.

Between species of animate life, however—between (for example) humans on the one hand and cats or rats on the other—the morally relevant differences are enormous, and almost universally appreciated. Humans engage in moral reflection; humans are morally autonomous; humans are members of moral communities, recognizing just claims against their own interest. Human beings do have rights; theirs is a moral status very different from that of cats or rats.

I am a speciesist. Speciesism is not merely plausible; it is essential for right conduct, because those who will not make the morally relevant distinctions among species are almost certain, in consequence, to misapprehend their true obligations. The analogy between speciesism and racism is insidious. Every sensitive moral judgment requires that the differing natures of the beings to whom obligations are owed be considered. If all forms of animate life—or vertebrate animal life?—must be treated equally, and if therefore in evaluating a research program the pains of a rodent count equally with the pains of a human, we are forced to conclude (1) that neither humans nor rodents possess rights, or (2) that rodents possess all the rights that humans possess. Both alternatives are absurd. Yet one or the other must be swallowed if the moral equality of all species is to be defended.

> **Insidious**
> Deceitful or treacherous.

Humans owe to other humans a degree of moral regard that cannot be owed to animals. Some humans take on the obligation to support and heal others, both humans and animals, as a principal duty in their lives; the fulfillment of that duty may require the sacrifice of many animals. If biomedical investigators abandon the effective pursuit of their professional objectives because they are convinced that they may not do to animals what the service of humans requires, they will fail, objectively, to do their duty. Refusing to recognize the moral differences among species is a sure path to calamity. . . .

Those who claim to base their objection to the use of animals in biomedical research on their reckoning of the net pleasures and pains produced make a second error, equally grave. Even if it were true—as it is surely not—that the pains of all animate beings must be counted equally, a cogent utilitarian calculation requires that we weigh all the consequences of the use, and of the nonuse, of animals in laboratory research. Critics relying (however mistakenly) on animal rights may claim to ignore the beneficial results of such research, rights being trump cards to which interest and advantage must give way. But an argument that is explicitly framed in terms of interest and benefit for all over the long run must attend also to the disadvantageous consequences of not using animals in research, and to all the achievements attained and attainable only through their use. The sum of the benefits of their use is utterly beyond quantification. The elimination of horrible disease, the increase of longevity, the avoidance of great pain, the saving of lives, and the improvement of the quality of lives (for humans and for animals) achieved through research using animals is so incalculably great that the argument of these critics, systematically pursued, establishes not their conclusion but its reverse: to refrain from using animals in biomedical research is, on utilitarian grounds, morally wrong.

When balancing the pleasures and pains resulting from the use of animals in research, we must not fail to place on the scales the terrible pains that would have resulted, would be suffered now, and would long continue had animals not been used. Every disease eliminated, every vaccine developed, every method of pain relief devised, every surgical procedure invented, every prosthetic device implanted—indeed, virtually every modern medical therapy is due, in part or in whole, to experimentation using animals. Nor may we ignore, in the balancing process, the predictable gains in human (and animal) well-being that are probably achievable in the future but that will not be achieved if the decision is made now to desist from such research or to curtail it. . . .

If the morally relevant differences between humans and animals are borne in mind, and if all relevant considerations are weighed, the calculation of long-term consequences must give overwhelming support for biomedical research using animals.

Concluding Remarks
Substitution

The humane treatment of animals requires that we desist from experimenting on them if we can accomplish the same result using alternative methods—in vitro experimentation, computer simulation, or others. Critics of some experiments using animals rightly make this point.

It would be a serious error to suppose, however, that alternative techniques could soon be used in most research now using live animal subjects. No other methods now on the horizon—or perhaps ever to be available—can fully replace the testing of a drug, a procedure, or a vaccine, in live organisms. . . .

Every advance in medicine—every new drug, new operation, new therapy of any kind—must sooner or later be tried on a living being for the first time. That trial, controlled or uncontrolled, will be an experiment. The subject of that experiment, if it is not an animal, will be a human being. Prohibiting the use of live animals in biomedical research, therefore, or sharply restricting it, must result either in the blockage of much valuable research or in the replacement of animal subjects with human subjects. These are the consequences—unacceptable to most reasonable persons—of not using animals in research.

Reduction

Should we not at least reduce the use of animals in biomedical research? No, we should increase it, to avoid when feasible the use of humans as experimental subjects. . . . Some experimental risks are substantial. When an experimental protocol that entails substantial risk to humans comes before an institutional review board, what response is appropriate? . . . May not the investigators be fairly asked, "Have you done all that you can to eliminate risk to humans by the extensive testing of that drug, that procedure, or that device on animals?" To achieve maximal safety for humans we are right to require thorough experimentation on animal subjects before humans are involved.

Opportunities to increase human safety in this way are commonly missed. . . . Humans are sometimes subjected to risks that animals could have borne, and

> **Institutional review board**
> A committee composed of researchers, physicians, an ethicist, a lawyer, and community representatives that reviews research protocols to determine that they meet legal and ethical guidelines governing research on humans. They are found in universities, hospitals, and other research institutions. In Canada these committees are referred to as research ethics boards.

should have borne, in their place. To maximize the protection of human subjects, I conclude, the wide and imaginative use of live animal subjects should be encouraged rather than discouraged. This enlargement in the use of animals is our obligation.

Consistency

Finally, . . . one cannot coherently object to the killing of animals in biomedical investigations while continuing to eat them. Anaesthetics and thoughtful animal husbandry render the level of actual animal distress in the laboratory generally lower than that in the abattoir. So long as death and discomfort do not substantially differ in the two contexts, the consistent objector must not only refrain from all eating of animals but also protest as vehemently against others eating them as against others experimenting on them. No less vigorously must the critic object to the wearing of animal hides in coats and shoes, to employment in any industrial enterprise that uses animal parts, and to any commercial development that will cause death or distress to animals. . . . How can the many common uses of animals be judged morally worthy, while their use in scientific investigation is judged unworthy?

> **Abattoir**
> A slaughterhouse.

The number of animals used in research is but the tiniest fraction of the total used to satisfy assorted human appetites. That these appetites, often base and satisfiable in other ways, morally justify the far larger consumption of animals, whereas the quest for improved human health and understanding cannot justify the far smaller, is wholly implausible. Aside from the numbers of animals involved, the distinction in terms of worthiness of use, drawn with regard to any single animal, is not defensible. A given sheep is surely not more justifiably used to put lamb chops on the supermarket counter than to serve in testing a new contraceptive or a new prosthetic device. The needless killing of animals is wrong; if the common killing of them for our food or convenience is right, the less common but more humane uses of animals in the service of medical science are certainly not less right.

Scrupulous vegetarianism, in matters of food, clothing, shelter, commerce, and recreation, and in all other spheres, is the only fully coherent position the critic may adopt. . . .

Study Questions

1. Cohen replies to the objection that his view of the basis of the possession of a right entails that humans who lack moral autonomy (e.g., the senile, the severely mentally impaired, infants, and so on) do not have rights. He argues that "the capacity for moral judgment that distinguishes humans from animals is not a test to be administered to human beings one by one." Is this reply persuasive?

2. Cohen maintains that "the analogy between speciesism and racism is insidious." What is the substance of this analogy? Is Cohen right?

3. What is the basis for Cohen's claim that the interests of animals count for less than the very same interests of humans. Is this claim well justified?

Notes

1. Regan, T. *The case for animal rights.* Berkeley, Calif.: University of California Press, 1983.
2. Singer, P. *Animal Liberation.* New York: Avon Books, 1977.
3. Kant, I. *Fundamental principles of the metaphysics of morals.* 1785. New York: Liberal Arts Press, 1949.
4. Rollin, BE. *Animal rights and human morality.* New York: Prometheus Books, 1981.
5. Singer, P. *Ten years of animal liberation.* New York Review of Books. 1985; 31:46-52.
6. Bentham, J. *Introduction to the principles of morals and legislation.* London: Athlone Press, 1970.
7. Singer. *Animal Liberation.*

TWO The Rights of Humans and Other Animals

Tom Regan | *Ethics & Behavior* 1997; 7: 103–11.

The Nature and Importance of Human Rights

. . . Human rights place justified limits on what people are free to do to one another. For example, the right to bodily integrity disallows physically assaulting another person's body simply on the grounds that others might benefit as a result. One cannot justify the Nazi hypothermia research because what was learned might help other people who suffer from exposure. Or take what I call the Mickey Mantle case. Mickey has a good heart, good kidneys, and, recently, a good liver. Suppose that Cal Ripken, Bobby Bonds, and Kirby Puckett each need one of these vital organs. Would it be permissible to transplant Mickey's organs, against his will, in these other ball players? After all, other things being equal, the world would be a better place with three healthy ball players in it than it is with just one aging former player.

Well, this is not something that is permissible, given that Mickey has a right to bodily integrity. There are some things that *morally cannot be done* to the individual even if others stand to benefit as a result of doing it. As Ronald Dworkin (1984) said, the rights of the individual "trump" the collective interest. In the moral game, the rights card is the trump card.

Even with these very few comments about rights on the table, I think we should be able to see why . . . the idea of animal rights is a very important idea, one fraught with massive potential practical significance. Because if animals have rights—including, for example, the right to bodily integrity and the right not to be made to suffer gratuitously—it is difficult to see how anything less than the total abolition of animal model research could be morally acceptable. In particular, if animals have rights, certain familiar ways of defending animal model research will be silenced. No longer will we want to listen to the long list of benefits attributed to research of this kind. If animals have rights, and if rights are the trump card in the moral game, their rights override any benefits, real or imagined, we have gained, or stand to gain, from using them in biomedical research. . . .

Utilitarianism

All utilitarians think that the morality of what we do—whether our acts are morally right or wrong—depends on what happens as a result of the choices we make. Utilitarianism is a forward-looking view. The consequences, results, or effects of our actions determine their morality. And by our actions we should be trying to make the world better, to bring about the best possible consequences or results, in any given situation.

What is best all considered, however, is not necessarily what is best for each individual. Utilitarians are committed to aggregating—to adding and subtracting—the positive and negative consequences experienced by different individuals. This means that one person might lose a lot so that another might gain. The Mickey Mantle case illustrates this general point. Mickey (literally) loses everything, but the three other ball players each get back a healthy life. From the point of view of utilitarianism, it is an open moral question whether anything wrong would be done if Mickey were treated in this way.

Now, the utilitarian has two choices. He could try to tell some story or another that is supposed to show why the consequences really would be better if Mickey's organs were not transplanted in the way we have imagined. This manoeuvre is known as *the utilitarian shuffle*. Or he could say, "Look, sometimes you just have to bite the bullet. If the world really would be a better place without Mickey, but with Mickey's

---

Nazi hypothermia research
Hypothermia results when the body's core or internal temperature drops below 35 degrees Celsius. This usually occurs after prolonged exposure to cold. During World War II the Nazis performed research on hypothermia in order to discover ways of preventing it. The researchers coerced Jews and other who were imprisoned in concentration camps to participate in these experiments, which involved, among other things, being submerged in vats of ice water for prolonged periods.

Mickey Mantle
An American baseball player (1931–95) who played for the New York Yankees. He holds many records, and he is arguably one of the game's best switch-hitters.

organs redistributed, then that is the right thing to do."

Whichever option the utilitarian chooses, the essential point is that his utilitarianism is, in my view, a fundamentally mistaken way to think about morality. Here is a simple test case that I think makes my point. Some time back four teenage boys raped and in other ways sexually abused a seriously retarded teenage girl. . . .

I assume that no one will question that the abuse this poor girl suffered was wrong. But I hope you will notice that the utilitarian's theory cannot easily explain why it is wrong. After all, there were four boys and just the one girl, and the boys evidently had a very good time. Shuffling along, the utilitarian might suggest that there are other consequences that need to be taken into account—for example, the insecurity experienced by other young girls as a result of what happened to this one, and so on.

But this is not the central point. The central point is that, before the utilitarian can pass a moral judgment in this case, his theory requires that we take the pleasures the four boys experienced into account— that we count *their* equal interests equally. By my lights, however, the pleasures experienced by these four boys are *totally irrelevant* to assessing the morality of their actions. More generally, the interests of those who do what is morally wrong have no bearing on the determination of the wrong they do. It is because utilitarianism requires that we count these interests, *and weigh them equally with those of the victims of wrongdoing*, that I think this way of thinking is fundamentally mistaken.

Thus, the importance of human rights, in my view. Because if we suppose that this young girl has rights, then the good time had by the boys—the benefits they derived from abusing her—emerge as beside the moral point. Her rights trump their good time; indeed, their good time has no bearing whatsoever on assessing the morality of what they did. If there is a valid way of defending or justifying our moral judgments, I believe that it involves thinking along the lines I have just sketched, crude as that sketch is.

Animal Welfare and Animal Rights

I turn now to the topic of animal rights, beginning with some comments on the distinction between animal welfarists and animal rightists. As the name suggests, animal welfarists are in theory committed to taking the welfare of animals seriously. Animals should not be caused gratuitous physical pain; their psychological well-being should not be diminished unnecessarily. These are among the principles that guide a conscientious welfarist.

As such, welfarists can, and some of them sometimes do, call for important reforms, in the name of humane improvements, regarding how humans utilize nonhuman animals. Provided, however, that the welfare interests of these animals are taken into account and counted fairly, we do nothing wrong in principle by utilizing them to advance human interests. In particular, the use of nonhuman animals in biomedical research is in principle morally right, from a welfarist perspective, even if this human endeavour occasionally goes wrong in practice, as when a particular researcher neglects or otherwise mistreats animals in his laboratory.

Animal welfarism, therefore, can be seen to embody utilitarianism. . . . The many benefits allegedly derived from animal model research outweigh the many harms experienced by the animals. . . .

Animal rightists differ from animal welfarists. Although animal welfarists can have reformist aspirations, animal rightists are necessarily abolitionists. From their perspective, the use of nonhuman animals in scientific research is wrong in principle, not simply occasionally wrong in practice. These animals do not belong in laboratories in the first place: They do not belong there because placing them there, in the hope of gaining benefits for others, violates their rights. Rights being the trump card in the moral game, it is not larger cages, but empty cages, that animal rightists call for.

Animal Rights

But *do* animals have rights? And if they do, what rights do they have? My answers to these questions are explained in my book, *The Case for Animal Rights* (1983), and it is this work that I recommend to anyone who is interested seriously in what my answers are and why I answer as I do. Concerning the latter point, let me remind you that all the philosophers writing on this issue agree that we do not offer answers to moral questions just by saying how we happen to feel or what we happen to like, or by making reference to the dominant customs in America today, or by citing selected passages in the Bible or some other sacred book. Our moral thinking needs to move in a different direction than those these paths open up to us.

But if not in these ways, how? No easy question, this; certainly not for the philosophically faint of heart. But here is *a* way, although certainly not the only way, to proceed.

Suppose we begin by assuming that humans have rights and ask how we might be able to illuminate or explain why we do. . . . If humans have rights, there must be something about being human that helps explain or illuminates why we have them. Put another way, there must be some characteristic or set of characteristics (for brevity's sake, I refer to these possibilities as C) that makes the attribution of rights plausible in our case and implausible in the case of, for example, clouds, negative afterimages, and mircrofungi. The question is: What could this C be?

Possible answers are many. . . . [A] promising . . . candidate is rational autonomy. It is because humans are rational autonomous agents, and because clouds, negative afterimages, and microfungi are not, that we have rights and they do not.

Suppose we grant this candidate for C for the moment; then we can ask how nonhuman animals would fare. In other words, we can ask, "Are any nonhuman animals rational and autonomous?" Because if some are, it would smack of prejudice to deny that they have rights but to affirm that we do.

Whether any nonhuman animals are rational and autonomous is a very difficult empirical question, one that we are unlikely to settle on this occasion. My own view, for what it is worth, is that there are many species of animals whose members satisfy these conditions. Nonhuman primates are the most obvious example. Next are the great whales and other mammals. Obviously, where we draw the line that separates those animals who are rational and autonomous from those who are not will be neither easy nor free of controversy. Indeed, it may be that there is no clearly defined line we can draw with confidence, given the abundance of our individual and collective ignorance. However, it is enough for our purposes to recognize that some nonhuman animals are like humans in being rational and autonomous. So if rational autonomy explains or illuminates why we have rights, consistency requires that we make the same judgment in the case of these other animals: They, too, would have rights.

There is, however, a problem. Not all human beings are rational, autonomous agents. Infants are not, although most of them some day will be, and older people who suffer from serious mental deterioration are not, although most of them once were. Plus there are those many thousands of humans who, like the young woman raped by the four teenage boys, are seriously mentally retarded throughout their entire lives. In any or all of these cases we have individuals who *are* human beings but who are *not* rational and autonomous. So if C is rational autonomy, it appears that billions of human beings lack rights and, in lacking them, lack the most important card in the moral game. In their case, we cannot say that it would be wrong to harm them in the hope of benefiting others because their rights trump the collective interest. In the nature of the case, they have no rights.

This problem can be avoided by putting forth a different candidate for C. Instead of using "cognitive criteria," criteria such as rationality, we might instead rely on noncognitive criteria, criteria such as sentience (the capacity to be able to experience pain and pleasure) or emotion. And this does seem to be a more promising way to think about C, especially because all those humans who were denied rights, given the criterion of rational autonomy, seem to satisfy these noncognitive criteria.

Noncognitive criteria do more than increase the number of human beings who qualify as rights holders. These same criteria also increase the number of nonhuman animals who qualify. Line drawing problems doubtless will persist, but, wherever one reasonably draws the line, it seems evident that there are many more nonhuman animals who are sentient or who feel emotions than there are nonhuman animals who are rational and autonomous.

Although much more needs to be said to complete the argument for animal rights, some features of the central plot emerge from the little that has been said here. We face a choice: *Either* we can set the criteria of rights possession (C) rather high, so to speak, requiring capacities such as rationality and autonomy, *or* we can set the criteria of rights possession lower, requiring noncognitive capacities such as sentience. If we choose the former, some (but not a great many) nonhuman animals arguably will qualify as possessors of rights; but many human beings also will fail to qualify. If we choose the latter alternative, these humans will be enfranchised within the class of rights holders; but so will many nonhuman animals. Rationally, we cannot have it both ways—cannot, that is, rationally defend the view that all and only human beings have rights. . . .

Which choice should we make? Informed people of good will can answer this question differently. I favour a view of rights that enfranchises the most vulnerable humans among us. Infants and young children, the elderly who suffer from degenerative diseases of the brain, the seriously mentally retarded of all ages are the most obvious examples. I do not think those of us who are more fortunate should be free to utilize these human beings—in biomedical research, for example—in the hope that we might learn something that will benefit us or others. . . . If we recognize the rights of these humans, however, we recognize that they hold trump cards that have greater ethical force than what is in the general interest. And that certainly is the position I hold and recommend in their case.

I also recognize, however, that any plausible criterion that would enfranchise these humans within the class of rights holders will spill over the species boundary, so to speak, and enfranchise many hundreds, possibly many thousands of species of animals. That being the case, these animals also must be viewed as holding the trump card in the moral game. And because the rights they have should not be overridden in the name of seeking benefits for ourselves or others, it follows that none of these animals should be in any laboratory for that purpose. From an animal rights perspective, as noted earlier, it is not larger cages, it is empty cages that recognition of animal rights requires.

Study Questions

1. Is Regan right that utilitarianism is a defective theory of morality?

2. Regan relies on the assumption that humans have rights. Is this assumption plausible?

3. Regan's view is that animal research is impermissible regardless of the benefits it may produce. Do you accept this? Justify your answer.

References

Dworkin, R. (1984). Rights as trumps. In J. Waldron (Ed.), *Theories of rights*. Oxford, UK: Oxford University Press.

Regan, T. (1983). *The case for animal rights*. Berkeley: University of California Press.

THREE Animal Welfare and Animals Rights
L. Wayne Sumner | *The Journal of Medicine and Philosophy* 1988; 13: 159-75.

. . . In this paper, . . . I shall assume that at least some animals have some form of moral standing. My concern is with an intramural dispute among those who share this assumption. . . . Roughly speaking, to have (some form and degree of) moral standing is to count or matter morally (in some respect and to some extent).[1] Every moral framework will, implicitly or explicitly, circumscribe a domain of creatures whom it treats as worthy of moral consideration in their own right. Different frameworks may, notoriously, define different moral domains, but they may also diverge at a deeper level. . . . I want to focus on the consequentialist/nonconsequentialist dichotomy. . . .

Consequentialists, as a class, are committed to the idea that the right thing to do is always whatever will bring about the best overall outcome (from some impersonal point of view).[2] All consequentialists are therefore committed (1) to some set of basic and ultimate values, and (2) to some operation for combining these values into a global evaluation of outcomes. . . . There are many possible forms of consequentialism. But on all of them a creature has moral standing if it possesses whatever the theory deems ultimately valuable. . .[1] For instance, if with utilitarians we start by thinking that the only ultimate value is welfare and that the best outcome is the one that maximizes welfare, then we will treat having moral standing as having something that can be included in a calculation of the general welfare and we will therefore distribute it to all creatures with interests. . . .

Nonconsequentialists, by contrast, are committed to the idea that the right thing to do is at least sometimes not what will bring about the best overall outcome (from any impersonal point of view). All nonconsequentialists are therefore committed (1) to some set of basic and ultimate values, and (2) to some set of constraints on consequentialist cost/benefit reasoning. There are also many possible forms of nonconsequentialism. But on all of them a creature will have moral standing if it possesses whatever the theory deems ultimately valuable. For instance, if with some rights theorists we start by thinking that the only ultimate value is welfare and that the basic form of moral protection is possession of rights, then we will treat having moral standing as having rights and we will likewise distribute it to all creatures with interests.

Frameworks on opposite sides of the divide may agree on who has moral standing while disagreeing on what it means to have such standing. This will occur whenever rival theories share a common menu of ultimate values. Because I wish to focus on competing interpretations of moral standing, and on the implications of these interpretations, it will suit my purposes well to assume agreement at the level of a theory of value. Thus I shall confine my attention to theories that agree that welfare is the only ultimate value. . . . I shall further confine my attention to utilitarianism on the one hand and to rights theories on the other. . . .

We are imagining, therefore, that a utilitarian and a rights theorist agree on who has moral standing but disagree about what it means to have such standing. . . . The two most influential defenders of the moral standing of (some) animals are related in just this way. In *Animal Liberation* Peter Singer has defended giving equal consideration to the interests of all creatures, human and nonhuman, in utilitarian cost/benefit calculations, while in *The Case for Animal Rights* Tom Regan has defended protecting the interests of all creatures, human and nonhuman, by means of basic rights. . . . Regan has argued at considerable length that his rights framework has implications for our practices involving animals that diverge considerably from those of Singer's utilitarianism.[3]. . . My aim is not to show that one's theoretical affiliation makes

no difference in these cases (that would be astonishing, if true) but only that it might make less difference than Regan thinks. . . .

It must be conceded that the appearances in some respects favour Regan's thesis of divergence. . . . Utilitarians seem to be committed to assessing particular cases from an impersonal or global point of view in which the moral weight of a harm is exhausted by its inclusion as a cost in a cost/benefit calculation. Thus they seem to be committed to treating the outcome of such a calculation as decisive on each particular occasion. Rights theorists, on the other hand, must treat at least some harms as having a moral weight which cannot be entirely captured in a cost/benefit calculation and which thus constrains acting on the outcome of such a calculation. Furthermore, utilitarians seem also to be committed to assigning some positive weight to all benefits, regardless of the means by which they are obtained, while rights theorists tend to discount entirely any benefits that are obtained at the cost of violating rights.[4] Surely, it will be said, moral frameworks that diverge in these ways at the foundational level can lead only to a similar divergence at the practical level. . . .

It is easy to be so impressed by these differences that we lose sight of the affinities between the two approaches, at both the theoretical and practical levels. The most important of these affinities I have mentioned already. Both animal welfarists and animal rightists can, and typically do, agree that (1) a creature has moral standing just in case it has interests, (2) having interests requires sentience, or the capacity for experience, and (3) many animals have interests (in this sense) and thus have moral standing. It is also worth emphasizing just how significant and powerful this area of agreement is. . . .

I want to try to show that, . . . while the gap between the animal welfare and animal rights viewpoints cannot be entirely closed, it can at least be significantly narrowed. . . . I shall begin construction on the animal rights side. . . . As we have seen, every rights framework necessarily raises some barriers against acting from the impersonal point of view represented by a global cost/benefit calculation. But some rights are more stringent than others. . . . At the one extreme, a framework that treats some set of basic rights as indefeasible by consequentialist considerations—which holds, that is, that these rights must be respected whatever the global costs of doing so—will indeed keep its distance from utilitarianism. But if the same rights are treated as defeasible, thus as surmountable thresholds against consequentialist calculation, then this distance will diminish. . . . As the global costs that a theory considers sufficient to override its rights are lowered, the gap between that theory and a straightforward form of utilitarianism will correspondingly be narrowed.

By way of illustration, I shall consider the rights that Regan defends in *The Case for Animal Rights*. Regan argues that every creature with a welfare of its own has inherent value, and that we have a basic duty to treat such creatures with the respect due them as bearers of inherent value. We may say, therefore, that the basic right in his system is the right to this respect. But both the notion of inherent value and that of respect require interpretation if this abstract basic right is to yield more concrete derivative rights. This interpretation is provided by Regan's "harm principle," which stipulates that we have a prima facie duty not to harm individuals. While the basic right to be treated with respect is indefeasible, the derivative right not to be harmed can be overridden. The real distance between Regan's rights framework and utilitarianism will therefore largely depend on the conditions that he accepts as sufficient to override this right. . . . For Reagan, certain very special circumstances aside, infringing an individual's right not to be harmed cannot be justified by the fact that doing so will produce a better outcome on the whole. Regan's basic right thus erects an insurmountable barrier against consequentialist reasoning, and Regan's own abolitionist conclusions about our practices involving animals depend essentially on that barrier. . . .

Thus there is a genuine gap at the practical level between Regan's version of an animal rights view and any version of . . . utilitarianism. . . .

One possible rapprochement between animal welfare and animal rights would involve treating rights as defeasible by global cost/benefit considerations. To say that rights are defeasible by such considerations is not to say that they are always defeated by them, for that would render the rights entirely redundant. But it is to say that they are sometimes defeated by them, so that rights may justifiably be infringed if the costs of respecting them exceed

Rapprochement
The establishment of peaceful or harmonious relations. This is a French word meaning to bring together.

some threshold. . . . We could say, for instance, that every individual with a welfare has a prima facie (defeasible) right not to be harmed, but that this right is overridden when respecting it would cause, or allow, a substantial aggregate harm. Any such theory would be messier than Regan's, since it would have to determine when an aggregate harm counts as substantial, but it would still be a genuine rights theory since its rights would still stand as barriers against unimpeded utilitarian cost/benefit reasoning. . . .

This modification of a rights framework would weaken rights across the board, thus the rights of humans and nonhumans alike. But it would probably also have the effect of weakening the rights of (most) nonhumans relative to those of (most) humans. It is a well-known feature of utilitarianism that it gives equal weight in its cost/benefit calculation to equal costs and equal benefits, regardless of whose they are. The other side of this coin, of course, is that when costs or benefits are unequal, they will count unequally. . . . Therefore, in any case in which some form of treatment is more harmful to other animals than to us it will be harder to justify inflicting it on them than on us. But it also follows that in any case in which some form of treatment is more harmful to us than to other animals it will be harder to justify inflicting it on us than on them. In these latter cases, although animals have exactly the same de jure moral standing as us, their (lesser) interests will de facto count for less in a utilitarian cost/ benefit calculation. . . .

De jure
A Latin term used in the law meaning in principle.

De facto
A Latin term meaning in fact, in reality, or in practice.

Once a rights theory allows that the right not to be harmed can be overridden by a sufficiently favourable balance of benefits over harms (however this standard is set), then it cannot avoid making interspecific comparisons of harms and benefits. Whenever such comparisons support the conclusion that some group of animals will be harmed less by the infringement of this right than will some group of human beings, then the rights of those animals will effectively count for less in the theory's own terms than will the rights of those human beings, despite the fact that both groups have the same basic rights and the same moral standing.

Thus far I have tried to move rights frameworks a little closer to the territory traditionally occupied by utilitarianism. It bears repeating that making rights defeasible, in some situations, by utilitarian considerations will not close the gap between the frameworks. . . . But it will narrow the gap, and it will also have the effect of requiring the devotees of rights to engage in a considerable amount of piecemeal, case-by-case analysis. . . . For this reason, sweeping abolitionist conclusions are less likely to be supported by a rights framework, especially for practices such as animal experimentation where the cost/benefit balance varies dramatically from case to case. But then at the level of practice animal rightists will begin to look a little more like animal welfarists.

The gap can also be narrowed, however, by building from the other side. Although utilitarianism is a (fairly) determinate theory rather than a broad family of theories, it still comes in different versions. Some of these versions are friendlier toward rights than others.[5] . . .

The story of how rights might be built into a utilitarian framework is a long and complicated one, and it can be only briefly summarized here. Every moral framework must include two different components. The first is an ultimate criterion of right and wrong. The function of this criterion, together with the facts of the matter, is to determine what the right thing to do is on each occasion of choice. This criterion is objective in the sense that it always yields the right answer even though no one—neither the agent nor any bystander—may be in a position to discover that answer. It thus takes the point of view of an omniscient observer, rather than that of agents embedded in the world. The second component is a decision-making procedure designed to help agents discover the right answer on each occasion of choice. This procedure is subjective in the sense that it takes account of the peculiarities and limitations of an agent's position in the world, including such factors as incomplete or unreliable information, fallibility in information processing, a tendency toward partiality, weakness of will, and so on. Thus while the ultimate criterion furnishes the moral target we are to hit, the decision procedure tells us how best to hit it.

One obvious decision strategy for any theory is a straightforward one: just aim directly at the target. This might be the best strategy for hitting the target, but it also might not. When we take into account the peculiarities and limitations of our positions in the world, we might do better to adopt some indirect or constrained strategy. There is no a priori answer in a theory to the question of which decision strategy we should adopt. In particular, the fact that a strategy is straightforward or direct is not itself a point in its favour; we must select a strategy for its efficacy in hitting the target and not for its simplicity or elegance. . . .

> **A priori**
> A Latin term meaning prior to; in this context the author is referring to the idea that we cannot select the right decision procedure prior to or without appeal to experience.

There is good reason for thinking that utilitarians will do better to adopt some indirect strategy when they evaluate our practices involving animals.[6] Consider once again the issue of animal experimentation.[7] For animal welfarists there is no avoiding the burden of piecemeal, case-by-case evaluation. To the extent that effective evaluation is possible at all, it happens in committees that are empowered to subject protocols for animal research to ethical review. Anyone who has ever served on such committees will not need to be reminded of the many defects and impediments that afflict their operations. The review committee does not initiate proposals, but merely accepts or rejects (or sometimes amends) those that happen to come along. It depends for information about the experiment's projected (animal) costs and (human) benefits on the researcher, who is an interested party in the affair, or on other practitioners in the field, who are likely to subscribe to the researcher's professional standards. While it may be fairly clear just what is in store for the animal subjects, the expected benefits are generally much more diffuse and speculative; furthermore, the committee has little opportunity to follow up on experiments to see whether these benefits are ever in fact realized. Lay members of review committees thus function on an alien territory in which, lacking both expertise and reliable information, they must reach a consensus with scientific members who have their own agenda of commitments and concerns. . . .

If animal welfarists do choose to function on review committees, what ethical standards should they employ and urge their fellow members to adopt? It would be folly to propose a direct utilitarian strategy, since they will never have access to the information they need in order to employ it effectively.

> **Omniscient**
> All knowing.

Thus even if they think that the utilitarian criterion provides the right answer in each case they will do better to switch to an indirect strategy. Since the costs to the animal subjects are generally immediate and certain, and the compensating human benefits by comparison distant and uncertain, one obvious device is to require that the benefits, even when discounted for their uncertainty, must substantially outweigh the costs. This is equivalent to determining what will count as an acceptable cost/benefit ratio for an experimental protocol. It is also equivalent to assigning the animal subjects a defeasible right not to be harmed which raises a threshold, though not an insurmountable threshold, against straightforward cost/benefit calculation.

If this is correct then animal welfarists have a good practical reason for taking seriously something like the defeasible rights that (some) animal rightists endorse.

The fact that these rights are basic in a rights framework and derivative in a utilitarian framework will be of theoretical interest but of little practical importance. Since we have no guarantee that the rights that animal welfarists should take seriously are identical to those endorsed by animal rightists, we cannot assume that the gap between the two groups has been closed. But it has been narrowed yet further. . . . For what it is worth, my own speculation is that, once animal rightists have accepted that rights can be defeasible even though basic and animal welfarists have accepted that rights can be important even though derivative, they will agree in rejecting most (but not all) animal research as unjustifiable. But even if their practical conclusions never converge entirely, they will surely converge over a very wide range of issues. And if this is the case, they have better reason than ever to form a common front against their common enemies.

Study Questions

1. Sumner suggests that animal rights theorists and utilitarians may agree that an animal has moral standing just in case it has interests. Is this a plausible basis for granting moral standing to animals?

2. Sumner argues that a rights theorist may hold that certain rights (e.g., the right against being harmed) are defeasible, and that such a right is defeated only when respecting it would produce or permit *substantial* aggregate harm. What is the most acceptable interpretation of "substantial?"

3. At the conclusion of his article, Sumner suggests that the modified versions of the rights theory and of utilitarianism will agree "in rejecting most (but not all) animal research as unjustifiable." Why might Sumner hold this view?

Notes

1. For further elaboration see my *Abortion and Moral Theory* (Sumner, 1981).
2. The impersonal point of view to which consequentialists are committed is explored in Samuel Scheffler, *The Rejection of Consequentialism* (1982, esp. ch. 1), and in Thomas Nagel, *The View from Nowhere* (1986, esp. chs. 8 and 9).
3. See Regan, *The Case for Animal Rights* (1983, ch. 9, esp. pp. 349–51 and 392–4).
4. See, for example, Regan, *The Case for Animal Rights* (1983, p. 393)
5. Some of the issues at stake here are explored in the essays in R. G. Frey (ed.), *Utility and Rights* (1984).
6. For a defence of this view see Derek Parfit, *Reasons and Persons* (1984, ch. 1).
7. I consider the parallel case of human experimentation in "Utilitarian goals and Kantian constraints (Or: always true to you, darling, in my fashion)" (Sumner, 1988).

References

Cooper, W. E. et al. (ed.): 1979, *New Essays on John Stuart Mill and Utilitarianism*, Canadian Association for Publishing in Philosophy, Guelph.

Frey, R. G. (ed.): 1984, *Utility and Rights*, University of Minnesota Press, Minneapolis.

Nagel, T.: 1986, *The View From Nowhere*, Oxford University Press, New York.

Parfit, D.: 1984, *Reasons and Persons*, Clarendon Press, Oxford.

Regan, T.: 1983, *The Case for Animal Rights*, University of California Press, Berkeley.

Scheffler, S.: 1982, *The Rejection of Consequentialism*, Clarendon Press, Oxford.

Singer, P.: 1975, *Animal Liberation*, New York Review, New York.

Sumner, L. W.: 1981, *Abortion and Moral Theory*, Princeton University Press, Princeton.

Sumner, L. W.: 1986, Review of *The Case for Animal Rights*, *Nous*, Vol. 20, No. 3.

Sumner, L. W.: 1979, 'The good and the right', in W. E. Cooper et al. (eds.), *New Essays on John Stuart Mill and Utilitarianism*, Canadian Association for Publishing in Philosophy, Guelph.

Sumner, L. W.: 1988, "Utilitarian goals and Kantian constraints (Or: Always True to You, Darling, In My Fashion), in Baruch A. Brody (ed.), *Moral Theory and Moral Judgments in Medical Ethics*, Kluwer Academic Publishers, Dordrecht.

Chapter Study Questions

1. Compare and contrast the account of rights defended by Cohen with the accounts defended by Regan and Sumner.

2. Do Sumner's modifications to utilitarianism deflect Regan's criticisms of this view? Is Sumner doing what Regan calls the "utilitarian shuffle"?

3. All of the authors in this chapter agree that we have obligations to animals. What are the main differences between them on this issue?

Critical Analysis

Consider the following from the article by Tom Regan:

"If humans have rights, there must be something about being human that helps explain or illuminates why we have them. Possible answers are many. A promising candidate is rational autonomy. It is because humans are rational autonomous agents, and because clouds, negative afterimages, and microfungi are not, that we have rights and they do not.

There is, however, a problem. Not all human beings are rational, autonomous agents. Infants are not, although most of them some day will be, and older people who suffer from serious mental deterioration are not, although most of them once were. Plus there are those many thousands of humans who…are seriously mentally retarded throughout their entire lives. In any or all of these cases we have individuals who are human beings but who are not rational and autonomous. So if . . . [the correct basis of rights] is rational autonomy, it appears that billions of human beings lack rights and, in lacking them, lack the most important card in the moral game. In their case, we cannot say that it would be wrong to harm them in the hope of benefiting others because their rights trump the collective interest. In the nature of the case, they have no rights."

Outline Regan's argument in your own words, paying particular attention to the premises that he relies on to support his main conclusion. Choose one premise for evaluation. Try to think of at least one objection to this premise.

Case Study

In Canada, there is no federal legislation dealing specifically with the use of animals in research, teaching and product testing. Instead, national standards are articulated and enforced by the Canadian Council on Animal Care (CCAC). Its mission, in its own words, is to "ensure through programs of education, assessment and guidelines that the use of animals, where necessary, for research, teaching and testing employs optimal physical and psychological care according to acceptable scientific standards, and to promote an increased level of knowledge, awareness and sensitivity to relevant ethical principles." Conformity to its standards is, however, voluntary. It is required only in cases in which a researcher or a research institution aims to acquire funding from a federal granting agency, e.g., the Natural Sciences and Engineering Council of Canada. The CCAC requires those participating in its programme to abide by a number of principles. In particular, it maintains that "the use of animals in research, teaching, and testing is acceptable ONLY if it promises to contribute to understanding of fundamental biological principles, or to the development of knowledge that can reasonably be expected to benefit humans or animals." It is therefore interested in promoting two distinct values: understanding or knowledge, and benefits to the health and well-being of humans and animals. It does not hold that any means to achieve these is acceptable. It says that the following procedures are unacceptable because they cause excessive pain: "utilization of muscle relaxants or paralytics . . . alone, without anesthetics, during surgical procedures" and "traumatizing procedures involving crushing, burning, striking or beating in unanesthetized animals." Although the CCAC encourages its members to reduce the number of animals it uses, to seek out alternatives to animals, and to reduce pain and suffering where possible, it does not explicitly demand that researchers demonstrate that the benefits in terms of knowledge and/or human and animal well-being that they seek outweigh the costs to animals in terms of pain, suffering, and distress. In addition, it forbids "painful experiments or multiple invasive procedures on an individual animal, conducted solely for the instruction of students in the classroom." However, in 2009 its members reported that tens of thousands of animals were subjected to at least "moderate to severe distress or discomfort" in training and educating students in post-secondary institutions.

1. Should the guidelines set out by the CCAC be mandatory for all institutions conducting research and cognate activities employing animals? Are the guidelines acceptable in your view? For more on the guidelines, see http://www.ccac.ca/en_/standards/policies/policy-ethics_animal_investigation

2. Do you think that researchers should be required to demonstrate that the benefits of their research outweigh its costs? Are some benefits (e.g., knowledge) more difficult to justify than others (e.g., health and well-being)?

3. Is there a conflict between the requirement that there be no "painful experiments or multiple invasive procedures on an individual animal, conducted solely for the instruction of students in the classroom" and the fact that members of the CCAC programme report that tens of thousands of animals were subject to such procedures in this context?

Further Reading

Animal Rights Canada [Internet]. Available from: http://www.animalrightscanada.com/. Date Accessed: 8 June 2012.

Canadian Council on Animal Care [Internet]. Available from: http://www.ccac.ca/. Date Accessed: 8 June 2012.

Montgomery, C. *Blood relations: animals, humans, and politics.* Toronto: Between the Lines; 2000.

Sorenson, J. *About Canada: animal rights.* Black Point, Nova Scotia: Fernwood Publishing; 2010.

16

Neuroenhancement

In this chapter, we explore the ethical permissibility of using drugs to enhance cognitive functions. A wide variety of drugs are used to treat diseases that affect attention, memory, and mood. For example, methylphenidate (Ritalin) is used to treat children with attention deficit hyperactivity disorder, donepezil (Aricept) is used to treat memory loss in patients with dementia, and fluoxetine (Prozac) is used to treat depression. The fact that cognitive abilities exist on a spectrum suggests that in addition to treating disease, some drugs might be used to enhance cognitive abilities in normally functioning individuals. Thus, methylphenidate might be used to increase attentiveness in a college student studying for exams, or fluoxetine could be used to help someone with who does not suffer from a mood disorder to feel "better than well." But so-called "neuroenhancement" or "cognitive enhancement" raises a number of thorny ethical issues.

In the literature, three broad ethical issues have been raised regarding neuroenhancement. First, while the desire to improve ourselves is basic, some have argued that it matters how the ends of self-improvement are achieved. Imagine, if you will, that all the knowledge potentially obtained in an undergraduate university degree could be gained by taking a single pill. Would you take it? Critics of neuroenhancement have argued that taking the pill—as opposed to working hard for four years in college—is illegitimate because the knowledge obtained would be inauthentic, that is, one wouldn't have earned it through one's own will, desire, and hard work. Second, the safety of drugs capable of enhancing normal cognitive functions has been questioned. Cognitive functions are complex and the consequences of enhancing them may be difficult to predict. Certainly further study (including studies with long-term follow-up) will be required to ensure that drugs used for this purpose are both safe and effective. Finally, some have worried about the effect that neuroenhancement will have on society, particularly on increasing social inequalities. Drugs for cognitive enhancement are likely to be viewed as cosmetic—akin to face lifts or other plastic surgery—and, as a result, would not be covered by public or private health insurance. This may mean that the benefits of such neuroenhancement are enjoyed by the rich and effectively denied to the poor. If neuroenhancement allows people to become more competitive in the workplace, the economic disparities between rich and poor could be magnified by the competitive advantages conferred by these drugs.

In the first reading, Carl Elliott criticizes the expanded use of antidepressants that goes beyond the treatment of standard psychiatric illnesses such as depression and anxiety. He questions whether it is appropriate for psychiatrists to use drugs to treat "alienation"—a feeling of being disconnected from one's self, one's culture, or even the meaning of life altogether. For Elliott, alienation is a state that—while unpleasant—has a moral purpose: an unhappy job, a failing marriage, or a life that seems to lack purpose, all call for feelings of alienation. As Elliott says, "given certain circumstances, alienation is the proper response." Presumably, such feelings may be the impetus for important life changes: a new and more rewarding career, an overdue divorce, or the active pursuit of new meaning in life. But psychiatry's narrow focus on internal psychic well-being leaves it blind to the moral purpose of alienation, and attempts to medicate a mismatch between people's lives and the external structures that give their lives meaning are, he believes, short-sighted.

In the second reading, Peter Kramer takes issue with Elliott's claim that alienation has a deeper moral purpose. Kramer points out that Elliott marshals his examples of alienation selectively and with purpose: all are sensitive individuals surrounded by those who (for Elliott at least) are philistines. In these circumstances, it is not surprising that alienation should seem to have a moral purpose. But Kramer invites us to consider another example. In rural Greece, the culturally defined mourning period when a woman loses her husband is five years. Consider two women: a sanguine woman in rural Greece who has recovered well from her husband's death after six months, and a sensitive Greek-American woman in the United States whose feelings of loss continue several years after her husband's death. Both feel disconnected from the mores of the cultures that surround them; both feel alienated. If the two women permanently traded places and thereby lost their sense of alienation, would we want to say that they had lost an "aspect of their humanity"? Seemingly not. Kramer argues that what Elliott is in fact valuing is not alienation but melancholy or sadness. There is a great tradition of melancholy among both philosophers and writers and thus it is not surprising that many value it—and even romanticize it. But this suggests that melancholy is merely an aesthetic good—a matter of taste, if you will—rather than anything of real moral significance.

In the third reading, Glannon challenges the suggestion that neuroenhancement will lead to an inauthentic or "alien" self. Authenticity for Glannon means identifying with our own mental states, and this identification is the result of reflecting and acting on our own desires and beliefs. So long as one's mental states are the product of critical reflection and voluntary action, they are authentic. Viewed this way, neuroenhancement does not seem to threaten authenticity. Consider the above example of obtaining a university education through four years of hard work versus consuming a pill. In both instances the decision to seek out and obtain the education may be the product of deliberating on one's own beliefs and desires and acting upon them. In the latter case, the "drug is merely the means through which the change in mental states is effected." Thus, Glannon argues that either course of action results in an education that is authentic. This somewhat unrealistic example aside, his worry is that too little is known about the safety of cognitive enhancing drugs. Until more research establishes that such drugs are safe and effective, those who choose to use them should be, to the fullest extent possible, apprised of their risks.

ONE   Pursued by Happiness and Beaten Senseless: Prozac and the American Dream

Carl Elliott | *Hastings Center Report* 2000; 30(2): 7-12.

Selective serotonin reuptake inhibitors
A class of drugs commonly used to treat depression, obsessive compulsive disorder, and other psychiatric conditions. As the name suggests, the drugs are thought to function by increasing the amount of serotonin available to neurons in the brain.

. . . In the decade or so since the development of the selective serotonin reuptake inhibitors, many thoughtful (and some not so thoughtful) voices have urged caution, or at least a damper on our enthusiasm for the drugs, most notably in the debate prompted by Peter Kramer's splendid book, *Listening to Prozac*. Scholars have worried that Prozac treats the self rather than proper diseases, that it alters personality, that it feeds dangerously into the American obsession with competition and worldly success, and that

Prozac
Fluoxetine; one of the first selective serotonin reuptake inhibitors available and, as the article explains, one of the drugs at the centre of a debate about the scope of proper prescribing of psychiatric medications.

Walker Percy
(1916–90) was a writer from the American South whose novels often deal with philosophical themes. Some of his best known novels include *The Moviegoer* (1960), *The Last Gentleman* (1966), and *Love in the Ruins* (1971; referred to in this article).

Ontological Lapsometer
A (fictional) invention of Dr Tom More, the psychiatrist and main character of Walker Percy's novel *Love in the Ruins*, that is used to diagnose and cure spiritual ailments.

it offers a mechanistic cure for spiritual problems of the sort predicted by Walker Percy in his novel *Love in the Ruins*, in which the psychiatrist Tom More treats existential ailments with his Ontological Lapsometer. But in the years since I first read Kramer's book I have begun to suspect that the problem may go deeper than Prozac; that the problem is not merely Prozac but the stance of psychiatry itself. Wittgenstein once wrote, "The sickness of a time is cured by an alteration in the mode of life of human beings, and it was possible for the sickness of philosophical problems to get cured only through a changed mode of thought and of life, not through a medicine invented by an individual."[1] He was talking about philosophy, not psychopharmacology, but the point is apt either way. At least part of the nagging worry about Prozac and its ilk is that for all the good they do, the ills that they treat are part and parcel of the lonely, forgetful, unbearably sad place where we live.

I am slightly reluctant to use the term "alienation," coming as it does with baggage that I do not necessarily want to take with me, but so be it: here, I think, it can serve a useful purpose. Alienation seems to describe at least some of the symptoms that bring people to the attention of a psychiatrist. How many patients this is, and whether Prozac actually cures them, remains to be seen. It may be very small in comparison to, say, the number who use Prozac for depression. But I take it from my psychiatric colleagues, from the case histories in Kramer's book and others, and from my many friends and acquaintances who have used the drug, that whether it affects alienation is at least an open question.

Alienation, it seems to me, differs from most of the kinds of descriptors that psychiatry ordinarily uses for psychiatric patients—descriptors like anxiety, obsessiveness, even unhappiness. These

Alienation
A loss of identity in which the self feels disconnected from the expectations of friends, family, community, or culture; a state in which life loses its meaning in some important sense.

descriptors describe internal psychic states. They are about (to use a slightly misleading metaphor) what's in my own head. Relationships with things outside myself can affect my happiness or unhappiness, or for that matter, my depression or my anxiety or my obsessions; if I am in a miserable job, or if my relationship with my wife is on the rocks, or even if (as we say down South) I am not right with God, I might be more unhappy, or more anxious or depressed. But the concepts themselves are by and large measures of my internal psychic well-being.

This makes them different from alienation. Alienation generally describes an incongruity between the self and external structures of meaning—a lack of fit between the way you are and the way you are expected to be, say, or a mismatch between the way you are living a life and the structures of meaning that tell you how to live a life. Alienated people are alienated from something—their families, their cultures, their jobs, their Gods. This isn't a purely internal matter; it isn't just in the alienated person's head. It is about a mismatch between a person and something outside himself. This, I think, is why it makes some sense (although one could contest this) to say that sometimes a person should be alienated—that given certain circumstances, alienation is the proper response. Some external circumstances call for alienation.

Alienation comes in many varieties, or so I think, many of which blur into one another. For the sake of simplicity, let me mention three, with the caveat that these divisions are artificial and overlapping. The first is a kind of personal alienation, a sense that you don't conform with social expectations of someone in your particular circumstances. It might be that your character doesn't quite fit into place as it should, so that you feel ill at ease among the other Princeton men or Milwaukee Rotarians or suburban high school cheerleaders. It may be that you feel alienated from the social role you are expected to occupy. You are not cut out to be a Washington political wife, or a Virginia gentleman, or the inheritor of the family hardware

Rotarians
Members of Rotary International, an organization dedicated to bringing together business and professional leaders for humanitarian service.

business. Or perhaps the direction your life is moving simply doesn't mesh with the way it's expected to move, like a New Hampshire housewife who at the age of fifty says this isn't the life for me, divorces her husband, sells the house, and goes off to Swaziland with the Peace Corps. For North Americans, these may be the most familiar kinds of alienation. They seem to be characteristic of times when a person's identity is in question or under re-evaluation, such as when we are in our early twenties and are expected to decide what to do with our lives: What should I do for a living? Where should I live? Should I marry? If so, whom? Or in mid-life, when we start to look back on the decisions we have made and how they have turned out: Why did I marry him? Why didn't we have children? How in God's name did I wind up in accounting?

> **Peace Corps**
> An American organization, created in response to President Kennedy's famous call to public service in 1961, that promotes peace through international volunteer work. Volunteers live and work in a single community for a two-year period.

A second type of alienation that comes to mind, related to the first, is cultural alienation. This often involves the sense that a particular form of life is changing beneath your feet, and that you no longer have the equipment to manage in the new way. Something like this kind of alienation seems to be a motivating force behind a lot of social criticism. You step outside of your own socialization (or you are pushed) and look at your own culture from a standpoint of detachment. Perhaps the most extreme example of this kind of alienation would be characteristic of colonized and displaced peoples—Native Americans whose traditional ways of life have been erased, among refugees marooned in Minnesota, Pacific Islanders colonized by the American military so that instead of fishing and harvesting tropical fruit they subsist on a diet of imported canned foods. I take it that this is also part of what Cornel West is getting at when, writing of the disappearance of traditional African American social institutions, he states that "the major enemy of black survival in America is neither oppression nor exploitation but rather the nihilistic threat—that is, loss of hope and absence of meaning."[2] . . . Part of the nagging worry about Prozac and its ilk is that the ills they treat are part and parcel of the lonely, forgetful, unbearably sad place where we live. . . .

But cultural alienation need not involve cultural change. In fact, perhaps the most recognizable symbols of American alienation are houses in the suburbs, which are seen as alienating precisely because of their static, anonymous conformity. . . . That your life is just an average life, and your story so ordinary it is not even worth telling. Anything that reminds you of this fact, anything that betrays the illusion that you are really, deep-down, quite an extraordinarily unique individual, is going to cut very close to the bone indeed. It is enough to make you think about an antidepressant.

Which leads to a third variety of alienation, one that I will call (with some trepidation) existential alienation. This kind of alienation involves questioning the very terms on which a life is built. By virtue of when, where, and to whom we are born, we inherit a sense of what it is possible to do with a human life, what kinds of lives are honourable or pointless or meaningful. . . . Calling into question your own form of life involves calling into question your own values, the very stuff out of which you are built. This is not just realizing that your own particular castle is built on thin air. It is realizing you are built out of air yourself. It is radically disorienting: the ultimate, dizzying high-wire act, like Wile E. Coyote after he runs off a cliff, glances down, and realizes where he is standing.

> **Wile E. Coyote**
> The Road Runner's *soi-disant* super-genius nemesis in a series of "Looney Toons" and "Merrie Melodies" cartoons created by animator Chuck Jones. Wile E. Coyote's numerous and absurdly complex schemes to kill—and eat—the Road Runner invariably fail and result in grievous injury to himself.

Many of the case histories surrounding Prozac gesture at this kind of alienation—the sense that not only don't you know what to do with your life, you don't know what could possibly tell you what to do. The structures that might have given life its sense and meaning are now contested or in question. The result is not just the feeling that you are ill-suited for your own particular form of life, or that your form of life is fading away; rather, it is a calling into question of the foundations of any form of life. . . . The result of these kinds of questions can be the sense that no form of life can really have the kind of justification that you feel you need. It is a sense that there is no rhyme and reason to your form of life other than the exigencies of biology and history, that the big picture is really nothing more than a big picture. . . .

What is left for those of us who are lost at sea? Apparently we have to make do with secular expertise, the professionals that Percy called the experts of the self. If we are alienated and impoverished and can't figure out why, we turn to doctors, psychologists, advice columnists, self-help authors, personal trainers, alternative healers, philosophical counsellors, or (let us admit it) ethicists, who will set us on the path to righteousness, personal fitness, and sound mental hygiene. . . . Experts of the self create facilities such as the Geriatrics Rehabilitation Unit in Percy's *Love in the Ruins*, where old folks often grow inexplicably sad despite the fact that their every need is met. "Though they may live in the pleasantest Senior Settlements where their every need is filled, every recreation provided, every sort of hobby encouraged, nevertheless many grow despondent in their happiness, sit slack and empty-eyed at shuffleboard and ceramic oven. Fishing poles fall from tanned and healthy hands. Golf clubs rust. Readers Digests go unread. Many old folk pine away and even die from unknown causes like a voodoo curse."[3]

Here is the key to the problem psychiatry has with a notion like alienation. The measure of psychiatric success is internal psychic well-being. The aim of psychiatry is (among other things) to get rid of anxieties, obsessions, compulsions, phobias, and various other barriers to good social functioning. Within this framework, where the measure of success is psychic well-being through good social functioning, alienation is something to be eliminated. It is a psychiatric complaint. It is a barrier to psychic well-being. Whereas what I want to suggest is that maybe psychic well-being isn't everything. Some lives are better than others, quite apart from the psychic well-being of the person who is leading them. I don't mean this in any ultimate, metaphysical sense. I'm not arguing that God prefers some lives to others, or that some lives are better than others because they are more rational or well-ordered. I just mean that the notion that some lives are better than others is part of the moral background to the way we live our lives. We all recognize that it is possible for a life to be a failure or a success, even if we aren't always able to say exactly why. . . .

By ignoring such matters as how a person lives his life, by steadfastly refusing to pass judgment on whether the ideals he lives by are worthy or wasteful or honourable or demeaning, psychiatry can say nothing useful whatsoever about alienation. It places itself in the position of neutrality about the broader structures of meaning within which lives are lived, and from which they might be alienated. What could

a psychiatrist say to the happy slave? What could he say to an alienated Sisyphus as he pushes the boulder up the mountain? That he would push the boulder more enthusiastically, more creatively, more insightfully, if he were on Prozac?

> **Sisyphus**
> In Greek mythology, he was a King who offended Zeus with his arrogance and who was punished by being made to repeatedly roll a large boulder up a steep hill, only to have it roll down the hill before he reached the top—an endless and vain struggle.

Already I can hear the protests. Do you want to deny Prozac to Sisyphus? Who are you to criticize him for taking it? Very well then. Perhaps I spoke hastily. My purpose was not to level any moral criticism. Sisyphus may well be happier on an antidepressant. His psychic well-being will probably be improved. Certainly he is entitled to the drug, if his managed care organization will pay for it. I only wish to point out that his predicament is not simply a matter of his internal psychic well-being. Any strategy that ignores certain larger aspects of his situation is going to sound a little hollow. . . .

I suspect that part of the worry many people have about Prozac has less to do with the drug itself than with the enthusiasm with which Americans in particular have embraced it. Why we have embraced it (apart from the merits of the drug itself, which are not at all inconsiderable) is a matter for speculation: a multibillion dollar pharmaceutical industry, a native enthusiasm for technology, an ethic of competitive individualism, a constitutional right to the pursuit of happiness. Yet along with that enthusiasm is the suspicion that psychopharmacology alone cannot account for the predicament in which we find ourselves; that this predicament is not something that can be cured, as Wittgenstein says, with a medicine invented by an individual, but rather by a change in our manner of living. And not by my own personal manner of living, or at least not solely, but by the way we all live now, together: by what Wittgenstein might call our form of life.

Of course, it may be that antidepressants will often cure depression without touching alienation, leaving a person alienated but not depressed. Whether this would be a good state to be in or not will depend on how you see our collective situation—whether, as Percy would say, you think we are in a predicament. Yet as long as we fail to take any account of these broader frameworks of significance, we cannot take account of alienation from them. Unless we think about meaning, we cannot take the measure of meaninglessness; unless we think about home, we cannot take the measure of homelessness; unless we recognize the fact of the journey, we cannot take account of the person who is lost. If, in Clifford Geertz's famous paraphrase of Weber, we are suspended in webs of significance that we ourselves have spun, then it is only by looking closely at how we are situated in those webs that we can see how we may be trapped there, or falling, or gazing contentedly at the ceiling.

Study Questions

1. According to Elliott, what is alienation? What does he mean when he says, "sometimes a person should be alienated"?

2. What is the aim of psychiatry? How does this conflict with seeing potential moral value in alienation?

3. What is the target of Elliott's critique? Prozac? Psychiatry? American culture?

Notes

1. L. Wittgenstein, *Remarks on the Foundations of Mathematics*, ed. G. E. Anscombe (Oxford: Basil Blackwell, 1956), p. 57.
2. C. West, *Race Matters* (Boston: Beacon Press, 1993), p. 15.
3. W. Percy, *Love in the Ruins* (New York: Ivy Books, 1971), pp. 12–13.

TWO The Valorization of Sadness: Alienation and the Melancholic Temperament
Peter D. Kramer | *Hastings Center Report* 2000; 30(2): 13-18.

At the heart of *Listening to Prozac* is a thought experiment: Imagine that we have to hand a medication that can move a person from a normal psychological state to another normal psychological state that is more desired or better socially rewarded.[1] What are the moral consequences of that potential, the one I called "cosmetic psychopharmacology"? The question would be overgeneral except that it occurs in the context of a discussion of psychic consequences of technologies. People now experience the self in the light of psychotherapeutic medications as lately they experienced it through psychoanalysis. . . .

To my delight, moral philosophers have taken up this thought experiment, particularly the medical ethicist Carl Elliott, in a series of essays distinguished by their literary appeal. These discussions are a continuation of *Listening to Prozac*, but they are also a form of backtracking, because the element that interests Elliott is cosmesis' goal. Elliott is worried about the diminution of alienation.

I hope here to use Elliott's essays to ask, as rule-keeper for a certain sort of game, whether the concept of alienation successfully identifies grounds on which cosmetic psychopharmacology might be morally suspect. At the same time, I will want to reopen the issue of the legitimate goals of treatment. To preview my conclusion—my impression is that the concern over Prozac, and with imagined medications extrapolated from experience with Prozac, turns almost entirely on an aesthetic valuation of melancholy.

Elliott's central claim is that addressing alienation as a psychiatric issue is like treating holy communion as a dietary issue—a category mistake. Included in this claim is the understanding that alienation has a particular

> **Cosmetic psychopharmacology**
> Using psychiatric drugs outside of the scope of the treatment of psychiatric disease; the use of such drugs to produce merely individually valued or socially desirable effects.

> **Melancholy**
> An emotional state of sadness of long duration. Someone who is chronically sad might be referred to as "melancholic."

> **Category mistake**
> Conflating two conceptually distinct kinds of things; putting a thing in a class to which it does not belong.

moral worth. Neither of these assertions strikes me as obvious. In particular, I want to say that both are thrown into doubt by a premise of our discussion, namely that medication can lessen alienation. The nature of the technology may cause us to reassess the category, and the significance, of the target.

To begin with the question of category: Clearly *some* alienation is an aspect of mental illness, indeed alienation is an element in schizophrenia. It is not absurd to imagine that alienation might be "psychiatric". Often Elliott equates alienation with depression, as when he paraphrases Walker Percy to this effect: "Take a look around you; it would take a moron not to be depressed."[2] The arguments Elliott makes regarding depression and alienation, as worrisome targets for pharmacology, are identical. It is not always clear whether the depression referred to is a stance or a syndrome.

> **Schizophrenia**
> A serious mental illness characterized by flat emotional responses, detachment from reality, and hallucinations.

As regards category, then, the question is, alienation of what sort? Elliott recognizes that alienation comes in many forms, and he describes personal, cultural, and existential alienation. But from a psychiatric point of view, the people Elliott suggests as candidates for antidepressant use are homogeneous. . . .

When I say that the premise "medication diminishes alienation" casts its shadow on questions of category, I mean that our likely beliefs about category are susceptible to being altered by our beliefs about how that diminution occurs. We do not expect medication to work directly on the cognitive component of alienation, just as we do not imagine there is a pill for, say, atheism or chauvinism—that sort of imagining would violate the rule that the drug we have in mind is a good deal like Prozac. Presumably, our hypothetic medication tones down obsessionality, pessimism, and social anxiety, so that, secondarily, a person feels less impelled to resist the ambient culture. It alters affective aspects of personality, where affect extends to such phenomena as sense of status in social groups.

That is to say, our premise brings into play the basis of personality. If we were certain, as many mid-century psychoanalysts were, that personality is the detailed psychic encoding of a person's experience in the world, relatively fixed but responsive to insight, then the parameters for a discussion of the pharmacologic enhancement of alienation would be clearer. Equally, if we were to discover that even minor depression is in

all instances caused by a virus that deforms brain anatomy, the discussion would be stable at a different point of equilibrium. The range of philosophical arguments might remain similar—one can approach character armour as a medical condition and one can define living with microbes as an expectable state of human life—but in each instance we would be more inclined to entertain particular ones.

> **Character armour**
> A term in psychoanalysis for deeply engrained defence mechanisms to prevent emotional excitement or harm.

To clarify the interplay of target and technology: Setting aside Prozac, let us imagine that it is discovered that moderate doses of vitamin C decrease a person's sense of isolation. Would the taking of vitamins seem worrisome? The answer depends on how we "listen" to the medication. We might decide that alienation of that sort was in all probability something like a vitamin deficiency. We might even decide in retrospect that our objection to cosmesis had resulted from an aesthetic assessment of the technology employed to achieve it. That is, previously (when it was a matter of using Prozac, rather than vitamins, to the same end) we had objected because the technology was artificial, scientifically complex, and manufactured and advertised by a large corporation—partaking of the very qualities we believe ought to lead to alienation, on, say, a political basis. Once vitamin C's effect was discovered, we might come to believe that Prozac had, after all, been repairing medical damage to the self. Starting with the premise that medication can mitigate alienation, it is not hard to imagine evidence in light of which alienation would be most parsimoniously understood as at least in part a psychiatric issue.

I should add that as a clinician, I find the argument by category mistake suspect because generally category mistakes are in the opposite direction from the one that perturbs Elliott. Mental illness has too often been too narrowly understood—misunderstood—as a principled response to social conditions; this error is one R. D. Laing made with regard to schizophrenia when he claimed that psychosis is a response to the absurd pressures of bourgeois family life. My own belief is that the conundrum necessarily is played out at a historical moment, ours, when the categorization of alienation remains ambiguous.

Elliott goes on to argue that alienation is circumstantially appropriate and morally valuable. Regarding personal and cultural alienation—the mismatch between particular self and the particulars of the social surround—Elliott writes that you might feel ill at ease among Milwaukee Rotarians. Elliott would disfavour your being offered Prozac in this instance because "Some external circumstances call for alienation."

Now I hope it is the case that no one is dispensing medication as an alternative to dropping membership in the Milwaukee Rotary. But if Elliott is at some distance from the clinical moment here, he is nonetheless successful in depicting one sort of unease, that of the sensitive person stuck in a group of philistines. Walker Percy, in a passage cited by Elliott, works the same vein as regards depression: "Consider the only adults who are never depressed: chuckle-heads, California surfers, and fundamentalist Christians who believe they have had a personal encounter with Jesus and are saved once and for all. Would you trade your depression to become any one of these?"[3]

> **Chuckle-head**
> A person of low intelligence.

These examples are amusing, but I fear that because they are all of a type, they prejudice the jury. Elliott's and Percy's comments succeed, on first reading, not because we value every instance of alienation—any sort of fish out of any sort of water—but because of a cultural preference for the melancholic over the sanguine. Consider the alienation or depression of a hockey player (a potential future Rotarian) rooming with poets; we may not want him to resist integration. . . .

In *Listening to Prozac*, I addressed a similar issue—alienation from what?—in regard to mourning rituals. Those who consider the American grieving period too brief and therefore alienating to the sensitive have pointed with admiration to rural Greece, where widows mourn predeceasing husbands for five years. But enforced mourning is restrictive for resilient widows; they are the alienated in a traditional culture. If alienation means a sense of incompatibility with the environment, then people of differing temperaments will be alienated in different settings. Do we honour both the sensitive and the resilient? Is it permissible for resilient Greek women to move to a society with shorter grieving periods? More to the point, if the sensitive move to rural Greece, will the consequent loss of alienation rob them of an aspect of their humanity? This sort of example might convince us that it is not personal or cultural alienation that we value, but the melancholic temperament or aspects of it, such as loyalty and sensitivity—and that we honour a sufferer in any setting, even one from which she is not personally or culturally alienated.

Effectively, Elliott conflates personal and cultural alienation. The notion of cultural alienation is invisibly buttressed by what I might call the Woody Allen effect. The prominently neurotic today are often political liberals, and this correlation has more or less held since the Romantic era. Soft left, hard right. But even if this conjunction is real and has an explanation (and what sort of explanation do we have in mind?), it is hardly universal. A sanguine person may be alarmed by apartheid, just as a melancholic might attribute his disaffection to the ending of apartheid. If Prozac induces conformity, it is to an ideal of assertiveness; but assertiveness can be in the service of social reform of the sort ordinarily understood as nonconformity or rebellion. The political effects of medicating the disaffected will be various. . . .

> **Romantic era**
> An artistic movement, reflected in literature, painting, and music, in the late 18th and early 19th century in Europe—widely understood as a reaction against the industrial revolution—that validated strong emotional reaction as the core of aesthetic experience.

Elliott's third category is existential alienation—"questioning the very terms on which a life is built," an unease such as one might suffer even on a desert island, or, as Robert Coles might put it, under any moon. Here we seem to be getting to the heart of the matter, alienation that has nothing to do with distance from a particular social surround.

We could perhaps obviate this consideration by arguing that if existential alienation is neither personal nor cultural, it should be part of being human, for all people in all times. If normal life is a project, then change qualifies as cosmetic only when life remains a project. Even for "good responders" to medication, existence remains hedged round by death, chance, unfairness, and absurdity.

But empirically, we know that angst grabs different people differently. Some people are more constantly aware of the universal existential condition. But what is it to be aware in this sense? Even existential alienation might be intertwined with temperament. Elliott leans toward that recognition when he writes, "Alienation of any type might go together with depression, of course, but I suspect that the two don't necessarily go hand in hand." But that is the question at issue: to what extent is affect, such as anxiety or depression, constitutive of existential alienation? To put the matter differently: If, medicated, one retains an intellectual unease but with diminished emotional discomfort, does being in that state constitute existential alienation? . . .

I have come to believe that much of the discussion of cosmetic psychopharmacology is not about pharmacology at all—that is to say, not about the technology. Rather, "cosmetic pharmacology" is a stand-in for worries over threats to melancholy. That psychotherapy caused less worry may speak to our lack of confidence in its efficacy.

We do, as a culture, value melancholy. Some months ago, I attended an exhibition of the paintings of "the young Picasso." Seeing the early canvases, I thought, "Here is a marvellous technician." I turned a corner to confront the works of the Blue Period, Picasso's response to the suicide of his friend Carlos Casagemas. Instantly I thought (as I believe the curator intended): "How profound." That pairing—melancholic/deep—is a central trope of the culture. Or to allude to another recent museum exhibition, for years the rap on Pierre Bonnard was that his paintings were too cheerful to be important. Here is the corresponding trope: happy/superficial.

> **Trope**
> Theme; figure of speech in which words are used for their metaphorical rather than literal meaning.

Surely the central tenet of literary criticism is Kafka's: "I think we ought to read only the kind of books that wound and stab us . . . [W]e need the books that affect us like a disaster, that grieve us deeply, like the death of someone we loved more than ourselves, like being banished into forests far from every one, like a suicide."[4] This need may even be pragmatic. In his poetry (I am thinking of "Terence, this is stupid stuff"), A. E. Housman argues that painful literature immunizes us against the pain of life's disappointments.

And here I want to lay down two linked challenges that are intentionally provocative. The first is to say that the literary aesthetic makes most sense in relation to a particular temperament (the melancholic, in which one feels great pain in response to loss) in a particular culture (one lacking technologies to prevent or diminish that pain). What if Mithradates had an antidote, so that he did not require prophylactic arsenic and strychnine? Might poetry appropriate to the antidepressant era be more like beer-drinking? And might that new art still prove authentic to the way of the world?

> **Mithradates**
> (134–63 BCE) King of Pontus and Armenia Minor (now part of modern Turkey) who was a formidable enemy of Rome. To protect himself from assassination, he took small daily doses of poison to build up a tolerance to its toxic effects.

The second challenge is yet more provocative, call it intentionally hyperbolic: to say that there is no neutral venue for this debate over alienation or cosmesis because our sensibility has been largely formed by melancholics. Much of philosophy is written, and much art has been created, by melancholics or the outright depressed, as a response to their substantial vulnerabilities. To put the matter only slightly less provocatively (and to return to the first challenge), much of philosophy is directed at depression as a threatening element of the human condition.

As Martha Nussbaum's *The Therapy of Desire* demonstrates in detail, classical moral philosophy is a means for coping with extremes of affect that follow upon loss.[5] The ancient Greeks' recommendations for the good life, in the writings of the Cynics and Stoics and Epicureans and Aristotelians, amount to ways to buffer the vicissitudes of attachment. If loss were less painful, the good life might be characterized not by ataraxia but by gusto. . . .

As for literature, studies indicate that an astonishing percentage, perhaps a vast majority, of serious writers are depressives. Researchers have speculated on the cause of that connection—does depression put one in touch with important issues, of deterioration and loss? But no one has asked what it means for us as a culture or even as a species that our unacknowledged legislators suffer from mood disorders, or something like. If there is no inherent moral distinction between melancholy and sanguinity, then we will need to worry about the association between creativity and mood. What if there is a consistent bias in the intellectual assessment of the good life or the wise perspective on life, an inherent bias against sanguinity hidden (and apparent) in philosophy and art?

> **Ataraxia**
> A tranquil state characterized by freedom from worry or passions.

An argument of this sort is worrisome—more worrisome than the conundrum we began with. And yet can we in good faith ignore the question of who sets the values? I have been in effect proposing still another thought experiment: Imagine a medication that diminishes the extremes of emotional response to loss, imparting the resilience already enjoyed by those with an even, sunny disposition. What would be the central philosophical questions in a culture where the use of this medication is widespread?

Aesthetic values do change in the light of changing views of health and illness. Elsewhere, I have asked why we are no longer charmed by suicidal melancholies—Goethe's Werther or Chateaubriand's Rene or Chekov's Ivanov.[6] Because we see major depression and affectively driven personality disorders as medically pathologic, what once exemplified authenticity now looks like immaturity or illness—as if the romantic writers had made a category error. . . .

I have offered an extreme version of an argument that might be more palatable in subtler form. I hope I have been convincing, or at least troubling, in one regard, the assertion that there is no privileged place to stand, no way to get outside the problem of authenticity as regards temperament.

Elliott asks whether we do not lose sight of something essential about ourselves when we see alienation and guilt as symptoms to be treated rather than as clues to our condition as human beings. The answer is in part empirical, in part contingent (on the social conditions of human life, a culture's technological resources, and such), and altogether aesthetic. If extremes of alienation are shown to arise from neuropathology, and if aspects of that pathology respond to treatment, our notion of the essential will change. And it may be that what remains of the experience and the concept of alienation will be yet more morally admirable: alienation stripped of compulsion, alienation independent of genetic happenstance, alienation that arises from free choice.

I want to end by saying that, like Percy and Elliott, in my private aesthetic, I value depression and alienation, see them as postures that have salience for the culture and inherent beauty. But the role of philosophy is to question preferences. The case for and against alienation seems to me at this moment wide open. It has become easy, in the light of the debate over Prozac, to imagine material circumstances that might cause us to reassess which aspects of alienation fall into which category. The challenge of Prozac is precisely that it puts in question our tastes and values.

Study Questions

1. What is cosmetic psychopharmacology?

2. Explain how Kramer's example of the grieving process in rural Greece shows that it is not alienation that we actually value.

3. Why is valuing melancholy merely aesthetic rather than moral?

Notes

1. P.D . Kramer, *Listening to Prozac* (New York: Viking Press, 1993).

2. C. Elliott, "The Tyranny of Happiness: Ethics and Cosmetic Psychopharmacology," in *Enhancing Human Traits: Ethical and Social Implications*, ed. E. Parens (Washington, D.C.: Georgetown University Press, 1998), pp. 177–88, at 183.

3. W Percy, *Lost in the Cosmos* (New York: Washington Square Press, 1983), p. 79, quoted in C. Elliott, "Prozac and the Existential Novel: Two Therapies," in *The Last Physician: Walker Percy and the Moral Life of Medicine*, ed. C. Elliott and J Lantos (Durham, N.C.: Duke University Press, 1999), p. 65.

4. F Kafka, letter to Oskar Polluck, 27 January 1904.

5. M. Nussbaum, *The Therapy of Desire: Theory and Practice in Hellenistic Ethics* (Princeton: Princeton University Press, 1994).

6. See Kramer, *Listening to Prozac*, p. 297, and P D. Kramer, "Stage View: What Ivanov Needs Is an Antidepressant," New York Times, 21 December 1997.

THREE   Psychopharmacological Enhancement

Walter Glannon | *Neuroethics* 2008; 1: 45-54.

Introduction

Many drugs have therapeutic off-label uses for which they were not originally intended. These uses were not part of the approval of the drugs and are not included in their labelling. Some drugs designed to treat neuro-psychiatric disorders can enhance certain normal cognitive functions. Methylphenidate (Ritalin) can help people with ADHD (Attention deficit hyperactivity disorder) to focus attention and carry out cognitive tasks. This same drug might also help university students and others who do not have this disorder to increase their concentration and perform better on exams or in their work. . . . Other drugs are being designed to enhance the consolidation, storage, and retrieval of memory for people without any memory impairment. SSRIs (selective serotonin reuptake inhibitors) such as fluoxetine (Prozac) are prescribed for the treatment of depression and anxiety disorders. Yet some who have not been diagnosed with these disorders take these drugs to enhance their mood and feel "better than well."[1,2]

Some philosophers and bioethicists are concerned that the use of these and other drugs to enhance normal cognition and mood would result in a state of inauthenticity.[3,4] The drugs would create states of mind that would in some sense be alien to people taking them. I will show that this concern about authenticity is unfounded. Then I will discuss what I believe are more ethically significant questions about the safety of enhancement drugs and consider the potential benefits and risks of using them for this purpose. . . . Finally, I will address the question of whether cognitive enhancement would fundamentally alter the doctor-patient relationship. Because the long-term effects of cognitive and affective enhancement are not known and could be harmful, a precautionary principle may be warranted. Safety concerns seem to justify limiting its use. As an expression of autonomy, though, competent individuals should be permitted to take enhancing agents. But they need to be aware of the risks in chronic use of these agents and to take responsibility for their effects. A reasonable middle ground between these positions is to warn those who choose to enhance that doing so entails risks.

Alienation? Inauthenticity?

One concern about enhancing normal cognitive capacities with drugs is that it would result in alienation from our true selves. Our selves consist partly in a unified set of psychological properties that are generated and sustained by normally functioning processes in the brain and central nervous system. We come to have authentic selves by identifying with our mental states. The state of identification results from a process of critical reflection on our desires, beliefs, intentions, and other states of mind. It is through this reflection

---

Off-label use

The use of a drug for an indication that is not listed in its terms of licensure from the drugs regulatory authority (in Canada, the Therapeutic Products Directorate). There may or may not be good evidence supporting the safety and efficacy of off-label uses of drugs.

Attention deficit hyperactivity disorder

A syndrome of inattentiveness, over-activity, or impulsiveness (or some combination thereof) out of the range of normal childhood behaviour. The diagnosis of ADHD has increased dramatically in recently years and it is now thought to affect up to 5 per cent of school-aged children.

Inauthenticity

Not genuine; failing to act faithfully and in accord with the will or needs of one's own inner being.

Enhancement drugs

Using a drug to expand normal function rather than to restore it, treat, or cure disease. Examples of enhancement discussed in this paper include reducing the need for sleep, improving memory, and diminishing performance anxiety. Drugs used for enhancement often have standard medical indications.

Precautionary principle

A rule invoked in the face of uncertainty regarding the consequences of a course of action when those consequences may be severe and irreversible; in such circumstances, the principle dictates that one ought not undertake the action without evidence that it is in fact safe to do so. The precautionary principle is contentious because it shifts the burden of proof from those who oppose an action to those who support it.

that we reinforce or reject them as the springs of our actions. Having an authentic self consists in having the higher-order reflective capacity to control which motivational states issue in our actions.[5-7] This capacity is a necessary condition for authentic and responsible agency, and insofar as agency is an essential component of selfhood, being an authentic agent is part of being an authentic self. Altering the process of critical reflection and the motivational states that result from it with psychotropic drugs presumably would result in alienation of our true selves from these states. We could not identify with these altered states and could not have authentic selves because something alien to us would be the agent of the change.

But it is not obvious that any drugs used to enhance cognition or mood would make ourselves inauthentic. If an individual with the capacity for practical reasoning freely decides to take a cognition- or mood-enhancing agent, then he or she is the agent of change. The drug is merely the means through which the change in mental states is effected. Provided that the individual has the capacity to critically reflect on the reasons for and against enhancement and to voluntarily act on these reasons, the change in mental states would not necessarily result in an alien or inauthentic self. The individual would have the capacity to foresee the change in mental states, and insofar as this is what he or she desires, intends, and decides to do after critical reflection, the change would be of his or her own doing. The realization of the intention to alter some of one's mental states would not necessarily alter numerical identity. Despite the changes, one could remain the same person after taking the drug, though it would depend on how substantial the changes were. The alteration could also be consistent with one's narrative identity. It could be an essential part of the unified set of values and interests over the course of one's entire biographical life.[8,9]

Even if one claimed that any psychological discontinuity between the earlier and later mental states would be substantial enough to result in distinct selves, the capacity to foresee the consequences of enhancement would be enough to make one responsible for them. Consider Stevenson's tale of Dr Jekyll and Mr Hyde. Jekyll transforms himself into the evil Hyde by voluntarily taking a potion. Later, when his curiosity moves him to repeat the experiment, he finds himself the subject of the involuntary mental states that characterize Hyde. Although it is Hyde who commits the evil deeds, Jekyll is responsible for them because he has the capacity to know that they are the likely consequences of his experiment and to prevent them by not taking the potion in the first place. Foreseeability makes the responsibility transfer from the earlier to the later time. This seems to be the point of Jekyll's admission, when speaking of Hyde, that "this too was myself."[10]

Attention and Alertness

Methylphenidate is a central nervous system stimulant and dopamine reuptake inhibitor. When used as a form of enhancement, it can increase attention in people whose dopamine levels are normal. Yet in brains with normal levels of dopamine, methylphenidate may cause dopamine dysregulation in various neural networks and lead to cognitive and conative abnormalities such as addiction. This has occurred, for example, in some patients taking dopamine for Parkinson's disease.[11] The drugs overcompensated for the dopamine depletion in the basal ganglia and other regions implicated in the disease.

Experiments using modafinil have shown that it can keep people alert and engaged in mental activities despite long periods of sleep deprivation.[12,13] It is believed that this drug activates dopamine, which then activates norepinephrine and histamine in a process that blocks the hypothalamus from promoting sleep. Modafinil does not appear to produce the same hyperactive and addictive effects of stimulants like amphetamines and cocaine because of its selectivity in targeting the dopamine pathway that controls wakefulness.

If the use of modafinil resulted in long-term REM sleep deprivation, however, then it could have deleterious effects on the brain and body.[14,15] . . . Drugs such as

> **Conative**
> Pertaining to the desire or the will to perform an action. In addiction, conation can overpower cognition; that is, the desire to take a drug can overpower a reasoning process that concludes that one ought not do so.

> **REM sleep**
> Rapid eye movement sleep; a phase of normal sleep characterized by rapid eye movements, paralysis, and dreaming. In an average night of sleep, a person will have 4–5 periods of REM sleep totalling 1.5–2.0 hours.

modafinil that limited NREM sleep could disrupt brain metabolism and interfere with the brain's ability to support cognitive tasks. Sleep also plays an important role in maintaining neural plasticity. Limiting sleep through pharmacological means could impair the brain's ability to adapt to changing environments or to adjust to injury. People who are chronically sleep-deprived (four hours or less per night) generally are at greater risk of morbidity and mortality than those who sleep six to eight hours per night. . . . There are established contraindications for modafinil. It should be used with caution in patients with a history of psychosis or cardiovascular disease. Its side effects are similar to those of other stimulants. . . .

Memory

Research into the mechanisms of memory suggests that novel pharmacological agents could enhance the encoding and storage of episodic and semantic memory of events and facts. "Smart" drugs targeting the transcription factor cyclic AMP response element binding protein (CREB), which influences the encoding and storage of long-term memory, might increase memory capacity in our brains.[16,17] . . . Memory enhancement could result in more effective cognitive capacities such as problem-solving and decision-making. Would these drugs enable us to form and store more memories and retrieve them more quickly? Or would increasing the storage capacity of memories impair our capacity to retrieve them? . . .

Another possible consequence of increased memory would be difficulty in learning new things, which depends on a certain degree of forgetting. The most famous case of this condition was the patient Shereshevkii, as reported by the neuropsychologist A. R. Luria.[18] Shereshevkii's formidable ability to remember facts and events resulted in his inability to process new information. The only employment he could sustain was that of a travelling mnemonist. . . .

As Daniel Schacter and Donna Rose Addis point out, "remembering the gist of what happened is an economical way of storing the most important aspects of our experiences without cluttering memory with trivial details."[19] They also note that "information about

the past is useful only to the extent that it allows us to anticipate what may happen in the future."[20] The extent to which we can learn new things is a function of the meaning we can construct from our past experience.[21] Memory is not just a reproduction of past events. The brain and mind do not function as a video recorder, or as a bank from which we withdraw particular memories of facts and events stored in specific sites in the brain. . . .

Memory researcher James McGaugh insists that we should be wary of inferring that if a certain amount of memory is good, then more memory is better.[22,23] Our capacity to form and store more memories might leave us too focused on the past, which might alter our phenomenological experience of persisting from the past to the future. Our cognitive capacities could be diminished by our ability to recall more facts and events that had little or no meaning or purpose for us. Before we pharmacologically tinker with memory systems, we need to consider how this might affect our neurological and mental capacities that mediate the content and meaning of memory. . . .

Keeping One's Cool

Anxiolytics are prescribed and taken for conditions falling within generalized anxiety disorder (GAD). These drugs include benzodiazepines such as diazepam (Valium) and lorazepam (Ativan), which block the release of stress hormones such as adrenaline. Yet these drugs are now being used by people who do not have GAD in order to remain calm when they have to act or interact with others in public. The beta-adrenergic antagonist propranolol is primarily an antihypertensive and antiarrhythmic drug designed to reduce the cardiovascular excitatory response to adrenaline and norepinephrine. By reducing this response in the brain as well, propranolol can attenuate or prevent anxiety. . . .

One musician taking propranolol told me that while his performances seemed to improve, the lack of an "adrenaline rush" blunted the normal experiential

> **Generalized anxiety disorder**
> A psychiatric disorder characterized by frequent or constant worry over different activities and events.

> **Antiarrhythmic drug**
> A drug used to convert an abnormal heart rhythm into a normal one or used to prevent the occurrence of abnormal heart rhythms.

> **Mnemonist**
> An individual with the ability to perform unusual feats of memory, such as rapidly memorizing an unfamiliar sequence of numbers, playing cards, words, or dates.

"feel" of these performances for him. He also noted that he had only a vague memory of some of his performances. . . . An anti-anxiety drug may enable one to keep one's cool during a performance, only to block the memory of that performance. Moreover, it is not known what effects the continued use of a drug that blocked a natural hormonal response might have on systems other than the cardiovascular and central nervous systems. . . .

Suppose that a 10-year-old female is a piano prodigy. Her parents and teachers believe that she is destined for greatness in the musical world. But she becomes anxious before her public performances. To prevent anxiety, her parents give her propranolol, which calms her and ensures a flawless musical performance in every instance. Encouraged by her parents, the child identifies with her musical prowess and desires to be a world-class musician. It appears that the child's ability to perform at the highest level will be an essential component of her well-being over the course of her life. Would there by anything objectionable about using propranolol in this case?

The fact that the pianist is not a mature minor or adult and does not have the decisional capacity to carefully think through the benefits and risks of chronic use of propranolol is significant. She, not her parents, would experience any long-term adverse effects of the drug. Because she does not have decisional capacity, and because the drug may involve some risk to her health, one could object to the parents' decision to allow her to take propranolol. It is not obvious that chronic use of this drug would be in her long-term best interests. This is a decision she could make on her own once she is competent enough to weigh the benefits and risks of the drug. . . . By insisting that their daughter take propranolol, the parents may be interfering with her right to an open future, which will only begin to take shape once she is capable of making her own decisions.[24] Only in cases where anxiety significantly limits a child's ability to function in everyday life would parental consent to the child's use of propranolol or any anxiolytic be justified. In these cases, anxiolytics would be justified for therapeutic uses, but not for enhancement. . . .

Right to an open future
The purported right of a child to a future that maximizes the scope of his or her autonomous choice. For instance, schooling a child in a particular religion may constrain the future choice of the child to adopt a different set of beliefs when the capacity for such choice develops.

Some mature adolescents or adults may take an SSRI instead of an anxiolytic for a similar purpose. Shyness may underlie their anxiety, and they may believe that an antidepressant may enable them to overcome this condition and become more successful in all of their projects. . . . However, there are potentially serious side effects of SSRIs in people with normal levels of serotonin, norepinephrine, and dopamine. Because antidepressants can increase the availability of these neurotransmitters, they may result in hypomania or mania in some biologically vulnerable people. . . .

It is not known what the long-term cognitive, affective, or conative effects of drugs to enhance alertness, memory, or public performance might be. What is known is that most drugs have side effects. Admittedly, this concern is not unique to enhancement drugs but applies to therapeutic drugs as well. Still, it is one thing to administer a drug with potential adverse effects for therapeutic treatment of a mental disorder. It is quite another thing to administer a drug with potential adverse effects to enhance normal mental functions. This raises the question of why one would take the risk of experiencing adverse effects of a drug if there is no medical need for it. . . . Yet because the long-term effects of enhancement are not yet known, it would be difficult to advocate for a policy that prohibited their use for this purpose. It should be up to individuals to choose whether to take cognition- or mood-enhancing drugs, provided that they are warned of the risks.

Some may question the selective concern about the drugs I have discussed. Many people take certain foods or supplements to improve cognitive and affective states of mind. Why is there such concern about drugs when food and supplements are taken to produce the same effects? Others may question why some drugs but not others concern us. Why do we not worry as much about the effects of nicotine or alcohol as we do about the effects of modafinil, CREB enhancers, anxiolytics, or SSRIs to enhance cognition or mood? . . .

Implications for the Doctor-Patient Relationship

Suppose that cognition- and mood-enhancing drugs were proven to be safe as well as effective. But they would not be available over the counter or the

Internet. Suppose further that a person wanted a drug to enhance his or her cognitive functions or mood and asked a doctor to prescribe it for him or her. Assuming that the drug was safe, there would be no risk of harm to the individual, and the doctor would be permitted to prescribe it. But there would be no therapeutic relationship between doctor and patient, given that the individual in such a case would not have a disease or illness in any sense of these terms. Even if we construe "therapy" loosely, it is unclear how an intervention that did not restore a patient to, or maintain a patient at, a normal level of mental and physical functioning could be described as therapeutic. . . .

Some have speculated that the possibility of neurocognitive enhancement could fundamentally alter the doctor-patient relationship.[25–27] Whether it does this will depend on physicians' views on what it means to have a therapeutic relationship with patients, whether this is a fiduciary relationship, and what it means to act in patients' best interests. It will depend on how physicians conceive of and exercise their professional autonomy in discharging their duty of care to patients. There may be considerable variation among physicians in how they exercise this autonomy, which would reflect their views on which psychopharmacological interventions they considered to be therapy, and which they considered to be enhancement. . . .

Conclusion

A significant body of data on the long-term effects of psychopharmacology to enhance normal levels of cognition or mood is not yet available. So there is no decisive reason for a policy that would prohibit the use of drugs for this purpose. Nevertheless, the potential harm from chronic use of enhancing drugs could be significant, which would seem to justify erring on the side of safety and adopting a precautionary principle limiting their use. At the same time, as an expression of autonomy competent individuals should be permitted to take enhancing drugs and to take responsibility for their effects. In adopting a reasonable middle ground between these two positions, we should issue the warning: "User Beware."

Study Questions

1. Do drugs that enhance cognition or mood threaten authenticity? Why?

2. Glannon argues that "we come to have authentic selves by identifying with our mental states." Is this a plausible view about how we acquire authentic selves?

3. Why does Glannon believe that we ought to adopt a precautionary approach with drugs that enhance cognition or mood? Do you agree?

Notes

1. Elliott, C. 2003. *Better than well: American medicine meets the American dream.* New York: Norton.
2. Kramer, P. 1993. *Listening to Prozac: A psychiatrist explores antidepressant drugs and the remaking of the self.* New York: Penguin.
3. Elliot, Better than well.
4. Parens, E. 2005. Authenticity and ambivalence: Toward understanding the enhancement debate. *Hastings Center Report* 353: 35–41. (May–June).
5. Frankfurt, H. 1989. *The importance of what we care about.* New York: Cambridge University Press.
6. Frankfurt, H. 1992. The faintest passion. Proceedings and Addresses of the American Philosophical Association 6: 5–16.
7. Mele, A. 1995. *Autonomous agents: From self-control to autonomy.* New York: Oxford University Press.
8. DeGrazia, D. 2005. *Human identity and bioethics.* New York: Cambridge University Press.
9. Schechtman, M. 1997. *The constitution of selves.* Ithaca, NY: Cornell University Press.
10. Stevenson, R.L. 1984. *Dr. Jekyll and Mr. Hyde, and other stories.* New York: Grosset and Dunlap.
11. Dodd, M.L., et al. 2005. Pathological gambling caused by drugs used to treat Parkinson disease. *Archives of Neurology* 62: 579–83.
12. Turner, D., et al. 2003. Cognitive enhancing effects of modafinil in healthy volunteers. *Psychopharmacology* 165: 260–9.
13. Vastag, B. 2004. *Poised to challenge need for sleep, 'wakefulness enhancer' rouses concerns. JAMA* 291: 167–70.
14. Siegel, J. 2001. The REM sleep–memory consolidation hypothesis. *Science* 294: 1058–63.
15. Stickgold, R., and M. Walker. 2005. Memory consolidation and reconsolidation: What's the role of sleep? Trends in *Neuroscience* 28: 408–15.

16. Lynch, G. 2002. Memory enhancement: The search for mechanism-based drugs. *Nature Neuroscience* 5: 1035–38.
17. Tully, T., et al. 2003. Targeting the CREB pathway for memory enhancers. *Nature Reviews: Drug Discovery* 2: 267–77.
18. Luria, A.R. 1969. *The mind of a mnemonist.* London: Jonathan Cape.
19. Schacter, D., and D. Rose Addis. 2007. The ghosts of past and future. *Nature* 445: 27.
20. Ibid.
21. Hassabis, D., et al. 2007. Patients with hippocampal amnesia cannot imagine new experiences. *Proceedings of the National Academy of Science of the United States of America* 104: 1726–31.
22. McGaugh, J. 2002. Remembering and forgetting: Physiological and pharmacological aspects. Testimony before US President's Council on Bioethics. Seventh Meeting, 17 October, session 3.

Transcript available at: www.bioethics.gov/transcripts/oct02/session3/html.
23. McGaugh, J. 2003. *Memory and emotion: The making of lasting memories.* New York: Columbia University Press.
24. Feinberg, J. 1992. A child's right to an open future. In *Freedom and fulfilment: Philosophical essays*, ed. J. Feinberg, 76–97. Princeton: Princeton University Press.
25. Caplan, A., and P. McHugh. 2004. Shall we enhance? A debate. *Cerebrum* 6: 13–29.
26. Chatterjee, A. 2006. The promise and predicament of cosmetic neurology. *Journal of Medical Ethics* 32: 110–13.
27. Farah, M.J., et al. 2004. Neurocognitive enhancement: What can we do and what should we do? *Nature Reviews: Neuroscience* 5: 421–5.

Chapter Study Questions

1. Explain how Kramer characterizes Elliott's position as a culturally bound affirmation of melancholy (rather than alienation). How might Elliott respond?

2. Outline Elliott and Glannon's arguments on alienation and authenticity. Whose arguments are more compelling? Why?

3. Is, as Kramer claims, Elliott's argument aesthetic rather than moral? What difference does this make? How does this relate to the role of philosophy as envisioned by both authors?

Critical Analysis

Consider the following selection from Glannon's article:

"Suppose . . . that a person wanted a drug to enhance his or her cognitive functions or mood and asked a doctor to prescribe it for him or her. Assuming that the drug was safe, there would be no risk of harm to the individual, and the doctor would be permitted to prescribe it. But there would be no therapeutic relationship between doctor and patient, given that the individual in such a case would not have a disease or illness in any sense of these terms. Even if we construe 'therapy' loosely, it is unclear how an intervention that did not restore a patient to, or maintain a patient at, a normal level of mental and physical functioning could be described as therapeutic."

Outline Glannon's argument in your own words, paying particular attention to the premises that he relies on to support his main conclusion. Choose one of the premises for evaluation. Try to think of at least one objection to this premise.

Case Study

The film *Limitless* (2011), based on the 2001 novel *The Dark Fields* by Alan Glynn, asks "how many of us ever know what it is to become the perfect version of ourselves?" In the film the main character, Eddie Morra (played by Bradley Cooper), is a failed writer with chronic writer's block—he can't complete the first word of his overdue novel. A chance meeting with his ex-wife's brother leads to an unexpected opportunity: a chance to take a pill that will change his luck. The drug, called NZT-48, possesses the remarkable property of allowing him to use 100 per cent of his brain. Suddenly, he can recall everything he has ever seen or heard; he can learn a language in a day; and he sees patterns in complex events that allow him to make predictions that others cannot. His overdue novel is finished in four days, and submitted to a surprised publisher. His ability to see patterns in complex data allows him to invest money in the stock market with enormous success.

In a few weeks, he turns a few thousand dollars into a few million. As success piles upon success, the main character himself seems to transform from a rough-hewn writer into a slick and confident investor. NZT-48 seems like a miracle save for the fact that if he stops taking it he will become sick and, if deprived of it for long enough, will die.

1. Is the novel written after taking NZT-48 an authentic product of the labours of Eddie Morra? Why?

2. How might a drug like NZT-48 threaten social equality?

3. Should a drug like NZT-48 ever be made available? If so, under what conditions?

Further Reading

Elliott C. *Better than well: American medicine meets the American dream.* New York: W.W. Norton and Company; 2004.

Glannon W. *Bioethics and the brain.* New York: Oxford University Press; 2008.

Greely H, Sahakian B, Harris J, Kessler RC, Gazzaniga M, Campbell P, Farah MJ. Towards responsible use of cognitive-enhancing drugs by the healthy. Nature [Internet]. 2008;456(7223):702–5. Available from: http://repository.upenn.edu/neuroethics_pubs/42/. Date accessed: 8 June 2012.

Kramer PD. *Listening to Prozac: the landmark book about antidepressants and the remaking of the self.* New York: Penguin; 1997.

Parens E. Authenticity and ambivalence: toward understanding the enhancement debate. *Hastings Cent Rep.* 2005;35(3):34–41.

Sexual Justice and Health Care

I n this chapter, we explore sexual justice and health care. Everyone, at some point in their lives, experiences illness and, eventually, death. This shared experience gives rise to certain social obligations to ensure that some amount of health care is available to everyone, despite disagreement about the nature and limits of those obligations. The concept of sexual justice, on the other hand, might be less familiar. What do philosophers mean when they use this concept? Sexual justice refers to the general moral requirement that we treat all persons with equal care and respect their sexual and gender identity. More specifically, sexual justice demands that our institutions such as education, government, and health care be equally accessible to all persons across the spectrum of sexuality and gender. The readings in this chapter push us to think about the moral significance of sexual diversity in human life, where sexual diversity encompasses, among others, gays, bisexuals, lesbians, transgendered, and transsexual persons. The values and beliefs that health care professionals hold affect their ability to adequately address the claims of justice. Judgments about whether and how to develop and administer the technologies and services required for gender transition will vary, but many health care professionals will misunderstand or hold discriminatory attitudes towards those who do not identify with the sex or gender to which they were assigned at birth. How should conflicting values and beliefs be addressed in questions about sexual justice in the context of health care? Should some values be given greater priority than others?

In the first reading, Alice Miller considers the appropriateness of a human rights approach to justice for sexual minorities in matters of health care. Miller notes that "Human rights claims regarding sexuality—including claims of broadly defined sexual rights, more narrowly tailored sexual health rights, and identity-based rights such as lesbian rights or transsexual non-discrimination rights—are being made in many places worldwide." She examines arguments that centre on the concepts of health and global sexual rights, and finds that although this approach seems to hold some promise, the conceptions of both health and sexual rights require clarification. As Chapter 13 illustrates, definitions of health (and illness) rest on certain assumptions about what is normal (physiologically and psychologically) and that these assumptions may undermine efforts to promote sexual justice. Viewing health issues through the framework of medicine, meanwhile, tends to emphasize exclusively medical approaches. Yet, many of the health problems facing sexual minorities have social origins, such as lack of access to food, housing, and shelter. A human rights approach to human sexuality must not overlook the social determinants of health. The concept of global sexual rights, Miller argues, is premised on fixed identities. To counter these preconceptions, scholars and community activists seek to deconstruct fixed sexual and gender identities, and allow individuals to choose to become male or female, or even to avoid committing to any single category of gender or sexual orientation. Miller worries that the rights-based approach to sexual justice in the context of health care is ultimately

Social determinants of health
Social factors (e.g., socioeconomic status, profession) that combine to affect the health of individuals and communities.

too narrow. The approach is too narrow in that it leaves out some issues it ought to take into account, such as the social determinants of health, and in that it tends to use fixed understandings of sexual identity, which may or may not apply to the individuals affected.

In the second reading, Greta Bauer and colleagues draw on research from their Ontario-based project, Trans PULSE, which studies the effects of marginalization and invisibility in the health care system. They use the term "trans" to cover those individuals whose gender identity or expression diverges from prevailing societal expectations. According to the authors, "Trans includes transsexual, transitioned, transgender, and genderqueer people, as well as some two-spirit people." Bauer and colleagues detail the many difficulties faced by trans people, arguing that the lack of research into trans health issues results in a great deal of ignorance not only on the part of the general public but also amongst doctors and nurses, who receive relatively little education on the subject. The little education they do receive is often lumped together with gay health issues, which bear little resemblance to trans health issues.

Trans men and women are harmed by the division of so much of the health care system into men's and women's health. The norm that only women are meant to see gynecologists is obviously problematic in the context of trans people. Trans patients report that they spend a lot of time and energy educating health professionals about their lives. Bureaucratic hurdles, such as gender specific billing codes, also get in the way. Bauer and colleagues bring a wide range of negative experiences to light but say less about what should be done to remedy the situation.

The third reading continues our theme of our obligations to sexual minority patients, looking more specifically at the doctor-patient relationship. Ami Harbin, Brenda Beagan, and Lisa Goldberg use qualitative interviews with gay, lesbian, bisexual and trans patients and with doctors who treat such individuals to explore how routine practices of health care can perpetuate or challenge marginalization. The authors use feminist phenomenology to analyze transcripts of meetings with queer and trans patients and of meetings with their doctors. Health care practitioners are encouraged to become more comfortable with gay, lesbian, bisexual and trans patients but the authors raise the question of whether increased comfort translates to better care. The authors discuss a variety of strategies that both doctors and patients engage in to promote comfort—such as changing doctors, pairing up queer patients with queer doctors, denying differences—but the authors worry that these strategies deny doctors the opportunity to really think about and reflect on

> **Feminist phenomenology**
> An approach within philosophy that focuses on experiences, on what a life feels like from a certain subjective point of view, and understands such experiences and such subjective orientations in the context of sexism and oppression.

the assumptions that are guiding their provision of healthcare. Remaining comfortable may require not asking difficult questions or thinking very much about what a patient has said and so can hinder the process of rational reflection which is a necessary element in good medical decision-making and in doctor/patient communication. According to Harbin et al. we need to move beyond the language of comfort and the strategies that promote it if we are to provide sexual minority patients with the kind of health care that justice requires.

ONE   Uneasy Promises: Sexuality, Health, and Human Rights

Alice M. Miller | *Journal of Medical Ethics* 2003; 29: 153-6.

This commentary highlights some elements of a health and human rights approach to sexuality that might prove useful to health policy and practice in the context of diverse sexualities. At the same time,

it perversely unsettles some of those very same concepts. In part, this is to better capture the challenges that those working for global sexual rights, a contentious but increasingly recognized area of human rights work, face on a daily basis. It also suggests that neither human rights nor health should be employed without an examination of the ways in which each concept functions. . . .

A health and human rights approach to sexuality can, if used critically, be part of politically astute and self-conscious coalition strategies. Because of its focus on one category of marginalized persons—here, persons of nonheteronormative sexualities—this approach can contribute both to reviving calls for social justice in health for the most diverse range of people and to transforming the nature and practice of state accountability in "ensuring the conditions in which all persons can be healthy."[1] . . .

> **Nonheteronormative**
> Heteronormative is the assumption that heterosexual sexuality is normal underlies this term, and everything else—e.g., homosexuality, bisexuality—is a deviation from that, not merely in a statistical sense but also in the sense of what is proper or right. Nonheteronormative refers to sexualities which do not fit within this framework.

Health and Human Rights

The formal system of rights work asserts entitlements as legal obligations and thus as tools for political and legal accountability. But one strength of human rights work is that it meshes formal treaty doctrines with grassroots activism and critiques of power, "the legitimate territory of those who make political demands about basic justice."[2] Key principles that underlie *both* formal and informal rights work, and that have special relevance to a health and human rights approach to sexuality, are the primacy of non-discrimination and equality, a focus on the dignity of the person, the understanding that all rights are interconnected and interdependent in their realization, and the participation of individuals and groups in the determination of issues affecting them.

In addition, while rights are almost never absolute, the limitations imposed on their exercise—some rights, for example, can be limited in the interest of public health—must be strictly scrutinized for such features as excessive breadth, arbitrariness, and effectiveness. In 1994, an authoritative opinion was issued by the Human Rights Committee, the group of United Nations experts that reviews the implementation of the International Covenant on Civil and Political Rights (to which the United States has bound itself). This opinion stated that the "criminalization of homosexual practices cannot be considered a reasonable means or proportionate measure to achieve the aim of *preventing* the spread of HIV/AIDS."[3] They stated that the invasion of privacy and the discriminatory impact of Tasmania's sodomy laws could not be justified by reference to public health needs.

In addition, human rights obligations include a tripartite ordering of governmental responsibility. Governments are required to *respect* rights (the state and its agents must not through their own actions violate rights), *protect* rights, (the state must organize all branches to ensure that no other entity—private person or corporation—abuses human rights), and *fulfill* rights (the state must also ensure that its actions, at all levels, make the enjoyment of rights possible). In the case of (sexual) health, obligations to fulfill rights could be met through taking steps to ensure that mechanisms are in place that adequately respond to epidemic diseases such as HIV/AIDS or by setting in place the infrastructure for an open and diverse society—for example, by ensuring that gay and lesbian advocacy groups can carry out health advocacy without legal strictures or fear of violence.

> **Sodomy laws**
> Legal prohibitions against any contact between the genitals of one person, and the mouth or anus of another. About 70 countries in the world have sodomy laws, and a majority of these prohibit sexual activities between men only.

> **Tripartite**
> Composed of or split into three parts.

These principles—as part of legally binding treaties and as critical ways of demanding accountability locally—are key components of health and human rights arguments. But, just as critically, the formal system of rights establishes health itself as a human right. The International Covenant on Economic, Social, and Cultural Rights, which the United States has signed but not ratified, states in Article 12 that "States . . . recognize the rights of everyone to the highest attainable standard of physical and mental health."[4] Other treaties either require guarantees of the conditions for health or focus on non-discrimination in health services. Note that this is not a Utopian guarantee to the right to be *healthy*, but rather an obligation to create the conditions of health. It functions as any other rights claim, not as a magic grant of health but as a tool for demanding attention, for compelling action. The specific, useful actions to build health must be developed locally, whereas the right to make the claim is global.

Contextualized understandings of steps required for health have developed in tandem with a conceptual framework stressing the *interrelated nature* of the enjoyment of rights. This framework examines the ways that the enjoyment of various rights must work together to make any right real. For example, if "the human rights of women include their right to have control over and decide freely and responsibly on matters related to their sexuality, including sexual and reproductive health, free of coercion, discrimination and violence,"[5] a range of rights is needed. They include rights such as non-discrimination, freedom of information, protection of physical integrity (freedom from torture, liberty, and security of the person), the right to enjoy the benefits of scientific progress, the right of individuals and groups to participate in issues affecting them, and the right to equal protection by the law. Through a strategy of interconnected rights claims, advocates have transformed bundles of existing legal obligations into claims for sexual rights.

Building Sexual Rights Inside the Developing World of Human Rights

Human rights claims regarding sexuality—including claims of broadly defined sexual rights, more narrowly tailored sexual health rights, and identity-based rights such as lesbian rights or transsexual non-discrimination rights—are being made in many places worldwide. Human rights activism aimed at building new norms for sexual rights has occurred in world conferences, in treaty-based strategies of reporting and submitting complaints, and in national invocations of regional and international rights standards. It has taken such forms as (1) combating state violations against persons based on their sexual orientation (classic human rights); (2) establishing the conditions for sexual health in the context of women's reproductive health (feminist health rights); and (3) opposing discrimination based on sexual identity and practice and demanding access to health care in the context of the global HIV/AIDS pandemic (a fusion of the violations approach and the conditions-of-health approach).[6–8]

But a critical review of these strategies reveals that they cannot by themselves encompass the wide range of sexual orientations, practices, and identities among persons of marginalized sexualities. Many strategies mobilize sexual and other identities as part of visibility movements, often promoting the idea that specific sexual identities are constitutive of universal and ahistorical (or unchanging) minority groups or are immutable identities that ought to be protected under human rights-based anti-discrimination norms. These strategies are in tension with the scholarly work that deconstructs identities according to specific historical processes. And they engage us with the real political question of whether it is possible to deconstruct and defend sexual identities at the same time, particularly in regard to the operation of state power. . . .

In 2000, the committee that oversees the implementation of the International Covenant on Economic, Social, and Cultural Rights issued an authoritative statement on state obligations with regard to "health" and included an important, first-ever reference to sexual orientation in this kind of general interpretation. Notably, this statement is also applicable across sex, race, and age and other identities. General Comment 14 reads in part:

> *"The Covenant proscribes any discrimination in health care and underlying determinants of health, as well as the means and entitlements for their procurement, on the grounds of race, colour, sex, language, religion, political or other opinion, national or social origin, property, birth, physical or mental disability, health status (including HIV/AIDS), sexual orientation, and civil, political, social or other status, which has the intention or effect of nullifying or impairing the equal exercise of the right to health."[9]*

The committee authors crafted their understanding of discrimination in health to include not simply discrimination in health care but the "underlying determinants of health." Through this short phrase, the committee opened up the possibility that the entire treaty could be used to evaluate governmental obligations to end discrimination on sexual orientation as it affects health. . . .

Is Health Safe for Sexual Rights?

Health cannot be presumed to be a benign site for sexuality—especially homosexuality. In addition to the history of medical and psychological interventions that oppress lesbians, gay men, and bisexual persons, including the very naming of homosexuality as a disease, and the complicated relationship between trans-sexuality and medical intervention, numerous scholars have pointed out the dangers of the urge to medicalize talk about sexuality.[10]

First, even progressive strategies for better care and services for persons of disparate sexualities must face the reality that medicine can also function as a regime of control, alone or in partnership with law, including criminal laws and public health legislation.[11,12] Next, talking about sexuality within the context of health does not imply that all of the demands of sexuality are encompassed within the domain of health. Focuses on sexual health as a strategy to develop and claim sexual rights have been important, and many gains have arisen from this approach. Nonetheless, although it appears politically tempting to claim more aspects of sexual rights through this approach (as it sidesteps certain condemnations based on religion, culture, or morals), we should be wary of over-medicalizing a constellation of social and biological processes that encompass domains of imagination, expression and communication, law, religion, and economics, as well as the body.[13,14] Conversely, because one's sexuality is not the only aspect of identity or behaviour affecting health status, a sexual health and rights approach should constantly relink sexual health to the many social determinants, such as occupational environment, job and social security, poverty, housing, and education, factored across other key variables, such as race and sex, that affect health status. While access to health care does not equal good health, good health nonetheless requires available, accessible, acceptable, and quality health services.

Finally, concepts of sexual health and healthy sexuality have dangerous tendencies to slide from denoting sexual behaviours carried out without coercion, violence, or exposure to disease to connoting normal, naturalized sex, and creating a hierarchy that excludes diverse—or to some, perverse—sexualities.[15]. . .

Taking Sexual Rights Beyond (Homo)sexual Orientation

This commentary has addressed the dangers and benefits of the fact that the most progressive formulations of how and where sexuality might fit within traditional human rights obligations have arisen in health contexts. While acknowledging the benefits of this approach, we cannot rest with health as the full universe of sexuality, nor with homosexuality as the sole focus of human rights claims to sexuality, as these immediately progressive steps may in the long run impoverish the richness of human sexuality. The work to create the conditions by which all persons can develop and enjoy their full personality as the Universal Declaration of Human Rights would have it—alone, in love, in lust, and in community—returns us to two core challenges.

First, health, including sexual health, needs to be resituated in social justice and the broader social transformation of society. Second, as you cannot diversify what you have not yet established, building rights for sexual diversity must begin with broad-based efforts toward a core rights claim for sexuality as a key aspect of all human beings and a worthy object of transformed rights work.

Study Questions

1. According to Miller, what are the strengths associated with taking a health and human rights approach to sexual justice?

2. What are the limitations of taking this approach?

3. What dangers does Miller identify with framing sexual justice issues in terms of health?

Notes

1. Committee for the Study of the Future of Public Health, Institute of Medicine. *The Future of Public Health*. Washington, DC: National Academy Press; 1988:40.

2. Freedman L. Censorship and manipulation of reproductive health information: an issue of human rights and women's health. In: Coliver S, ed. *The Right to Know: Human Rights and Access to Reproductive Health Information*. London, England; ARTICLE 19; 1955:1–37.

3. *Nicholas Toonen v. Australia*, UN GAOR, Hum Rts Cte, 15th Sess, Case 488/1992, UN Doc CCPR/c/D/488/1992, April 1994.

4. *International Covenant on Economic, Social, and Cultural Rights*, GA Res 2200(XXI), UN GAOR, Supp No. 16, at 49, UN Doc A 6316 (1966).

5. Platform for Action of the Fourth World Conference on Women, September 1995, UN Doc A/CONF.177/20 (17 October 1995), para. 96.

6. Parker R. Sexual rights: concepts and action, *Health Hum Rights*. 1997;2:31–8.
7. Abeyesekera S. Activism for sexual and reproductive rights: progress and challenges. *Health Hum Rights*. 1997;2:39–44.
8. Miller A. Sexual but not reproductive: exploring the junction and disjunction of sexual and reproductive rights. *Health Hum Rights*. 2000;4:68–109.
9. General Comment 14, CESCR, UN Doc E/C12/2000/4 (4 July 2000).
10. Vance CS. Anthropology Rediscovers Sexuality: A Theoretical Comment. *Soc Sci Med*. 1991;33:875–84.
11. Foucault M. *The History of Sexuality*. Hurley R, trans. New York, NY: Vintage Books; 1987.

12. Otto D. Rethinking the "universality" of human rights law. *Columbia Hum Rights Law Rev*. Fall 1997;29:1–46.
13. Vance CS. Pleasure and danger: towards a politics of sexuality. In: Vance CS, ed. *Pleasure and Danger: Exploring Female Sexuality*. London, England: Pandora Press; 1992:1–28.
14. Correa S, Petchesky R. Reproductive and sexual rights: a feminist perspective. In: Sen G, Germaine A, Chen LC, eds. *Population Policies Reconsidered: Health, Empowerment and Rights*. Cambridge, Mass: Harvard University Press; 1997: 107–26.
15. Rubin G. Thinking sex: notes for a radical theory of the politics of sexuality. In Vance CS, ed. *Pleasure and Danger: Exploring Female Sexuality*. London, England: Pandora Press; 1992:267–319.

TWO   "I Don't Think This is Theoretical; This is Our Lives": How Erasure Impacts Health Care for Transgender People

Greta R. Bauer, Rebecca Hammond, Robb Travers, Matthias Kaay, Karin M. Hohenadel, and Michelle Boyce | *Journal of the Association of Nurses in AIDS Care* **2009; 20(5): 348–61.**

Trans is an umbrella term that encompasses a diverse group of people whose gender identity or expression diverts from prevailing societal expectations. Trans includes transsexual, transitioned, transgender, and genderqueer people, as well as some "two-spirit" people. The corresponding terms *cissexual* and *cisgender* typically describe nontrans people. . . .

Background and Significance

Despite consistent documentation that trans people are routinely exposed to direct and indirect experiences of discrimination and harassment and are often unable to access health and social services, analyses that have attempted to explain how such marginalization gets produced have been notably absent. When explanations for the exclusion that trans people experience have been provided, the tendency has been to attribute the marginalization as a consequence of transphobia (i.e., fear or hatred of transgenderism or transsexuality). Whereas transphobia may be a useful concept in understanding the motivations underlying the actions of individuals, its use as an explanation has obscured the more systematic nature of trans marginalization by isolating the particular problem to acts rather than embedding the problem in broader cultural and political contexts. . . .

This article provides one of the first schemas for understanding the process through which trans people come to experience marginalization and vulnerability, with a focus specifically on the processes that exclude trans people from accessible and appropriate health services. The concept of erasure, described by Namaste (2000) as "'a defining condition of how transsexuality is managed in culture and institutions, a condition that ultimately inscribes transsexuality as impossible,'" . . . is used as a framework.[1]

The Trans PULSE Project

Trans PULSE is an Ontario-wide project that aims to broadly understand how social exclusion impacts the health of trans people. . . . Trans PULSE is a mixed-methods study using both qualitative and quantitative components. Phase I consisted of a set of "community soundings," or focus groups, designed to elicit concerns about a range of health and health care issues among trans people in various Ontario communities. . . .

Results

Although community soundings covered a broad range of topics, much of the discussion focused on experiences within health care systems and included the following difficulties: interacting with physicians, nurses, staff, and mental health providers; finding accurate information; and accessing primary, hospital, mental health, and transition-related care. . . .

Erasure appeared in two key domains in the analysis: informational systems, and institutional policies and practices. Erasure could be passive or active. Passive erasure included a lack of knowledge of trans issues and the assumption that this information was neither important nor relevant. Active erasure could involve a range of responses from visible discomfort to refusal of services to violent responses that aimed to intimidate or harm. Active and passive erasure within these two domains produced systemic barriers to care and served to reinforce the erasure of individual trans people and, by extension, trans communities.

Informational Erasure

Informational erasure encompasses both a lack of knowledge regarding trans people and trans issues and the assumption that such knowledge does not exist even when it may. It is manifest in research studies, curricula, and textbooks, and in the information learned by or readily accessible to health care providers and policy makers.

Health research often erroneously presumes that all research participants are cissexual, that their partners or family members are cissexual, and that their sex and gender have been consistent over the lifetime. Thus, trans people who have been research participants have been systematically erased, and by extension, trans experience and subjectivity have been rendered invisible. The social exclusion produced has a cumulative impact, because trans bodies are not counted or not recognized. Social exclusion is experienced profoundly by individuals. One participant put it frankly, as follows:

"I'm one of the dead ones. Remember [this], just because you're TS [transsexual], you're one of the dead ones. All of this time that I've survived, I'm one of the walking dead, because we're not counted, we're not represented anywhere."

The lack of research on trans lives and trans issues has resulted in a dearth of information on health-related topics, including issues related to family practice, mental health, and trans-specific health care, which includes transition-related as well as primary health care concerns. A participant elaborated on this theme:

"I think that one of the things that bothers me personally is the lack of information on long-term worries healthwise. Here I am, I've had SRS [sex reassignment surgery]. How is it all going to work in 40 years? I have no idea. Do I have to worry about breast cancer? Do I have to worry about prostate cancer? There's a few studies, but they are so little

that they can't really tell us what the heck is going to happen to us eventually. I think we need that kind of data. I'd like to ask my doctor 'Well, what should I worry about?" and not hear 'Well, I have no frickin' idea'." . . .

The lack of information on how gender identity relates or does not relate to mental health allows provider assumptions to manifest in ways that erect barriers to care. Although research results have shown that transsexual people are no more likely to suffer from psychopathology than cissexual people,[2] providers may perceive unrelated mental health issues to stem from a person's gender identity. One participant explained as follows:

". . . [S]ometimes we have other mental illnesses. So if we're trying to get help, some doctors may blame it on the trans aspect of reality, when in fact there's an actual illness."

Another participant explained that conversely, providers might assume that a person's gender identity stems from mental health issues and is not legitimate in the comment that, "sometimes the trans issues are discarded. 'Oh, you're not really trans, you're dealing with such and such an issue.'" . . . Providers rarely receive information presented in a way that allows them to see a person's mental health issues as separate from trans status and tend to discount one or the other, or link what may be unrelated issues. This blurring or blinding of issues may result in inadequate or inappropriate care. . . .

When [research] has been produced, it is often not incorporated into textbooks, educational curricula, health care protocols, or other summary documents, or it is incorporated in a way that conflates gender identity with sexual orientation. This erasure reflects the priorities, biases, and oversights of writers and publishers who function in a cisnormative system, one in which people are assumed to be cissexual. One participant elaborated as follows:

". . . [In] the first-year class, transsexual . . . was not even half a paragraph in the 500 giant-page book, and it wasn't even its own section. It came under the section, and this is seriously the title, 'Homosexuality'. . . ."

Information on community-sensitive policies and practices in health care . . . often omit specific issues of trans clients or erroneously assume that issues around gender identity are similar to issues around sexual orientation. A participant clarified; "Trans and gay is [sic] not necessarily the same thing. Just because someone knows a lot about gay stuff doesn't mean they know a lot about trans stuff or they are even accepting."

This pervasive absence of information, along with stunted knowledge production and dissemination, greatly affect the ability of trans people to access health care services. It manifests in an unwillingness on the part of providers to transcend obstacles to gain access to information or to use the information that has been made available. A participant explained as follows:

> "I've had more issues with lack of knowledge, having to [educate] my GP [general practitioner] and my gyno [gynecologist] . . . Not only do they not have the knowledge, but they have no interest to learn. You can give them information, you can offer them resources, but they cannot be bothered. So they would much rather pass you off and get you out of the office—'pass the tranny'."

. . . The theme of having to educate one's own providers was shared by many participants. Providers had not received education on trans health issues and working with trans patients or clients. Thus, when a trans person walked through the door, providers were not prepared. . . .

Health care providers' lack of preparation for working with trans patients or clients stems in part from inaccurate current estimates of the size of trans populations. Given oft-cited estimates from the Netherlands of 1 in 30,400 born females and 1 in 11,900 born males being transsexual,[3] there would be approximately 615 such people in Ontario, including children and infants. Although actual numbers are unknown, one publicly funded community health centre in Toronto, which is mandated to provide primary health care services to LGBT communities, currently has more trans clients than should exist in the entire province, given these estimates. . . . Several participants identified a concern regarding the underestimation of the size of the trans community:

> "In my opinion, until we blow that myth out of the water, we're only going to get funding that's based on 1 in 30,000 of the population. If we are, as some would believe, 1 in 1500 to 2000, then we should get 15 times the attention and funding."

The perception that trans people are rare reinforces an erasure of trans communities and the continuing treatment of trans people as isolated cases. . . . These widely cited population estimates come from assessments of surgery-seeking transsexual people, who represent only a portion of the broader trans community. A participant elaborated as follows:

> "Health care professionals need to have a sensitivity . . . that there are so many different kinds of trans people, you can't have any assumption, because there is such a huge range about what it means to be trans."

Assumptions about what a trans person looks like, what their issues are, or what they need result from a lack of research characterizing the diversity within trans communities. Trans participants in the authors' community soundings had varied gender identities, came from a wide variety of ethnic communities, were born in numerous countries, and worked across the full range of professions. Research into the specific needs of particular groups (e.g., trans men, trans women, genderqueer or bi-gendered people, two-spirit trans people, trans immigrants, trans sex workers, trans people living "stealth" or living in isolated communities, trans youth, trans seniors) is needed to understand the full scope of health-related needs within trans communities.

Institutional Erasure

Institutional erasure occurs through a lack of policies that accommodate trans identities or trans bodies, including the lack of knowledge that such policies are even necessary. This form of erasure is actualized in several ways. The possibility of trans identities can be excluded from the outset in bureaucratic applications such as texts and forms. This is most often apparent on referral forms, administrative intake forms, prescriptions, and other documents. One participant described difficulties based on the sex designation on their provincial insurance card . . . as follows:

> "Even just not seeing the doctor [is affecting my health]; like, I am not going . . . telling them I am trans and have to drop my drawers, like forget it. And now my health card reads male, and I had to get an ultrasound, and it's the second time I had problems going for an ultrasound. The first time my health card read female, and the second time it

read male, both times I sort of had a problem . . . I couldn't get a consult with a gynecologist anywhere, with any of the doctors—my nurse practitioner called every single one. So, like, that is scary."

Sex designations on health-related documents can affect a patient's experience while receiving care. Staff may assume it is an error and try to get it corrected, or alternately, it may "out" a patient as trans. Sex designations play another critical role in care, because billing systems are often set up with an assumption of concordance between listed sex and body parts and allow billing for sex-specific procedures only to individuals of that designated sex. Thus, it becomes problematic to bill for such things as a hysterectomy for a male patient or prostate-related treatments for a female patient. In these examples, erasure is embedded, both in the omission of a designation for trans individuals and in the attempt to reinscribe or "correct" a designation for access to service.

From an institutional standpoint, trans identities are erased through an absence of safe, trans-inclusive spaces. In sex-segregated systems such as hospital wards or women's clinics, trans people are often forced to choose between accessing services according to their birth sex or foregoing services entirely. . . .

"I felt like shit. Here I am in this women's ward, on this women's floor, the only guy, and it's pretty awkward . . . it's so uncomfortable. I felt like shit."

. . . Broadly, trans people seeking health care are often faced with the acute realization that many providers are not familiar with or willing to accept the possibility of trans identities, which impacts both the availability and quality of care. Embedded in this particular configuration of institutional erasure is a politics of recognition regarding being in the appropriate place or possessing the correct anatomy to be provided service. A participant recalled the following:

"I got told by one of those three doctors that I should probably seek health care elsewhere . . . because, for some reason, he did not know [that I was trans] in advance, because that wasn't what I was seeing him for, and when he found out, he pretty much said word for word, "Please go someplace else," so that he wouldn't have to deal with it . . . it bothers me immensely that we're still treated that way by people who should know better."

. . . The erasure of trans people in institutional contexts functions with information erasure to form a mutually reinforcing system. . . . The lack of information, along with the failure to synthesize existing information into curricula and texts, contributes to the impression of research scarcity and, by extension, minimizes the importance of trans-related research. . . . Lack of consideration of trans people in protocols and policies provides for continued erasure of trans people's needs and does not signal their importance or even existence to staff and providers. . . . The continuing underestimation of the size or strength of trans populations allows for continued assumptions that systems do not need to be adapted to be trans-appropriate and that trans people can be dealt with on an individual basis. These assumptions serve to make a given system inaccessible for potential trans clients and affect the quality of care that can be provided.

Discussion

Cisnormativity

Underlying the processes of erasure is cisnormativity. Cisnormativity describes the expectation that all people are cissexual, that those assigned male at birth always grow up to be men and those assigned female at birth always grow up to be women. . . . Cisnormativity disallows the possibility of trans existence or trans visibility. As such, the existence of an actual trans person within systems such as health care is too often unanticipated and produces a social emergency of sorts because both staff and systems are unprepared for this reality. . . .

Navigating Cisnormative Systems

Data from this study showed numerous challenges that trans participants have in navigating cisnormative health care systems. They have difficulty finding health care providers who can provide trans-competent care, both in terms of providing a trans-friendly environment and having specific knowledge of trans health issues. Trans patients have often taken on the burden of attempting to educate the providers they have gone to for specific expertise. Trans patients have had to endure the indignity of being placed in sex-segregated wards or sent to sex-specific service clinics that were not appropriate to their felt or visible gender. Negative experiences, or fears of having negative experiences, have caused some people to avoid health care settings or to self-treat.

Others have chosen to not disclose their trans status whenever possible. For trans people who have the option of passing as cissexual, the choice often exists as to where and when and to whom to disclose. Yet choice is often an illusion in which all options carry risks. For example, a trans person in need of emergency health care has the "choice" to self-disclose his or her medical history and hormone use. Disclosure involves the risk of denial of care or mistreatment; lack of disclosure involves the risk of inappropriate health care and possible unintentional disclosure through medical examinations or testing. The onus should not be on trans people to make themselves visible in vulnerable situations, to educate persons in positions of greater power, or to try to change policies to accommodate their needs, especially at a time of distress. . . .

Conclusion

This project was undertaken not merely to describe the challenges that trans people experience. Rather, the information was obtained to provide an understanding of the ways in which these challenges are brought into existence. As patterns emerged in the experiences that were shared, it was difficult to understand how social determinants of health, such as access to health care, affect the lives of trans people without understanding the processes through which trans people are actively and passively erased. . . . Although this work sought to expand the theoretical basis for social exclusion of trans people, the theoretical and practical are not discrete areas. One participant phrased it well, as follows:

> "[T]he barriers remain within the larger society and even within the larger LGBTTQ [lesbian, gay, bisexual, trans, two-spirit, and queer] community, acceptance of who we are as equal and deserving of the same resources, the same attention. And what's the word? Erasure—which all of [us] are familiar with as a theoretical and practical term. I don't think this is theoretical; this is our lives."

Study Questions

1. Explain institutional and informational erasure, and give an example of each.

2. Explain how institutional and informational erasure interact with and reinforce one another.

3. What do the authors argue are the main reasons for the lack of information and knowledge about trans people?

Notes

1. Namaste, V. K. (2000). *Invisible lives: The erasure of transsexual and transgendered people*. Chicago: University of Chicago Press.
2. Haraldsen, I. R., & Dahl, A. A. (2000). Symptom profiles of gender dysphoric patients of transsexual type compared to patients with personality disorders and healthy adults. *Acta Psychiatrica Scandinavica*, 102, 276-81.
3. Bakker, A., Van Kesteren, P. J. M., Gooren, L. J. G., & Bezemer, P. D. (1993). The prevalence of transsexualism in the Netherlands. *Acta Psychiatrica Scandinavica*, 87, 237-8.

THREE Discomfort, Judgment, and Health Care for Queers

Ami Harbin, Brenda Beagan, and Lisa Goldberg | *Journal of Bioethical Inquiry* 2012; 9(2): 149-160.

This paper draws on findings from qualitative interviews with queer (self-identified as lesbian, gay, bisexual, or queer) and transgendered women and with physicians providing care to queer and trans patients in Halifax, Nova Scotia, Canada, to explore how routine practices of health care can perpetuate or challenge the marginalization of queers. . . . We argue that an ethical approach to care would in fact require attending

Heteronormative
The assumption that opposite sex relations are not just normal in the sense that they are statistically more common than same sex relationships but also that they are the way relationships are supposed to be, that one ought to be heterosexual.

Gender normative
The assumption that social roles which are based on male and female biological identity ought to guide our behaviour. For example, it's gender normative to assume that all women want children and are naturally better at caring for small infants.

Theoretical Approach: Feminist Bioethics, Cultural Competence, and Queer Contexts

[B]ioethicists . . . have shown how membership in oppressed groups can make it more likely both that individuals will experience serious health problems and that they will go unrecognized in current systems . . . (Baylis et al. 2008; Betancourt 2006; Fowler et al. 2007; Joseph et al. 2007; McNair 2003; Sherwin 1992; Shildrick and Mykitiuk 2005; Tong 1996). Attending particularly to queer and transgender individuals' experiences, researchers in contexts of care have shown that heteronormativity positions heterosexuality as the assumed sexual identity of patients, while a persistently assumed gender binary insists patients are necessarily either men or women.

Gender binary
The assumption that that there are only two distinct and opposite genders, masculine and feminine when in reality many people—including some transgendered persons—think that gender is much more like a spectrum, admitting of a great deal of diversity.

Gender-queer
A person whose gender identity does not fit in the usual categories of male or female.

ily either men or women. Heteronormativity and gendernormativity function together to make queer, transgender, and gender-queer lives invisible and make the particular needs of queer and trans patients less likely to be met (Barbara et al. 2001; Fryer 2008; Goldberg et al. 2009; Goldberg et al. 2011; Ryan-Flood 2009; Salamon 2009; Steele et al. 2006; Sullivan 2008; Valanis et al. 2000; also the Queer Bioethics Consortium n.d.). . . .

At the same time, sociologists and others have closely to instances of discomfort, which may signal for both patients and physicians moments where heteronormative and gender-normative assumptions may be challenged or may challenge good care. . . .

challenged . . . the adequacy of cultural competence education that encourages health care professionals to learn about . . . and develop tolerance and appreciation for others (Dogra et al. 2010; Gustafson and Reitmanova 2010; Kumas-Tan et al. 2007; Reitmanova 2011; Turner 2005; Wear 2003). . . . [D]ominant models of cultural competence training fail to address power relations, systemic sources of social inequities, and connections between social inequities and normative assumptions. Moreover, the measure of successful learning, the hallmark of "cultural competence," tends to be increased comfort and confidence among learners, rather than skills in critical reflexivity (Kumas-Tan et al. 2007; Reitmanova 2011). . . .

[W]e argue that generally well-intentioned physicians and patients setting out to maximize comfort—their own and the others'—in a care interaction can nonetheless unwittingly reproduce normative assumptions that marginalize and unfairly burden queer and trans patients. We explore here how an emphasis on comfort in health care interactions may in fact hinder the critical reflexivity needed to improve ethical and equitable care. . . .

Critical reflexivity
Intellectually challenging one's thoughts about one's role in the social structure—such as doctor, nurse, or patient—in a way that has the potential to change both one's practices, one's beliefs about those practices, and the power relations between people in different roles.

Causes of Discomfort

[T]he queer women we interviewed described more discomfort than their physicians did and bore such discomfort in a way compounded by fear that they will be denied safe and good health care as a result of being queer. . . .

Queer patients expressed discomfort in nearly every decision about whether or when to "come out" to a health care provider. Una described multiple levels of fear regarding coming out:

"I want to say something but I'm scared and I don't know how to say it, and I keep thinking, "How am I going to say it?" . .. If I tell her, what will she say? If I tell her, will she still be my doctor? If I tell her, who will I go see, who is she going to refer me to?"

. . . Queer women also expressed discomfort in moments of registering queer relationships. Women described being questioned about the name they recorded as partner for next of kin or emergency contacts. In one incident, Heather was told that she must have spelled her (female) partner's name incorrectly. In another incident, queer participant Kim described a refusal to accept her definition of family:

> *So I'm sitting there—I think this is probably the most uncomfortable I've ever felt—with this sick baby and feeling vulnerable and afraid and not sure what's going on, . . . and ah, the [woman doing the intake] was just so insensitive and she said, "Well what's the relationship," and I said mother, and she says, "Aren't you the mother?" I said, "Yes, she has two mothers." "Well how can that be?" . . . And then I had to dig through my bag to find this piece of paper that I carry around that confirms this Legal Guardian in Health Care, so she looks at it and the whole time she's looking at me like I've got six heads and she's saying all of this loudly enough that the people behind me are hearing and I noticed people looking at me, and then she's looking at my document and then she goes, "Well that's not going to fit in my slot."*

. . . Participants regularly described discomfort around health care providers' insistence about the need for pregnancy tests or contraception. For one trans woman we interviewed (Jackie), discomfort accompanied moments of identification as simple as getting a prescription in her current name, while the pharmacy needed it written in her pre-transition name . . . Women also expressed discomfort around descriptions of sexual practice . . . Some women described discomfort around being queer and unpartnered, [which] meant that their queerness could be more easily contested or treated as irrelevant in health care contexts.

. . . Physicians often noted that they feel discomfort when they mistake a patient's sexuality or when they can't tell if the person with a patient is a queer partner. Many expressed feeling discomfort when they did not know how to provide care but felt that professionalism requires that they not disclose uncertainty (cf. Fox 1980). Many physicians claimed that, other than requiring different approaches to sexual health, queer women's needs were the same as any other woman's. Some, like Helen, acknowledged their lack of knowledge . . . : "Some of our reactions come from pure ignorance and being caught flat-footed to say, 'Oh my god, I have no idea.' More so that, than perhaps judging." . . .

Discomfort about providing care to trans patients was something that almost all physicians readily admitted, even those who said they felt comfortable with all queer patients. Some physicians' expressions of discomfort were also confused expressions of concern about the power they have to decide courses of treatment in cases where they feel underprepared and ultimately responsible for trans patients' health. . . .

Strategies for Avoiding Discomfort

Strategy 1:
Avoid Discomfort by Avoiding Each Other

On this strategy, if a queer woman is uncomfortable with her physician, she should find a different physician. If a physician is uncomfortable with queer patients, she should refer them to someone else. One physician, Mona, noted that if queer patients feel uncomfortable, it would likely be with their own identities:

> *"I don't feel awkward or uncomfortable or nervous. . . . If people were really uncomfortable . . . I'd probably have them see [the gay medical director] . . . or just tell them that they can go to psychological services and that people over there should be very comfortable and capable of helping them, 'cause they would all have the training . . . if they were uncomfortable with how they saw themselves and they needed more information. . . ."*

By positioning queer patients' discomfort as the source of the problem in such cases, and ending uncomfortable physician–patient relationships early, the discomfort of any particular physician does not get challenged.

Strategy 2:
Avoid Discomfort by Putting Like With Like

On this strategy, if a queer woman is seeking care, she should seek queer providers. Straight providers should help match queer patients with queer providers. Queer providers should make themselves especially available to queer patients. As noted above, physician Mona thought referring her queer patients to her gay colleagues was appropriate. . . .

Strategy 3: Avoid Discomfort
by Not Discussing Anything Uncomfortable

Queer patients should only come out to health care providers when directly necessary, on this strategy.

Providers should ask about patients' sexual orientation or gender identity only when directly necessary. Helen said that she would not ask about sexual orientation or partners until a patient brings it up, even if it takes years, saying that to do otherwise would show disrespect . . .

This approach means that patients and physicians are responsible for determining in advance the health care circumstances in which queerness is directly necessary. . . . [W]hen physicians treat this aspect of patients' lives as private, the message appears to be that this aspect of patient lives is too private or shameful to discuss.

Strategy 4: Avoid Discomfort by Not Expressing It

Both patients and providers noted the felt need to never express discomfort. . . . [Physician] Gina expressed how discomfort, like an illness, might intensify or be more easily spread to others, and should therefore be avoided.

"I have to be comfortable and that will come out if I'm not comfortable and will probably add to their discomfort or create discomfort, so I don't want to do that if at all possible. I try to avoid it."

Strategy 5:
Avoid Discomfort by Denying Difference

On this strategy, providers and patients who are uncomfortable should characterize all patients as the same. Retreating to the sense that everyone needs just the same kind of treatment can create ease and suggest that queerness is irrelevant and thus not the cause of discomfort, whether giving or receiving treatment. When asked how her practice might change when a patient discloses queerness, Debbie responded: "Not at all. They would have the same needs." . . .

Strategy 6: Avoid Discomfort by Becoming "Happy in Your Skin"

This approach was aimed at queers, though the sentiment was expressed by both patients and providers. On this strategy, queer women are encouraged to cultivate more comfort in health care encounters for themselves and their providers by simply being less ill-at-ease and more open and happy with their queer identities. For Joan, a physician participant, the easiest queer patient is "somebody who's happy in their skin":

". . . I think if they're happy, if they are happy with their choice . . . happy maybe isn't the word, ah, content maybe, or at one with their choice, ah, that's easier to handle than someone who doesn't know themselves."

Queer participant Kim echoed the point:

"People take their lead from what you say and how you are. And if you're just matter-of-fact and okay with it, then they are too. . . . People's discomfort often comes from not knowing how to respond, . . . so I think if you're just upfront and give people the language to use then they're generally fine. . . . Every time, the heart pounds, you know, there's that anxiety, but generally it's been okay."

Here, queer patients are seen by both provider and patient as bearing most of the responsibility for maintaining a comfortable atmosphere in a health care interaction. The belief seems to be that it's not a patient's queerness that makes a provider–patient interaction uncomfortable so much as her discomfort with her queerness. If a patient is happy in her skin, her provider will be supportive and the care she receives will be as good as it should be.

Discomfort is seen as a serious enough problem in health contexts that patients and providers both suggested that patients leave if they are uncomfortable. Participant Ella highlighted explicitly the worry that a practitioner's discomfort would signal not just personal judgment but also professional misinformation: "If they're uncomfortable, they're probably not informed and so you're probably not getting the true level of health care that you need and deserve, so if you can, move on." Sarah, a physician, echoed the sentiment: "I would hope that most patients if they're uncomfortable will be brave enough to leave that practice . . ." Both patients and physicians articulated this in a city where, like many Canadian cities, virtually no general practitioners are accepting new patients. . . .

Critically Evaluating Comfort

Physicians' discomfort around providing care to queer patients expresses the ways health care practices remain heteronormative and gender-normative, inadequately attentive to the social harms queers may face in all realms of life, including in ways that affect their physical and emotional health. . . .

From a feminist perspective, the first five strategies for avoiding discomfort . . . are troubling in their own ways, if the goal is health care that takes into account rather than denies the position of queers in heteronormative and gendernormative contexts. The sixth strategy is particularly disconcerting insofar as it seems to charge queer patients alone with the task of ensuring comfort in health care interactions . . .

Who is it serving for queer women patients not to be able to express struggles with their identifications to their physicians? How is discomfort something inherent when queerness enters a heteronormative health care context . . . [I]n this case, the discomfort becomes a problem for which the queer patient is responsible. The problem is that she is uncomfortable and this is a problem she should fix. . . .

Providers and queer patients . . . rarely address what would happen if they were to acknowledge discomfort with each other or to allow for moments of discomfort around each other. [Physician] Gina suggests that it may be important to express rather than avoid discomfort and that her and other physicians' worries about introducing more discomfort for patients may prevent more open expressions that could be useful. Addressing the question of how to structure anti-heteronormative education for practitioners, . . . she suggested . . . that uncomfortable physicians should "be able to say that out loud without worrying about getting in trouble," where opportunities for more open expression might facilitate their ability "to say maybe where that comes from and then how can they address it.". . .

Anti-heteronormative education might be reshaped to allow for some expressions of discomfort with queerness apart from patient interaction, but it is also possible that moments of uncomfortable interaction between patients and providers may reshape norms of clinical interaction. Under Gina's explanation of the promise of expressions of discomfort, we hear a general will to improve, to challenge her own heteronormative and gender-normative practices, and thereby to provide better care for queers. Given the often unconscious character of oppression and the perpetuation of micro-inequalities, physicians may benefit more from training in critical reflexivity than standard cultural competence training. . . .

> **Micro-inequalities**
> Small inequalities, that are often unintentional, which produce harms that are sometimes too small to notice on their own, but yet can add up to much larger social wrongs.

Critically reflective practitioners ask themselves not only questions about how they felt and what assumptions they may have been making, but also questions about where their assumptions came from and how assumptions and actions/inactions may reinforce or contradict existing social and power relations.

Discomfort and Judgment

For many of the queer women in our study, feelings of comfort indicated that their health care provider was not judging them. . . . Feelings and especially expressions of discomfort were associated with a failure, with a provider having communicated judgment of a patient . . . Although the queer patient's experience of judgment is more centrally at issue, physicians could also feel judged by queer patients. . . . [J]udgments and discernments in both directions may incorporate ideas of what "people do" as "normal," socialized adults or as "progressive, non-bigoted, liberal-minded professionals." . . .

[So] both [patients and providers may] develop heightened sensitivity to what physicians are allowed to say in response to patients' queerness. When physicians are uncertain about the particular needs of their queer patients and uncertain about how fully their own feelings about queerness align with neutrality and "cultural competence," they may have little sense of which questions are appropriate to ask their patients and which will reveal unprofessional or biased judgments of queerness that should be kept to themselves (see Beagan and Kumas-Tan 2009). Even so, persistent societal heteronormativity makes it likely that practitioners are forming judgments of their patients' sexualities, whether or not they express them in ways their patients perceive. . . .

Physicians could still regularly judge (i.e., discriminate against) women behind postures of comfort and acceptance. When providers achieve comfort in their interactions with queer patients by not encouraging patients to express much about their sexuality, by treating all patients the same, or by hiding the discomfort they feel about not being well informed about holistic queer or trans care, comfort is not a sure sign of freedom from judgment. Beyond judgments of unnaturalness, physicians might wrongly judge that queerness is an immature phase in sexuality, that queers' needs for care are no different than nonqueers' needs, that queer sexual practice is inherently unhealthy, and so on. It can be that some uncomfortable moments allow physicians' judgments and insecurities and patients' realities to be expressed and worked through, actually improving the kind of care accessible to queer patients.

Conclusion

. . . In the case of health care for queers, oppressed patients stand to receive better care as a result of uncomfortable physician–patient interactions than they do if moments of discomfort are figured as uniformly bad practice. Less harmful practitioner–patient relations may come in part from sharing responsibility for resolving discomfort, rather than asymmetrically assigning this responsibility to patients, and from being open about discomfort, rather than fearing it or feigning comfort. The way shared moments of discomfort are handled may transform underlying heteronormativity and gender-normativity in the physician–patient relationship . . .

It might be that discomfort can produce joint efforts to recognize what causes discomfort and joint efforts to challenge underlying judgments—efforts that may not happen otherwise.

Study Questions

1. What is "marginalization" and why does it matter in the ethics of health care?

2. The authors of this paper set out to show routine practices of health care can perpetuate or challenge the marginalization of queers. Give an example of a routine health care practice and say how and in what way it might result in the marginalization of queer patients?

3. One of the authors' main worries is that the focus on health care professionals being "comfortable" with their sexual minority patients may result in less than adequate care for those same patients. How might the maintenance of "comfortableness" get in the way of the relationship between a queer patient and his/her health care professional? Again, can you think of an example of how this might happen?

References

Ahmed, S. 2006. *Queer phenomenology: Orientations, objects, others.* Durham, and London: Duke University Press.

Barbara, A., S. Quandt, and R. Anderson. 2001. Experiences of lesbians in the health care environment. *Women & Health* 34(1): 45–62.

Baylis, F., N.P. Kenny, and S. Sherwin. 2008. A relational account of public health ethics. *Public Health Ethics* 1(3):196–209.

Beagan, B., and Z. Kumas-Tan. 2009. Approaches to diversity in family medicine: "I have always tried to be colour blind." *Canadian Family Physician* 55(8): e21–e28.

Betancourt, J.R. 2006. Eliminating racial and ethnic disparities in health care: What is the role of academic medicine? *Academic Medicine* 81(9): 788–92.

Champaneria, M., and S. Axtell. 2004. Cultural competence training in US medical schools. *Journal of the American Medical Association* 291(17): 2142. doi:10.1001/jama.291.17.2142.

Diprose, R. 1994. *The bodies of women: Ethics, embodiment and sexual difference.* New York: Routledge.

Diprose, R. 2002. *Corporeal generosity: On giving with Nietzsche, Merleau-Ponty, and Levinas.* Albany: SUNY Press.

Dogra, N., S. Reitmanova, and O. Carter-Pokras. 2010. Teaching cultural diversity: Current status in UK, US, and Canadian medical schools. *Journal of General Internal Medicine* 25(Supplement 2): S164–8.

Fowler, R.A., N. Sabur, P. Li, et al. 2007. Sex- and age-based differences in the delivery and outcomes of critical care. *Canadian Medical Association Journal* 177(12): 1513–19. E-publication 14 November.

Fox, R.C. 1980. The evolution of medical uncertainty. The Milbank Memorial Fund Quarterly. *Health and Society* 58(1): 1–49.

Fryer, D.R. 2008. *Thinking queerly: Posthumanist essays on ethics and identity.* Eastbourne: Gardners Books.

Goldberg, L., A. Ryan, and J. Sawchyn. 2009. Feminist and queer phenomenology: A framework for perinatal nursing practice, research, and education for advancing lesbian health. *Health Care for Women International* 30(6): 536–49.

Goldberg, L., A. Harbin, and S. Campbell. 2011. Queering the birthing space: Phenomenological interpretations of the relationships between lesbian couples and perinatal nurses in the context of birthing care. *Sexualities* 14(2): 173–92.

Grosz, E. 1994. *Volatile bodies: Toward a corporeal feminism.* Bloomington: Indiana University Press.

Gustafson, D.L., and S. Reitmanova. 2010. How are we "doing" cultural diversity? A look across English Canadian undergraduate medical school programmes. *Medical Teacher* 32(10): 816–23.

Harbin, A. 2012. Bodily disorientation and moral change. *Hypatia* 27(2). doi:10.1111/j.1527-2001.2011.01263.x.

Heyes, C. 2007. *Self-transformations: Foucault, ethics, and normalized bodies.* Oxford: Oxford University Press.

Joseph, K.S., R.M. Liston, L. Dodds, L. Dahlgren, and A.C. Allen. 2007. Socioeconomic status and perinatal outcomes in a setting with universal access to essential health care services. *Canadian Medical Association Journal* 177(6): 583–90.

Kumas-Tan, Z.O., B. Beagan, C. Loppie, A. MacLeod, and B. Frank. 2007. Measuring cultural competence: Examining hidden assumptions. *Academic Medicine* 82(6): 548–57.

McNair, R. 2003. Lesbian health inequalities: A cultural minority issue for health professionals. *The Medical Journal of Australia* 178(2): 643–5. Queer Bioethics Consortium. No date. Bioethics, sexuality, gender identity. http://www.queerbioethics.org.

Reitmanova, S. 2011. Cross-cultural undergraduate medical education in North America: Theoretical concepts and educational approaches. *Teaching and Learning in Medicine* 23(2): 197–203.

Ryan-Flood, R. 2009. *Lesbian motherhood: Gender, families and sexual citizenship.* New York: Palgrave Macmillan.

Salamon, G. 2009. The sexual schema: Transposition and transgender. In *You've changed: Sex reassignment and personal identity*, ed. L.J. Shrage, 81–97. Oxford: Oxford University Press.

Sherwin, S. 1992. *No longer patient: Feminist ethics and health care.* Philadelphia: Temple University Press.

Shildrick, M., and R. Mykitiuk (eds.). 2005. *Ethics of the body: Postconventional challenges.* New York: MIT Press.

Steele, L.S., J.M. Tinmouth, and A. Lu. 2006. Regular health care use by lesbians: A path analysis of predictive factors. *Family Practice* 23(6): 631–6. E-publication 23 June.

Sullivan, N. 2008. Dis-orienting paraphilias? Disability, desire, and the question of (Bio) ethics. *Journal of Bioethical Inquiry* 5(2–3): 183–92.

Tong, R. 1996. *Feminist approaches to bioethics.* Boulder: Westview Press.

Turner, L. 2005. Is cultural sensitivity sometimes insensitive? *Canadian Family Physician* 51(4): 478–80.

Valanis, B.G., D.J. Bowen, T. Bassford, E. Whitlock, P. Charney, and R.A. Carter. 2000. Sexual orientation and health: Comparisons in the women's health initiative sample. *Archives of Family Medicine* 9(9): 843–53.

Wear, D. 2003. Insurgent multiculturalism: Rethinking how and why we teach culture in medical education. *Academic Medicine* 78(6): 549–54.

Weiss, G. 1999. *Body images: Embodiment as intercorporeality.* New York: Routledge.

Young, I.M. 2005. *On female body experience: Throwing like a girl and other essays.* Oxford: Oxford University Press.

Chapter Study Questions

1. How ought the rights of trans identified patients be secured: by ensuring that all doctors receive education about alternate sex and gender identities, or by ensuring that all trans patients have access to doctors who specialize in trans health care? What are the moral and political differences between these two approaches? What might Bauer et al. and Harbin et al. have to say about this issue?

2. According to Miller and Bauer and colleagues, what is sexual justice and how do they argue

for it? Are their views complementary to one another? How so?

3. Both Harbin et al. and Bauer et al. worry that too much of the burden of educating doctors about issues facing trans patients falls on the patients themselves. But Harbin's approach seems to speak in favour of more conversations, rather then fewer, between doctors and patients. How might Harbin's approach avoid the problem that both articles point out?

Critical Analysis

Consider the following selection from the Miller article:

"Health" cannot be presumed to be a benign site for sexuality—especially homosexuality. In addition to the history of medical and psychologic

interventions that oppress lesbians, gay men, and bisexual persons, including the very naming of "homosexuality" as a disease, and the

complicated relationship between trans-sexuality and medical intervention, numerous scholars have pointed out the dangers of the urge to medicalize talk about sexuality.

First, even progressive strategies for better care and services for persons of disparate sexualities must face the reality that medicine can also function as a regime of control, alone or in partnership with law, including criminal laws and public health legislation. Next, talking about sexuality within the context of health does not imply that all of the demands of sexuality are encompassed within the domain of health. Focuses on sexual health as a strategy to develop and claim "sexual rights" have been important, and many gains have arisen from this approach. Nonetheless, although it appears politically tempting to claim more aspects of sexual rights through this approach (as it sidesteps certain condemnations based on religion, culture, or morals), we should be wary of over-medicalizing a constellation of social and biological processes that encompass domains of imagination, expression and communication, law, religion, and economics, as well as the body.

Conversely, because one's sexuality is not the only aspect of identity or behaviour affecting health status, a "sexual health and rights" approach should constantly relink sexual health to the many social determinants, such as occupational environment, job and social security, poverty, housing, and education, factored across other key variables, such as race and sex, that affect health status. While access to health care does not equal good health, good health nonetheless requires available, accessible, acceptable, and quality health services. Finally, concepts of "sexual health" and "healthy sexuality" have dangerous tendencies to slide from denoting sexual behaviours carried out without coercion, violence, or exposure to disease to connoting "normal, naturalized" sex, and creating a hierarchy that excludes diverse—or to some, perverse—sexualities."

Outline Miller's argument in your own words, paying particular attention to the premises that she relies on to support her main conclusion. Choose one of the premises for evaluation. Try to think of at least one objection to this premise.

Case Study

After years of living in Vancouver, Joe returned home to a small town near Ottawa, Ontario, where his mother and old friends still lived. Shortly thereafter, Joe woke up with a sore throat and fever. Two days later, symptoms had moved to Joe's chest, and continued to worsen for a week. At the encouragement of his girlfriend and family, Joe reluctantly decided that a visit to the doctor was necessary. However, in Vancouver, both Joe and the doctor were comfortable with addressing Joe's health care needs, such as a regular pap test, and the doctor was unfazed by Joe's tattoos, chest hair, and piercings, or by the fact that Joe was queer. Joe knew that it was highly unlikely, though, that there would be a walk-in clinic in this small Ontario hamlet with someone who would be knowledgeable or sensitive to the issues and needs of someone who was queer and transgendered.

Instead, Joe found a walk-in clinic in downtown Ottawa that had rainbow flags all over its website, suggesting that it would be sensitive to Joe's needs. But when Joe called to make an appointment, and explained the situation, the receptionist explained unsympathetically that Joe was outside of the catchment area, and would have to find somewhere closer to home. Unable to face the prospect of seeing a doctor in the local community, Joe called back and asked to speak to the clinic director. The clinic director apologized profusely and assured Joe that a terrible mistake had been made: even though Joe lives outside of Ottawa, his employment in the city means he is eligible for treatment at the walk-in clinic. The clinic director invited Joe to come in the next day and see a doctor—one who would be comfortable addressing Joe's health care needs. (Case adapted from Coyote 2008; see reference below).

1. How does Joe's experience illustrate the concept of erasure discussed by Bauer and colleagues?

2. What health risks does Joe face as a result of erasure?

3. Does Joe have a right to a health care provider who is knowledgeable about trans bodies and trans lives? How might this be brought about?

Further Reading

Trans Pulse [Internet]. Available from: http://www. transpulseproject.ca. Date accessed: 10 June 2012.

Trans-Health: The online magazine of health and fitness for transsexual and transgendered people [Internet]. Available from: http://www.trans-health. com. Date accessed: 10 June 2012.

Coyote IE. Which doctor. *Xtra National* [Internet]. 6 June 2008. Available from: http://www.xtra.ca/

public/National/Which_doctor-4897.aspx. Date accessed: 10 June 2012.

Meyer IH, Northridge ME, editors. *The health of sexual minorities: public health perspectives on lesbian, gay, bisexual and transgender population.* New York: Springer; 2007.

Project on Bioethics, sexuality, and gender identity [Internet]. Available from: http://www.queerbio-ethics.org/. Date accessed: 10 June 2012.

Credits

Grateful acknowledgment is made for permission to use the following material:

Chapter 1

Sagan, A. and Singer, P. "The Moral Status of Stem Cells" in *Metaphilosophy* 2007; 38: 264-284 (Wiley-Blackwell).

Holm, S. "The Ethical Case against Stem Cell Research" in *Cambridge Quarterly of Health Care* 2003; 12: 372-383 (Cambridge University Press).

McLeod, C. and Baylis, F. "Feminists on the Inalienability of Human Embryos" *Hypatia* 2006; 21: 1-14. (Wiley-Blackwell).

Chapter 2

Marquis, D. "Why Abortion is Immoral" in *The Journal of Philosophy* 1989; 86: 183-202 (The Journal of Philosophy, Inc.).

Sumner, L.W., *Abortion and Moral Theory.* © 1981 Princeton University Press. Reprinted by permission of Princeton University Press.

Little, M. O. "Abortion, Intimacy, and the Duty to Gestate" in *Ethical Theory and Moral Practice* 1999; 2: 295-312.

Chapter 3

Savulescu, Julian. "Procreative Beneficence: Why we should select the Best Children." *Bioethics* 2001; 15: 413-426.

Gedge, Elizabeth. "'Healthy' Human Embryos and Symbolic Harm" in Nisker, J., Baylis, F., Karpin, I., McLeod, C. and Mykitiuk, R. (eds.,). *The 'Healthy' Embryo: Social, Biomedical, Legal and Philosophical Perspectives.* Cambridge: Cambridge University Press, 2010: 233-250. Reprinted with the permission of Cambridge University Press.

Kukla, Rebecca. "Measuring Mothering". *International Journal of Feminist Approaches to Bioethics* 2008; 1: 67-90. By permission of Indian University Press.

Chapter 4

Buchanan, A. and Brock, D. W. "Deciding for Others: Competence" in *The Milbank Quarterly* 1986; 64.2: 17-94. Reproduced with permission of Blackwell Ltd.

Freedman, B. "'A Moral Theory of Informed Consent" in *Hastings Center Report* 1975; 5.4: 32-39.

Misak, Cheryl. "ICU Psychosis and Patient Autonomy: Some Thoughts from the Inside". *Journal of Medicine and Philosophy* 2005; 30(4): 411–30.

Chapter 5

Schneiderman, Lawrence J. and Jecker, Nancy S. and Jonsen, Albert R. "Medical Futility: Its Meaning and Ethical Implications" in *Annals of Internal Medicine* 1990; 112: 949-954.

Truog, Robert D. and Brett, Allan S. and Frader, Joel. "The Problem with Futility" in *New England Journal of Medicine* 1992; 326: 1560-1564.

Charles Weijer, Peter A. Singer, Bernard M. Dickens, Stephen Workman. "Dealing with Demands for Inappropriate Treatment" in *Canadian Medical Association Journal* 1998; 159: 817-821.

Chapter 6

Freedman, B. "Equipoise and the Ethics of Clinical Research" in *New England Journal of Medicine* 1987; 317: 141-145.

Miller, Franklin G. and Brody, Howard. "A Critique of Clinical Equipoise: Therapeutic Misconception in the Ethics of Clinical Trials" in *Hastings Center Report* 2003; 33(3): 19-28.

Miller, Paul B. and Weijer, Charles. "Trust Based Obligations of the State and Physician-Researchers to Patient-Subjects" in *Journal of Medical Ethics* 2006; 32: 542–547.

Chapter 7

Narveson, Jan. The Medical Minimum: Zero. *The Journal of Medicine and Philosophy* 2012. Licensed via Rightslink.

Joseph Heath. Permission obtained from Joseph Heath, joseph.heath@utoronto.ca. (Article was originally published in French).

Chapter 8

Sreenivasan, Gopal. "Health and Justice in our Non-ideal World" in *Politics, Philosophy & Economics* 2007; 6: 218-236. Sage Journals.

From *The Life You Can Save: Acting Now To End World Poverty* by Peter Singer, copyright © 2009 by Peter Singer. Used by permission of Random House, Inc.

Chung, Ryoa . "Domination and Destitution in an Unjust World" in *Canadian Journal of Philosophy*, Supplementary Volume 2005; 31: 311-334.

Chapter 9

Schuklenk, U., van Delden, J, Downie, J, Mclean, S, Upshur, R., Weinstock, D. *The Royal Society of Canada Expert Panel: End-of-Life Decision Making.* 2011 Report In Brief: http://www.rsc-src.ca/creports.php. Permission obtained via comm-assistant@rsc-src.ca.

Freedman, Benjamin. The Rodriguez Case: Sticky Questions and Slippery Answers. *McGill Law Journal* 1994; 39: 644-656.

Downie, J. and Sherwin, S. A Feminist Exploration of Issues Around Assisted Death. *St. Louis University Public Law Review* 1995-1996; 15: 303-330. Reprinted with permission of the Saint Louis University Public Law Review © 1996 St. Louis University School of Law, St. Louis, Missouri.

Chapter 10

Pojman, Louis P. from Pojman. *Life and Death*, 2e. © 2000 Wadsworth, a part of Cengage Learning, Inc. Reproduced by permission.

Puccetti, Roland. "Does Anyone Survive Neocortical Death?" in Zaner, RM (ed.). *Death: Beyond Whole-Brain Criteria*. Dordrecht, The Netherlands: Kluwer Academic Publishers, 1988: 75-90. With kind permission from Springer Science+Business Media B.V.

Emanuel, Linda L. "Re-examining Death: The Asymptotic Model and a Bounded Zone Definition" in *Hastings Center Report* 1995; 25(4): 27-35.

Chapter 11

Aaron Spital and James Stacey Taylor."Routine Recovery of Cadaveric Organs for Transplantation: Consistent, Fair, and Life-Saving" in *Clinical Journal of the American Society of Nephrology* 2007; 2: 300-303.

Glannon, Walter. "Do the Sick Have a Right to Cadaveric Organs?" in *Journal of Medical Ethics* 2003; 29: 153-156.

Erin, Charles A. and John Harris. "An Ethical Market in Human Organs" in *Journal of Medical Ethics* 2003; 29: 137-138.

Chapter 12

Hare, R.M. "Public Policy in a Pluralist Society" in Singer, P, Kuhse, H, Buckle, S, Dawson, K, Kasimba, P (eds.). *Embryo Experimentation*. New York: Cambridge University Press, 1990: 183-194. Reprinted with the permission of Cambridge University Press.

Ainslie, Donald C. "Bioethics and the Problem of Pluralism" in *Social Philosophy and Policy* 2002; 19: 1-28.

Kymlicka, Will. "Moral Philosophy and Public Policy: The Case of New Reproductive Technologies" in Sumner, L.W., Boyle J. (eds.). *Philosophical Perspectives on Bioethics*. Toronto: University of Toronto Press, 1996: 244-270. Reprinted with permission of the publisher.

Chapter 13

Boorse, Christopher. "On the Distinction Between Disease and Illness" in *Philosophy and Public Affairs* 1975; 5.1: 49-68. Used with permission of Blackwell Publishing Ltd.

Hacking , Ian. "Madness: Biological or Constructed?'" in Hacking I. *The Social Construction of What?* Cambridge, MA: Harvard University Press, 1999: 100-124.

Callahan, Joan C. "Menopause: Taking the Cures or Curing the Takes?" in Margaret Urban Walker (ed.). *Mother Time: Women, Aging and Ethics*. New York: Rowman & Littlefield, 2000: 151-174.

Chapter 14

James F. Childress, Ruth R. Faden, Ruth D. Gaare, Lawrence O. Gostin, Jeffrey Kahn, Richard J. Bonnie, Nancy E. Kass, Anna C. Mastroianni, Jonathan D. Moreno, and Phillip Nieburg. "Public Health Ethics: Mapping the Terrain" in *The Journal of Law, Medicine & Ethics* 2002; 30(2): 170-178.

Wilson, James. "Towards a Normative Framework for Public Health Ethics and Policy'" in *Public Health Ethics*; 2009 2(2): 184-194.

Alison K. Thompson, Karen Faith, Jennifer L. Gibson, and Ross E.G. Upshur. "Pandemic Influenza Preparedness: An Ethical Framework to Guide Decision-making" in *BMC Medical Ethics* 2006; E12. © 2006 Thompson et al; licensee BioMed Central Ltd.

Chapter 15

Cohen, Carl. "The Case for the Use of Animals in Biomedical Research" in *New England Journal of Medicine* 1986; 315: 865-870.

Regan, Tom. "The Rights of Humans and Other Animals" in *Ethics & Behavior* 1997; 7: 103-111.

Sumner, L. Wayne. "Animal Welfare and Animals Rights" in *The Journal of Medicine and Philosophy* 1988; 13: 159-175.

Chapter 16

Elliott, Carl. "Pursued by Happiness and Beaten Senseless: Prozac and the American Dream" in *Hastings Center Report* 2000; 30(2): 7-12.

Kramer, Peter D. "The Valorization of Sadness: Alienation and the Melancholic Temperament" in *Hastings Center Report* 2000; 30(2): 13-18.

Glannon, W. "Psychopharmacological Enhancement" in *Neuroethics* 2008; 1: 45-54.

Chapter 17

Miller, Alice M. "Uneasy Promises: Sexuality, Health, and Human Rights" in *American Journal of Public Health*, June 2001, Vol. 91, No. 6.

Greta R. Bauer, Rebecca Hammond, Robb Travers, Matthias Kaay, Karin M. Hohenadel, Michelle Boyce. "'I Don't Think This is Theoretical; This is Our Lives: How Erasure Impacts Health Care for Transgender People" in *Journal of the Association of Nurses in AIDS Care* 2009; 20(5): 348–361.

Ami Harbin & Brenda Beagan & Lisa Goldberg, "Discomfort, Judgment, and Health Care for Queers", *Bioethical Inquiry* (2012) 9:149–160.

Case Study based on: Coyote IE. "Which doctor." *Xtra National*. June 6, 2008.

Index